BARLOW'S TABLES

OF

SQUARES
CUBES
SQUARE ROOTS
CUBE ROOTS

AND

RECIPROCALS

OF ALL INTEGERS UP TO

12,500

Edited by
L. J. COMRIE, M.A., Ph.D.

FOURTH EDITION
TENTH IMPRESSION

NEW YORK:
CHEMICAL PUBLISHING Co. Inc., 212 Fifth Avenue, 10 NY.
1965

First Edition	1814
Second Edition	1840
Third Edition	1930
Fourth Edition	1941
Reprinted	1946
Reprinted	1947
Reprinted	1950
Reprinted	1952
Reprinted	1954
Reprinted	1956
Reprinted	1958
Reprinted	1960
Reprinted	1961
Reprinted	1962
Reprinted	1965

Printed in Great Britain by
Straker Brothers Ltd., 194/200 Bishopsgate, London, E.C.2

SQUARES
CUBES
SQUARE ROOTS
CUBE ROOTS

AND

RECIPROCALS

OF ALL INTEGERS UP TO

12,500

FROM THE PREFACE TO THE ORIGINAL EDITION

IN presenting the following Mathematical Tables to the attention of the public, the far greater part of which are the result of laborious calculation, little need be said to prove that I have not had in view the accomplishment of any pecuniary object; as the time employed in the computation, the expense of publication, and the limited number of purchasers, which from the nature of the subject is to be apprehended, preclude every idea of adequate remuneration. And as little is to be expected of mathematical reputation; nothing more being requisite for the execution of such an undertaking than a moderate skill in computation and a persevering industry and attention; which are not precisely the qualifications a mathematician is most anxious to be thought to possess.

In fact, the only motive which prompted me to engage in this unprofitable task was the utility that I conceived might result from my labour; and if I have succeeded in facilitating any of the more abstruse arithmetical calculations, and thereby rendered mathematical investigations more pleasant and easy, I have obtained the principal object I had in view.

With respect to the execution, it is shown in the introduction that the methods employed in the construction of the tables were such as nearly to preclude the possibility of error in the computations, and the same care has been taken in superintending the work through the press; for being well aware that the utility of the performance depended wholly upon its accuracy, I have been the more cautious of guarding it from an imperfection, which could not fail of depreciating its value in the estimation of the public.

PETER BARLOW

Royal Military Academy, Woolwich
July 1, 1814

FROM THE PREFACE TO THE EDITION
OF 1840

This reprint of Mr. Barlow's Tables, as well as that of Lalande which preceded it, was suggested by me to the Society for the Diffusion of Useful Knowledge on two grounds. The intrinsic merit of both works made me desirous of seeing them printed in a better type than any in which they had ever appeared; added to which, the latter could only be procured from abroad, and the former was wholly out of print. In the second place, I had long been satisfied that the old numeral symbols, in which most of the figures had heads or tails, were many times more legible than those of uniform height, introduced, I believe, by Dr. Hutton. From the time when the reprint of Lalande appeared (about twelve months ago) I have heard no one contest this position; and the present work will show that it is as true of a heavy page (as the printers call it) as of one in which there are fewer figures.

At the same time, I cannot claim any credit whatever for the accuracy with which either work has been examined and corrected, except that of knowing where to find those who could do both much better than myself. Mr. Farley, of the Nautical Almanac Office, is answerable for the work on these points: and I feel very sure that the large number of computers to whom it will prove useful will admit his skill and accuracy; though it must take years of trial and use of the tables to establish their freedom from error.

I cannot ascertain that any tables of square roots, cube roots or reciprocals comparable in extent to those of Mr. Barlow were ever printed before his. The tables of squares and cubes up to 10,000 were printed by Guldinus in 1635, by J. P. Buckner (according to Murhard) in 1701, and by Séguin in 1801. The cubes to 10000^3, and the squares up to 25400^2, by Dr. Hutton, were published by the Board of Longitude in 1781.

A. DE MORGAN

University College
December 23, 1839

PREFACE TO THE THIRD EDITION

BARLOW's Tables first appeared in 1814. In 1840 De Morgan edited a new edition, the stereo plates for which were used for all subsequent editions. Certain tables included in the first edition were omitted, notably factors, the first ten powers of all numbers from 1 to 100, fourth and fifth powers up to 1000, prime numbers from 1 to 100,000, and hyperbolic (natural) logarithms to eight decimals for all numbers from 1000 to 10,000.

The present edition has come into existence partly because the stereo plates that had been used for 90 years showed evidence of wear, but mainly because the ever-increasing demand for these tables has made it possible for the publishers to face the expense of resetting the work in modern type. In addition to improved typography, this has permitted the introduction of other improvements that were needed. The tables of powers in the original edition have been restored. The square and cube roots have been cut down to eight significant figures—the greatest number usually employed in present day computing. The addition of interlinear differences will greatly facilitate interpolation of the tabular values.

The most valuable new feature, however, is the addition of a column showing the square root of 10 times the number in the argument column, in other words giving the square root of every 10th number between 10,000 and 100,000. This enables the user, when extracting a square root, to have the benefit of a four-figure argument in all cases. The values from 2500 to 10,000 were computed by interpolating to tenths the 14-figure values from 250 to 1000 given in Hülsse's edition of Vega's *Sammlung Mathematischer Tafeln*. Values from 1000 to 2500 were obtained by dividing by two every fourth value from 4000 to 10,000. The initial stages of the interpolation were done by a Hollerith tabulating machine, and the final stage, consisting of a building up from second differences, with the printing of number, square root, first and second differences, was done on a Class 11 Burroughs adding machine, which lends itself perfectly to the art of constructing tables by integration in the manner contemplated by Babbage when he attempted to build his difference engine.

Every effort has been made to secure freedom from error. In addition to a comparison with the edition of 1840 and with Jahn's *Tafeln . . . der Quadratzahlen und Kubikzahlen*, the columns of squares and cubes were built up, the former on a Monroe machine, and the latter on a Brunsviga-Dupla. A further check is given by the fact that the last two figures of the squares repeat on each page, while the last four figures repeat after 5000. The last triad of the cubes repeats after 1000. The square and cube roots were compared with those in Hülsse's Vega, while the reciprocals were read against Oakes's *Table of Reciprocals* and Picarte's *La Division Reduite a une Addition*. The squares, cubes and reciprocals of numbers up to 1000 and the square roots, cube roots and powers of numbers up to 100 were compared with those in Gelin's *Recueil de Tables Numériques*.

The work of revision has shown that there are no errors in the squares and cubes of the 1840 edition. In the square and cube roots errors of a unit of the last decimal are frequent (in the cube roots about one-seventh of the values are affected), while there are occasional errors of two units. This limit is exceeded only in the case of cube roots between 9600 and 9800, where the error is systematic, rising to 9 units of the last decimal, and averaging 8 units between 9650 and 9750. In the reciprocals there are 60 errors of a unit in the last decimal, but none greater. A list of errata in the fourth and higher powers of the 1814 edition is given by Cunningham in *Messenger of Mathematics*, XXXV, 13 (1905).

PREFACE

In the 1797 edition of Vega's Tables there is a table of cube roots to 7 decimals of the numbers from 1–100, of which 24 are in error by one unit and 3 (65, 69 and 73) in error by two units of the last decimal. This table was copied by Barlow in 1814, but with the correction of the cube root of 73. Hülsse has also copied this table, correcting the values for 9 and 73. After 100 the two tables are entirely independent. In the cube roots of Hülsse there are occasional errors of a unit in the last decimal, while the differencing of the square roots showed that the error of the twelfth decimal does not exceed a unit; considering that this work was performed nearly a century ago, it is a remarkable piece of computing. The following errors have been found:—

$\sqrt[3]{357}$	For	9712	read	9709
$\sqrt[3]{483}$	,,	0132	,,	0134
$\sqrt{687}$	,,	212684	,,	210684
$\sqrt[3]{5607}$	,,	5762	,,	4762
$\sqrt[3]{6363}$	,,	5872	,,	5072
$\sqrt[3]{6808}$	,,	7034	,,	7914
$\sqrt[3]{9590}$	,,	7993	,,	7893

Jahn's Table is one of the most inaccurate ever printed. 51 errors were found in the squares, and 341 in the cubes up to 10,000. Some of these may be printers' errors, but the greater number, especially in the cubes, are obviously computing errors; in many cases the difference between the value given for n^3 and the true value is a multiple of n. Cunningham (*loc. cit.*), who examined the table of 4th to 9th powers up to 50, remarked that "the numerous errors (25) found in one page shake one's confidence in the main Table (of Squares and Cubes)."

No errors were found in the portions of Oakes and Picarte used. The only error found in Gelin is in the cube root of 57, which should read 3·84850 11313, not 3·84850 10693.

L. J. COMRIE

H.M. Nautical Almanac Office
Royal Naval College
*London, S.E.*10
1930 *January*

PREFACE TO THE FOURTH EDITION

In this new edition the tables have been extended from 10,000 to 12,500 particularly in order to avoid discontinuities when working with numbers just below and just above unity. The work of preparation has been greatly facilitated by a 6-register National machine, which lends itself to any work of a tabular nature.

L. J. COMRIE

Scientific Computing Service, Limited
23 *Bedford Square*
*London, W.C.*1
January, 1941

INTRODUCTION

Arrangements of the Tables. In addition to the squares, cubes, square roots, cube roots and reciprocals of all numbers up to 12,500 the tables give (pages 2–3) the factorials of numbers up to 100, the fourth power and the reciprocals of the square roots of numbers up to 1000 (pages 2–21), powers up to the tenth of numbers up to 100 and up to the twentieth of numbers up to 10 (pages 252–256). On page 257 will be found tables of binomial coefficients and of constants.

The division of the squares and cubes into pairs and triads will facilitate the formation of squares and cubes of decimal quantities. A movement of the decimal point through one figure in the number results in a corresponding movement through two figures in the square or three in the cube.

In order to economise space the numbers in the columns square root, square root of $10n$, cube root and reciprocal have been divided into two groups—a leading and a following. The following group is contained in the body of the table, and the leading group at the head and foot of each column. A change in the leading group is clearly indicated by an asterisk at the point of change; the leading group at the head of the column is associated with following groups above the asterisk, and the leading group at the foot of the column with following groups below the asterisk. Thus

$$\sqrt{2724} = 52\cdot191953$$
$$\sqrt{27240} = 165\cdot045448$$
$$\sqrt[3]{2724} = 13\cdot965903$$
$$\frac{1}{2724} = 0\cdot0003671072$$

For values of n less 6250 the leading group of the square root of $10n$ is always a multiple of 10; for values greater than 6250 it is an integer. There are no asterisks in the column of reciprocals.

Interpolation. The columns of square roots, cube roots and reciprocals may be interpolated in the usual way, using the printed differences, in the portion of 1000–10,000. The maximum errors that can arise through neglect of the second differences are, in units of the last decimal tabulated:

n	$\sqrt{n}$	$\sqrt{10n}$	$\sqrt[3]{n}$	$\frac{1}{n}$
1000	1·0	3·1	0·3	2·5
2000	0·3	1·1	0·1	0·3
3000	0·2	0·6	0·0	0·1
4000	0·1	0·4	0·0	0·0
5000	0·1	0·3	0·0	0·0
10000	0·0	0·1	0·0	0·0

Function Diffs.

f_{-1}

$\quad a$

$f_0 \qquad d$

$\quad b$

$f_1 \qquad e$

$\quad c$

f_2

The effect of second differences on an interpolate may be easily and accurately allowed for. Denote four consecutive values of the function by f_{-1}, f_0, f_1, f_2, and their differences by a, b, c and d, e as in the accompanying scheme. The value f_n of the function at a point n^* between 0 and 1 is given by Bessel's formula as

$$f_n = f_0 + nb + \frac{n(n-1)}{2}\frac{d+e}{2}$$

Putting $B'' = \dfrac{n(n-1)}{4}$ this becomes

$$f_n = f_0 + nb + B''(c-a)$$

A critical table giving values of B'' to the degree of accuracy necessary in this table will be found on the last page.

Example: Required the square root of 10056. From page 22

$$
\begin{aligned}
&f_{-1}\quad 100{\cdot}199800 \\
&\qquad\qquad\qquad\qquad 49888 = a \\
&f_0\quad\ \ 100{\cdot}249688 \\
&\qquad\qquad\qquad\qquad 49863 = b \\
&f_1\quad\ \ 100{\cdot}299551 \\
&\qquad\qquad\qquad\qquad 49839 = c \\
&f_2\quad\ \ 100{\cdot}349390
\end{aligned}
$$

$n = {\cdot}6 \qquad c - a = -49 \qquad B'' = -{\cdot}06$

$\qquad\qquad\qquad\qquad\qquad\quad f_0 = 100{\cdot}249688$

$\qquad nb = {\cdot}6 \times 49863 = \quad + 299178$

$B''(c-a) = -{\cdot}06 \times -49 = \quad + \qquad 29$

$\qquad\qquad\qquad \sqrt{10056} = 100{\cdot}279609$

If the user has a calculating machine the term f_0 may be set on the keyboard and thence in the product register, leaving as many decimals in the multiplier register as there are in the fraction n. b is then set on the keyboard, and a single turn produces f_1, the checking of which checks the setting of both f_0 and b. Multiplication by n then produces $f_0 + nb$.

It will be noted that for a square root the first and second difference corrections are always positive, while for a reciprocal they are always negative. The cube root may be regarded as linear throughout.

Square Roots. In obtaining a square root the position of the decimal point and the value of the first figure should be obtained by inspection of the number. The value of the first figure will determine whether the column $\sqrt{n}$ or the column $\sqrt{10n}$ is to be used. Thus

$$\sqrt{23{\cdot}95} = 4{\cdot}8938737 \text{ from the column } \sqrt{n}$$
$$\sqrt{0{\cdot}02395} = 0{\cdot}154757875 \text{ from the column } \sqrt{10n}$$

Square roots to eight significant figures are readily obtained by interpolation of the tabular values. If more significant figures are required than are given by the tables it suffices to divide the number by its approximate root, and take the mean or average of divisor and quotient. By this means the number of figures correctly known at first will be doubled. Thus a root that is known to five figures may be used to determine the root to 9 or 10 figures.

* This is the usual notation for the "phase" or interpolating factor, or fraction of the interval, and should not be confused with the n of the tables.

INTRODUCTION

If x be a number and $\sqrt{x} + \epsilon$ is the approximate root, the mean of divisor and quotient will be $\sqrt{x} + \dfrac{\epsilon^2}{2\sqrt{x}}$, so that, if ϵ is of the first order of smallness, ϵ^2 is of the second order. Since ϵ^2 is always positive the root thus obtained will tend to be too great numerically, so that, if the original root contains f figures, and the $2f$th figure of the quotient is odd, it should be diminished by 1 before dividing by 2. Thus the approximate root of 23·95 is 4·8939

$$\frac{23·95}{4·8939} = 4·893847443$$

$$\sqrt{23·95} = \tfrac{1}{2}(4·8939 + 4·893847442)$$

$$= 4·893873721 \text{ which is correct to the last decimal.}$$

Cube Roots. In obtaining a cube root the position of the decimal point and the value of the first figure should be obtained by inspection of the number, which is first divided into triads commencing from the decimal. A critical table for determining the first figure is given on the last page.

Examples:

$\sqrt[3]{23950}$	=	2*· ...	$\sqrt[3]{0·2395}$	=	0·6 ...
$\sqrt[3]{2395}$	=	1*· ...	$\sqrt[3]{0·02395}$	=	0·2 ...
$\sqrt[3]{239·5}$	=	6· ...	$\sqrt[3]{0·002395}$	=	0·1 ...
$\sqrt[3]{23·95}$	=	2· ...	$\sqrt[3]{0·0002395}$	=	0·06 ...
$\sqrt[3]{2·395}$	=	1· ...	$\sqrt[3]{0·00002395}$	=	0·02 ...

As it is not convenient to tabulate $\sqrt[3]{10n}$ and $\sqrt[3]{100n}$, provision must be made for cases which fall outside the part between 1250 and 12,500, which is the convenient range of the table. The number may be multiplied by a factor that will bring it within this range, and the root thus obtained divided by the cube root of this factor. Various factors will be required according to the value of the first triad. Thus:

1st triad	Multiplier	Divisor
001 to 012	Not required	—
010 to 100	125	5
020 to 195	64	4
046 to 460	27	3
156 to 1560	8	2

The factor 8 is, of course, the most convenient, and fortunately, covers the largest range if the first triad is allowed to extend to 1560.

Examples:

$$\sqrt[3]{23950} = \tfrac{1}{4}\sqrt[3]{23950 \times 64} = \tfrac{10}{4}\sqrt[3]{1532·8} = 28·824945$$
$$= \tfrac{1}{5}\sqrt[3]{23950 \times 125} = 2\sqrt[3]{2993·75} = 28·824946$$
$$\sqrt[3]{239·5} = \tfrac{1}{2}\sqrt[3]{239·5 \times 8} = \tfrac{1}{2}\sqrt[3]{1916} = 6·2101465$$
$$= \tfrac{1}{3}\sqrt[3]{239·5 \times 27} = \tfrac{1}{3}\sqrt[3]{6466·5} = 6·2101463$$

Another method consists in using inverse interpolation of the column of cubes. To obtain eight significant figures the first five significant figures of the difference of the cubes may be used, and second differences neglected.

Example: $\sqrt[3]{23950}$. The first figure of the root is 2; enter the column n^3 between $n = 2000$ and $n = 3000$ at the figures 2395. The root is therefore

$$28·82 \frac{12327}{24926} = 28·824945$$

Similarly $$\sqrt[3]{239 \cdot 5} = 6 \cdot 210\ \frac{1694}{11571} = 6 \cdot 2101464$$

This method is more exact than that first described if the accuracy of the 8th significant figure is important. It should, of course, be used when only four or five significant figures are required.

If the user has a calculating machine the number may be brought into the range of the tables by multiplying by a power of ten. The cube root then found must be multiplied by 2154434690 or 4641588834 and the decimal suitably adjusted. Multiplication by the second factor may be replaced by division by the first, especially if the keyboard of the machine has only eight or nine columns. These factors are given for convenience on the last page. Thus

$$\sqrt[3]{23950} = \sqrt[3]{2395} \times 2 \cdot 1544347 = 28 \cdot 824947$$
$$\sqrt[3]{239 \cdot 5} = \sqrt[3]{2395} \div 2 \cdot 1544347 = 6 \cdot 2101464$$

An even more expeditious method with a calculating machine is as follows. Obtain four figures correctly from the column n by entering the column n^3. Divide the number by n^2 (found on the same line) and take one third of $2n +$ the quotient. This yields eight significant figures, but if the approximate cube root is known to five figures, a value to ten figures may be obtained. If x be a number and $\sqrt[3]{x} + \epsilon$ an approximate cube root, this process yields $\sqrt[3]{x} + \dfrac{\epsilon^2}{3\sqrt[3]{x}}$

Example: $\sqrt[3]{23950}$ The approximate root is $28 \cdot 82$, the square of which is $830 \cdot 5924$.

$$\frac{23950}{830 \cdot 5924} = 28 \cdot 834841$$

$$\sqrt[3]{23950} = \tfrac{1}{3}\ (28 \cdot 82 + 28 \cdot 82 + 28 \cdot 834841) = 28 \cdot 824947$$

This method is, in general, the most accurate if the correctness of the 8th figure is important. If the cube root to ten significant figures is required.

$$\frac{23950}{28 \cdot 825^2} = 28 \cdot 82483871$$

Hence $$\sqrt[3]{23950} = 28 \cdot 82494624$$

In actual practice nothing need be written except the final answer.

Reciprocals. Every user of calculating machines knows the value of reciprocals when performing several divisions by the same divisor. The use of a table of reciprocals represents a distinct saving of time and effort, and not infrequently renders the use of reciprocals profitable in cases where the subsequent saving would not be sufficient to justify the time required to form them by the machine itself. They are also useful in the evaluation of $y = a + \dfrac{b}{x}$ for various values of x when a and b are constant.

Special uses of the Tables. Attention may be drawn to the use of the tables in computing the roots of the quadratic equation $ax^2 + bx + c = 0$. The roots are

$$x = \frac{-b \pm \sqrt{b^2 + (c - a)^2 - (c + a)^2}}{2a}$$

Similarly in a triangle A B C

$$\cos A = \frac{(b + c)^2 + (b - c)^2 - 2a^2}{(b + c)^2 - (b - c)^2}$$

SQUARES
CUBES
SQUARE ROOTS
CUBE ROOTS

AND

RECIPROCALS

OF ALL INTEGERS UP TO

12,500

No. n	Square n^2	Cube n^3	Fourth power n^4	$\dfrac{1}{\sqrt{n}}$	Factorial* $n!$	Sq. root $\sqrt{n}$	Cube root $\sqrt[3]{n}$	Reciprocal $\dfrac{1}{n}$
				0·				0·
1	1	1	1		1	1·0000000	1·0000000	
2	4	8	16	7071068	2	1·4142136	1·2599210	500000000
3	9	27	81	5773503	6	1·7320508	1·4422496	333333333
4	16	64	256	5000000	24	2·0000000	1·5874011	250000000
5	25	125	625	4472136	120	2·2360680	1·7099759	200000000
6	36	216	1296	4082483	720	2·4494897	1·8171206	166666667
7	49	343	2401	3779645	5040	2·6457513	1·9129312	142857143
8	64	512	4096	3535534	40320	2·8284271	2·0000000	125000000
9	81	729	6561	3333333	362880	3·0000000	2·0800838	111111111
10	1 00	1 000	1 0000	3162278	0·3628800 7	3·1622777	2·1544347	100000000
11	1 21	1 331	1 4641	3015113	3·9916800 7	3·3166248	2·2239801	090909091
12	1 44	1 728	2 0736	2886751	4·7900160 8	3·4641016	2·2894285	083333333
13	1 69	2 197	2 8561	2773501	6·2270208 9	3·6055513	2·3513347	076923077
14	1 96	2 744	3 8416	2672612	8·7178291 10	3·7416574	2·4101423	071428571
15	2 25	3 375	5 0625	2581989	1·3076744 12	3·8729833	2·4662121	066666667
16	2 56	4 096	6 5536	2500000	2·0922790 13	4·0000000	2·5198421	062500000
17	2 89	4 913	8 3521	2425356	3·5568743 14	4·1231056	2·5712816	058823529
18	3 24	5 832	10 4976	2357023	6·4023737 15	4·2426407	2·6207414	055555556
19	3 61	6 859	13 0321	2294157	1·2164510 17	4·3588989	2·6684016	052631579
20	4 00	8 000	16 0000	2236068	2·4329020 18	4·4721360	2·7144176	050000000
21	4 41	9 261	19 4481	2182179	5·1090942 19	4·5825757	2·7589242	047619048
22	4 84	10 648	23 4256	2132007	1·1240007 21	4·6904158	2·8020393	045454545
23	5 29	12 167	27 9841	2085144	2·5852017 22	4·7958315	2·8438670	043478261
24	5 76	13 824	33 1776	2041241	6·2044840 23	4·8989795	2·8844991	041666667
25	6 25	15 625	39 0625	2000000	1·5511210 25	5·0000000	2·9240177	040000000
26	6 76	17 576	45 6976	1961161	4·0329146 26	5·0990195	2·9624961	038461538
27	7 29	19 683	53 1441	1924501	1·0888869 28	5·1961524	3·0000000	037037037
28	7 84	21 952	61 4656	1889822	3·0488834 29	5·2915026	3·0365890	035714286
29	8 41	24 389	70 7281	1856953	8·8417620 30	5·3851648	3·0723168	034482759
30	9 00	27 000	81 0000	1825742	2·6525286 32	5·4772256	3·1072325	033333333
31	9 61	29 791	92 3521	1796053	8·2228387 33	5·5677644	3·1413807	032258065
32	10 24	32 768	104 8576	1767767	2·6313084 35	5·6568542	3·1748021	031250000
33	10 89	35 937	118 5921	1740777	8·6833176 36	5·7445626	3·2075343	030303030
34	11 56	39 304	133 6336	1714986	2 9523280 38	5·8309519	3·2396118	029411765
35	12 25	42 875	150 0625	1690309	1·0333148 40	5·9160798	3·2710663	028571429
36	12 96	46 656	167 9616	1666667	3·7199333 41	6·0000000	3·3019272	027777778
37	13 69	50 653	187 4161	1643990	1·3763753 43	6·0827625	3·3322219	027027027
38	14 44	54 872	208 5136	1622214	5·2302262 44	6·1644140	3·3619754	026315789
39	15 21	59 319	231 3441	1601282	2·0397882 46	6·2449980	3·3912114	025641026
40	16 00	64 000	256 0000	1581139	8·1591528 47	6·3245553	3·4199519	025000000
41	16 81	68 921	282 5761	1561738	3·3452527 49	6·4031242	3·4482172	024390244
42	17 64	74 088	311 1696	1543034	1·4050061 51	6·4807407	3·4760266	023809524
43	18 49	79 507	341 8801	1524986	6·0415263 52	6·5574385	3·5033981	023255814
44	19 36	85 184	374 8096	1507557	2·6582716 54	6·6332496	3·5303483	022727273
45	20 25	91 125	410 0625	1490712	1·1962222 56	6·7082039	3·5568933	022222222
46	21 16	97 336	447 7456	1474420	5·5026222 57	6·7823300	3·5830479	021739130
47	22 09	103 823	487 9681	1458650	2·5862324 59	6·8556546	3·6088261	021276596
48	23 04	110 592	530 8416	1443376	1·2413916 61	6·9282032	3·6342412	020833333
49	24 01	117 649	576 4801	1428571	6·0828186 62	7·0000000	3·6593057	020408163
50	25 00	125 000	625 0000	1414214	3·0414093 64	7·0710678	3·6840315	020000000

*The number following $n!$ is the power of 10 by which the given tabular quantity must be multiplied.

No. n	Square n^2	Cube n^3	Fourth power n^4	$\frac{1}{\sqrt{n}}$	Factorial* $n!$	Sq. root $\sqrt{n}$	Cube root $\sqrt[3]{n}$	Reciprocal $\frac{1}{n}$
				0·				0·0
50	25 00	125 000	625 0000	1414214	3·0414093 64	7·0710678	3·6840315	20000000
51	26 01	132 651	676 5201	1400280	1·5511188 66	7·1414284	3·7084298	19607843
52	27 04	140 608	731 1616	1386750	8·0658175 67	7·2111026	3·7325112	19230769
53	28 09	148 877	789 0481	1373606	4·2748833 69	7·2801099	3·7562858	18867925
54	29 16	157 464	850 3056	1360828	2·3084370 71	7·3484692	3·7797631	18518519
55	30 25	166 375	915 0625	1348400	1·2696403 73	7·4161985	3·8029525	18181818
56	31 36	175 616	983 4496	1336306	7·1099859 74	7·4833148	3·8258624	17857143
57	32 49	185 193	1055 6001	1324532	4·0526920 76	7·5498344	3·8485011	17543860
58	33 64	195 112	1131 6496	1313064	2·3505613 78	7·6157731	3·8708766	17241379
59	34 81	205 379	1211 7361	1301889	1·3868312 80	7·6811457	3·8929964	16949153
60	36 00	216 000	1296 0000	1290994	8·3209871 81	7·7459667	3·9148676	16666667
61	37 21	226 981	1384 5841	1280369	5·0758021 83	7·8102497	3·9364972	16393443
62	38 44	238 328	1477 6336	1270001	3·1469973 85	7·8740079	3·9578916	16129032
63	39 69	250 047	1575 2961	1259882	1·9826083 87	7·9372539	3·9790572	15873016
64	40 96	262 144	1677 7216	1250000	1·2688693 89	8·0000000	4·0000000	15625000
65	42 25	274 625	1785 0625	1240347	8·2476506 90	8·0622577	4·0207258	15384615
66	43 56	287 496	1897 4736	1230915	5·4434494 92	8·1240384	4·0412400	15151515
67	44 89	300 763	2015 1121	1221694	3·6471111 94	8·1853528	4·0615481	14925373
68	46 24	314 432	2138 1376	1212678	2·4800355 96	8·2462113	4·0816551	14705882
69	47 61	328 509	2266 7121	1203859	1·7112245 98	8·3066239	4·1015659	14492754
70	49 00	343 000	2401 0000	1195229	1·1978572 100	8·3666003	4·1212853	14285714
71	50 41	357 911	2541 1681	1186782	8·5047769 101	8·4261498	4·1408177	14084507
72	51 84	373 248	2687 3856	1178511	6·1234458 103	8·4852814	4·1601676	13888889
73	53 29	389 017	2839 8241	1170411	4·4701155 105	8·5440037	4·1793392	13698630
74	54 76	405 224	2998 6576	1162476	3·3078854 107	8·6023253	4·1983365	13513514
75	56 25	421 875	3164 0625	1154701	2·4809141 109	8·6602540	4·2171633	13333333
76	57 76	438 976	3336 2176	1147079	1·8854947 111	8·7177979	4·2358236	13157895
77	59 29	456 533	3515 3041	1139606	1·4518309 113	8·7749644	4·2543209	12987013
78	60 84	474 552	3701 5056	1132277	1·1324281 115	8·8317609	4·2726587	12820513
79	62 41	493 039	3895 0081	1125088	8·9461821 116	8·8881944	4·2908404	12658228
80	64 00	512 000	4096 0000	1118034	7·1569457 118	8·9442719	4·3088694	12500000
81	65 61	531 441	4304 6721	1111111	5·7971286 120	9·0000000	4·3267487	12345679
82	67 24	551 368	4521 2176	1104315	4·7536433 122	9·0553851	4·3444815	12195122
83	68 89	571 787	4745 8321	1097643	3·9455240 124	9·1104336	4·3620707	12048193
84	70 56	592 704	4978 7136	1091089	3·3142401 126	9·1651514	4·3795191	11904762
85	72 25	614 125	5220 0625	1084652	2·8171041 128	9·2195445	4·3968297	11764706
86	73 96	636 056	5470 0816	1078328	2·4227095 130	9·2736185	4·4140050	11627907
87	75 69	658 503	5728 9761	1072113	2·1077573 132	9·3273791	4·4310476	11494253
88	77 44	681 472	5996 9536	1066004	1·8548264 134	9·3808315	4·4479602	11363636
89	79 21	704 969	6274 2241	1059998	1·6507955 136	9·4339811	4·4647451	11235955
90	81 00	729 000	6561 0000	1054093	1·4857160 138	9·4868330	4·4814047	11111111
91	82 81	753 571	6857 4961	1048285	1·3520015 140	9·5393920	4·4979414	10989011
92	84 64	778 688	7163 9296	1042572	1·2438414 142	9·5916630	4·5143574	10869565
93	86 49	804 357	7480 5201	1036952	1·1567725 144	9·6436508	4·5306549	10752688
94	88 36	830 584	7807 4896	1031421	1·0873662 146	9·6953597	4·5468359	10638298
95	90 25	857 375	8145 0625	1025978	1·0329978 148	9·7467943	4·5629026	10526316
96	92 16	884 736	8493 4656	1020621	9·9167793 149	9·7979590	4·5788570	10416667
97	94 09	912 673	8852 9281	1015346	9·6192760 151	9·8488578	4·5947009	10309278
98	96 04	941 192	9223 6816	1010153	9·4268904 153	9·8994949	4·6104363	10204082
99	98 01	970 299	9605 9601	1005038	9·3326215 155	9·9498744	4·6260650	10101010
100	100 00 00	1000 000	10000 0000	1000000	9·3326215 157	10·0000000	4·6415888	10000000

*The number following n! is the power of 10 by which the given tabular quantity must be multiplied.

3

No. n	Square n^2	Cube n^3	Fourth power n^4	$\dfrac{1}{\sqrt{n}}$	Square root $\sqrt{n}$	Cube root $\sqrt[3]{n}$	Reciprocal $\dfrac{1}{n}$
				0·0			0·00
100	1 00 00	1 000 000	1 0000 0000		10·0000000	4·6415888	
101	1 02 01	1 030 301	1 0406 0401	995037	10·0498756	4·6570095	9900990
102	1 04 04	1 061 208	1 0824 3216	990148	10·0995049	4·6723287	9803922
103	1 06 09	1 092 727	1 1255 0881	985329	10·1488916	4·6875481	9708738
104	1 08 16	1 124 864	1 1698 5856	980581	10·1980390	4·7026694	9615385
105	1 10 25	1 157 625	1 2155 0625	975900	10·2469508	4·7176940	9523810
106	1 12 36	1 191 016	1 2624 7696	971286	10·2956301	4·7326235	9433962
107	1 14 49	1 225 043	1 3107 9601	966736	10·3440804	4·7474594	9345794
108	1 16 64	1 259 712	1 3604 8896	962250	10·3923048	4·7622032	9259259
109	1 18 81	1 295 029	1 4115 8161	957826	10·4403065	4·7768562	9174312
110	1 21 00	1 331 000	1 4641 0000	953463	10·4880885	4·7914199	9090909
111	1 23 21	1 367 631	1 5180 7041	949158	10·5356538	4·8058955	9009009
112	1 25 44	1 404 928	1 5735 1936	944911	10·5830052	4·8202845	8928571
113	1 27 69	1 442 897	1 6304 7361	940721	10·6301458	4·8345881	8849558
114	1 29 96	1 481 544	1 6889 6016	936586	10·6770783	4·8488076	8771930
115	1 32 25	1 520 875	1 7490 0625	932505	10·7238053	4·8629441	8695652
116	1 34 56	1 560 896	1 8106 3936	928477	10·7703296	4·8776990	8620690
117	1 36 89	1 601 613	1 8738 8721	924500	10·8166538	4·8909732	8547009
118	1 39 24	1 643 032	1 9387 7776	920575	10·8627805	4·9048681	8474576
119	1 41 61	1 685 159	2 0053 3921	916698	10·9087121	4·9186847	8403361
120	1 44 00	1 728 000	2 0736 0000	912871	10·9544512	4·9324241	8333333
121	1 46 41	1 771 561	2 1435 8881	909091	11·0000000	4·9460874	8264463
122	1 48 84	1 815 848	2 2153 3456	905357	11·0453610	4·9596757	8196721
123	1 51 29	1 860 867	2 2888 6641	901670	11·0905365	4·9731898	8130081
124	1 53 76	1 906 624	2 3642 1376	898027	11·1355287	4·9866310	8064516
125	1 56 25	1 953 125	2 4414 0625	894427	11·1803399	5·0000000	8000000
126	1 58 76	2 000 376	2 5204 7376	890871	11·2249722	5·0132979	7936508
127	1 61 29	2 048 383	2 6014 4641	887357	11·2694277	5·0265257	7874016
128	1 63 84	2 097 152	2 6843 5456	883883	11·3137085	5·0396842	7812500
129	1 66 41	2 146 689	2 7692 2881	880451	11·3578167	5·0527743	7751938
130	1 69 00	2 197 000	2 8561 0000	877058	11·4017543	5·0657970	7692308
131	1 71 61	2 248 091	2 9449 9921	873704	11·4452231	5·0787531	7633588
132	1 74 24	2 299 968	3 0359 5776	870388	11·4891253	5·0916434	7575758
133	1 76 89	2 352 637	3 1290 0721	867110	11·5325626	5·1044687	7518797
134	1 79 56	2 406 104	3 2241 7936	863868	11·5758369	5·1172299	7462687
135	1 82 25	2 460 375	3 3215 0625	860663	11·6189500	5·1299278	7407407
136	1 84 96	2 515 456	3 4210 2016	857493	11·6619038	5·1425632	7352941
137	1 87 69	2 571 353	3 5227 5361	854358	11·7046999	5·1551367	7299270
138	1 90 44	2 628 072	3 6267 3936	851257	11·7473401	5·1676493	7246377
139	1 93 21	2 685 619	3 7330 1041	848189	11·7898261	5·1801015	7194245
140	1 96 00	2 744 000	3 8416 0000	845154	11·8321596	5·1924941	7142857
141	1 98 81	2 803 221	3 9525 4161	842152	11·8743421	5·2048279	7092199
142	2 01 64	2 863 288	4 0658 6896	839181	11·9163753	5·2171034	7042254
143	2 04 49	2 924 207	4 1816 1601	836242	11·9582607	5·2293215	6993007
144	2 07 36	2 985 984	4 2998 1696	833333	12·0000000	5·2414828	6944444
145	2 10 25	3 048 625	4 4205 0625	830455	12·0415946	5·2535879	6896552
146	2 13 16	3 112 136	4 5437 1856	827606	12·0830460	5·2656374	6849315
147	2 16 09	3 176 523	4 6694 8881	824786	12·1243557	5·2776321	6802721
148	2 19 04	3 241 792	4 7978 5216	821995	12·1655251	5·2895725	6756757
149	2 22 01	3 307 949	4 9288 4401	819232	12·2065556	5·3014592	6711409
150	2 25 00	3 375 000	5 0625 0000	816497	12·2474487	5·3132928	6666667

No. n	Square n^2	Cube n^3	Fourth power n^4	$\dfrac{1}{\sqrt{n}}$	Square root $\sqrt{n}$	Cube root $\sqrt[3]{n}$	Reciprocal $\dfrac{1}{n}$
				0·0			0·00
150	2 25 00	3 375 000	5 0625 0000	816497	12·2474487	5·3132928	6666667
151	2 28 01	3 442 951	5 1988 5601	813788	12·2882057	5·3250740	6622517
152	2 31 04	3 511 808	5 3379 4816	811107	12·3288280	5·3368033	6578947
153	2 34 09	3 581 577	5 4798 1281	808452	12·3693169	5·3484812	6535948
154	2 37 16	3 652 264	5 6244 8656	805823	12·4096736	5·3601084	6493506
155	2 40 25	3 723 875	5 7720 0625	803219	12·4498996	5·3716854	6451613
156	2 43 36	3 796 416	5 9224 0896	800641	12·4899960	5·3832126	6410256
157	2 46 49	3 869 893	6 0757 3201	798087	12·5299641	5·3946907	6369427
158	2 49 64	3 944 312	6 2320 1296	795557	12·5698051	5·4061202	6329114
159	2 52 81	4 019 679	6 3912 8961	793052	12·6095202	5·4175015	6289308
160	2 56 00	4 096 000	6 5536 0000	790569	12·6491106	5·4288352	6250000
161	2 59 21	4 173 281	6 7189 8241	788110	12·6885775	5·4401218	6211180
162	2 62 44	4 251 528	6 8874 7536	785674	12·7279221	5·4513618	6172840
163	2 65 69	4 330 747	7 0591 1761	783260	12·7671453	5·4625556	6134969
164	2 68 96	4 410 944	7 2339 4816	780869	12·8062485	5·4737037	6097561
165	2 72 25	4 492 125	7 4120 0625	778499	12·8452326	5·4848066	6060606
166	2 75 56	4 574 296	7 5933 3136	776151	12·8840987	5·4958647	6024096
167	2 78 89	4 657 463	7 7779 6321	773823	12·9228480	5·5068784	5988024
168	2 82 24	4 741 632	7 9659 4176	771517	12·9614814	5·5178484	5952381
169	2 85 61	4 826 809	8 1573 0721	769231	13·0000000	5·5287748	5917160
170	2 89 00	4 913 000	8 3521 0000	766965	13·0384048	5·5396583	5882353
171	2 92 41	5 000 211	8 5503 6081	764719	13·0766968	5·5504991	5847953
172	2 95 84	5 088 448	8 7521 3056	762493	13·1148770	5·5612978	5813953
173	2 99 29	5 177 717	8 9574 5041	760286	13·1529464	5·5720547	5780347
174	3 02 76	5 268 024	9 1663 6176	758098	13·1909060	5·5827702	5747126
175	3 06 25	5 359 375	9 3789 0625	755929	13·2287566	5·5934447	5714286
176	3 09 76	5 451 776	9 5951 2576	753778	13·2664992	5·6040787	5681818
177	3 13 29	5 545 233	9 8150 6241	751646	13·3041347	5·6146724	5649718
178	3 16 84	5 639 752	10 0387 5856	749532	13·3416641	5·6252263	5617978
179	3 20 41	5 735 339	10 2662 5681	747435	13·3790882	5·6357408	5586592
180	3 24 00	5 832 000	10 4976 0000	745356	13·4164079	5·6462162	5555556
181	3 27 61	5 929 741	10 7328 3121	743294	13·4536240	5·6566528	5524862
182	3 31 24	6 028 568	10 9719 9376	741249	13·4907376	5·6670511	5494505
183	3 34 89	6 128 487	11 2151 3121	739221	13·5277493	5·6774114	5464481
184	3 38 56	6 229 504	11 4622 8736	737210	13·5646600	5·6877340	5434783
185	3 42 25	6 331 625	11 7135 0625	735215	13·6014705	5·6980192	5405405
186	3 45 96	6 434 856	11 9688 3216	733236	13·6381817	5·7082675	5376344
187	3 49 69	6 539 203	12 2283 0961	731272	13·6747943	5·7184791	5347594
188	3 53 44	6 644 672	12 4919 8336	729325	13·7113092	5·7286543	5319149
·189	3 57 21	6 751 269	12 7598 9841	727393	13·7477271	5·7387935	5291005
190	3 61 00	6 859 000	13 0321 0000	725476	13·7840488	5·7488971	5263158
191	3 64 81	6 967 871	13 3086 3361	723575	13·8202750	5·7589652	5235602
192	3 68 64	7 077 888	13 5895 4496	721688	13·8564065	5·7689983	5208333
193	3 72 49	7 189 057	13 8748 8001	719816	13·8924440	5·7789966	5181347
194	3 76 36	7 301 384	14 1646 8496	717958	13·9283883	5·7889604	5154639
195	3 80 25	7 414 875	14 4590 0625	716115	13·9642400	5·7988900	5128205
196	3 84 16	7 529 536	14 7578 9056	714286	14·0000000	5·8087857	5102041
197	3 88 09	7 645 373	15 0613 8481	712470	14·0356688	5·8186479	5076142
198	3 92 04	7 762 392	15 3695 3616	710669	14·0712473	5·8284767	5050505
199	3 96 01	7 880 599	15 6823 9201	708881	14·1067360	5·8382725	5025126
200	4 00 00	8 000 000	16 0000 0000	707107	14·1421356	5·8480355	5000000

5

No. n	Square n^2	Cube n^3	Fourth power n^4	$\dfrac{1}{\sqrt{n}}$	Square root $\sqrt{n}$	Cube root $\sqrt[3]{n}$	Reciprocal $\dfrac{1}{n}$
				0·0			0·00
200	4 00 00	8 000 000	16 0000 0000	707107	14·1421356	5·8480355	5000000
201	4 04 01	8 120 601	16 3224 0801	705346	14·1774469	5·8577660	4975124
202	4 08 04	8 242 408	16 6496 6416	703598	14·2126704	5·8674643	4950495
203	4 12 09	8 365 427	16 9818 1681	701862	14·2478068	5·8771307	4926108
204	4 16 16	8 489 664	17 3189 1456	700140	14·2828569	5·8867653	4901961
205	4 20 25	8 615 125	17 6610 0625	698430	14·3178211	5·8963685	4878049
206	4 24 36	8 741 816	18 0081 4096	696733	14·3527001	5·9059406	4854369
207	4 28 49	8 869 743	18 3603 6801	695048	14·3874946	5·9154817	4830918
208	4 32 64	8 998 912	18 7177 3696	693375	14·4222051	5·9249921	4807692
209	4 36 81	9 129 329	19 0802 9761	691714	14·4568323	5·9344721	4784689
210	4 41 00	9 261 000	19 4481 0000	690066	14·4913767	5·9439220	4761905
211	4 45 21	9 393 931	19 8211 9441	688428	14·:·8390	5·9533418	4739336
212	4 49 44	9 528 128	20 1996 3136	686803	14·5602198	5·9627320	4716981
213	4 53 69	9 663 597	20 5834 6161	685189	14·5945195	5·9720928	4694836
214	4 57 96	9 800 344	20 9727 3616	683586	14·6287388	5·9814240	4672897
215	4 62 25	9 938 375	21 3675 0625	681994	14·6628783	5·9907264	4651163
216	4 66 56	10 077 696	21 7678 2336	680414	14·6969385	6·0000000	4629630
217	4 70 89	10 218 313	22 1737 3921	678844	14·7309199	6·0092450	4608295
218	4 75 24	10 360 232	22 5853 0576	677285	14·7648231	6·0184617	4587156
219	4 79 61	10 503 459	23 0025 7521	675737	14·7986486	6·0276502	4566210
220	4 84 00	10 648 000	23 4256 0000	674200	14·8323970	6·0368107	4545455
221	4 88 41	10 793 861	23 8544 3281	672673	14·8660687	6·0459436	4524887
222	4 92 84	10 941 048	24 2891 2656	671156	14·8996644	6·0550489	4504505
223	4 97 29	11 089 567	24 7297 3441	669650	14·9331845	6·0641270	4484305
224	5 01 76	11 239 424	25 1763 0976	668153	14·9666295	6·0731779	4464286
225	5 06 25	11 390 625	25 6289 0625	666667	15·0000000	6·0822020	4444444
226	5 10 76	11 543 176	26 0875 7776	665190	15·0332964	6·0911993	4424779
227	5 15 29	11 697 083	26 5523 7841	663723	15·0665192	6·1001702	4405286
228	5 19 84	11 852 352	27 0233 6256	662266	15·0996689	6·1091147	4385965
229	5 24 41	12 008 989	27 5005 8481	660819	15·1327460	6·1180332	4366812
230	5 29 00	12 167 000	27 9841 0000	659380	15·1657509	6·1269257	4347826
231	5 33 61	12 326 391	28 4739 6321	657952	15·1986842	6·1357924	4329004
232	5 38 24	12 487 168	28 9702 2976	656532	15·2315462	6·1446337	4310345
233	5 42 89	12 649 337	29 4729 5521	655122	15·2643375	6·1534495	4291845
234	5 47 56	12 812 904	29 9821 9536	653720	15·2970585	6·1622401	4273504
235	5 52 25	12 977 875	30 4980 0625	652238	15·3297097	6·1710058	4255319
236	5 56 96	13 144 256	31 0204 4416	650945	15·3622915	6·1797466	4237288
237	5 61 69	13 312 053	31 5495 6561	649570	15·3948043	6·1884628	4219409
238	5 66 44	13 481 272	32 0854 2736	648204	15·4272486	6·1971544	4201681
239	5 71 21	13 651 919	32 6280 8641	646846	15·4596248	6·2058218	4184100
240	5 76 00	13 824 000	33 1776 0000	645497	15·4919334	6·2144650	4166667
241	5 80 81	13 997 521	33 7340 2561	644157	15·5241747	6·2230843	4149378
242	5 85 64	14 172 488	34 2974 2096	642824	15·5563492	6·2316797	4132231
243	5 90 49	14 348 907	34 8678 4401	641500	15·5884573	6·2402515	4115226
244	5 95 36	14 526 784	35 4453 5296	640184	15·6204994	6·2487998	4098361
245	6 00 25	14 706 125	36 0300 0625	638877	15·6524758	6·2573247	4081633
246	6 05 16	14 886 936	36 6218 8256	637577	15·6843871	6·2658266	4065041
247	6 10 09	15 069 223	37 2209 8081	636285	15·7162336	6·2743054	4048583
248	6 15 04	15 252 992	37 8274 2016	635001	15·7480157	6·2827613	4032258
249	6 20 01	15 438 249	38 4412 4001	633724	15·7797338	6·2911946	4016064
250	6 25 00	15 625 000	39 0625 0000	632456	15·8113883	6·2996052	4000000

6

No. n	Square n^2	Cube n^3	Fourth power n^4	$\dfrac{1}{\sqrt{n}}$	Square root $\sqrt{n}$	Cube root $\sqrt[3]{n}$	Reciprocal $\dfrac{1}{n}$
				0·0			0·00
250	6 25 00	15 625 000	39 0625 0000	632456	15·8113883	6·2996052	4000000
251	6 30 01	15 813 251	39 6912 6001	631194	15·8429795	6·3079935	3984064
252	6 35 04	16 003 008	40 3275 8016	629941	15·8745079	6·3163596	3968254
253	6 40 09	16 194 277	40 9715 2081	628695	15·9059737	6·3247035	3952569
254·	6 45 16	16 387 064	41 6231 4256	627456	15·9373775	6·3330255	3937008
255	6 50 25	16 581 375	42 2825 0625	626224	15·9687194	6·3413257	3921569
256	6 55 36	16 777 216	42 9496 7296	625000	16·0000000	6·3496042	3906250
257	6 60 49	16 974 593	43 6247 0401	623783	16·0312195	6·3578612	3891051
258	6 65 64	17 173 512	44 3076 6096	622573	16·0623784	6·3660968	3875969
259	6 70 81	17 373 979	44 9986 0561	621370	16·0934769	6·3743111	3861004
260	6 76 00	17 576 000	45 6976 0000	620174	16·1245155	6·3825043	3846154
261	6 81 21	17 779 581	46 4047 0641	618984	16·1554944	6·3906765	3831418
262	6 86 44	17 984 728	47 1199 8736	617802	16·1864141	6·3988279	3816794
263	6 91 69	18 191 447	47 8435 0561	616626	16·2172747	6·4069586	3802281
264	6 96 96	18 399 744	48 5753 2416	615457	16·2480768	6·4150687	3787879
265	7 02 25	18 609 625	49 3155 0625	614295	16·2788206	6·4231583	3773585
266	7 07 56	18 821 096	50 0641 1536	613139	16·3095064	6·4312276	3759398
267	7 12 89	19 034 163	50 8212 1521	611990	16·3401346	6·4392767	3745318
268	7 18 24	19 248 832	51 5868 6976	610847	16·3707055	6·4473057	3731343
269	7 23 61	19 465 109	52 3611 4321	609711	16·4012195	6·4553148	3717472
270	7 29 00	19 683 000	53 1441 0000	608581	16·4316767	6·4633041	3703704
271	7 34 41	19 902 511	53 9358 0481	607457	16·4620776	6·4712736	3690037
272	7 39 84	20 123 648	54 7363 2256	606339	16·4924225	6·4792236	3676471
273	7 45 29	20 346 417	55 5457 1841	605228	16·5227116	6·4871541	3663004
274	7 50 76	20 570 824	56 3640 5776	604122	16·5529454	6·4950653	3649635
275	7 56 25	20 796 875	57 1914 0625	603023	16·5831240	6·5029572	3636364
276	7 61 76	21 024 576	58 0278 2976	601929	16·6132477	6·5108301	3623188
277	7 67 29	21 253 933	58 8733 9441	600842	16·6433170	6·5186839	3610108
278	7 72 84	21 484 952	59 7281 6656	599760	16·6733320	6·5265189	3597122
279	7 78 41	21 717 639	60 5922 1281	598684	16·7032931	6·5343351	3584229
280	7 84 00	21 952 000	61 4656 0000	597614	16·7332005	6·5421326	3571429
281	7 89 61	22 188 041	62 3483 9521	596550	16·7630546	6·5499116	3558719
282	7 95 24	22 425 768	63 2406 6576	595491	16·7928556	6·5576722	3546099
283	8 00 89	22 665 187	64 1424 7921	594438	16·8226038	6·5654144	3533569
284	8 06 56	22 906 304	65 0539 0336	593391	16·8522995	6·5731385	3521127
285	8 12 25	23 149 125	65 9750 0625	592349	16·8819430	6·5808444	3508772
286	8 17 96	23 393 656	66 9058 5616	591312	16·9115345	6·5885323	3496503
287	8 23 69	23 639 903	67 8465 2161	590281	16·9410743	6·5962023	3484321
288	8 29 44	23 887 872	68 7970 7136	589256	16·9705627	6·6038545	3472222
289	8 35 21	24 137 569	69 7575 7441	588235	17·0000000	6·6114890	3460208
290	8 41 00	24 389 000	70 7281 0000	587220	17·0293864	6·6191059	3448276
291	8 46 81	24 642 171	71 7087 1761	586210	17·0587221	6·6267054	3436426
292	8 52 64	24 897 088	72 6994 9696	585206	17·0880075	6·6342874	3424658
293	8 58 49	25 153 757	73 7005 0801	584206	17·1172428	6·6418522	3412969
294	8 64 36	25 412 184	74 7118 2096	583212	17·1464282	6·6493998	3401361
295	8 70 25	25 672 375	75 7335 0625	582223	17·1755640	6·6569302	3389831
296	8 76 16	25 934 336	76 7656 3456	581238	17·2046505	6·6644437	3378378
297	8 82 09	26 198 073	77 8082 7681	580259	17·2336879	6·6719403	3367003
298	8 88 04	26 463 592	78 8615 0416	579284	17·2626765	6·6794200	3355705
299	8 94 01	26 730 899	79 9253 8801	578315	17·2916165	6·6868831	3344482
300	9 00 00	27 000 000	81 0000 0000	577350	17·3205081	6·6943295	3333333

7

No. n	Square n^2	Cube n^3	Fourth power n^4	$\frac{1}{\sqrt{n}}$	Square root $\sqrt{n}$	Cube root $\sqrt[3]{n}$	Reciprocal $\frac{1}{n}$
				0·0			0·00
300	9 00 00	27 000 000	81 0000 0000	577350	17·3205081	6·6943295	3333333
301	9 06 01	27 270 901	82 0854 1201	576390	17·3493516	6·7017594	3322259
302	9 12 04	27 543 608	83 1816 9616	575435	17·3781472	6·7091729	3311258
303	9 18 09	27 818 127	84 2889 2481	574485	17·4068952	6·7165700	3300330
304	9 24 16	28 094 464	85 4071 7056	573539	17·4355958	6·7239508	3289474
305	9 30 25	28 372 625	86 5365 0625	572598	17·4642492	6·7313155	3278689
306	9 36 36	28 652 616	87 6770 0496	571662	17·4928557	6·7386641	3267974
307	9 42 49	28 934 443	88 8287 4001	570730	17·5214155	6·7459967	3257329
308	9 48 64	29 218 112	89 9917 8496	569803	17·5499288	6·7533134	3246753
309	9 54 81	29 503 629	91 1662 1361	568880	17·5783958	6·7606143	3236246
310	9 61 00	29 791 000	92 3521 0000	567962	17·6068169	6·7678995	3225806
311	9 67 21	30 080 231	93 5495 1841	567048	17·6351921	6·7751690	3215434
312	9 73 44	30 371 328	94 7585 4336	566139	17·6635217	6·7824229	3205128
313	9 79 69	30 664 297	95 9792 4961	565233	17·6918060	6·7896613	3194888
314	9 85 96	30 959 144	97 2117 1216	564333	17·7200451	6·7968844	3184713
315	9 92 25	31 255 875	98 4560 0625	563436	17·7482393	6·8040921	3174603
316	9 98 56	31 554 496	99 7122 0736	562544	17·7763888	6·8112846	3164557
317	10 04 89	31 855 013	100 9803 9121	561656	17·8044938	6·8184619	3154574
318	10 11 24	32 157 432	102 2606 3376	560772	17·8325545	6·8256242	3144654
319	10 17 61	32 461 759	103 5530 1121	559893	17·8605711	6·8327715	3134796
320	10 24 00	32 768 000	104 8576 0000	559017	17·8885438	6·8399038	3125000
321	10 30 41	33 076 161	106 1744 7681	558146	17·9164729	6·8470213	3115265
322	10 36 84	33 386 248	107 5037 1856	557278	17·9443584	6·8541240	3105590
323	10 43 29	33 698 267	108 8454 0241	556415	17·9722008	6·8612120	3095975
324	10 49 76	34 012 224	110 1996 0576	555556	18·0000000	6·8682855	3086420
325	10 56 25	34 328 125	111 5664 0625	554700	18·0277564	6·8753443	3076923
326	10 62 76	34 645 976	112 9458 8176	553849	18·0554701	6·8823888	3067485
327	10 69 29	34 965 783	114 3381 1041	553001	18·0831413	6·8894188	3058104
328	10 75 84	35 287 552	115 7431 7056	552158	18·1107703	6·8964345	3048780
329	10 82 41	35 611 289	117 1611 4081	551318	18·1383571	6·9034359	3039514
330	10 89 00	35 937 000	118 5921 0000	550482	18·1659021	6·9104232	3030303
331	10 95 61	36 264 691	120 0361 2721	549650	18·1934054	6·9173964	3021148
332	11 02 24	36 594 368	121 4933 0176	548821	18·2208672	6·9243556	3012048
333	11 08 89	36 926 037	122 9637 0321	547997	18·2482876	6·9313008	3003003
334	11 15 56	37 259 704	124 4474 1136	547176	18·2756669	6·9382321	2994012
335	11 22 25	37 595 375	125 9445 0625	546358	18·3030052	6·9451496	2985075
336	11 28 96	37 933 056	127 4550 6816	545545	18·3303028	6·9520533	2976190
337	11 35 69	38 272 753	128 9791 7761	544735	18·3575598	6·9589433	2967359
338	11 42 44	38 614 472	130 5169 1536	543928	18·3847763	6·9658198	2958580
339	11 49 21	38 958 219	132 0683 6241	543125	18·4119526	6·9726826	2949853
340	11 56 00	39 304 000	133 6336 0000	542326	18·4390889	6·9795320	2941176
341	11 62 81	39 651 821	135 2127 0961	541530	18·4661853	6·9863680	2932551
342	11 69 64	40 001 688	136 8057 7296	540738	18·4932420	6·9931907	2923977
343	11 76 49	40 353 607	138 4128 7201	539949	18·5202592	7·0000000	2915452
344	11 83 36	40 707 584	140 0340 8896	539164	18·5472370	7·0067961	2906977
345	11 90 25	41 063 625	141 6695 0625	538382	18·5741756	7·0135791	2898551
346	11 97 16	41 421 736	143 3192 0656	537603	18·6010752	7·0203490	2890173
347	12 04 09	41 781 923	144 9832 7281	536828	18·6279360	7·0271058	2881844
348	12 11 04	42 144 192	146 6617 8816	536056	18·6547581	7·0338497	2873563
349	12 18 01	42 5( ) 549	148 3548 3601	535288	18·6815417	7·0405806	2865330
350	12 25 00	42 875 000	150 0625 0000	534522	18·7082869	7·0472987	2857143

No. n	Square n²	Cube n³	Fourth power n⁴	$\frac{1}{\sqrt{n}}$	Square root $\sqrt{n}$	Cube root $\sqrt[3]{n}$	Reciprocal $\frac{1}{n}$
				0·0			0·00
350	12 25 00	42 875 000	150 0625 0000	534522	18·7082869	7·0472987	2857143
351	12 32 01	43 243 551	151 7848 6401	533761	18·7349940	7·0540041	2849003
352	12 39 04	43 614 208	153 5220 1216	533002	18·7616630	7·0606967	2840909
353	12 46 09	43 986 977	155 2740 2881	532246	18·7882942	7·0673766	2832861
354	12 53 16	44 361 864	157 0409 9856	531494	18·8148877	7·0740440	2824859
355	12 60 25	44 738 875	158 8230 0625	530745	18·8414437	7·0806988	2816901
356	12 67 36	45 118 016	160 6201 3696	529999	18·8679623	7·0873411	2808989
357	12 74 49	45 499 293	162 4324 7601	529256	18·8944436	7·0939709	2801120
358	12 81 64	45 882 712	164 2601 0896	528516	18·9208879	7·1005885	2793296
359	12 88 81	46 268 279	166 1031 2161	527780	18·9472953	7·1071937	2785515
360	12 96 00	46 656 000	167 9616 0000	527046	18·9736660	7·1137866	2777778
361	13 03 21	47 045 881	169 8356 3041	526316	19·0000000	7·1203674	2770083
362	13 10 44	47 437 928	171 7252 9936	525588	19·0262976	7·1269360	2762431
363	13 17 69	47 832 147	173 6306 9361	524864	19·0525589	7·1334925	2754821
364	13 24 96	48 228 544	175 5519 0016	524142	19·0787840	7·1400370	2747253
365	13 32 25	48 627 125	177 4890 0625	523424	19·1049732	7·1465695	2739726
366	13 39 56	49 027 896	179 4420 9936	522708	19·1311265	7·1530901	2732240
367	13 46 89	49 430 863	181 4112 6721	521996	19·1572441	7·1595988	2724796
368	13 54 24	49 836 032	183 3965 9776	521286	19·1833261	7·1660957	2717391
369	13 61 61	50 243 409	185 3981 7921	520579	19·2093727	7·1725809	2710027
370	13 69 00	50 653 000	187 4161 0000	519875	19·2353841	7·1790544	2702703
371	13 76 41	51 064 811	189 4504 4881	519174	19·2613603	7·1855162	2695418
372	13 83 84	51 478 848	191 5013 1456	518476	19·2873015	7·1919663	2688172
373	13 91 29	51 895 117	193 5687 8641	517780	19·3132079	7·1984050	2680965
374	13 98 76	52 313 624	195 6529 5376	517088	19·3390796	7·2048321	2673797
375	14 06 25	52 734 375	197 7539 0625	516398	19·3649167	7·2112479	2666667
376	14 13 76	53 157 376	199 8717 3376	515711	19·3907194	7·2176522	2659574
377	14 21 29	53 582 633	202 0065 2641	515026	19·4164878	7·2240451	2652520
378	14 28 84	54 010 152	204 1583 7456	514345	19·4422221	7·2304268	2645503
379	14 36 41	54 439 939	206 3273 6881	513665	19·4679223	7·2367972	2638522
380	14 44 00	54 872 000	208 5136 0000	512989	19·4935887	7·2431564	2631579
381	14 51 61	55 306 341	210 7171 5921	512316	19·5192213	7·2495045	2624672
382	14 59 24	55 742 968	212 9381 3776	511645	19·5448203	7·2558415	2617801
383	14 66 89	56 181 887	215 1766 2721	510976	19·5703858	7·2621674	2610966
384	14 74 56	56 623 104	217 4327 1936	510310	19·5959179	7·2684824	2604167
385	14 82 25	57 066 625	219 7065 0625	509647	19·6214169	7·2747863	2597403
386	14 89 96	57 512 456	221 9980 8016	508987	19·6468827	7·2810794	2590674
387	14 97 69	57 960 603	224 3075 3361	508329	19·6723156	7·2873616	2583979
388	15 05 44	58 411 072	226 6349 5936	507673	19·6977156	7·2936330	2577320
389	15 13 21	58 863 869	228 9804 5041	507020	19·7230829	7·2998937	2570694
390	15 21 00	59 319 000	231 3441 0000	506370	19·7484177	7·3061436	2564103
391	15 28 81	59 776 471	233 7260 0161	505722	19·7737199	7·3123828	2557545
392	15 36 64	60 236 288	236 1262 4896	505076	19·7989899	7·3186114	2551020
393	15 44 49	60 698 457	238 5449 3601	504433	19·8242276	7·3248294	2544529
394	15 52 36	61 162 984	240 9821 5696	503793	19·8494332	7·3310369	2538071
395	15 60 25	61 629 875	243 4380 0625	503155	19·8746069	7·3372339	2531646
396	15 68 16	62 099 136	245 9125 7856	502519	19·8997487	7·3434205	2525253
397	15 76 09	62 570 773	248 4059 6881	501886	19·9248588	7·3495966	2518892
398	15 84 04	63 044 792	250 9182 7216	501255	19·9499373	7·3557624	2512563
399	15 92 01	63 521 199	253 4495 8401	500626	19·9749844	7·3619178	2506266
400	16 00 00	64 000 000	256 0000 0000	500000	20·0000000	7·3680630	2500000

9

No. n	Square n^2	Cube n^3	Fourth power n^4	$\dfrac{1}{\sqrt{n}}$	Square root $\sqrt{n}$	Cube root $\sqrt[3]{n}$	Reciprocal $\dfrac{1}{n}$
				0·0			0·00
400	16 00 00	64 000 000	256 0000 0000	500000	20·0000000	7·3680630	2500000
401	16 08 01	64 481 201	258 5696 1601	499376	20·0249844	7·3741979	2493766
402	16 16 04	64 964 808	261 1585 2816	498755	20·0499377	7·3803227	2487562
403	16 24 09	65 450 827	263 7668 3281	498135	20·0748599	7·3864373	2481390
404	16 32 16	65 939 264	266 3946 2656	497519	20·0997512	7·3925418	2475248
405	16 40 25	66 430 125	269 0420 0625	496904	20·1246118	7·3986362	2469136
406	16 48 36	66 923 416	271 7090 6896	496292	20·1494417	7·4047206	2463054
407	16 56 49	67 419 143	274 3959 1201	495682	20·1742410	7·4107951	2457002
408	16 64 64	67 917 312	277 1026 3296	495074	20·1990099	7·4168595	2450980
409	16 72 81	68 417 929	279 8293 2961	494468	20·2237484	7·4229141	2444988
410	16 81 00	68 921 000	282 5761 0000	493865	20·2484567	7·4289588	2439024
411	16 89 21	69 426 531	285 3430 4241	493264	20·2731349	7·4349937	2433090
412	16 97 44	69 934 528	288 1302 5536	492665	20·2977831	7·4410189	2427184
413	17 05 69	70 444 997	290 9378 3761	492068	20·3224014	7·4470342	2421308
414	17 13 96	70 957 944	293 7658 8816	491473	20·3469899	7·4530399	2415459
415	17 22 25	71 473 375	296 6145 0625	490881	20·3715488	7·4590359	2409639
416	17 30 56	71 991 296	299 4837 9136	490290	20·3960781	7·4650223	2403846
417	17 38 89	72 511 713	302 3738 4321	489702	20·4205779	7·4709991	2398082
418	17 47 24	73 034 632	305 2847 6176	489116	20·4450483	7·4769664	2392344
419	17 55 61	73 560 059	308 2166 4721	488532	20·4694895	7·4829241	2386635
420	17 64 00	74 088 000	311 1696 0000	487950	20·4939015	7·4888724	2380952
421	17 72 41	74 618 461	314 1437 2081	487370	20·5182845	7·4948112	2375297
422	17 80 84	75 151 448	317 1391 1056	486792	20·5426386	7·5007407	2369668
423	17 89 29	75 686 967	320 1558 7041	486217	20·5669638	7·5066607	2364066
424	17 97 76	76 225 024	323 1941 0176	485643	20·5912603	7·5125715	2358491
425	18 06 25	76 765 625	326 2539 0625	485071	20·6155281	7·5184730	2352941
426	18 14 76	77 308 776	329 3353 8576	484502	20·6397674	7·5243652	2347418
427	18 23 29	77 854 483	332 4386 4241	483934	20·6639783	7·5302482	2341920
428	18 31 84	78 402 752	335 5637 7856	483368	20·6881609	7·5361220	2336449
429	18 40 41	78 953 589	338 7108 9681	482805	20·7123152	7·5419867	2331002
430	18 49 00	79 507 000	341 8801 0000	482243	20·7364414	7·5478423	2325581
431	18 57 61	80 062 991	345 0714 9121	481683	20·7605395	7·5536888	2320186
432	18 66 24	80 621 568	348 2851 7376	481125	20·7846097	7·5595263	2314815
433	18 74 89	81 182 737	351 5212 5121	480569	20·8086520	7·5653548	2309469
434	18 83 56	81 746 504	354 7798 2736	480015	20·8326667	7·5711743	2304147
435	18 92 25	82 312 875	358 0610 0625	479463	20·8566536	7·5769849	2298851
436	19 00 96	82 881 856	361 3648 9216	478913	20·8806130	7·5827865	2293578
437	19 09 69	83 453 453	364 6915 8961	478365	20·9045450	7·5885793	2288330
438	19 18 44	84 027 672	368 0412 0336	477818	20·9284495	7·5943633	2283105
439	19 27 21	84 604 519	371 4138 3841	477274	20·9523268	7·6001385	2277904
440	19 36 00	85 184 000	374 8096 0000	476731	20·9761770	7·6059049	2272727
441	19 44 81	85 766 121	378 2285 9361	476190	21·0000000	7·6116626	2267574
442	19 53 64	86 350 888	381 6709 2496	475651	21·0237960	7·6174116	2262443
443	19 62 49	86 938 307	385 1367 0001	475114	21·0475652	7·6231519	2257336
444	19 71 36	87 528 384	388 6260 2496	474579	21·0713075	7·6288836	2252252
445	19 80 25	88 121 125	392 1390 0625	474045	21·0950231	7·6346067	2247191
446	19 89 16	88 716 536	395 6757 5056	473514	21·1187121	7·6403212	2242152
447	19 98 09	89 314 623	399 2363 6481	472984	21·1423745	7·6460272	2237136
448	20 07 04	89 915 392	402 8209 5616	472456	21·1660105	7·6517247	223·143
449	20 16 01	90 518 849	406 4296 3201	471929	21·1896201	7·6574137	2227171
450	20 25 00	91 125 000	410 0625 0000	471405	21·2132034	7·6630943	2222222

No. n	Square n²	Cube n³	Fourth power n⁴	$\frac{1}{\sqrt{n}}$	Square root $\sqrt{n}$	Cube root $\sqrt[3]{n}$	Reciprocal $\frac{1}{n}$
				0·0			0·00
450	20 25 00	91 125 000	410 0625 0000	471405	21·2132034	7·6630943	2222222
451	20 34 01	91 733 851	413 7196 6801	470882	21·2367606	7·6687665	2217295
452	20 43 04	92 345 408	417 4012 4416	470360	21·2602916	7·6744303	2212389
453	20 52 09	92 959 677	421 1073 3681	469841	21·2837967	7·6800857	2207506
454	20 61 16	93 576 664	424 8380 5456	469323	21·3072758	7·6857328	2202643
455	20 70 25	94 196 375	428 5935 0625	468807	21·3307290	7·6913717	2197802
456	20 79 36	94 818 816	432 3738 0096	468293	21·3541565	7·6970023	2192982
457	20 88 49	95 443 993	436 1790 4801	467780	21·3775583	7·7026246	2188184
458	20 97 64	96 071 912	440 0093 5696	467269	21·4009346	7·7082388	2183406
459	21 06 81	96 702 579	443 8648 3761	466760	21·4242853	7·7138448	2178649
460	21 16 00	97 336 000	447 7456 0000	466252	21·4476106	7·7194426	2173913
461	21 25 21	97 972 181	451 6517 5401	465746	21·4709106	7·7250324	2169197
462	21 34 44	98 611 128	455 5834 1136	465242	21·4941853	7·7306141	2164502
463	21 43 69	99 252 847	459 5406 8161	464739	21·5174348	7·7361877	2159827
464	21 52 96	99 897 344	463 5236 7616	464238	21·5406592	7·7417533	2155172
465	21 62 25	100 544 625	467 5325 0625	463739	21·5638587	7·7473109	2150538
466	21 71 56	101 194 696	471 5672 8336	463241	21·5870331	7·7528605	2145923
467	21 80 89	101 847 563	475 6281 1921	462745	21·6101828	7·7584023	2141328
468	21 90 24	102 503 232	479 7151 2576	462250	21·6333077	7·7639361	2136752
469	21 99 61	103 161 709	483 8284 1521	461757	21·6564078	7·7694620	2132196
470	22 09 00	103 823 000	487 9681 0000	461266	21·6794834	7·7749801	2127660
471	22 18 41	104 487 111	492 1342 9281	460776	21·7025344	7·7804904	2123142
472	22 27 84	105 154 048	496 3271 0656	460287	21·7255610	7·7859928	2118644
473	22 37 29	105 823 817	500 5466 5441	459800	21·7485632	7·7914875	2114165
474	22 46 76	106 496 424	504 7930 4976	459315	21·7715411	7·7969745	2109705
475	22 56 25	107 171 875	509 0664 0625	458831	21·7944947	7·8024538	2105263
476	22 65 76	107 850 176	513 3668 3776	458349	21·8174242	7·8079253	2100840
477	22 75 29	108 531 333	517 6944 5841	457869	21·8403297	7·8133892	2096436
478	22 84 84	109 215 352	522 0493 8256	457389	21·8632111	7·8188455	2092050
479	22 94 41	109 902 239	526 4317 2481	456912	21·8860686	7·8242942	2087683
480	23 04 00	110 592 000	530 8416 0000	456435	21·9089023	7·8297353	2083333
481	23 13 61	111 284 641	535 2791 2321	455961	21·9317122	7·8351688	2079002
482	23 23 24	111 980 168	539 7444 0976	455488	21·9544984	7·8405948	2074689
483	23 32 89	112 678 587	544 2375 7521	455016	21·9772610	7·8460134	2070393
484	23 42 56	113 379 904	548 7587 3536	454545	22·0000000	7·8514244	2066116
485	23 52 25	114 084 125	553 3080 0625	454077	22·0227155	7·8568280	2061856
486	23 61 96	114 791 256	557 8855 0416	453609	22·0454077	7·8622242	2057613
487	23 71 69	115 501 303	562 4913 4561	453143	22·0680765	7·8676130	2053388
488	23 81 44	116 214 272	567 1256 4736	452679	22·0907220	7·8729944	2049180
489	23 91 21	116 930 169	571 7885 2641	452216	22·1133444	7·8783684	2044990
490	24 01 00	117 649 000	576 4801 0000	451754	22·1359436	7·8837352	2040816
491	24 10 81	118 370 771	581 2004 8561	451294	22·1585198	7·8890946	2036660
492	24 20 64	119 095 488	585 9498 0096	450835	22·1810730	7·8944468	2032520
493	24 30 49	119 823 157	590 7281 6401	450377	22·2036033	7·8997917	2028398
494	24 40 36	120 553 784	595 5356 9296	449921	22·2261108	7·9051294	2024291
495	24 50 25	121 287 375	600 3725 0625	449467	22·2485955	7·9104599	2020202
496	24 60 16	122 023 936	605 2387 2256	449013	22·2710575	7·9157832	2016129
497	24 70 09	122 763 473	610 1344 6081	448561	22·2934968	7·9210994	2012072
498	24 80 04	123 505 992	615 0598 4016	448111	22·3159136	7·9264084	2008032
499	24 90 01	124 251 499	620 0149 8001	447661	22·3383079	7·9317104	2004008
500	25 00 00	125 000 000	625 0000 0000	447214	22·3606798	7·9370053	2000000

No. n	Square n²	Cube n³	Fourth power n⁴	$\frac{1}{\sqrt{n}}$	Square root √n	Cube root ∛n	Reciprocal $\frac{1}{n}$
				0·0			0·00
500	25 00 00	125 000 000	625 0000 0000	447214	22·3606798	7·9370053	2000000
501	25 10 01	125 751 501	630 0150 2001	446767	22·3830293	7·9422931	1996008
502	25 20 04	126 506 008	635 0601 6016	446322	22·4053565	7·9475739	1992032
503	25 30 09	127 263 527	640 1355 4081	445878	22·4276615	7·9528476	1988072
504	25 40 16	128 024 064	645 2412 8256	445435	22·4499443	7·9581144	1984127
505	25 50 25	128 787 625	650 3775 0625	444994	22·4722051	7·9633742	1980198
506	25 60 36	129 554 216	655 5443 3296	444554	22·4944438	7·9686271	1976285
507	25 70 49	130 323 843	660 7418 8401	444116	22·5166605	7·9738731	1972387
508	25 80 64	131 096 512	665 9702 8096	443678	22·5388553	7·9791122	1968504
509	25 90 81	131 872 229	671 2296 4561	443242	22·5610283	7·9843444	1964637
510	26 01 00	132 651 000	676 5201 0000	442807	22·5831796	7·9895697	1960784
511	26 11 21	133 432 831	681 8417 6641	442374	22·6053091	7·9947883	1956947
512	26 21 44	134 217 728	687 1947 6736	441942	22·6274170	8·0000000	1953125
513	26 31 69	135 005 697	692 5792 2561	441511	22·6495033	8·0052049	1949318
514	26 41 96	135 796 744	697 9952 6416	441081	22·6715681	8·0104031	1945525
515	26 52 25	136 590 875	703 4430 0625	440653	22·6936114	8·0155946	1941748
516	26 62 56	137 388 096	708 9225 7536	440225	22·7156334	8·0207793	1937984
517	26 72 89	138 188 413	714 4340 9521	439799	22·7376340	8·0259574	1934236
518	26 83 24	138 991 832	719 9776 8976	439375	22·7596134	8·0311287	1930502
519	26 93 61	139 798 359	725 5534 8321	438951	22·7815715	8·0362934	1926782
520	27 04 00	140 608 000	731 1616 0000	438529	22·8035085	8·0414515	1923077
521	27 14 41	141 420 761	736 8021 6481	438108	22·8254244	8·0466030	1919386
522	27 24 84	142 236 648	742 4753 0256	437688	22·8473193	8·0517479	1915709
523	27 35 29	143 055 667	748 1811 3841	437269	22·8691933	8·0568862	1912046
524	27 45 76	143 877 824	753 9197 9776	436852	22·8910463	8·0620180	1908397
525	27 56 25	144 703 125	759 6914 0625	436436	22·9128785	8·0671432	1904762
526	27 66 76	145 531 576	765 4960 8976	436021	22·9346899	8·0722620	1901141
527	27 77 29	146 363 183	771 3339 7441	435607	22·9564806	8·0773742	1897533
528	27 87 84	147 197 952	777 2051 8656	435194	22·9782506	8·0824800	1893939
529	27 98 41	148 035 889	783 1098 5281	434783	23·0000000	8·0875794	1890359
530	28 09 00	148 877 000	789 0481 0000	434372	23·0217289	8·0926723	1886792
531	28 19 61	149 721 291	795 0200 5521	433963	23·0434372	8·0977589	1883229
532	28 30 24	150 568 768	801 0258 4576	433555	23·0651252	8·1028390	1879699
533	28 40 89	151 419 437	807 0655 9921	433148	23·0867928	8·1079128	1876173
534	28 51 56	152 273 304	813 1394 4336	432742	23·1084400	8·1129803	1872659
535	28 62 25	153 130 375	819 2475 0625	432338	23·1300670	8·1180414	1869159
536	28 72 96	153 990 656	825 3899 1616	431934	23·1516738	8·1230962	1865672
537	28 83 69	154 854 153	831 5668 0161	431532	23·1732605	8·1281447	1862197
538	28 94 44	155 720 872	837 7782 9136	431131	23·1948270	8·1331870	1858736
539	29 05 21	156 590 819	844 0245 1441	430730	23·2163735	8·1382230	1855288
540	29 16 00	157 464 000	850 3056 0000	430331	23·2379001	8·1432528	1851852
541	29 26 81	158 340 421	856 6216 7761	429934	23·2594067	8·1482764	1848429
542	29 37 64	159 220 088	862 9728 7696	429537	23·2808935	8·1532939	1845018
543	29 48 49	160 103 007	869 3593 2801	429141	23·3023604	8·1583051	1841621
544	29 59 36	160 989 184	875 7811 6096	428746	23·3238076	8·1633102	1838235
545	29 70 25	161 878 625	882 2385 0625	428353	23·3452351	8·1683092	1834862
546	29 81 16	162 771 336	888 7314 9456	427960	23·3666429	8·1733020	1831502
547	29 92 09	163 667 323	895 2602 5681	427569	23·3880311	8·1782888	1828154
548	30 03 04	164 566 592	901 8249 2416	427179	23·4093998	8·1832695	1824818
549	30 14 01	165 469 149	908 4256 2801	426790	23·4307490	8·1882441	1821494
550	30 25 00	166 375 000	915 0625 0000	426401	23·4520788	8·1932127	1818182

12

No. n	Square n^2	Cube n^3	Fourth power n^4	$\dfrac{1}{\sqrt{n}}$	Square root $\sqrt{n}$	Cube root $\sqrt[3]{n}$	Reciprocal $\dfrac{1}{n}$
				0·0			0·00
550	30 25 00	166 375 000	915 0625 0000	426401	23·4520788	8·1932127	1818182
551	30 36 01	167 284 151	921 7356 7201	426014	23·4733892	8·1981753	1814882
552	30 47 04	168 196 608	928 4452 7616	425628	23·4946802	8·2031319	1811594
553	30 58 09	169 112 377	935 1914 4481	425243	23·5159520	8·2080825	1808318
554	30 69 16	170 031 464	941 9743 1056	424859	23·5372046	8·2130271	1805054
555	30 80 25	170 953 875	948 7940 0625	424476	23·5584380	8·2179657	1801802
556	30 91 36	171 879 616	955 6506 6496	424094	23·5796522	8·2228985	1798561
557	31 02 49	172 808 693	962 5444 2001	423714	23·6008474	8·2278254	1795332
558	31 13 64	173 741 112	969 4754 0496	423334	23·6220236	8·2327463	1792115
559	31 24 81	174 676 879	976 4437 5361	422955	23·6431808	8·2376614	1788909
560	31 36 00	175 616 000	983 4496 0000	422577	23·6643191	8·2425706	1785714
561	31 47 21	176 558 481	990 4930 7841	422200	23·6854386	8·2474740	1782531
562	31 58 44	177 504 328	997 5743 2336	421825	23·7065392	8·2523715	1779359
563	31 69 69	178 453 547	1004 6934 6961	421450	23·7276210	8·2572633	1776199
564	31 80 96	179 406 144	1011 8506 5216	421076	23·7486842	8·2621492	1773050
565	31 92 25	180 362 125	1019 0460 0625	420703	23·7697286	8·2670294	1769912
566	32 03 56	181 321 496	1026 2796 6736	420331	23·7907545	8·2719038	1766784
567	32 14 89	182 284 263	1033 5517 7121	419961	23·8117618	8·2767725	1763668
568	32 26 24	183 250 432	1040 8624 5376	419591	23·8327506	8·2816355	1760563
569	32 37 61	184 220 009	1048 2118 5121	419222	23·8537209	8·2864928	1757469
570	32 49 00	185 193 000	1055 6001 0000	418854	23·8746728	8·2913443	1754386
571	32 60 41	186 169 411	1063 0273 3681	418487	23·8956063	8·2961902	1751313
572	32 71 84	187 149 248	1070 4936 9856	418121	23·9165215	8·3010305	1748252
573	32 83 29	188 132 517	1077 9993 2241	417756	23·9374184	8·3058651	1745201
574	32 94 76	189 119 224	1085 5443 4576	417392	23·9582971	8·3106941	1742160
575	33 06 25	190 109 375	1093 1289 0625	417029	23·9791576	8·3155175	1739130
576	33 17 76	191 102 976	1100 7531 4176	416667	24·0000000	8·3203353	1736111
577	33 29 29	192 100 033	1108 4171 9041	416305	24·0208243	8·3251475	1733102
578	33 40 84	193 100 552	1116 1211 9056	415945	24·0416306	8·3299542	1730104
579	33 52 41	194 104 539	1123 8652 8081	415586	24·0624188	8·3347553	1727116
580	33 64 00	195 112 000	1131 6496 0000	415227	24·0831892	8·3395509	1724138
581	33 75 61	196 122 941	1139 4742 8721	414870	24·1039416	8·3443410	1721170
582	33 87 24	197 137 368	1147 3394 8176	414513	24·1246762	8·3491256	1718213
583	33 98 89	198 155 287	1155 2453 2321	414158	24·1453929	8·3539047	1715266
584	34 10 56	199 176 704	1163 1919 5136	413803	24·1660919	8·3586784	1712329
585	34 22 25	200 201 625	1171 1795 0625	413449	24·1867732	8·3634466	1709402
586	34 33 96	201 230 056	1179 2081 2816	413096	24·2074369	8·3682094	1706485
587	34 45 69	202 262 003	1187 2779 5761	412744	24·2280829	8·3729668	1703578
588	34 57 44	203 297 472	1195 3891 3536	412393	24·2487113	8·3777187	1700680
589	34 69 21	204 336 469	1203 5418 0241	412043	24·2693222	8·3824653	1697793
590	34 81 00	205 379 000	1211 7361 0000	411693	24·2899156	8·3872065	1694915
591	34 92 81	206 425 071	1219 9721 6961	411345	24·3104916	8·3919424	1692047
592	35 04 64	207 474 688	1228 2501 5296	410997	24·3310501	8·3966729	1689189
593	35 16 49	208 527 857	1236 5701 9201	410651	24·3515913	8·4013981	1686341
594	35 28 36	209 584 584	1244 9324 2896	410305	24·3721152	8·4061180	1683502
595	35 40 25	210 644 875	1253 3370 0625	409960	24·3926218	8·4108326	1680672
596	35 52 16	211 708 736	1261 7840 6656	409616	24·4131112	8·4155419	1677852
597	35 64 09	212 776 173	1270 2737 5281	409273	24·4335834	8·4202459	1675042
598	35 76 04	213 847 192	1278 8062 0816	408930	24·4540385	8·4249447	1672241
599	35 88 01	214 921 799	1287 3815 7601	408589	24·4744765	8·4296383	1669449
600	36 00 00	216 000 000	1296 0000 0000	408248	24·4948974	8·4343267	1666667

13

No. n	Square n^2	Cube n^3	Fourth power n^4	$\dfrac{1}{\sqrt{n}}$	Square root $\sqrt{n}$	Cube root $\sqrt[3]{n}$	Reciprocal $\dfrac{1}{n}$
				0·0			0·00
600	36 00 00	216 000 000	1296 0000 0000	408248	24·4948974	8·4343267	1666667
601	36 12 01	217 081 801	1304 6616 2401	407909	24·5153013	8·4390098	1663894
602	36 24 04	218 167 208	1313 3665 9216	407570	24·5356883	8·4436877	1661130
603	36 36 09	219 256 227	1322 1150 4881	407231	24·5560583	8·4483605	1658375
604	36 48 16	220 348 864	1330 9071 3856	406894	24·5764115	8·4530281	1655629
605	36 60 25	221 445 125	1339 7430 0625	406558	24·5967478	8·4576906	1652893
606	36 72 36	222 545 016	1348 6227 9696	406222	24·6170673	8·4623479	1650165
607	36 84 49	223 648 543	1357 5466 5601	405887	24·6373700	8·4670001	1647446
608	36 96 64	224 755 712	1366 5147 2896	405554	24·6576560	8·4716472	1644737
609	37 08 81	225 866 529	1375 5271 6161	405220	24·6779254	8·4762892	1642036
610	37 21 00	226 981 000	1384 5841 0000	404888	24·6981781	8·4809261	1639344
611	37 33 21	228 099 131	1393 6856 9041	404557	24·7184142	8·4855579	1636661
612	37 45 44	229 220 928	1402 8320 7936	404226	24·7386338	8·4901847	1633987
613	37 57 69	230 346 397	1412 0234 1361	403896	24·7588368	8·4948065	1631321
614	37 69 96	231 475 544	1421 2598 4016	403567	24·7790234	8·4994233	1628664
615	37 82 25	232 608 375	1430 5415 0625	403239	24·7991935	8·5040350	1626016
616	37 94 56	233 744 896	1439 8685 5936	402911	24·8193473	8·5086417	1623377
617	38 06 89	234 885 113	1449 2411 4721	402585	24·8394847	8·5132435	1620746
618	38 19 24	236 029 032	1458 6594 1776	402259	24·8596058	8·5178403	1618123
619	38 31 61	237 176 659	1468 1235 1921	401934	24·8797106	8·5224321	1615509
620	38 44 00	238 328 000	1477 6336 0000	401610	24·8997992	8·5270190	1612903
621	38 56 41	239 483 061	1487 1898 0881	401286	24·9198716	8·5316009	1610306
622	38 68 84	240 641 848	1496 7922 9456	400963	24·9399278	8·5361780	1607717
623	38 81 29	241 804 367	1506 4412 0641	400642	24·9599679	8·5407501	1605136
624	38 93 76	242 970 624	1516 1366 9376	400320	24·9799920	8·5453174	1602564
625	39 06 25	244 140 625	1525 8789 0625	400000	25·0000000	8·5498797	1600000
626	39 18 76	245 314 376	1535 6679 9376	399680	25·0199920	8·5544372	1597444
627	39 31 29	246 491 883	1545 5041 0641	399362	25·0399681	8·5589899	1594896
628	39 43 84	247 673 152	1555 3873 9456	399043	25·0599282	8·5635377	1592357
629	39 56 41	248 858 189	1565 3180 0881	398726	25·0798724	8·5680807	1589825
630	39 69 00	250 047 000	1575 2961 0000	398410	25·0998008	8·5726189	1587302
631	39 81 61	251 239 591	1585 3218 1921	398094	25·1197134	8·5771523	1584786
632	39 94 24	252 435 968	1595 3953 1776	397779	25·1396102	8·5816809	1582278
633	40 06 89	253 636 137	1605 5167 4721	397464	25·1594913	8·5862047	1579779
634	40 19 56	254 840 104	1615 6862 5936	397151	25·1793566	8·5907237	1577287
635	40 32 25	256 047 875	1625 9040 0625	396838	25·1992063	8·5952380	1574803
636	40 44 96	257 259 456	1636 1701 4016	396526	25·2190404	8·5997476	1572327
637	40 57 69	258 474 853	1646 4848 1361	396214	25·2388589	8·6042524	1569859
638	40 70 44	259 694 072	1656 8481 7936	395904	25·2586619	8·6087526	1567398
639	40 83 21	260 917 119	1667 2603 9041	395594	25·2784493	8·6132480	1564945
640	40 96 00	262 144 000	1677 7216 0000	395285	25·2982213	8·6177388	1562500
641	41 08 81	263 374 721	1688 2319 6161	394976	25·3179778	8·6222248	1560062
642	41 21 64	264 609 288	1698 7916 2896	394669	25·3377189	8·6267062	1557632
643	41 34 49	265 847 707	1709 4007 5601	394362	25·3574447	8·6311830	1555210
644	41 47 36	267 089 984	1720 0594 9696	394055	25·3771551	8·6356551	1552795
645	41 60 25	268 336 125	1730 7680 0625	393750	25·3968502	8·6401226	1550388
646	41 73 16	269 586 136	1741 5264 3856	393445	25·4165301	8·6445855	1547988
647	41 86 09	270 840 023	1752 3349 4881	393141	25·4361947	8·6490437	1545595
648	41 99 04	272 097 792	1763 1936 9216	392837	25·4558441	8·6534974	1543210
649	42 12 01	273 359 449	1774 1028 2401	392534	25·4754784	8·6579465	1540832
650	42 25 00	274 625 000	1785 0625 0000	392232	25·4950976	8·6623911	1538462

14

No. n	Square n^2	Cube n^3	Fourth power n^4	$\dfrac{1}{\sqrt{n}}$	Square root $\sqrt{n}$	Cube root $\sqrt[3]{n}$	Reciprocal $\dfrac{1}{n}$
				0·0			0·00
650	42 25 00	274 625 000	1785 0625 0000	392232	25·4950976	8·6623911	1538462
651	42 38 01	275 894 451	1796 0728 7601	391931	25·5147016	8·6668310	1536098
652	42 51 04	277 167 808	1807 1341 0816	391630	25·5342907	8·6712665	1533742
653	42 64 09	278 445 077	1818 2463 5281	391330	25·5538647	8·6756974	1531394
654	42 77 16	279 726 264	1829 4097 6656	391031	25·5734237	8·6801237	1529052
655	42 90 25	281 011 375	1840 6245 0625	390732	25·5929678	8·6845456	1526718
656	43 03 36	282 300 416	1851 8907 2896	390434	25·6124969	8·6889630	1524390
657	43 16 49	283 593 393	1863 2085 9201	390137	25·6320112	8·6933759	1522070
658	43 29 64	284 890 312	1874 5782 5296	389841	25·6515107	8·6977843	1519757
659	43 42 81	286 191 179	1885 9998 6961	389545	25·6709953	8·7021882	1517451
660	43 56 00	287 496 000	1897 4736 0000	389249	25·6904652	8·7065877	1515152
661	43 69 21	288 804 781	1908 9996 0241	388955	25·7099203	8·7109827	1512859
662	43 82 44	290 117 528	1920 5780 3536	388661	25·7293607	8·7153734	1510574
663	43 95 69	291 434 247	1932 2090 5761	388368	25·7487864	8·7197596	1508296
664	44 08 96	292 754 944	1943 8928 2816	388075	25·7681975	8·7241413	1506024
665	44 22 25	294 079 625	1955 6295 0625	387783	25·7875939	8·7285187	1503759
666	44 35 56	295 408 296	1967 4192 5136	387492	25·8069758	8·7328917	1501502
667	44 48 89	296 740 963	1979 2622 2321	387202	25·8263431	8·7372604	1499250
668	44 62 24	298 077 632	1991 1585 8176	386912	25·8456960	8·7416246	1497006
669	44 75 61	299 418 309	2003 1084 8721	386622	25·8650343	8·7459846	1494768
670	44 89 00	300 763 000	2015 1121 0000	386334	25·8843582	8·7503401	1492537
671	45 02 41	302 111 711	2027 1695 8081	386046	25·9036677	8·7546914	1490313
672	45 15 84	303 464 448	2039 2810 9056	385758	25·9229628	8·7590383	1488095
673	45 29 29	304 821 217	2051 4467 9041	385472	25·9422435	8·7633809	1485884
674	45 42 76	306 182 024	2063 6668 4176	385186	25·9615100	8·7677192	1483680
675	45 56 25	307 546 875	2075 9414 0625	384900	25·9807621	8·7720532	1481481
676	45 69 76	308 915 776	2088 2706 4576	384615	26·0000000	8·7763830	1479290
677	45 83 29	310 288 733	2100 6547 2241	384331	26·0192237	8·7807084	1477105
678	45 96 84	311 665 752	2113 0937 9856	384048	26·0384331	8·7850296	1474926
679	46 10 41	313 046 839	2125 5880 3681	383765	26·0576284	8·7893466	1472754
680	46 24 00	314 432 900	2138 1376 0000	383482	26·0768096	8·7936593	1470588
681	46 37 61	315 821 241	2150 7426 5121	383201	26·0959767	8·7979679	1468429
682	46 51 24	317 214 568	2163 4033 5376	382920	26·1151297	8·8022721	1466276
683	46 64 89	318 611 987	2176 1198 7121	382639	26·1342687	8·8065722	1464129
684	46 78 56	320 013 504	2188 8923 6736	382360	26·1533937	8·8108681	1461988
685	46 92 25	321 419 125	2201 7210 0625	382080	26·1725047	8·8151598	1459854
686	47 05 96	322 828 856	2214 6059 5216	381802	26·1916017	8·8194473	1457726
687	47 19 69	324 242 703	2227 5473 6961	381524	26·2106848	8·8237307	1455604
688	47 33 44	325 660 672	2240 5454 2336	381246	26·2297541	8·8280099	1453488
689	47 47 21	327 082 769	2253 6002 7841	380970	26·2488095	8·8322850	1451379
690	47 61 00	328 509 000	2266 7121 0000	380693	26·2678511	8·8365559	1449275
691	47 74 81	329 939 371	2279 8810 5361	380418	26·2868789	8·8408227	1447178
692	47 88 64	331 373 888	2293 1073 0496	380143	26·3058929	8·8450854	1445087
693	48 02 49	332 812 557	2306 3910 2001	379869	26·3248932	8·8493440	1443001
694	48 16 36	334 255 384	2319 7323 6496	379595	26·3438797	8·8535985	1440922
695	48 30 25	335 702 375	2333 1315 0625	379322	26·3628527	8·8578489	1438849
696	48 44 16	337 153 536	2346 5886 1056	379049	26·3818119	8·8620952	1436782
697	48 58 09	338 608 873	2360 1038 4481	378777	26·4007576	8·8663375	1434720
698	48 72 04	340 068 392	2373 6773 7616	378506	26·4196896	8·8705757	1432665
699	48 86 01	341 532 099	2387 3093 7201	378235	26·4386081	8·8748099	1430615
700	49 00 00	343 000 000	2401 0000 0000	377964	26·4575131	8·8790400	1428571

15

No. n	Square n^2	Cube n^3	Fourth power n^4	$\frac{1}{\sqrt{n}}$	Square root $\sqrt{n}$	Cube root $\sqrt[3]{n}$	Reciprocal $\frac{1}{n}$
				0·0			0·00
700	49 00 00	343 000 000	2401 0000 0000	377964	26·4575131	8·8790400	1428571
701	49 14 01	344 472 101	2414 7494 2801	377695	26·4764046	8·8832661	1426534
702	49 28 04	345 948 408	2428 5578 2416	377426	26·4952826	8·8874882	1424501
703	49 42 09	347 428 927	2442 4253 5681	377157	26·5141472	8·8917063	1422475
704	49 56 16	348 913 664	2456 3521 9456	376889	26·5329983	8·8959204	1420455
705	49 70 25	350 402 625	2470 3385 0625	376622	26·5518361	8·9001305	1418440
706	49 84 36	351 895 816	2484 3844 6096	376355	26·5706605	8·9043366	1416431
707	49 98 49	353 393 243	2498 4902 2801	376089	26·5894716	8·9085387	1414427
708	50 12 64	354 894 912	2512 6559 7696	375823	26·6082694	8·9127369	1412429
709	50 26 81	356 400 829	2526 8818 7761	375558	26·6270539	8·9169311	1410437
710	50 41 00	357 911 000	2541 1681 0000	375293	26·6458252	8·9211214	1408451
711	50 55 21	359 425 431	2555 5148 1441	375029	26·6645833	8·9253078	1406470
712	50 69 44	360 944 128	2569 9221 9136	374766	26·6833281	8·9294902	1404494
713	50 83 69	362 467 097	2584 3904 0161	374503	26·7020598	8·9336687	1402525
714	50 97 96	363 994 344	2598 9196 1616	374241	26·7207784	8·9378433	1400560
715	51 12 25	365 525 875	2613 5100 0625	373979	26·7394839	8·9420140	1398601
716	51 26 56	367 061 696	2628 1617 4336	373718	26·7581763	8·9461809	1396648
717	51 40 89	368 601 813	2642 8749 9921	373457	26·7768557	8·9503438	1394700
718	51 55 24	370 146 232	2657 6499 4576	373197	26·7955220	8 9545029	1392758
719	51 69 61	371 694 959	2672 4867 5521	372937	26·8141754	8·9586581	1390821
720	51 84 00	373 248 000	2687 3856 0000	372678	26·8328157	8·9628095	1388889
721	51 98 41	374 805 361	2702 3466 5281	372419	26·8514432	8·9669570	1386963
722	52 12 84	376 367 048	2717 3700 8656	372161	26·8700577	8·9711007	1385042
723	52 27 29	377 933 067	2732 4560 7441	371904	26·8886593	8·9752406	1383126
724	52 41 76	379 503 424	2747 6047 8976	371647	26·9072481	8·9793766	1381215
725	52 56 25	381 078 125	2762 8164 0625	371391	26·9258240	8·9835089	1379310
726	52 70 76	382 657 176	2778 0910 9776	371135	26·9443872	8·9876373	1377410
727	52 85 29	384 240 583	2793 4290 3841	370879	26·9629375	8·9917620	1375516
728	52 99 84	385 828 352	2808 8304 0256	370625	26·9814751	8·9958829	1373626
729	53 14 41	387 420 489	2824 2953 6481	370370	27·0000000	9·0000000	1371742
730	53 29 00	389 017 000	2839 8241 0000	370117	27·0185122	9·0041133	1369863
731	53 43 61	390 617 891	2855 4167 8321	369863	27·0370117	9·0082229	1367989
732	53 58 24	392 223 168	2871 0735 8976	369611	27·0554985	9·0123288	1366120
733	53 72 89	393 832 837	2886 7946 9521	369358	27·0739727	9·0164309	1364256
734	53 87 56	395 446 904	2902 5802 7536	369107	27·0924344	9·0205293	1362398
735	54 02 25	397 065 375	2918 4305 0625	368856	27·1108834	9·0246239	1360544
736	54 16 96	398 688 256	2934 3455 6416	368605	27·1293199	9·0287149	1358696
737	54 31 69	400 315 553	2950 3256 2561	368355	27·1477439	9·0328021	1356852
738	54 46 44	401 947 272	2966 3708 6736	368105	27·1661554	9·0368857	1355014
739	54 61 21	403 583 419	2982 4814 6641	367856	27·1845544	9·0409655	1353180
740	54 76 00	405 224 000	2998 6576 0000	367607	27·2029410	9·0450417	1351351
741	54 90 81	406 869 021	3014 8994 4561	367359	27·2213152	9·0491142	1349528
742	55 05 64	408 518 488	3031 2071 8096	367112	27·2396769	9·0531831	1347709
743	55 20 49	410 172 407	3047 5809 8401	366864	27·2580263	9·0572482	1345895
744	55 35 36	411 830 784	3064 0210 3296	366618	27·2763634	9·0613098	1344086
745	55 50 25	413 493 625	3080 5275 0625	366372	27·2946881	9·0653677	1342282
746	55 65 16	415 160 936	3097 1005 8256	366126	27·3130006	9·0694220	1340483
747	55 80 09	416 832 723	3113 7404 4081	365881	27·3313007	9·0734726	1338668
748	55 95 04	418 508 992	3130 4472 6016	365636	27·3495887	9·0775197	1336898
749	56 10 01	420 189 749	3147 2212 2001	365392	27·3678644	9·0815631	1335113
750	56 25 00	421 875 000	3164 0625 0000	365148	27·3861279	9·0856030	1333333

No. n	Square n^2	Cube n^3	Fourth power n^4	$\dfrac{1}{\sqrt{n}}$	Square root $\sqrt{n}$	Cube root $\sqrt[3]{n}$	Reciprocal $\dfrac{1}{n}$
				0·0			0·00
750	56 25 00	421 875 000	3164 0625 0000	365148	27·3861279	9·0856030	1333333
751	56 40 01	423 564 751	3180 9712 8001	364905	27·4043792	9·0896392	1331558
752	56 55 04	425 259 008	3197 9477 4016	364662	27·4226184	9·0936719	1329787
753	56 70 09	426 957 777	3214 9920 6081	364420	27·4408455	9·0977010	1328021
754	56 85 16	428 661 064	3232 1044 2256	364179	27·4590604	9·1017265	1326260
755	57 00 25	430 368 875	3249 2850 0625	363937	27·4772633	9·1057485	1324503
756	57 15 36	432 081 216	3266 5339 9296	363696	27·4954542	9·1097669	1322751
757	57 30 49	433 798 093	3283 8515 6401	363456	27·5136330	9·1137818	1321004
758	57 45 64	435 519 512	3301 2379 0096	363216	·27·5317998	9·1177931	1319261
759	57 60 81	437 245 479	3318 6931 8561	362977	27·5499546	9·1218010	1317523
760	57 76 00	438 976 000	3336 2176 0000	362738	27·5680975	9·1258053	1315789
761	57 91 21	440 711 081	3353 8113 2641	362500	27·5862284	9·1298061	1314060
762	58 06 44	442 450 728	3371 4745 4736	362262	27·6043475	9·1338034	1312336
763	58 21 69	444 194 947	3389 2074 4561	362024	27·6224546	9·1377971	1310616
764	58 36 96	445 943 744	3407 0102 0416	361787	27·6405499	9·1417874	1308901
765	58 52 25	447 697 125	3424 8830 0625	361551	27·6586334	9·1457743	1307190
766	58 67 56	449 455 096	3442 8260 3536	361315	27·6767050	9·1497576	1305483
767	58 82 89	451 217 663	3460 8394 7521	361079	27·6947648	9·1537375	1303781
768	58 98 24	452 984 832	3478 9235 0976	360844	27·7128129	9·1577139	1302083
769	59 13 61	454 756 609	3497 0783 2321	360609	27·7308492	9·1616869	1300390
770	59.29 00	456 533 000	3515 3041 0000	360375	27·7488739	9·1656565	1298701
771	59 44 41	458 314 011	3533 6010 2481	360141	27·7668868	9·1696226	1297017
772	59 59 84	460 099 648	3551 9692 8256	359908	27·7848880	9·1735852	1295337
773	59 75 29	461 889 917	3570 4090 5841	359675	27·8028771	9·1775445	1293661
774	59 90 76	463 684 824	3588 9205 3776	359443	27·8208555	9·1815003	1291990
775	60 06 25	465 484 375	3607 5039 0625	359211	27·8388218	9·1854528	1290323
776	60 21 76	467 288 576	3626 1593 4976	358979	27·8567766	9·1894018	1288660
777	60 37 29	469 097 433	3644 8870 5441	358748	27·8747197	9·1933474	1287001
778	60 52 84	470 910 952	3663 6872 0656	358517	27·8926514	9·1972897	1285347
779	60 68 41	472 729 139	3682 5599 9281	358287	27·9105715	9·2012286	1283697
780	60 84 00	474 552 000	3701 5056 0000	358057	27·9284801	9·2051641	1282051
781	60 99 61	476 379 541	3720 5242 1521	357828	27·9463772	9·2090962	1280410
782	61 15 24	478 211 768	3739 6160 2576	357599	27·9642629	9·2130250	1278772
783	61 30 89	480 048 687	3758 7812 1921	357371	27·9821372	9·2169505	1277139
784	61 46 56	481 890 304	3778 0199 8336	357143	28·0000000	9·2208726	1275510
785	61 62 25	483 736 625	3797 3325 0625	356915	28·0178515	9·2247914	1273885
786	61 77 96	485 587 656	3816 7189 7616	356688	28·0356915	9·2287068	1272265
787	61 93 69	487 443 403	3836 1795 8161	356462	28·0535203	9·2326189	1270648
788	62 09 44	489 303 872	3855 7145 1136	356235	28·0713377	9·2365277	1269036
789	62 25 21	491 169 069	3875 3239 5441	356009	28·0891438	9·2404333	1267427
790	62 41 00	493 039 000	3895 0081 0000	355784	28·1069386	9·2443355	1265823
791	62 56 81	494 913 671	3914 7671 3761	355559	28·1247222	9·2482344	1264223
792	62 72 64	496 793 088	3934 6012 5696	355335	28·1424946	9·2521300	1262626
793	62 88 49	498 677 257	3954 5106 4801	355110	28·1602557	9·2560224	1261034
794	63 04 36	500 566 184	3974 4955 0096	354887	28·1780056	9·2599115	1259446
795	63 20 25	502 459 875	3994 5560 0625	354663	28·1957444	9·2637973	1257862
796	63 36 16	504 358 336	4014 6923 5456	354441	28·2134720	9·2676798	1256281
797	63 52 09	506 261 573	4034 9047 3681	354218	28·2311884	9·2715592	1254705
798	63 68 04	508 169 592	4055 1933 4416	353996	28·2488938	9·2754352	1253133
799	63 84 01	510 082 399	4075 5583 6801	353775	·28·2665881	9·2793081	1251564
800	64 00 00	512 000 000	4096 0000 0000	353553	28·2842712	9·2831777	1250000

C

17

No. n	Square n^2	Cube n^3	Fourth power n^4	$\frac{1}{\sqrt{n}}$	Square root $\sqrt{n}$	Cube root $\sqrt[3]{n}$	Reciprocal $\frac{1}{n}$
				0·0			0·00
800	64 00 00	512 000 000	4096 0000 0000	353553	28·2842712	9·2831777	1250000
801	64 16 01	513 922 401	4116 5184 3201	353333	28·3019434	9·2870440	1248439
802	64 32 04	515 849 608	4137 1138 5616	353112	28·3196045	9·2909072	1246883
803	64 48 09	517 781 627	4157 7864 6481	352892	28·3372546	9·2947672	1245330
804	64 64 16	519 718 464	4178 5364 5056	352673	28·3548938	9·2986239	1243781
805	64 80 25	521 660 125	4199 3640 0625	352454	28·3725219	9·3024775	1242236
806	64 96 36	523 606 616	4220 2693 2496	352235	28·3901391	9·3063278	1240695
807	65 12 49	525 557 943	4241 2526 0001	352017	28·4077454	9·3101750	1239157
808	65 28 64	527 514 112	4262 3140 2496	351799	28·4253408	9·3140190	1237624
809	65 44 81	529 475 129	4283 4537 9361	351581	28·4429253	9·3178598	1236094
810	65 61 00	531 441 000	4304 6721 0000	351364	28·4604989	9·3216975	1234568
811	65 77 21	533 411 731	4325 9691 3841	351147	28·4780617	9·3255320	1233046
812	65 93 44	535 387 328	4347 3451 0336	350931	28·4956137	9·3293634	1231527
813	66 09 69	537 367 797	4368 8001 8961	350715	28·5131549	9·3331916	1230012
814	66 25 96	539 353 144	4390 3345 9216	350500	28·5306852	9·3370167	1228501
815	66 42 25	541 343 375	4411 9485 0625	350285	28·5482048	9·3408386	1226994
816	66 58 56	543 338 496	4433 6421 2736	350070	28·5657137	9·3446575	1225490
817	66 74 89	545 338 513	4455 4156 5121	349856	28·5832119	9·3484732	1223990
818	66 91 24	547 343 432	4477 2692 7376	349642	28·6006993	9·3522858	1222494
819	67 07 61	549 353 259	4499 2031 9121	349428	28·6181760	9·3560952	1221001
820	67 24 00	551 368 000	4521 2176 0000	349215	28·6356421	9·3599016	1219512
821	67 40 41	553 387 661	4543 3126 9681	349002	28·6530976	9·3637049	1218027
822	67 56 84	555 412 248	4565 4886 7856	348790	28·6705424	9·3675051	1216545
823	67 73 29	557 441 767	4587 7457 4241	348578	28·6879766	9·3713022	1215067
824	67 89 76	559 476 224	4610 0840 8576	348367	28·7054002	9·3750963	1213592
825	68 06 25	561 515 625	4632 5039 0625	348155	28·7228132	9·3788873	1212121
826	68 22 76	563 559 976	4655 0054 0176	347945	28·7402157	9·3826752	1210654
827	68 39 29	565 609 283	4677 5887 7041	347734	28·7576077	9·3864601	1209190
828	68 55 84	567 663 552	4700 2542 1056	347524	28·7749891	9·3902419	1207729
829	68 72 41	569 722 789	4723 0019 2081	347314	28·7923601	9·3940206	1206273
830	68 89 00	571 787 000	4745 8321 0000	347105	28·8097206	9·3977964	1204819
831	69 05 61	573 856 191	4768 7449 4721	346896	28·8270706	9·4015691	1203369
832	69 22 24	575 930 368	4791 7406 6176	346688	28·8444102	9·4053388	1201923
833	69 38 89	578 009 537	4814 8194 4321	346479	28·8617394	9·4091054	1200480
834	69 55 56	580 093 704	4837 9814 9136	346272	28·8790582	9·4128690	1199041
835	69 72 25	582 182 875	4861 2270 0625	346064	28·8963666	9·4166297	1197605
836	69 88 96	584 277 056	4884 5561 8816	345857	28·9136646	9·4203873	1196172
837	70 05 69	586 376 253	4907 9692 3761	345651	28·9309523	9·4241420	1194743
838	70 22 44	588 480 472	4931 4663 5536	345444	28·9482297	9·4278936	1193317
839	70 39 21	590 589 719	4955 0477 4241	345238	28·9654967	9·4316423	1191895
840	70 56 00	592 704 000	4978 7136 0000	345033	28·9827535	9·4353880	1190476
841	70 72 81	594 823 321	5002 4641 2961	344828	29·0000000	9·4391307	1189061
842	70 89 64	596 947 688	5026 2995 3296	344623	29·0172363	9·4428704	1187648
843	71 06 49	599 077 107	5050 2200 1201	344418	29·0344623	9·4466072	1186240
844	71 23 36	601 211 584	5074 2257 6896	344214	29·0516781	9·4503411	1184834
845	71 40 25	603 351 125	5098 3170 0625	344010	29·0688837	9·4540719	1183432
846	71 57 16	605 495 736	5122 4939 2656	343807	29·0860791	9·4577999	1182033
847	71 74 09	607 645 423	5146 7567 3281	343604	29·1032644	9·4615249	1180638
848	71 91 04	609 800 192	5171 1056 2816	343401	29·1204396	9·4652470	1179245
849	72 08 01	611 960 049	5195 5408 1601	343199	29·1376046	9·4689661	1177856
850	72 25 00	614 125 000	5220 0625 0000	342997	29·1547595	9·4726824	1176471

No. n	Square n^2	Cube n^3	Fourth power n^4	$\dfrac{1}{\sqrt{n}}$	Square root $\sqrt{n}$	Cube root $\sqrt[3]{n}$	Reciprocal $\dfrac{1}{n}$
				0·0			0·00
850	72 25 00	614 125 000	5220 0625 0000	342997	29·1547595	9·4726824	1176471
851	72 42 01	616 295 051	5244 6708 8401	342796	29·1719043	9·4763957	1175088
852	72 59 04	618 470 208	5269 3661 7216	342594	29·1890390	9·4801061	1173709
853	72 76 09	620 650 477	5294 1485 6881	342393	29·2061637	9·4838136	1172333
854	72 93 16	622 835 864	5319 0182 7856	342193	29·2232784	9·4875182	1170960
855	73 10 25	625 026 375	5343 9755 0625	341993	29·2403830	9·4912200	1169591
856	73 27 36	627 222 016	5369 0204 5696	341793	29·2574777	9·4949188	1168224
857	73 44 49	629 422 793	5394 1533 3601	341593	29·2745623	9·4986148	1166861
858	73 61 64	631 628 712	5419 3743 4896	341394	29·2916370	9·5023078	1165501
859	73 78 81	633 839 779	5444 6837 0161	341196	29·3087018	9·5059981	1164144
860	73 96 00	636 056 000	5470 0816 0000	340997	29·3257566	9·5096854	1162791
861	74 13 21	638 277 381	5495 5682 5041	340799	29·3428015	9·5133699	1161440
862	74 30 44	640 503 928	5521 1438 5936	340601	29·3598365	9·5170516	1160093
863	74 47 69	642 735 647	5546 8086 3361	340404	29·3768616	9·5207304	1158749
864	74 64 96	644 972 544	5572 5627 8016	340207	29·3938769	9·5244063	1157407
865	74 82 25	647 214 625	5598 4065 0625	340010	29·4108823	9·5280794	1156069
866	74 99 56	649 461 896	5624 3400 1936	339814	29·4278779	9·5317497	1154734
867	75 16 89	651 714 363	5650 3635 2721	339618	29·4448637	9·5354172	1153403
868	75 34 24	653 972 032	5676 4772 3776	339422	29·4618397	9·5390818	1152074
869	75 51 61	656 234 909	5702 6813 5921	339227	29·4788059	9·5427437	1150748
870	75 69 00	658 503 000	5728 9761 0000	339032	29·4957624	9·5464027	1149425
871	75 86 41	660 776 311	5755 3616 6881	338837	29·5127091	9·5500589	1148106
872	76 03 84	663 054 848	5781 8382 7456	338643	29·5296461	9·5537124	1146789
873	76 21 29	665 338 617	5808 4061 2641	338449	29·5465734	9·5573630	1145475
874	76 38 76	667 627 624	5835 0654 3376	338255	29·5634910	9·5610108	1144165
875	76 56 25	669 921 875	5861 8164 0625	338062	29·5803989	9·5646559	1142857
876	76 73 76	672 221 376	5888 6592 5376	337869	29·5972972	9·5682982	1141553
877	76 91 29	674 526 133	5915 5941 8641	337676	29·6141858	9·5719377	1140251
878	77 08 84	676 836 152	5942 6214 1456	337484	29·6310648	9·5755745	1138952
879	77 26 41	679 151 439	5969 7411 4881	337292	29·6479342	9·5792085	1137656
880	77 44 00	681 472 000	5996 9536 0000	337100	29·6647939	9·5828397	1136364
881	77 61 61	683 797 841	6024 2589 7921	336909	29·6816442	9·5864682	1135074
882	77 79 24	686 128 968	6051 6574 9776	336718	29·6984848	9·5900939	1133787
883	77 96 89	688 465 387	6079 1493 6721	336527	29·7153159	9·5937170	1132503
884	78 14 56	690 807 104	6106 7347 9936	336336	29·7321375	9·5973372	1131222
885	78 32 25	693 154 125	6134 4140 0625	336146	29·7489496	9·6009548	1129944
886	78 49 96	695 506 456	6162 1872 0016	335957	29·7657521	9·6045696	1128668
887	78 67 69	697 864 103	6190 0545 9361	335767	29·7825452	9·6081817	1127396
888	78 85 44	700 227 072	6218 0163 9936	335578	29·7993289	9·6117911	1126126
889	79 03 21	702 595 369	6246 0728 3041	335389	29·8161030	9·6153977	1124859
890	79 21 00	704 969 000	6274 2241 0000	335201	29·8328678	9·6190017	1123596
891	79 38 81	707 347 971	6302 4704 2161	335013	29·8496231	9·6226030	1122334
892	79 56 64	709 732 288	6330 8120 0896	334825	29·8663690	9·6262016	1121076
893	79 74 49	712 121 957	6359 2490 7601	334637	29·8831056	9·6297975	1119821
894	79 92 36	714 516 984	6387 7818 3696	334450	29·8998328	9·6333907	1118568
895	80 10 25	716 917 375	6416 4105 0625	334263	29·9165506	9·6369812	1117318
896	80 28 16	719 323 136	6445 1352 9856	334077	29·9332591	9·6405691	1116071
897	80 46 09	721 734 273	6473 9564 2881	333890	29·9499583	9·6441542	1114827
898	80 64 04	724 150 792	6502 8741 1216	333704	29·9666481	9·6477368	1113586
899	80 82 01	726 572 699	6531 8885 6401	333519	29·9833287	9·6513166	1112347
900	81 00 00	729 000 000	6561 0000 0000	333333	30·0000000	9·6548938	1111111

No. n	Square n^2	Cube n^3	Fourth power n^4	$\frac{1}{\sqrt{n}}$	Square root $\sqrt{n}$	Cube root $\sqrt[3]{n}$	Reciprocal $\frac{1}{n}$
				0·0			0·00
900	81 00 00	729 000 000	6561 0000 0000	333333	30·0000000	9·6548938	1111111
901	81 18 01	731 432 701	6590 2086 3601	333148	30·0166620	9·6584684	1109878
902	81 36 04	733 870 808	6619 5146 8816	332964	30·0333148	9·6620403	1108647
903	81 54 09	736 314 327	6648 9183 7281	332779	30·0499584	9·6656096	1107420
904	81 72 16	738 763 264	6678 4199 0656	332595	30·0665928	9·6691763	1106195
905	81 90 25	741 217 625	6708 0195 0625	332411	30·0832179	9·6727403	1104972
906	82 08 36	743 677 416	6737 7173 8896	332228	30·0998339	9·6763017	1103753
907	82 26 49	746 142 643	6767 5137 7201	332045	30·1164407	9·6798604	1102536
908	82 44 64	748 613 312	6797 4088 7296	331862	30·1330383	9·6834166	1101322
909	82 62 81	751 089 429	6827 4029 0961	331679	30·1496269	9·6869701	1100110
910	82 81 00	753 571 000	6857 4961 0000	331497	30·1662063	9·6905211	1098901
911	82 99 21	756 058 031	6887 6886 6241	331315	30·1827765	9·6940694	1097695
912	83 17 44	758 550 528	6917 9808 1536	331133	30·1993377	9·6976152	1096491
913	83 35 69	761 048 497	6948 3727 7761	330952	30·2158899	9·7011583	1095290
.914	83 53 96	763 551 944	6978 8647 6816	330771	30·2324329	9·7046989	1094092
915	83 72 25	766 060 875	7009 4570 0625	330590	30·2489669	9·7082369	1092896
916	83 90 56	768 575 296	7040 1497 1136	330409	30·2654919	9·7117723	1091703
917	84 08 89	771 095 213	7070 9431 0321	330229	30·2820079	9·7153051	1090513
918	84 27 24	773 620 632	7101 8374 0176	330049	30·2985148	9·7188354	1089325
919	84 45 61	776 151 559	7132 8328 2721	329870	30·3150128	9·7223631	1088139
920	84 64 00	778 688 000	7163 9296 0000	329690	30·3315018	9·7258883	1086957
921	84 82 41	781 229 961	7195 1279 4081	329511	30·3479818	9·7294109	1085776
922	85 00 84	783 777 448	7226 4280 7056	329332	30·3644529	9·7329309	1084599
923	85 19 29	786 330 467	7257 8302 1041	329154	30·3809151	9·7364484	1083424
924	85 37 76	788 889 024	7289 3345 8176	328976	30·3973683	9·7399634	1082251
925	85 56 25	791 453 125	7320 9414 0625	328798	30·4138127	9·7434758	1081081
926	85 74 76	794 022 776	7352 6509 0576	328620	30·4302481	9·7469857	1079914
927	85 93 29	796 597 983	7384 4633 0241	328443	30·4466747	9·7504931	1078749
928	86 11 84	799 178 752	7416 3788 1856	328266	30·4630924	9·7539979	1077586
929	86 30 41	801 765 089	7448 3976 7681	328089	30·4795013	9·7575003	1076426
930	86 49 00	804 357 000	7480 5201 0000	327913	30·4959014	9·7610001	1075269
931	86 67 61	806 954 491	7512 7463 1121	327737	30·5122926	9·7644974	1074114
932	86 86 24	809 557 568	7545 0765 3376	327561	30·5286750	9·7679922	1072961
933	87 04 89	812 166 237	7577 5109 9121	327385	30·5450487	9·7714845	1071811
934	87 23 56	814 780 504	7610 0499 0736	327210	30·5614136	9·7749743	1070664
935	87 42 25	817 400 375	7642 6935 0625	327035	30·5777697	9·7784617	1069519
936	87 60 96	820 025 856	7675 4420 1216	326860	30·5941171	9·7819465	1068376
937	87 79 69	822 656 953	7708 2956 4961	326686	30·6104557	9·7854289	1067236
938	87 98 44	825 293 672	7741 2546 4336	326512	30·6267857	9·7889087	1066098
939	88 17 21	827 936 019	7774 3192 1841	326338	30·6431069	9·7923861	1064963
940	88 36 00	830 584 000	7807 4896 0000	326164	30·6594194	9·7958611	1063830
941	88 54 81	833 237 621	7840 7660 1361	325991	30·6757233	9·7993336	1062699
942	88 73 64	835 896 888	7874 1486 8496	325818	30·6920185	9·8028036	1061571
943	88 92 49	838 561 807	7907 6378 4001	325645	30·7083051	9·8062711	1060445
944	89 11 36	841 232 384	7941 2337 0496	325472	30·7245830	9·8097363	1059322
945	89 30 25	843 908 625	7974 9365 0625	325300	30·7408523	9·8131989	1058201
946	89 49 16	846 590 536	8008 7464 7056	325128	30·7571130	9·8166592	1057082
947	89 68 09	849 278 123	8042 6638 2481	324956	30·7733651	9·8201169	1055966
948	89 87 04	851 971 392	·8076 6887 9616	324785	30·7896088	9·8235723	1054852
949	90 06 01	854 670 349	8110 8216 1201	324614	30·8058436	9·8270252	1053741
950	90 25 00	857 375 000	8145 0625 0000	324443	30·8220700	9·8304757	1052632

No. n	Square n^2	Cube n^3	Fourth power n^4	$\dfrac{1}{\sqrt{n}}$	Square root $\sqrt{n}$	Cube root $\sqrt[3]{n}$	Recipr. $\dfrac{1}{n}$
				0·0			0·00
950	90 25 00	857 375 000	8145 0625 0000	324443	30·8220700	9·8304757	1052632
951	90 44 01	860 085 351	8179 4116 8801	324272	30·8382879	9·8339238	1051525
952	90 63 04	862 801 408	8213 8694 0416	324102	30·8544972	9·8373695	1050420
953	90 82 09	865 523 177	8248 4358 7681	323932	30·8706981	9·8408127	1049318
954	91 01 16	868 250 664	8283 1113 3456	323762	30·8868904	9·8442536	1048218
955	91 20 25	870 983 875	8317 8960 0625	323592	30·9030743	9·8476920	1047120
956	91 39 36	873 722 816	8352 7901 2096	323423	30·9192497	9·8511280	1046025
957	91 58 49	876 467 493	8387 7939 0801	323254	30·9354166	9·8545617	1044932
958	91 77 64	879 217 912	8422 9075 9696	323085	30·9515751	9·8579929	1043841
959	91 96 81	881 974 079	8458 1314 1761	322917	30·9677251	9·8614218	1042753
960	92 16 00	884 736 000	8493 4656 0000	322749	30·9838668	9·8648483	1041667
961	92 35 21	887 503 681	8528 9103 7441	322581	31·0000000	9·8682724	1040583
962	92 54 44	890 277 128	8564 4659 7136	322413	31·0161248	9·8716941	1039501
963	92 73 69	893 056 347	8600 1326 2161	322245	31·0322413	9·8751135	1038422
964	92 92 96	895 841 344	8635 9105 5616	322078	31·0483494	9·8785305	1037344
965	93 12 25	898 632 125	8671 8000 0625	321911	31·0644491	9·8819451	1036269
966	93 31 56	901 428 696	8707 8012 0336	321745	31·0805405	9·8853574	1035197
967	93 50 89	904 231 063	8743 9143 7921	321578	31·0966236	9·8887673	1034126
968	93 70 24	907 039 232	8780 1397 6576	321412	31·1126984	9·8921749	1033058
969	93 89 61	909 853 209	8816 4775 9521	321246	31·1287648	9·8955801	1031992
970	94 09 00	912 673 000	8852 9281 0000	321081	31·1448230	9·8989830	1030928
971	94 28 41	915 498 611	8889 4915 1281	320915	31·1608729	9·9023835	1029866
972	94 47 84	918 330 048	8926 1680 6656	320750	31·1769145	9·9057817	1028807
973	94 67 29	921 167 317	8962 9579 9441	320585	31·1929479	9·9091776	1027749
974	94 86 76	924 010 424	8999 8615 2976	320421	31·2089731	9·9125712	1026694
975	95 06 25	926 859 375	9036 8789 0625	320256	31·2249900	9·9159624	1025641
976	95 25 76	929 714 176	9074 0103 5776	320092	31·2409987	9·9193513	1024590
977	95 45 29	932 574 833	9111 2561 1841	319928	31·2569992	9·9227379	1023541
978	95 64 84	935 441 352	9148 6164 2256	319765	31·2729915	9·9261222	1022495
979	95 84 41	938 313 739	9186 0915 0481	319601	31·2889757	9·9295042	1021450
980	96 04 00	941 192 000	9223 6816 0000	319438	31·3049517	9·9328839	1020408
981	96 23 61	944 076 141	9261 3869 4321	319275	31·3209195	9·9362613	1019368
982	96 43 24	946 966 168	9299 2077 6976	319113	31·3368792	9·9396364	1018330
983	96 62 89	949 862 087	9337 1443 1521	318950	31·3528308	9·9430092	1017294
984	96 82 56	952 763 904	9375 1968 1536	318788	31·3687743	9·9463797	1016260
985	97 02 25	955 671 625	9413 3655 0625	318626	31·3847097	9·9497479	1015228
986	97 21 96	958 585 256	9451 6506 2416	318465	31·4006369	9·9531138	1014199
987	97 41 69	961 504 803	9490 0524 0561	318304	31·4165561	9·9564775	1013171
988	97 61 44	964 430 272	9528 5710 8736	318142	31·4324673	9·9598389	1012146
989	97 81 21	967 361 669	9567 2069 0641	317982	31·4483704	9·9631981	1011122
990	98 01 00	970 299 000	9605 9601 0000	317821	31·4642654	9·9665549	1010101
991	98 20 81	973 242 271	9644 8309 0561	317660	31·4801525	9·9699095	1009082
992	98 40 64	976 191 488	9683 8195 6096	317500	31·4960315	9·9732619	1008065
993	98 60 49	979 146 657	9722 9263 0401	317340	31·5119025	9·9766120	1007049
994	98 80 36	982 107 784	9762 1513 7296	317181	31·5277655	9·9799599	1006036
995	99 00 25	985 074 875	9801 4950 0625	317021	31·5436206	9·9833055	1005025
996	99 20 16	988 047 936	9840 9574 4256	316862	31·5594677	9·9866489	1004016
997	99 40 09	991 026 973	9880 5389 2081	316703	31·5753068	9·9899900	1003009
998	99 60 04	994 011 992	9920 2396 8016	316544	31·5911380	9·9933289	1002004
999	99 80 01	997 002 999	9960 0599 5001	316386	31·6069613	9·9966656	1001001
1000	1 00 00 00	1 000 000 000	1 0000 0000 0000	316228	31·6227766	10·0000000	1000000

No. n	Square n²	Cube n³	Square root √n	Sq. rt. of 10n √10n	Cube root ∛n	Reciprocal 1/n
			31·	100 +	10·	0·000
1000	1 00 00 00	1 000 000 000	622777 (15807)	0·000000 (49988)	000000 (3332)	9990010 (9990)
1001	1 00 20 01	1 003 003 001	638584 (15800)	0·049988 (49962)	003332 (3330)	9980040 (9970)
1002	1 00 40 04	1 006 012 008	654384 (15791)	0·099950 (49938)	006662 (3328)	9970090 (9950)
1003	1 00 60 09	1 009 027 027	670175 (15784)	0·149888 (49912)	009990 (3326)	9960159 (9931)
1004	1 00 80 16	1 012 048 064	685959 (15776)	0·199800 (49888)	013316 (3323)	(9910)
1005	1 01 00 25	1 015 075 125	701735 (15768)	0·249688 (49863)	016639 (3321)	9950249 (9891)
1006	1 01 20 36	1 018 108 216	717503 (15760)	0·299551 (49839)	019960 (3319)	9940358 (9871)
1007	1 01 40 49	1 021 147 343	733263 (15753)	0·349390 (49813)	023279 (3317)	9930487 (9852)
1008	1 01 60 64	1 024 192 512	749016 (15744)	0·399203 (49789)	026596 (3314)	9920635 (9832)
1009	1 01 80 81	1 027 243 729	764760 (15737)	0·448992 (49764)	029910 (3313)	9910803 (9813)
1010	1 02 01 00	1 030 301 000	780497 (15729)	0·498756 (49740)	033223 (3310)	9900990 (9793)
1011	1 02 21 21	1 033 364 331	796226 (15721)	0·548496 (49715)	036533 (3308)	9891197 (9774)
1012	1 02 41 44	1 036 433 728	811947 (15714)	0·598211 (49690)	039841 (3306)	9881423 (9755)
1013	1 02 61 69	1 039 509 197	827661 (15706)	0·647901 (49666)	043147 (3304)	9871668 (9735)
1014	1 02 81 96	1 042 590 744	843367 (15698)	0·697567 (49641)	046451 (3301)	9861933 (9716)
1015	1 03 02 25	1 045 678 375	859065 (15690)	0·747208 (49617)	049752 (3299)	9852217 (9697)
1016	1 03 22 56	1 048 772 096	874755 (15682)	0·796825 (49593)	053051 (3298)	9842520 (9678)
1017	1 03 42 89	1 051 871 913	890437 (15675)	0·846418 (49568)	056349 (3295)	9832842 (9659)
1018	1 03 63 24	1 054 977 832	906112 (15667)	0·895986 (49544)	059644 (3292)	9823183 (9640)
1019	1 03 83 61	1 058 089 859	921779 (15660)	0·945530 (49519)	062936 (3291)	9813543 (9621)
1020	1 04 04 00	1 061 208 000	937439 (15652)	0·995049 (49496)	066227 (3289)	9803922 (9603)
1021	1 04 24 41	1 064 332 261	953091 (15644)	1·044545 (49471)	069516 (3286)	9794319 (9583)
1022	1 04 44 84	1 067 462 648	968735 (15636)	1·094016 (49446)	072802 (3284)	9784736 (9565)
1023	1 04 65 29	1 070 599 167	984371 (15629)	1·143462 (49423)	076086 (3282)	9775171 (9546)
1024	1 04 85 76	1 073 741 824	*000000 (15621)	1·192885 (49399)	079368 (3280)	9765625 (9527)
1025	1 05 06 25	1 076 890 625	015621 (15614)	1·242284 (49374)	082648 (3278)	9756098 (9509)
1026	1 05 26 76	1 080 045 576	031235 (15606)	1·291658 (49350)	085926 (3276)	9746589 (9491)
1027	1 05 47 29	1 083 206 683	046841 (15598)	1·341008 (49327)	089202 (3274)	9737098 (9472)
1028	1 05 67 84	1 086 373 952	062439 (15591)	1·390335 (49302)	092476 (3271)	9727626 (9453)
1029	1 05 88 41	1 089 547 389	078030 (15583)	1·439637 (49279)	095747 (3269)	9718173 (9435)
1030	1 06 09 00	1 092 727 000	093613 (15576)	1·488916 (49254)	099016 (3268)	9708738 (9417)
1031	1 06 29 61	1 095 912 791	109189 (15568)	1·538170 (49231)	102284 (3265)	9699321 (9399)
1032	1 06 50 24	1 099 104 768	124757 (15560)	1·587401 (49207)	105549 (3263)	9689922 (9380)
1033	1 06 70 89	1 102 302 937	140317 (15553)	1·636608 (49183)	108812 (3261)	9680542 (9362)
1034	1 06 91 56	1 105 507 304	155870 (15546)	1·685791 (49159)	112073 (3258)	9671180 (9344)
1035	1 07 12 25	1 108 717 875	171416 (15538)	1·734950 (49135)	115331 (3257)	9661836 (9326)
1036	1 07 32 96	1 111 934 656	186954 (15530)	1·784085 (49112)	118588 (3255)	9652510 (9308)
1037	1 07 53 69	1 115 157 653	202484 (15523)	1·833197 (49088)	121843 (3252)	9643202 (9291)
1038	1 07 74 44	1 118 386 872	218007 (15516)	1·882285 (49064)	125095 (3251)	9633911 (9272)
1039	1 07 95 21	1 121 622 319	233523 (15508)	1·931349 (49041)	128346 (3248)	9624639 (9254)
1040	1 08 16 00	1 124 864 000	249031 (15501)	1·980390 (49018)	131594 (3246)	9615385 (9237)
1041	1 08 36 81	1 128 111 921	264532 (15493)	2·029408 (48993)	134840 (3244)	9606148 (9219)
1042	1 08 57 64	1 131 366 088	280025 (15486)	2·078401 (48970)	138084 (3243)	9596929 (9201)
1043	1 08 78 49	1 134 626 507	295511 (15478)	2·127371 (48947)	141327 (3240)	9587728 (9184)
1044	1 08 99 36	1 137 893 184	310989 (15471)	2·176318 (48924)	144567 (3238)	9578544 (9166)
1045	1 09 20 25	1 141 166 125	326460 (15463)	2·225242 (48899)	147805 (3236)	9569378 (9149)
1046	1 09 41 16	1 144 445 336	341923 (15456)	2·274141 (48877)	151041 (3233)	9560229 (9131)
1047	1 09 62 09	1 147 730 823	357379 (15449)	2·323018 (48853)	154274 (3232)	9551098 (9113)
1048	1 09 83 04	1 151 022 592	372828 (15441)	2·371871 (48830)	157506 (3230)	9541985 (9097)
1049	1 10 04 01	1 154 320 649	388269 (15434)	2·420701 (48807)	160736 (3228)	9532888 (9078)
1050	1 10 25 00	1 157 625 000	403703 32·	2·469508 100 +	163964 10·	9523810 0·000

No. n	Square n^2	Cube n^3	Square root $\sqrt{n}$	Sq. rt. of 10n $\sqrt{10n}$	Cube root $\sqrt[3]{n}$	Reciprocal $\frac{1}{n}$
			32·	100 +	10·	0·000
1050	1 10 25 00	1 157 625 000	403703 $_{15427}$	2·469508 $_{48783}$	163964 $_{3225}$	9523810
1051	1 10 46 01	1 160 935 651	419130 $_{15419}$	2·518291 $_{48760}$	167189 $_{3224}$	9514748 $_{9062}$
1052	1 10 67 04	1 164 252 608	434549 $_{15412}$	2·567051 $_{48737}$	170413 $_{3221}$	9505703 $_{9045}$
1053	1 10 88 09	1 167 575 877	449961 $_{15405}$	2·615788 $_{48714}$	173634 $_{3220}$	9496676 $_{9027}$
1054	1 11 09 16	1 170 905 464	465366 $_{15398}$	2·664502 $_{48691}$	176854 $_{3217}$	9487666 $_{9010}$
1055	1 11 30 25	1 174 241 375	480764 $_{15390}$	2·713193 $_{48668}$	180071 $_{3216}$	9478673 $_{8993}$ $_{8976}$
1056	1 11 51 36	1 177 583 616	496154 $_{15382}$	2·761861 $_{48644}$	183287 $_{3213}$	9469697 $_{8959}$
1057	1 11 72 49	1 180 932 193	511536 $_{15376}$	2·810505 $_{48622}$	186500 $_{3212}$	9460738 $_{8942}$
1058	1 11 93 64	1 184 287 112	526912 $_{15368}$	2·859127 $_{48599}$	189712 $_{3209}$	9451796 $_{8925}$
1059	1 12 14 81	1 187 648 379	542280 $_{15361}$	2·907726 $_{48575}$	192921 $_{3207}$	9442871 $_{8909}$
1060	1 12 36 00	1 191 016 000	557641 $_{15354}$	2·956301 $_{48553}$	196128 $_{3206}$	9433962 $_{8891}$
1061	1 12 57 21	1 194 389 981	572995 $_{15346}$	3·004854 $_{48530}$	199334 $_{3203}$	9425071 $_{8875}$
1062	1 12 78 44	1 197 770 328	588341 $_{15340}$	3·053384 $_{48507}$	202537 $_{3201}$	9416196 $_{8858}$
1063	1 12 99 69	1 201 157 047	603681 $_{15332}$	3·101891 $_{48485}$	205738 $_{3199}$	9407338 $_{8842}$
1064	1 13 20 96	1 204 550 144	619013 $_{15325}$	3·150376 $_{48461}$	208937 $_{3198}$	9398496 $_{8825}$
1065	1 13 42 25	1 207 949 625	634338 $_{15317}$	3·198837 $_{48439}$	212135 $_{3195}$	9389671 $_{8808}$
1066	1 13 63 56	1 211 355 496	649655 $_{15311}$	3·247276 $_{48416}$	215330 $_{3193}$	9380863 $_{8792}$
1067	1 13 84 89	1 214 767 763	664966 $_{15303}$	3·295692 $_{48393}$	218523 $_{3192}$	9372071 $_{8775}$
1068	1 14 06 24	1 218 186 432	680269 $_{15296}$	3·344085 $_{48371}$	221715 $_{3189}$	9363296 $_{8759}$
1069	1 14 27 61	1 221 611 509	695565 $_{15289}$	3·392456 $_{48348}$	224904 $_{3187}$	9354537 $_{8743}$
1070	1 14 49 00	1 225 043 000	710854 $_{15282}$	3·440804 $_{48326}$	228091 $_{3186}$	9345794 $_{8726}$
1071	1 14 70 41	1 228 480 911	726136 $_{15275}$	3·489130 $_{48303}$	231277 $_{3183}$	9337068 $_{8710}$
1072	1 14 91 84	1 231 925 248	741411 $_{15268}$	3·537433 $_{48280}$	234460 $_{3181}$	9328358 $_{8694}$
1073	1 15 13 29	1 235 376 017	756679 $_{15260}$	3·585713 $_{48258}$	237641 $_{3180}$	9319664 $_{8677}$
1074	1 15 34 76	1 238 833 224	771939 $_{15254}$	3·633971 $_{48236}$	240821 $_{3177}$	9310987 $_{8661}$
1075	1 15 56 25	1 242 296 875	787193 $_{15246}$	3·682207 $_{48213}$	243998 $_{3176}$	9302326 $_{8646}$
1076	1 15 77 76	1 245 766 976	802439 $_{15239}$	3·730420 $_{48191}$	247174 $_{3173}$	9293680 $_{8629}$
1077	1 15 99 29	1 249 243 533	817678 $_{15232}$	3·778611 $_{48168}$	250347 $_{3172}$	9285051 $_{8613}$
1078	1 16 20 84	1 252 726 552	832910 $_{15225}$	3·826779 $_{48146}$	253519 $_{3169}$	9276438 $_{8597}$
1079	1 16 42 41	1 256 216 039	848135 $_{15218}$	3·874925 $_{48123}$	256688 $_{3168}$	9267841 $_{8582}$
1080	1 16 64 00	1 259 712 000	863353 $_{15211}$	3·923048 $_{48102}$	259856 $_{3165}$	9259259 $_{8565}$
1081	1 16 85 61	1 263 214 441	878564 $_{15204}$	3·971150 $_{48079}$	263021 $_{3164}$	9250694 $_{8550}$
1082	1 17 07 24	1 266 723 368	893768 $_{15197}$	4·019229 $_{48057}$	266185 $_{3162}$	9242144 $_{8534}$
1083	1 17 28 89	1 270 238 787	908965 $_{15190}$	4·067286 $_{48035}$	269347 $_{3160}$	9233610 $_{8518}$
1084	1 17 50 56	1 273 760 704	924155 $_{15183}$	4·115321 $_{48012}$	272507 $_{3157}$	9225092 $_{8502}$
1085	1 17 72 25	1 277 289 125	939338 $_{15176}$	4·163333 $_{47991}$	275664 $_{3156}$	9216590 $_{8487}$
1086	1 17 93 96	1 280 824 056	954514 $_{15169}$	4·211324 $_{47968}$	278820 $_{3154}$	9208103 $_{8471}$
1087	1 18 15 69	1 284 365 503	969683 $_{15162}$	4·259292 $_{47946}$	281974 $_{3152}$	9199632 $_{8456}$
1088	1 18 37 44	1 287 913 472	984845 $_{15155}$	4·307238 $_{47925}$	285126 $_{3150}$	9191176 $_{8440}$
1089	1 18 59 21	1 291 467 969	*000000 $_{15148}$	4·355163 $_{47902}$	288276 $_{3149}$	9182746 $_{8424}$
1090	1 18 81 00	1 295 029 000	015148 $_{15141}$	4·403065 $_{47880}$	291425 $_{3146}$	9174312 $_{8409}$
1091	1 19 02 81	1 298 596 571	030289 $_{15134}$	4·450945 $_{47859}$	294571 $_{3144}$	9165903 $_{8394}$
1092	1 19 24 64	1 302 170 688	045423 $_{15128}$	4·498804 $_{47836}$	297715 $_{3143}$	9157509 $_{8378}$
1093	1 19 46 49	1 305 751 357	060551 $_{15120}$	4·546640 $_{47815}$	300858 $_{3140}$	9149131 $_{8363}$
1094	1 19 68 36	1 309 338 584	075671 $_{15113}$	4·594455 $_{47793}$	303998 $_{3139}$	9140768 $_{8348}$
1095	1 19 90 25	1 312 932 375	090784 $_{15107}$	4·642248 $_{47771}$	307137 $_{3136}$	9132420 $_{8332}$
1096	1 20 12 16	1 316 532 736	105891 $_{15099}$	4·690019 $_{47749}$	310273 $_{3135}$	9124088 $_{8318}$
1097	1 20 34 09	1 320 139 673	120990 $_{15093}$	4·737768 $_{47727}$	313408 $_{3133}$	9115770 $_{8302}$
1098	1 20 56 04	1 323 753 192	136083 $_{15086}$	4·785495 $_{47706}$	316541 $_{3131}$	9107468 $_{8287}$
1099	1 20 78 01	1 327 373 299	151169 $_{15079}$	4·833201 $_{47684}$	319672 $_{3129}$	9099181 $_{8272}$
1100	1 21 00 00	1 331 000 000	166248	4·880885	322801	9090909
			33·	100 +	10·	0·000

No. n	Square n^2	Cube n^3	Square root $\sqrt{n}$	Sq. rt. of 10n $\sqrt{10n}$	Cube root $\sqrt[3]{n}$	Reciprocal $\frac{1}{n}$
			33·	100 +	10·	0·000
1100	1 21 00 00	1 331 000 000	166248 15072	4·880885 47662	322801 3127	9090909 8257
1101	1 21 22 01	1 334 633 301	181320 15065	4·928547 47641	325928 3126	9082652 8242
1102	1 21 44 04	1 338 273 208	196385 15059	4·976188 47619	329054 3123	9074410 8227
1103	1 21 66 09	1 341 919 727	211444 15051	5·023807 47597	332177 3122	9066183 8212
1104	1 21 88 16	1 345 572 864	226495 15045	5·071404 47576	335299 3119	9057971 8197
1105	1 22 10 25	1 349 232 625	241540 15038	5·118980 47555	338418 3118	9049774 8183
1106	1 22 32 36	1 352 899 016	256578 15032	5·166535 47533	341536 3116	9041591 8167
1107	1 22 54 49	1 356 572 043	271610 15024	5·214068 47511	344652 3114	9033424 8153
1108	1 22 76 64	1 360 251 712	286634 15018	5·261579 47490	347766 3112	9025271 8138
1109	1 22 98 81	1 363 938 029	301652 15010	5·309069 47469	350878 3110	9017133 8124
1110	1 23 21 00	1 367 631 000	316662 15005	5·356538 47447	353988 3108	9009009 8109
1111	1 23 43 21	1 371 330 631	331667 14997	5·403985 47426	357096 3107	9000900 8094
1112	1 23 65 44	1 375 036 928	346664 14991	5·451411 47404	360203 3105	8992806 8080
1113	1 23 87 69	1 378 749 897	361655 14984	5·498815 47383	363308 3102	8984726 8065
1114	1 24 09 96	1 382 469 544	376639 14977	5·546198 47362	366410 3101	8976661 8051
1115	1 24 32 25	1 386 195 875	391616 14970	5·593560 47341	369511 3099	8968610 8037
1116	1 24 54 56	1 389 928 896	406586 14964	5·640901 47320	372610 3098	8960573 8022
1117	1 24 76 89	1 393 668 613	421550 14957	5·688221 47298	375708 3095	8952551 8007
1118	1 24 99 24	1 397 415 032	436507 14950	5·735519 47277	378803 3094	8944544 7994
1119	1 25 21 61	1 401 168 159	451457 14944	5·782796 47256	381897 3091	8936550 7979
1120	1 25 44 00	1 404 928 000	466401 14937	5·830052 47235	384988 3090	8928571 7964
1121	1 25 66 41	1 408 694 561	481338 14930	5·877287 47214	388078 3088	8920607 7951
1122	1 25 88 84	1 412 467 848	496268 14924	5·924501 47193	391166 3086	8912656 7936
1123	1 26 11 29	1 416 247 867	511192 14917	5·971694 47172	394252 3085	8904720 7923
1124	1 26 33 76	1 420 034 624	526109 14911	6·018866 47151	397337 3082	8896797 7908
1125	1 26 56 25	1 423 828 125	541020 14903	6·066017 47130	400419 3081	8888889 7894
1126	1 26 78 76	1 427 628 376	555923 14898	6·113147 47109	403500 3079	8880995 7881
1127	1 27 01 29	1 431 435 383	570821 14890	6·160256 47088	406579 3077	8873114 7866
1128	1 27 23 84	1 435 249 152	585711 14884	6·207344 47068	409656 3075	8865248 7852
1129	1 27 46 41	1 439 069 689	600595 14878	6·254412 47046	412731 3073	8857396 7838
1130	1 27 69 00	1 442 897 000	615473 14870	6·301458 47026	415804 3072	8849558 7825
1131	1 27 91 61	1 446 731 091	630343 14865	6·348484 47005	418876 3070	8841733 7811
1132	1 28 14 24	1 450 571 968	645208 14857	6·395489 46984	421946 3068	8833922 7797
1133	1 28 36 89	1 454 419 637	660065 14851	6·442473 46963	425014 3066	8826125 7783
1134	1 28 59 56	1 458 274 104	674916 14845	6·489436 46943	428080 3064	8818342 7769
1135	1 28 82 25	1 462 135 375	689761 14838	6·536379 46922	431144 3063	8810573 7756
1136	1 29 04 96	1 466 003 456	704599 14832	6·583301 46901	434207 3061	8802817 7742
1137	1 29 27 69	1 469 878 353	719431 14825	6·630202 46881	437268 3059	8795075 7729
1138	1 29 50 44	1 473 760 072	734256 14818	6·677083 46860	440327 3057	8787346 7715
1139	1 29 73 21	1 477 648 619	749074 14812	6·723943 46840	443384 3055	8779631 7701
1140	1 29 96 00	1 481 544 000	763886 14806	6·770783 46819	446439 3054	8771930 7688
1141	1 30 18 81	1 485 446 221	778692 14798	6·817602 46798	449493 3052	8764242 7675
1142	1 30 41 64	1 489 355 288	793490 14793	6·864400 46778	452545 3050	8756567 7661
1143	1 30 64 49	1 493 271 207	808283 14786	6·911178 46758	455595 3048	8748906 7647
1144	1 30 87 36	1 497 193 984	823069 14780	6·957936 46737	458643 3047	8741259 7635
1145	1 31 10 25	1 501 123 625	837849 14773	7·004673 46717	461690 3044	8733624 7621
1146	1 31 33 16	1 505 060 136	852622 14766	7·051390 46696	464734 3043	8726003 7607
1147	1 31 56 09	1 509 003 523	867388 14761	7·098086 46676	467777 3041	8718396 7595
1148	1 31 79 04	1 512 953 792	882149 14754	7·144762 46656	470818 3040	8710801 7581
1149	1 32 02 01	1 516 910 949	896903 14747	7·191418 46635	473858 3038	8703220 7568
1150	1 32 25 00	1 520 875 000	911650	7·238053	476896	8695652
			33·	100 +	10·	0·000

24

No. n	Square n^2	Cube n^3	Square root $\sqrt{n}$	Sq. rt. of 10n $\sqrt{10n}$	Cube root $\sqrt[3]{n}$	Reciprocal $\dfrac{1}{n}$
			33·	100 +	10·	0·000
1150	1 32 25 00	1 520 875 000	911650 14741	7·238053 46615	476896 3035	8695652 7555
1151	1 32 48 01	1 524 845 951	926391 14734	7·284668 46595	479931 3035	8688097 7541
1152	1 32 71 04	1 528 823 808	941125 14729	7·331263 46575	482966 3032	8680556 7529
1153	1 32 94 09	1 532 808 577	955854 14722	7·377838 46554	485998 3031	8673027 7516
1154	1 33 17 16	1 536 800 264	970576 14715	7·424392 46534	489029 3028	8665511 7502
1155	1 33 40 25	1 540 798 875	985291 14709	7·470926 46514	492057 3028	8658009 7490
1156	1 33 63 36	1 544 804 416	*000000 14703	7·517440 46494	495085 3025	8650519 7477
1157	1 33 86 49	1 548 816 893	014703 14696	7·563934 46474	498110 3024	8643042 7463
1158	1 34 09 64	1 552 836 312	029399 14690	7·610408 46454	501134 3022	8635579 7451
1159	1 34 32 81	1 556 862 679	044089 14684	7·656862 46434	504156 3020	8628128 7438
1160	1 34 56 00	1 560 896 000	058773 14677	7·703296 46414	507176 3018	8620690 7426
1161	1 34 79 21	1 564 936 281	073450 14671	7·749710 46394	510194 3017	8613264 7412
1162	1 35 02 44	1 568 983 528	088121 14665	7·796104 46374	513211 3015	8605852 7400
1163	1 35 25 69	1 573 037 747	102786 14658	7·842478 46354	516226 3013	8598452 7387
1164	1 35 48 96	1 577 098 944	117444 14652	7·888832 46334	519239 3012	8591065 7374
1165	1 35 72 25	1 581 167 125	132096 14646	7·935166 46314	522251 3009	8583691 7362
1166	1 35 95 56	1 585 242 296	146742 14640	7·981480 46294	525260 3008	8576329 7349
1167	1 36 18 89	1 589 324 463	161382 14633	8·027774 46275	528268 3007	8568980 7336
1168	1 36 42 24	1 593 413 632	176015 14627	8·074049 46254	531275 3004	8561644 7324
1169	1 36 65 61	1 597 509 809	190642 14621	8·120303 46235	534279 3003	8554320 7311
1170	1 36 89 00	1 601 613 000	205263 14614	8·166538 46215	537282 3002	8547009 7299
1171	1 37 12 41	1 605 723 211	219877 14609	8·212753 46196	540284 2999	8539710 7287
1172	1 37 35 84	1 609 840 448	234486 14602	8·258949 46176	543283 2998	8532423 7274
1173	1 37 59 29	1 613 964 717	249088 14595	8·305125 46156	546281 2996	8525149 7261
1174	1 37 82 76	1 618 096 024	263683 14590	8·351281 46136	549277 2994	8517888 7250
1175	1 38 06 25	1 622 234 375	278273 14583	8·397417 46117	552271 2993	8510638 7237
1176	1 38 29 76	1 626 379 776	292856 14578	8·443534 46097	555264 2991	8503401 7224
1177	1 38 53 29	1 630 532 233	307434 14571	8·489631 46077	558255 2989	8496177 7213
1178	1 38 76 84	1 634 691 752	322005 14564	8·535708 46058	561244 2988	8488964 7200
1179	1 39 00 41	1 638 858 339	336569 14559	8·581766 46039	564232 2986	8481764 7188
1180	1 39 24 00	1 643 032 000	351128 14553	8·627805 46019	567218 2984	8474576 7175
1181	1 39 47 61	1 647 212 741	365681 14546	8·673824 45999	570202 2983	8467401 7164
1182	1 39 71 24	1 651 400 568	380227 14540	8·719823 45980	573185 2981	8460227 7152
1183	1 39 94 89	1 655 595 487	394767 14534	8·765803 45961	576166 2979	8453085 7139
1184	1 40 18 56	1 659 797 504	409301 14528	8·811764 45941	579145 2977	8445946 7127
1185	1 40 42 25	1 664 006 625	423829 14522	8·857705 45922	582122 2976	8438819 7116
1186	1 40 65 96	1 668 222 856	438351 14515	8·903627 45903	585098 2974	8431703 7103
1187	1 40 89 69	1 672 446 203	452866 14510	8·949530 45883	588072 2973	8424600 7092
1188	1 41 13 44	1 676 676 672	467376 14503	8·995413 45864	591045 2971	8417508 7079
1189	1 41 37 21	1 680 914 269	481879 14498	9·041277 45844	594016 2969	8410429 7068
1190	1 41 61 00	1 685 159 000	496377 14491	9·087121 45825	596985 2968	8403361 7055
1191	1 41 84 81	1 689 410 871	510868 14485	9·132946 45807	599953 2965	8396306 7044
1192	1 42 08 64	1 693 669 888	525353 14479	9·178753 45786	602918 2965	8389262 7032
1193	1 42 32 49	1 697 936 057	539832 14473	9·224539 45768	605883 2962	8382230 7021
1194	1 42 56 36	1 702 209 384	554305 14467	9·270307 45749	608845 2961	8375209 7008
1195	1 42 80 25	1 706 489 875	568772 14461	9·316056 45729	611806 2959	8368201 6997
1196	1 43 04 16	1 710 777 536	583233 14455	9·361785 45710	614765 2958	8361204 6985
1197	1 43 28 09	1 715 072 373	597688 14449	9·407495 45691	617723 2956	8354219 6974
1198	1 43 52 04	1 719 374 392	612137 14442	9·453186 45672	620679 2954	8347245 6961
1199	1 43 76 01	1 723 683 599	626579 14437	9·498858 45654	623633 2953	8340284 6951
1200	1 44 00 00	1 728 000 000	641016	9·544512	626586	8333333
			34·	100 +	10·	0·000

25

No. n	Square n²	Cube n³	Square root √n	Sq. rt. of 10n √10n	Cube root ∛n	Reciprocal 1/n
			34·	100 +	10·	0·000
1200	1 44 00 00	1 728 000 000	641016 14431	9·544512 45634	626586 2951	8333333 6938
1201	1 44 24 01	1 732 323 601	655447 14425	9·590146 45615	629537 2949	8326395 6927
1202	1 44 48 04	1 736 654 408	669872 14418	9·635761 45596	632486 2948	8319468 6916
1203	1 44 72 09	1 740 992 427	684290 14413	9·681357 45577	635434 2946	8312552 6904
1204	1 44 96 16	1 745 337 664	698703 14407	9·726934 45558	638380 2944	8305648 6893
1205	1 45 20 25	1 749 690 125	713110 14401	9·772492 45539	641324 2943	8298755 6881
1206	1 45 44 36	1 754 049 816	727511 14395	9·818031 45520	644267 2941	8291874 6870
1207	1 45 68 49	1 758 416 743	741906 14388	9·863552 45501	647208 2940	8285004 6858
1208	1 45 92 64	1 762 790 912	756294 14383	9·909053 45483	650148 2938	8278146 6847
1209	1 46 16 81	1 767 172 329	770677 14377	9·954536 45464	653086 2936	8271299 6836
1210	1 46 41 00	1 771 561 000	785054 14371	*0·000000 45445	656022 2935	8264463 6825
1211	1 46 65 21	1 775 956 931	799425 14365	0·045445 45427	658957 2933	8257638 6813
1212	1 46 89 44	1 780 360 128	813790 14360	0·090872 45407	661890 2932	8250825 6802
1213	1 47 13 69	1 784 770 597	828150 14353	0·136279 45389	664822 2930	8244023 6791
1214	1 47 37 96	1 789 188 344	842503 14347	0·181668 45370	667752 2928	8237232 6779
1215	1 47 62 25	1 793 613 375	856850 14342	0·227038 45352	670680 2927	8230453 6769
1216	1 47 86 56	1 798 045 696	871192 14335	0·272390 45333	673607 2925	8223684 6757
1217	1 48 10 89	1 802 485 313	885527 14330	0·317723 45314	676532 2923	8216927 6746
1218	1 48 35 24	1 806 932 232	899857 14324	0·363037 45296	679455 2922	8210181 6736
1219	1 48 59 61	1 811 386 459	914181 14317	0·408333 45277	682377 2920	8203445 6724
1220	1 48 84 00	1 815 848 000	928498 14312	0·453610 45259	685297 2919	8196721 6713
1221	1 49 08 41	1 820 316 861	942810 14307	0·498869 45240	688216 2917	8190008 6702
1222	1 49 32 84	1 824 793 048	957117 14300	0·544109 45221	691133 2916	8183306 6691
1223	1 49 57 29	1 829 276 567	971417 14294	0·589330 45203	694049 2913	8176615 6680
1224	1 49 81 76	1 833 767 424	985711 14289	0·634533 45185	696962 2913	8169935 6670
1225	1 50 06 25	1 838 265 625	*000000 14283	0·679718 45166	699875 2911	8163265 6658
1226	1 50 30 76	1 842 771 176	014283 14277	0·724884 45148	702786 2909	8156607 6648
1227	1 50 55 29	1 847 284 083	028560 14271	0·770032 45129	705695 2907	8149959 6637
1228	1 50 79 84	1 851 804 352	042831 14265	0·815161 45111	708602 2906	8143322 6625
1229	1 51 04 41	1 856 331 989	057096 14260	0·860272 45093	711508 2905	8136697 6616
1230	1 51 29 00	1 860 867 000	071356 14254	0·905365 45074	714413 2903	8130081 6604
1231	1 51 53 61	1 865 409 391	085610 14248	0·950439 45056	717316 2901	8123477 6594
1232	1 51 78 24	1 869 959 168	099858 14242	0·995495 45038	720217 2900	8116883 6583
1233	1 52 02 89	1 874 516 337	114100 14236	1·040533 45020	723117 2898	8110300 6572
1234	1 52 27 56	1 879 080 904	128336 14231	1·085553 45001	726015 2896	8103728 6562
1235	1 52 52 25	1 883 652 875	142567 14225	1·130554 44983	728911 2895	8097166 6551
1236	1 52 76 96	1 888 232 256	156792 14219	1·175537 44965	731806 2894	8090615 6541
1237	1 53 01 69	1 892 819 053	171011 14213	1·220502 44946	734700 2892	8084074 6530
1238	1 53 26 44	1 897 413 272	185224 14208	1·265448 44929	737592 2890	8077544 6519
1239	1 53 51 21	1 902 014 919	199432 14202	1·310377 44910	740482 2889	8071025 6509
1240	1 53 76 00	1 906 624 000	213634 14196	1·355287 44893	743371 2887	8064516 6498
1241	1 54 00 81	1 911 240 521	227830 14190	1·400180 44874	746258 2886	8058018 6488
1242	1 54 25 64	1 915 864 488	242020 14185	1·445054 44856	749144 2884	8051530 6478
1243	1 54 50 49	1 920 495 907	256205 14179	1·489910 44838	752028 2882	8045052 6467
1244	1 54 75 36	1 925 134 784	270384 14174	1·534748 44820	754910 2881	8038585 6456
1245	1 55 00 25	1 929 781 125	284558 14167	1·579568 44802	757791 2880	8032129 6447
1246	1 55 25 16	1 934 434 936	298725 14162	1·624370 44784	760671 2878	8025682 6436
1247	1 55 50 09	1 939 096 223	312887 14156	1·669154 44766	763549 2876	8019246 6436
1248	1 55 75 04	1 943 764 992	327043 14151	1·713920 44749	766425 2875	8012821 6425
1249	1 56 00 01	1 948 441 249	341194 14145	1·758669 44730	769300 2873	8006405 6416
1250	1 56 25 00	1 953 125 000	355339	1·803399	772173	8000000 6405
			35·	110 +	10·	0·000

No. n	Square n^2	Cube n^3	Square root $\sqrt{n}$		Sq. rt. of 10n $\sqrt{10n}$		Cube root $\sqrt[3]{n}$		Reciprocal $\frac{1}{n}$	
			35·		110 +		10·		0·000	
1250	1 56 25 00	1 953 125 000	355339	14139	1·803399	44712	772173	2872	8000000	6395
1251	1 56 50 01	1 957 816 251	369478	14134	1·848111	44695	775045	2871	7993605	6385
1252	1 56 75 04	1 962 515 008	383612	14128	1·892806	44677	777916	2868	7987220	6374
1253	1 57 00 09	1 967 221 277	397740	14122	1·937483	44658	780784	2868	7980846	6364
1254	1 57 25 16	1 971 935 064	411862	14117	1·982141	44642	783652	2865	7974482	6355
1255	1 57 50 25	1 976 656 375	425979	14111	2·026783	44623	786517	2864	7968127	6344
1256	1 57 75 36	1 981 385 216	440090	14106	2·071406	44605	789381	2863	7961783	6334
1257	1 58 00 49	1 986 121 593	454196	14100	2·116011	44588	792244	2861	7955449	6323
1258	1 58 25 64	1 990 865 512	468296	14094	2·160599	44570	795105	2860	7949126	6314
1259	1 58 50 81	1 995 616 979	482390	14089	2·205169	44553	797965	2858	7942812	6304
1260	1 58 76 00	2 000 376 000	496479	14083	2·249722	44534	800823	2857	7936508	6294
1261	1 59 01 21	2 005 142 581	510562	14077	2·294256	44517	803680	2855	7930214	6284
1262	1 59 26 44	2 009 916 728	524639	14072	2·338773	44500	806535	2853	7923930	6274
1263	1 59 51 69	2 014 698 447	538711	14067	2·383273	44482	809388	2852	7917656	6264
1264	1 59 76 96	2 019 487 744	552778	14060	2·427755	44464	812240	2851	7911392	6254
1265	1 60 02 25	2 024 284 625	566838	14056	2·472219	44446	815091	2849	7905138	6244
1266	1 60 27 56	2 029 089 096	580894	14049	2·516665	44430	817940	2848	7898894	6234
1267	1 60 52 89	2 033 901 163	594943	14045	2·561095	44411	820788	2846	7892660	6225
1268	1 60 78 24	2 038 720 832	608988	14038	2·605506	44394	823634	2844	7886435	6214
1269	1 61 03 61	2 043 548 109	623026	14033	2·649900	44377	826478	2843	7880221	6205
1270	1 61 29 00	2 048 383 000	637059	14028	2·694277	44359	829321	2842	7874016	6195
1271	1 61 54 41	2 053 225 511	651087	14022	2·738636	44341	832163	2840	7867821	6186
1272	1.61 79 84	2 058 075 648	665109	14017	2·782977	44325	835003	2839	7861635	6175
1273	1 62 05 29	2 062 933 417	679126	14011	2·827302	44306	837842	2837	7855460	6166
1274	1 62 30 76	2 067 798 824	693137	14005	2·871608	44290	840679	2835	7849294	6157
1275	1 62 56 25	2 072 671 875	707142	14000	2·915898	44272	843514	2835	7843137	6146
1276	1 62 81 76	2 077 552 576	721142	13995	2·960170	44255	846349	2832	7836997	6137
1277	1 63 07 29	2 082 440 933	735137	13989	3·004425	44237	849181	2831	7830854	6128
1278	1 63 32 84	2 087 336 952	749126	13983	3·048662	44220	852012	2830	7824726	6118
1279	1 63 58 41	2 092 240 639	763109	13979	3·092882	44203	854842	2828	7818608	6108
1280	1 63 84 00	2 097 152 000	777088	13972	3·137085	44186	857670	2827	7812500	6099
1281	1 64 09 61	2 102 071 041	791060	13968	3·181271	44168	860497	2826	7806401	6089
1282	1 64 34 24	2 106 997 768	805028	13961	3·225439	44151	863323	2823	7800312	6080
1283	1 64 60 89	2 111 932 187	818989	13957	3·269590	44134	866146	2823	7794232	6070
1284	1 64 86 56	2 116 874 304	832946	13951	3·313724	44116	868969	2821	7788162	6061
1285	1 65 12 25	2 121 824 125	846897	13945	3·357840	44100	871790	2819	7782101	6051
1286	1 65 37 96	2 126 781 656	860842	13940	3·401940	44082	874609	2818	7776050	6042
1287	1 65 63 69	2 131 746 903	874782	13935	3·446022	44066	877427	2817	7770008	6033
1288	1 65 89 44	2 136 719 872	888717	13929	3·490088	44048	880244	2815	7763975	6023
1289	1 66 15 21	2 141 700 569	902646	13924	3·534136	44031	883059	2813	7757952	6014
1290	1 66 41 00	2 146 689 000	916570	13918	3·578167	44014	885872	2812	7751938	6005
1291	1 66 66 81	2 151 685 171	930488	13914	3·622181	43997	888684	2811	7745933	5995
1292	1 66 92 64	2 156 689 088	944402	13907	3·666178	43980	891495	2809	7739938	5986
1293	1 67 18 49	2 161 700 757	958309	13902	3·710158	43963	894304	2808	7733952	5977
1294	1 67 44 36	2 166 720 184	972211	13897	3·754121	43946	897112	2807	7727975	5967
1295	1 67 70 25	2 171 747 375	986108	13892	3·798067	43929	899919	2805	7722008	5959
1296	1 67 96 16	2 176 782 336	*000000	13886	3·841996	43912	902724	2803	7716049	5949
1297	1 68 22 09	2 181 825 073	013886	13881	3·885908	43895	905527	2802	7710100	5940
1298	1 68 48 04	2 186 875 592	027767	13876	3·929803	43878	908329	2801	7704160	5931
1299	1 68 74 01	2 191 933 899	041643	13870	3·973681	43862	911130	2799	7698229	5921
1300	1 69 00 00	2 197 000 000	055513		4·017543		913929		7692308	
			36·		110 +		10·		0·000	

No. n	Square n^2	Cube n^3	Square root $\sqrt{n}$	Sq. rt. of 10n $\sqrt{10n}$	Cube root $\sqrt[3]{n}$	Reciprocal $\dfrac{1}{n}$
			36·	110 +	10·	0·000
1300	1 69 00 00	2 197 000 000	055513 13865	4·017543 43844	913929 2798	7692308 5913
1301	1 69 26 01	2 202 073 901	069378 13859	4·061387 43828	916727 2796	7686395 5903
1302	1 69 52 04	2 207 155 608	083237 13854	4·105215 43810	919523 2795	7680492 5895
1303	1 69 78 09	2 212 245 127	097091 13849	4·149025 43794	922318 2793	7674597 5885
1304	1 70 04 16	2 217 342 464	110940 13844	4·192819 43778	925111 2792	7668712 5877
1305	1 70 30 25	2 222 447 625	124784 13838	4·236597 43760	927903 2791	7662835 5867
1306	1 70 56 36	2 227 560 616	138622 13833	4·280357 43744	930694 2789	7656968 5859
1307	1 70 82 49	2 232 681 443	152455 13828	4·324101 43727	933483 2788	7651109 5849
1308	1 71 08 64	2 237 810 112	166283 13822	4·367828 43710	936271 2786	7645260 5841
1309	1 71 34 81	2 242 946 629	180105 13817	4·411538 43693	939057 2785	7639419 5831
1310	1 71 61 00	2 248 091 000	193922 13812	4·455231 43677	941842 2783	7633588 5823
1311	1 71 87 21	2 253 243 231	207734 13807	4·498908 43661	944625 2782	7627765 5814
1312	1 72 13 44	2 258 403 328	221541 13801	4·542569 43643	947407 2781	7621951 5805
1313	1 72 39 69	2 263 571 297	235342 13796	4·586212 43627	950188 2779	7616146 5796
1314	1 72 65 96	2 268 747 144	249138 13791	4·629839 43610	952967 2778	7610350 5787
1315	1 72 92 25	2 273 930 875	262929 13785	4·673449 43594	955745 2776	7604563 5779
1316	1 73 18 56	2 279 122 496	276714 13781	4·717043 43577	958521 2775	7598784 5770
1317	1 73 44 89	2 284 322 013	290495 13775	4·760620 43561	961296 2774	7593014 5761
1318	1 73 71 24	2 289 529 432	304270 13770	4·804181 43544	964070 2772	7587253 5752
1319	1 73 97 61	2 294 744 759	318040 13764	4·847725 43528	966842 2771	7581501 5743
1320	1 74 24 00	2 299 968 000	331804 13760	4·891253 43511	969613 2770	7575758 5735
1321	1 74 50 41	2 305 199 161	345564 13754	4·934764 43495	972383 2768	7570023 5726
1322	1 74 76 84	2 310 438 248	359318 13749	4·978259 43478	975151 2766	7564297 5718
1323	1 75 03 29	2 315 685 267	373067 13744	5·021737 43462	977917 2765	7558579 5709
1324	1 75 29 76	2 320 940 224	386811 13738	5·065199 43445	980682 2764	7552870 5700
1325	1 75 56 25	2 326 203 125	400549 13734	5·108644 43429	983446 2763	7547170 5692
1326	1 75 82 76	2 331 473 976	414283 13728	5·152073 43413	986209 2761	7541478 5683
1327	1 76 09 29	2 336 752 783	428011 13723	5·195486 43396	988970 2759	7535795 5675
1328	1 76 35 84	2 342 039 552	441734 13718	5·238882 43380	991729 2759	7530120 5666
1329	1 76 62 41	2 347 334 289	455452 13713	5·282262 43364	994488 2756	7524454 5657
1330	1 76 89 00	2 352 637 000	469165 13708	5·325626 43347	997244 2756	7518797 5649
1331	1 77 15 61	2 357 947 691	482873 13702	5·368973 43331	*000000 2754	7513148 5640
1332	1 77 42 24	2 363 266 368	496575 13698	5·412304 43315	002754 2753	7507508 5633
1333	1 77 68 89	2 368 593 037	510273 13692	5·455619 43299	005507 2751	7501875 5623
1334	1 77 95 56	2 373 927 704	523965 13687	5·498918 43282	008258 2750	7496252 5615
1335	1 78 22 25	2 379 270 375	537652 13682	5·542200 43266	011008 2749	7490637 5607
1336	1 78 48 96	2 384 621 056	551334 13677	5·585466 43250	013757 2747	7485030 5598
1337	1 78 75 69	2 389 979 753	565011 13671	5·628716 43234	016504 2746	7479432 5590
1338	1 79 02 44	2 395 346 472	578682 13667	5·671950 43218	019250 2745	7473842 5582
1339	1 79 29 21	2 400 721 219	592349 13661	5·715168 43201	021995 2743	7468260 5573
1340	1 79 56 00	2 406 104 000	606010 13657	5·758369 43185	024738 2742	7462687 5565
1341	1 79 82 81	2 411 494 821	619667 13651	5·801554 43170	027480 2740	7457122 5557
1342	1 80 09 64	2 416 893 688	633318 13646	5·844724 43153	030220 2739	7451565 5549
1343	1 80 36 49	2 422 300 607	646964 13642	5·887877 43137	032959 2738	7446016 5540
1344	1 80 63 36	2 427 715 584	660606 13636	5·931014 43121	035697 2736	7440476 5532
1345	1 80 90 25	2 433 138 625	674242 13631	5·974135 43105	038433 2735	7434944 5523
1346	1 81 17 16	2 438 569 736	687873 13626	6·017240 43089	041168 2734	7429421 5516
1347	1 81 44 09	2 444 008 923	701499 13621	6·060329 43073	043902 2732	7423905 5507
1348	1 81 71 04	2 449 456 192	715120 13615	6·103402 43057	046634 2731	7418398 5500
1349	1 81 98 01	2 454 911 549	728735 13611	6·146459 43041	049365 2729	7412898 5491
1350	1 82 25 00	2 460 375 000	742346	6·189500	052094	7407407
			36·	110 +	11·	0·000

No. n	Square n²	Cube n³	Square root √n	Sq. rt. of 10n √10n	Cube root ∛n	Reciprocal 1/n
			36·	110 +	11·	0·000
1350	1 82 25 00	2 460 375 000	742346 13606	6·189500 43026	052094 2729	7407407 5482
1351	1 82 53 01	2 465 846 551	755952 13601	6·232526 43009	054823 2727	7401925 5475
1352	1 82 79 04	2 471 326 208	769553 13595	6·275535 43009	057550 2725	7396450 5467
1353	1 83 06 09	2 476 813 977	783148 13591	6·318528 42993	060275 2724	7390983 5459
1354	1 83 33 16	2 482 309 864	796739 13586	6·361506 42978	062999 2723	7385524 5450
				42961		
1355	1 83 60 25	2 487 813 875	810325 13580	6·404467 42946	065722 2722	7380074 5443
1356	1 83 87 36	2 493 326 016	823905 13576	6·447413 42930	068444 2720	7374631 5434
1357	1 84 14 49	2 498 846 293	837481 13571	6·490343 42914	071164 2719	7369197 5427
1358	1 84 41 64	2 504 374 712	851052 13565	6·533257 42898	073883 2717	7363770 5418
1359	1 84 68 81	2 509 911 279	864617 13561	6·576155 42883	076600 2717	7358352 5411
1360	1 84 96 00	2 515 456 000	878178 13555	6·619038 42867	079317 2714	7352941 5402
1361	1 85 23 21	2 521 008 881	891733 13551	6·661905 42851	082031 2714	7347539 5395
1362	1 85 50 44	2 526 569 928	905284 13546	6·704756 42835	084745 2712	7342144 5387
1363	1 85 77 69	2 532 139 147	918830 13541	6·747591 42820	087457 2711	7336757 5379
1364	1 86 04 96	2 537 716 544	932371 13535	6·790411 42803	090168 2710	7331378 5371
1365	1 86 32 25	2 543 302 125	945906 13531	6·833214 42789	092878 2708	7326007 5363
1366	1 86 59 56	2 548 895 896	959437 13526	6·876003 42772	095586 2707	7320644 5355
1367	1 86 86 89	2 554 497 863	972963 13521	6·918775 42757	098293 2705	7315289 5347
1368	1 87 14 24	2 560 108 032	986484 13516	6·961532 42741	100998 2704	7309942 5340
1369	1 87 41 61	2 565 726 409	*000000 13511	7·004273 42726	103702 2703	7304602 5332
1370	1 87 69 00	2 571 353 000	013511 13506	7·046999 42710	106405 2702	7299270 5324
1371	1 87 96 41	2 576 987 811	027017 13501	7·089709 42695	109107 2700	7293946 5316
1372	1 88 23 84	2 582 630 848	040518 13497	7·132404 42679	111807 2699	7288630 5309
1373	1 88 51 29	2 588 282 117	054015 13491	7·175083 42663	114506 2698	7283321 5301
1374	1 88 78 76	2 593 941 624	067506 13486	7·217746 42648	117204 2696	7278020 5293
1375	1 89 06 25	2 599 609 375	080992 13482	7·260394 42632	119900 2696	7272727 5285
1376	1 89 33 76	2 605 285 376	094474 13477	7·303026 42617	122596 2693	7267442 5278
1377	1 89 61 29	2 610 969 633	107951 13471	7·345643 42602	125289 2693	7262164 5270
1378	1 89 88 84	2 616 662 152	121422 13467	7·388245 42586	127982 2691	7256894 5262
1379	1 90 16 41	2 622 362 939	134889 13462	7·430831 42570	130673 2690	7251632 5255
1380	1 90 44 00	2 628 072 000	148351 13457	7·473401 42555	133363 2688	7246377 5247
1381	1 90 71 61	2 633 789 341	161808 13453	7·515956 42540	136051 2688	7241130 5240
1382	1 90 99 24	2 639 514 968	175261 13447	7·558496 42524	138739 2686	7235890 5232
1383	1 91 26 89	2 645 248 887	188708 13442	7·601020 42509	141425 2684	7230658 5224
1384	1 91 54 56	2 650 991 104	202150 13438	7·643529 42494	144109 2684	7225434 5217
1385	1 91 82 25	2 656 741 625	215588 13433	7·686023 42478	146793 2682	7220217 5210
1386	1 92 09 96	2 662 500 456	229021 13428	7·728501 42463	149475 2681	7215007 5202
1387	1 92 37 69	2 668 267 603	242449 13423	7·770964 42448	152156 2679	7209805 5194
1388	1 92 65 44	2 674 043 072	255872 13418	7·813412 42432	154835 2678	7204611 5187
1389	1 92 93 21	2 679 826 869	269290 13414	7·855844 42417	157513 2677	7199424 5179
1390	1 93 21 00	2 685 619 000	282704 13408	7·898261 42402	160190 2676	7194245 5172
1391	1 93 48 81	2 691 419 471	296112 13404	7·940663 42387	162866 2674	7189073 5165
1392	1 93 76 64	2 697 228 288	309516 13399	7·983050 42371	165540 2673	7183908 5157
1393	1 94 04 49	2 703 045 457	322915 13394	8·025421 42356	168213 2672	7178751 5150
1394	1 94 32 36	2 708 870 984	336309 13390	8·067777 42341	170885 2671	7173601 5142
1395	1 94 60 25	2 714 704 875	349699 13384	8·110118 42326	173556 2669	7168459 5135
1396	1 94 88 16	2 720 547 136	363083 13380	8·152444 42311	176225 2668	7163324 5128
1397	1 95 16 09	2 726 397 773	376463 13375	8·194755 42295	178893 2667	7158196 5120
1398	1 95 44 04	2 732 256 792	389838 13370	8·237050 42280	181560 2665	7153076 5113
1399	1 95 72 01	2 738 124 199	403208 13366	8·279330 42266	184225 2664	7147963 5106
1400	1 96 00 00	2 744 000 000	416574	8·321596	186889	7142857
			37·	110 +	11·	0·000

No. n	Square n²	Cube n³	Square root √n	Sq. rt. of 10n √10n	Cube root ∛n	Reciprocal 1/n
			37·	110 +	11·	0·000
1400	1 96 00 00	2 744 000 000	416574	8·321596	186889	7142857
1401	1 96 28 01	2 749 884 201	429935 (13361)	8·363846 (42250)	189552 (2663)	7137759 (5098)
1402	1 96 56 04	2 755 776 808	443290 (13355)	8·406081 (42235)	192214 (2662)	7132668 (5091)
1403	1 96 84 09	2 761 677 827	456642 (13352)	8·448301 (42220)	194874 (2660)	7127584 (5084)
1404	1 97 12 16	2 767 587 264	469988 (13346)	8·490506 (42205)	197533 (2659)	7122507 (5077)
			(13342)	(42190)	(2658)	(5069)
1405	1 97 40 25	2 773 505 125	483330 (13337)	8·532696 (42175)	200191 (2657)	7117438 (5062)
1406	1 97 68 36	2 779 431 416	496667 (13332)	8·574871 (42160)	202848 (2655)	7112376 (5055)
1407	1 97 96 49	2 785 366 143	509999 (13327)	8·617031 (42145)	205503 (2654)	7107321 (5048)
1408	1 98 24 64	2 791 309 312	523326 (13323)	8·659176 (42130)	208157 (2653)	7102273 (5041)
1409	1 98 52 81	2 797 260 929	536649 (13318)	8·701306 (42115)	210810 (2652)	7097232 (5033)
1410	1 98 81 00	2 803 221 000	549967 (13313)	8·743421 (42100)	213462 (2650)	7092199 (5027)
1411	1 99 09 21	2 809 189 531	563280 (13308)	8·785521 (42085)	216112 (2649)	7087172 (5019)
1412	1 99 37 44	2 815 166 528	576588 (13304)	8·827606 (42071)	218761 (2648)	7082153 (5012)
1413	1 99 65 69	2 821 151 997	589892 (13299)	8·869677 (42055)	221409 (2646)	7077141 (5005)
1414	1 99 93 96	2 827 145 944	603191 (13295)	8·911732 (42041)	224055 (2646)	7072136 (4998)
1415	2 00 22 25	2 833 148 375	616486 (13289)	8·953773 (42025)	226701 (2644)	7067138 (4991)
1416	2 00 50 56	2 839 159 296	629775 (13285)	8·995798 (42011)	229345 (2643)	7062147 (4984)
1417	2 00 78 89	2 845 178 713	643060 (13281)	9·037809 (41996)	231988 (2641)	7057163 (4977)
1418	2 01 07 24	2 851 206 632	656341 (13275)	9·079805 (41981)	234629 (2641)	7052186 (4970)
1419	2 01 35 61	2 857 243 059	669616 (13271)	9·121786 (41967)	237270 (2639)	7047216 (4962)
1420	2 01 64 00	2 863 288 000	682887 (13267)	9·163753 (41952)	239909 (2638)	7042254 (4956)
1421	2 01 92 41	2 869 341 461	696154 (13261)	9·205705 (41936)	242547 (2636)	7037298 (4949)
1422	2 02 20 84	2 875 403 448	709415 (13257)	9·247641 (41923)	245183 (2636)	7032349 (4942)
1423	2 02 49 29	2 881 473 967	722672 (13253)	9·289564 (41907)	247819 (2634)	7027407 (4935)
1424	2 02 77 76	2 887 553 024	735925 (13247)	9·331471 (41893)	250453 (2633)	7022472 (4928)
1425	2 03 06 25	2 893 640 625	749172 (13243)	9·373364 (41878)	253086 (2631)	7017544 (4921)
1426	2 03 34 76	2 899 736 776	762415 (13239)	9·415242 (41863)	255717 (2631)	7012623 (4915)
1427	2 03 63 29	2 905 841 483	775654 (13233)	9·457105 (41849)	258348 (2629)	7007708 (4907)
1428	2 03 91 84	2 911 954 752	788887 (13229)	9·498954 (41834)	260977 (2628)	7002801 (4900)
1429	2 04 20 41	2 918 076 589	802116 (13225)	9·540788 (41819)	263605 (2627)	6997901 (4894)
1430	2 04 49 00	2 924 207 000	815341 (13220)	9·582607 (41805)	266232 (2625)	6993007 (4887)
1431	2 04 77 61	2 930 345 991	828561 (13215)	9·624412 (41790)	268857 (2625)	6988120 (4880)
1432	2 05 06 24	2 936 493 568	841776 (13210)	9·666202 (41776)	271482 (2623)	6983240 (4873)
1433	2 05 34 89	2 942 649 737	854986 (13206)	9·707978 (41761)	274105 (2622)	6978367 (4866)
1434	2 05 63 56	2 948 814 504	868192 (13202)	9·749739 (41747)	276727 (2620)	6973501 (4860)
1435	2 05 92 25	2 954 987 875	881394 (13197)	9·791486 (41731)	279347 (2620)	6968641 (4853)
1436	2 06 20 96	2 961 169 856	894591 (13192)	9·833217 (41718)	281967 (2618)	6963788 (4846)
1437	2 06 49 69	2 967 360 453	907783 (13187)	9·874935 (41703)	284585 (2617)	6958942 (4839)
1438	2 06 78 44	2 973 559 672	920970 (13183)	9·916638 (41688)	287202 (2616)	6954103 (4833)
1439	2 07 07 21	2 979 767 519	934153 (13179)	9·958326 (41674)	289818 (2614)	6949270 (4826)
1440	2 07 36 00	2 985 984 000	947332 (13174)	*0·000000 (41659)	292432 (2614)	6944444 (4819)
1441	2 07 64 81	2 992 209 121	960506 (13169)	0·041659 (41645)	295046 (2612)	6939625 (4812)
1442	2 07 93 64	2 998 442 888	973675 (13165)	0·083304 (41631)	297658 (2611)	6934813 (4806)
1443	2 08 22 49	3 004 685 307	986840 (13160)	0·124935 (41616)	300269 (2610)	6930007 (4799)
1444	2 08 51 36	3 010 936 384	*000000 (13156)	0·166551 (41602)	302879 (2608)	6925208 (4793)
1445	2 08 80 25	3 017 196 125	013156 (13151)	0·208153 (41587)	305487 (2608)	6920415 (4786)
1446	2 09 09 16	3 023 464 536	026307 (13146)	0·249740 (41573)	308095 (2606)	6915629 (4779)
1447	2 09 38 09	3 029 741 623	039453 (13142)	0·291313 (41559)	310701 (2605)	6910850 (4773)
1448	2 09 67 04	3 036 027 392	052595 (13138)	0·332872 (41544)	313306 (2603)	6906077 (4766)
1449	2 09 96 01	3 042 321 849	065733 (13133)	0·374416 (41530)	315909 (2603)	6901311 (4759)
1450	2 10 25 00	3 048 625 000	078866	0·415946	318512	6896552
			38·	120 +	11·	0·000

No. n	Square n²	Cube n³	Square root √n	Sq. rt. of 10n √10n	Cube root ∛n	Reciprocal 1/n
			38·	120 +	11·	0·000
1450	2 10 25 00	3 048 625 000	078866 [13128]	0·415946 [41515]	318512 [2601]	6896552
1451	2 10 54 01	3 054 936 851	091994 [13124]	0·457461 [41502]	321113 [2600]	6891799 [4753]
1452	2 10 83 04	3 061 257 408	105118 [13119]	0·498963 [41487]	323713 [2599]	6887052 [4747]
1453	2 11 12 09	3 067 586 677	118237 [13115]	0·540450 [41472]	326312 [2598]	6882312 [4740]
1454	2 11 41 16	3 073 924 664	131352 [13110]	0·581922 [41459]	328910 [2597]	6877579 [4733]
1455	2 11 70 25	3 080 271 375	144462 [13106]	0·623381 [41444]	331507 [2595]	6872852 [4727]
1456	2 11 99 36	3 086 626 816	157568 [13101]	0·664825 [41430]	334102 [2594]	6868132 [4720]
1457	2 12 28 49	3 092 990 993	170669 [13097]	0·706255 [41416]	336696 [2593]	6863418 [4714]
1458	2 12 57 64	3 099 363 912	183766 [13093]	0·747671 [41401]	339289 [2592]	6858711 [4707]
1459	2 12 86 81	3 105 745 579	196859 [13087]	0·789072 [41388]	341881 [2591]	6854010 [4701]
1460	2 13 16 00	3 112 136 000	209946 [13084]	0·830460 [41373]	344472 [2589]	6849315 [4695]
1461	2 13 45 21	3 118 535 181	223030 [13079]	0·871833 [41359]	347061 [2589]	6844627 [4688]
1462	2 13 74 44	3 124 943 128	236109 [13074]	0·913192 [41345]	349650 [2587]	6839945 [4682]
1463	2 14 03 69	3 131 359 847	249183 [13070]	0·954537 [41331]	352237 [2586]	6835270 [4675]
1464	2 14 32 96	3 137 785 344	262253 [13065]	0·995868 [41316]	354823 [2584]	6830601 [4669]
1465	2 14 62 25	3 144 219 625	275318 [13061]	1·037184 [41303]	357407 [2584]	6825939 [4662]
1466	2 14 91 56	3 150 662 696	288379 [13057]	1·078487 [41288]	359991 [2582]	6821282 [4657]
1467	2 15 20 89	3 157 114 563	301436 [13052]	1·119775 [41275]	362573 [2582]	6816633 [4649]
1468	2 15 50 24	3 163 575 232	314488 [13048]	1·161050 [41260]	365155 [2580]	6811989 [4644]
1469	2 15 79 61	3 170 044 709	327536 [13043]	1·202310 [41247]	367735 [2579]	6807352 [4637]
1470	2 16 09 00	3 176 523 000	340579 [13039]	1·243557 [41232]	370314 [2577]	6802721 [4631]
1471	2 16 38 41	3 183 010 111	353618 [13034]	1·284789 [41218]	372891 [2576]	6798097 [4624]
1472	2 16 67 84	3 189 506 048	366652 [13030]	1·326007 [41204]	375467 [2576]	6793478 [4619]
1473	2 16 97 29	3 196 010 817	379682 [13026]	1·367211 [41191]	378043 [2575]	6788866 [4612]
1474	2 17 26 76	3 202 524 424	392708 [13021]	1·408402 [41176]	380618 [2573]	6784261 [4605]
1475	2 17 56 25	3 209 046 875	405729 [13016]	1·449578 [41162]	383191 [2571]	6779661 [4600]
1476	2 17 85 76	3 215 578 176	418745 [13013]	1·490740 [41149]	385762 [2571]	6775068 [4593]
1477	2 18 15 29	3 222 118 333	431758 [13008]	1·531889 [41134]	388333 [2570]	6770481 [4587]
1478	2 18 44 84	3 228 667 352	444766 [13003]	1·573023 [41121]	390903 [2568]	6765900 [4581]
1479	2 18 74 41	3 235 225 239	457769 [12999]	1·614144 [41107]	393471 [2567]	6761325 [4575]
1480	2 19 04 00	3 241 792 000	470768 [12995]	1·655251 [41092]	396038 [2567]	6756757 [4568]
1481	2 19 33 61	3 248 367 641	483763 [12990]	1·696343 [41079]	398605 [2564]	6752194 [4563]
1482	2 19 63 24	3 254 952 168	496753 [12986]	1·737422 [41065]	401169 [2564]	6747638 [4556]
1483	2 19 92 89	3 261 545 587	509739 [12982]	1·778487 [41052]	403733 [2563]	6743088 [4550]
1484	2 20 22 56	3 268 147 904	522721 [12977]	1·819539 [41037]	406296 [2561]	6738544 [4544]
1485	2 20 52 25	3 274 759 125	535698 [12973]	1·860576 [41024]	408857 [2561]	6734007 [4537]
1486	2 20 81 96	3 281 379 256	548671 [12968]	1·901600 [41009]	411418 [2559]	6729475 [4532]
1487	2 21 11 69	3 288 008 303	561639 [12964]	1·942609 [40996]	413977 [2558]	6724950 [4525]
1488	2 21 41 44	3 294 646 272	574603 [12960]	1·983605 [40983]	416535 [2557]	6720430 [4520]
1489	2 21 71 21	3 301 293 169	587563 [12955]	2·024588 [40968]	419092 [2556]	6715917 [4513]
1490	2 22 01 00	3 307 949 000	600518 [12951]	2·065556 [40955]	421648 [2554]	6711409 [4508]
1491	2 22 30 81	3 314 613 771	613469 [12947]	2·106511 [40941]	424202 [2554]	6706908 [4501]
1492	2 22 60 64	3 321 287 488	626416 [12942]	2·147452 [40927]	426756 [2552]	6702413 [4495]
1493	2 22 90 49	3 327 970 157	639358 [12938]	2·188379 [40914]	429308 [2551]	6697924 [4489]
1494	2 23 20 36	3 334 661 784	652296 [12934]	2·229293 [40900]	431859 [2550]	6693440 [4484]
1495	2 23 50 25	3 341 362 375	665230 [12929]	2·270193 [40886]	434409 [2549]	6688963 [4477]
1496	2 23 80 16	3 348 071 936	678159 [12925]	2·311079 [40872]	436958 [2548]	6684492 [4471]
1497	2 24 10 09	3 354 790 473	691084 [12921]	2·351951 [40859]	439506 [2547]	6680027 [4465]
1498	2 24 40 04	3 361 517 992	704005 [12916]	2·392810 [40846]	442053 [2547]	6675567 [4460]
1499	2 24 70 01	3 368 254 499	716921 [12912]	2·433656 [40831]	444598 [2545]	6671114 [4453]
1500	2 25 00 00	3 375 000 000	729833 38·	2·474487 120 +	447142 11·	6666667 0·000 [4447]

No. n	Square n²	Cube n³	Square root √n	Sq. rt. of 10n √10n	Cube root ∛n	Reciprocal 1/n
			38·	120 +	11·	0·000
1500	2 25 00 00	3 375 000 000	729833 12908	2·474487 40818	447142 2544	6666667 4442
1501	2 25 30 01	3 381 754 501	742741 12904	2·515305 40805	449686 2542	6662225 4435
1502	2 25 60 04	3 388 518 008	755645 12899	2·556110 40790	452228 2541	6657790 4430
1503	2 25 90 09	3 395 290 527	768544 12895	2·596900 40778	454769 2540	6653360 4424
1504	2 26 20 16	3 402 072 064	781439 12890	2·637678 40763	457309 2538	6648936 4418
1505	2 26 50 25	3 408 862 625	794329 12887	2·678441 40751	459847 2538	6644518 4412
1506	2 26 80 36	3 415 662 216	807216 12882	2·719192 40736	462385 2536	6640106 4406
1507	2 27 10 49	3 422 470 843	820098 12878	2·759928 40723	464921 2536	6635700 4400
1508	2 27 40 64	3 429 288 512	832976 12873	2·800651 40710	467457 2534	6631300 4395
1509	2 27 70 81	3 436 115 229	845849 12869	2·841361 40696	469991 2533	6626905 4388
1510	2 28 01 00	3 442 951 000	858718 12865	2·882057 40683	472524 2532	6622517 4383
1511	2 28 31 21	3 449 795 831	871583 12861	2·922740 40669	475056 2531	6618134 4377
1512	2 28 61 44	3 456 649 728	884444 12857	2·963409 40656	477587 2530	6613757 4372
1513	2 28 91 69	3 463 512 697	897301 12852	3·004065 40642	480117 2529	6609385 4365
1514	2 29 21 96	3 470 384 744	910153 12848	3·044707 40629	482646 2527	6605020 4360
1515	2 29 52 25	3 477 265 875	923001 12844	3·085336 40616	485173 2527	6600660 4354
1516	2 29 82 56	3 484 156 096	935845 12839	3·125952 40602	487700 2525	6596306 4348
1517	2 30 12 89	3 491 055 413	948684 12835	3·166554 40589	490225 2524	6591958 4343
1518	2 30 43 24	3 497 963 832	961519 12832	3·207143 40575	492749 2523	6587615 4337
1519	2 30 73 61	3 504 881 359	974351 12826	3·247718 40562	495272 2522	6583278 4331
1520	2 31 04 00	3 511 808 000	987177 12823	3·288280 40549	497794 2521	6578947 4325
1521	2 31 34 41	3 518 743 761	*000000 12818	3·328829 40535	500315 2520	6574622 4320
1522	2 31 64 84	3 525 688 648	012818 12815	3·369364 40522	502835 2519	6570302 4314
1523	2 31 95 29	3 532 642 667	025633 12810	3·409886 40509	505354 2517	6565988 4308
1524	2 32 25 76	3 539 605 824	038443 12805	3·450395 40495	507871 2517	6561680 4303
1525	2 32 56 25	3 546 578 125	051248 12802	3·490890 40483	510388 2515	6557377 4297
1526	2 32 86 76	3 553 559 576	064050 12797	3·531373 40468	512903 2514	6553080 4292
1527	2 33 17 29	3 560 550 183	076847 12794	3·571841 40456	515417 2513	6548788 4285
1528	2 33 47 84	3 567 549 952	089641 12789	3·612297 40443	517930 2513	6544503 4281
1529	2 33 78 41	3 574 558 889	102430 12784	3·652740 40429	520443 2511	6540222 4274
1530	2 34 09 00	3 581 577 000	115214 12781	3·693169 40416	522954 2509	6535948 4269
1531	2 34 39 61	3 588 604 291	127995 12777	3·733585 40403	525463 2509	6531679 4264
1532	2 34 70 24	3 595 640 768	140772 12772	3·773988 40389	527972 2508	6527415 4258
1533	2 35 00 89	3 602 686 437	153544 12768	3·814377 40377	530480 2507	6523157 4252
1534	2 35 31 56	3 609 741 304	166312 12764	3·854754 40363	532987 2505	6518905 4247
1535	2 35 62 25	3 616 805 375	179076 12760	3·895117 40350	535492 2505	6514658 4241
1536	2 35 92 96	3 623 878 656	191836 12756	3·935467 40337	537997 2503	6510417 4236
1537	2 36 23 69	3 630 961 153	204592 12751	3·975804 40324	540500 2502	6506181 4230
1538	2 36 54 44	3 638 052 872	217343 12747	4·016128 40311	543002 2502	6501951 4225
1539	2 36 85 21	3 645 153 819	230090 12744	4·056439 40297	545503 2501	6497726 4220
1540	2 37 16 00	3 652 264 000	242834 12739	4·096736 40285	548004 2499	6493506 4213
1541	2 37 46 81	3 659 383 421	255573 12735	4·137021 40272	550503 2499	6489293 4209
1542	2 37 77 64	3 666 512 088	268308 12731	4·177293 40258	553000 2497	6485084 4203
1543	2 38 08 49	3 673 650 007	281039 12726	4·217551 40246	555497 2496	6480881 4197
1544	2 38 39 36	3 680 797 184	293765 12723	4·257797 40232	557993 2495	6476684 4192
1545	2 38 70 25	3 687 953 625	306488 12719	4·298029 40219	560488 2493	6472492 4187
1546	2 39 01 16	3 695 119 336	319207 12714	4·338248 40207	562981 2493	6468305 4181
1547	2 39 32 09	3 702 294 323	331921 12710	4·378455 40193	565474 2492	6464124 4176
1548	2 39 63 04	3 709 478 592	344631 12706	4·418648 40181	567966 2490	6459948 4170
1549	2 39 94 01	3 716 672 149	357337 12702	4·458829 40167	570456 2489	6455778 4165
1550	2 40 25 00	3 723 875 000	370039 39·	4·498996 120 +	572945 11·	6451613 0·000

No. n	Square n²	Cube n³	Square root √n	Sq. rt. of 10n √10n	Cube root ∛n	Reciprocal 1/n
			39·	**120 +**	**11·**	**0·000**
1550	2 40 25 00	3 723 875 000	370039 12698	4·498996 40154	572945 2489	6451613 4160
1551	2 40 56 01	3 731 087 151	382737 12694	4·539150 40142	575434 2487	6447453 4154
1552	2 40 87 04	3 738 308 608	395431 12690	4·579292 40129	577921 2486	6443299 4149
1553	2 41 18 09	3 745 539 377	408121 12686	4·619421 40115	580407 2485	6439150 4144
1554	2 41 49 16	3 752 779 464	420807 12681	4·659536 40103	582892 2484	6435006 4138
1555	2 41 80 25	3 760 028 875	433488 12678	4·699639 40090	585376 2483	6430868 4133
1556	2 42 11 36	3 767 287 616	446166 12673	4·739729 40077	587859 2482	6426735 4127
1557	2 42 42 49	3 774 555 693	458839 12670	4·779806 40064	590341 2481	6422608 4123
1558	2 42 73 64	3 781 833 112	471509 12665	4·819870 40052	592822 2479	6418485 4117
1559	2 43 04 81	3 789 119 879	484174 12661	4·859922 40038	595301 2479	6414368 4112
1560	2 43 36 00	3 796 416 000	496835 12658	4·899960 40026	597780 2478	6410256 4106
1561	2 43 67 21	3 803 721 481	509493 12653	4·939986 40012	600258 2476	6406150 4101
1562	2 43 98 44	3 811 036 328	522146 12649	4·979998 40000	602734 2476	6402049 4096
1563	2 44 29 69	3 818 360 547	534795 12645	5·019998 39988	605210 2474	6397953 4091
1564	2 44 60 96	3 825 694 144	547440 12641	5·059986 39974	607684 2474	6393862 4086
1565	2 44 92 25	3 833 037 125	560081 12637	5·099960 39962	610158 2472	6389776 4080
1566	2 45 23 56	3 840 389 496	572718 12633	5·139922 39949	612630 2472	6385696 4080
1567	2 45 54 89	3 847 751 263	585351 12629	5·179871 39936	615101 2471	6381621 4075
1568	2 45 86 24	3 855 122 432	597980 12625	5·219807 39923	617571 2470	6377551 4070
1569	2 46 17 61	3 862 503 009	610605 12621	5·259730 39911	620041 2470	6373486 4065
1570	2 46 49 00	3 869 893 000	623226 12616	5·299641 39898	622509 2467	6369427 4055
1571	2 46 80 41	3 877 292 411	635842 12613	5·339539 39885	624976 2466	6365372 4049
1572	2 47 11 84	3 884 701 248	648455 12609	5·379424 39873	627442 2465	6361323 4044
1573	2 47 43 29	3 892 119 517	661064 12605	5·419297 39860	629907 2464	6357279 4039
1574	2·47 74 76	3 899 547 224	673669 12601	5·459157 39847	632371 2463	6353240 4034
1575	2 48 06 25	3 906 984 375	686270 12596	5·499004 39835	634834 2462	6349206 4028
1576	2 48 37 76	3 914 430 976	698866 12593	5·538839 39822	637296 2461	6345178 4024
1577	2 48 69 29	3 921 887 033	711459 12589	5·578661 39809	639757 2459	6341154 4018
1578	2 49 00 84	3 929 352 552	724048 12585	5·618470 39797	642216 2459	6337136 4014
1579	2 49 32 41	3 936 827 539	736633 12581	5·658267 39784	644675 2458	6333122 4008
1580	2 49 64 00	3 944 312 000	749214 12577	5·698051 39771	647133 2457	6329114 4003
1581	2 49 95 61	3 951 805 941	761791 12573	5·737822 39759	649590 2455	6325111 3998
1582	2 50 27 24	3 959 309 368	774364 12569	5·777581 39747	652045 2455	6321113 3994
1583	2 50 58 89	3 966 822 287	786933 12564	5·817328 39734	654500 2453	6317119 3988
1584	2 50 90 56	3 974 344 704	799497 12561	5·857062 39721	656953 2453	6313131 3983
1585	2 51 22 25	3 981 876 625	812058 12558	5·896783 39709	659406 2451	6309148 3978
1586	2 51 53 96	3 989 418 056	824616 12553	5·936492 39696	661857 2451	6305170 3973
1587	2 51 85 69	3 996 969 003	837169 12549	5·976188 39684	664308 2449	6301197 3968
1588	2 52 17 44	4 004 529 472	849718 12545	6·015872 39671	666757 2449	6297229 3963
1589	2 52 49 21	4 012 099 469	862263 12541	6·055543 39659	669206 2447	6293266 3958
1590	2 52 81 00	4 019 679 000	874804 12537	6·095202 39646	671653 2447	6289308 3953
1591	2 53 12 81	4 027 268 071	887341 12534	6·134848 39634	674100 2445	6285355 3948
1592	2 53 44 64	4 034 866 688	899875 12529	6·174482 39622	676545 2444	6281407 3943
1593	2 53 76 49	4 042 474 857	912404 12526	6·214104 39609	678989 2444	6277464 3938
1594	2 54 08 36	4 050 092 584	924930 12521	6·253713 39596	681433 2442	6273526 3934
1595	2 54 40 25	4 057 719 875	937451 12518	6·293309 39585	683875 2441	6269592 3928
1596	2 54 72 16	4 065 356 736	949969 12513	6·332894 39571	686316 2440	6265664 3923
1597	2 55 04 09	4 073 003 173	962482 12510	6·372465 39560	688756 2440	6261741 3919
1598	2 55 36 04	4 080 659 192	974992 12506	6·412025 39547	691196 2438	6257822 3913
1599	2 55 68 01	4 088 324 799	987498 12502	6·451572 39534	693634 2437	6253909 3909
1600	2 56 00 00	4 096 000 000	*000000	6·491106	696071	6250000
			40·	**120 +**	**11·**	**0·000**

No. n	Square n^2	Cube n^3	Square root $\sqrt{n}$	Sq. rt. of 10n $\sqrt{10n}$	Cube root $\sqrt[3]{n}$	Reciprocal $\dfrac{1}{n}$
			40·	120 +	11·	0·000
1600	2 56 00 00	4 096 000 000	000000	6·491106	696071	6250000
1601	2 56 32 01	4 103 684 801	012498 12498	6·530629 39523	698507 2436	6246096 3904
1602	2 56 64 04	4 111 379 208	024992 12494	6·570139 39510	700942 2435	6242197 3899
1603	2 56 96 09	4 119 083 227	037482 12490	6·609636 39497	703376 2434	6238303 3894
1604	2 57 28 16	4 126 796 864	049969 12487	6·649122 39486	705810 2434	6234414 3889
					2432	3884
1605	2 57 60 25	4 134 520 125	062451 12482	6·688595 39473	708242 2432	6230530 3880
1606	2 57 92 36	4 142 253 016	074930 12479	6·728055 39460	710673 2431	6226650 3875
1607	2 58 24 49	4 149 995 543	087405 12475	6·767504 39449	713103 2430	6222775 3870
1608	2 58 56 64	4 157 747 712	099875 12470	6·806940 39436	715532 2429	6218905 3865
1609	2 58 88 81	4 165 509 529	112342 12467	6·846364 39424	717960 2428	6215040 3860
					2427	
1610	2 59 21 00	4 173 281 000	124805 12463	6·885775 39411	720387 2426	6211180 3855
1611	2 59 53 21	4 181 062 131	137264 12459	6·925175 39400	722813 2425	6207325 3851
1612	2 59 85 44	4 188 852 928	149720 12456	6·964562 39387	725238 2424	6203474 3846
1613	2 60 17 69	4 196 653 397	162171 12451	7·003937 39375	727662 2423	6199628 3841
1614	2 60 49 96	4 204 463 544	174619 12448	7·043300 39363	730085 2423	6195787 3837
					2423	
1615	2 60 82 25	4 212 283 375	187063 12444	7·082650 39350	732508 2421	6191950 3831
1616	2 61 14 56	4 220 112 896	199502 12439	7·121989 39339	734929 2420	6188119 3827
1617	2 61 46 89	4 227 952 113	211939 12437	7·161315 39326	737349 2419	6184292 3822
1618	2 61 79 24	4 235 801 032	224371 12432	7·200629 39314	739768 2418	6180470 3818
1619	2 62 11 61	4 243 659 659	236799 12428	7·239931 39302	742186 2417	6176652 3812
1620	2 62 44 00	4 251 528 000	249224 12425	7·279221 39290	744603 2416	6172840 3809
1621	2 62 76 41	4 259 406 061	261644 12420	7·318498 39277	747019 2415	6169031 3803
1622	2 63 08 84	4 267 293 848	274061 12417	7·357764 39266	749434 2414	6165228 3803
1623	2 63 41 29	4 275 191 367	286474 12413	7·397017 39253	751848 2414	6161429 3799
1624	2 63 73 76	4 283 098 624	298883 12409	7·436259 39242	754261 2413	6157635 3794
					2412	3789
1625	2 64 06 25	4 291 015 625	311289 12406	7·475488 39229	756673 2412	6153846 3784
1626	2 64 38 76	4 298 942 376	323690 12401	7·514705 39217	759085 2410	6150062 3784
1627	2 64 71 29	4 306 878 883	336088 12398	7·553910 39205	761495 2409	6146281 3781
1628	2 65 03 84	4 314 825 152	348482 12394	7·593103 39193	763904 2408	6142506 3775
1629	2 65 36 41	4 322 781 189	360872 12390	7·632284 39181	766312 2407	6138735 3771
						3766
1630	2 65 69 00	4 330 747 000	373258 12386	7·671453 39169	768719 2406	6134969 3761
1631	2 66 01 61	4 338 722 591	385641 12383	7·710610 39157	771125 2406	6131208 3757
1632	2 66 34 24	4 346 707 968	398020 12379	7·749755 39145	773531 2404	6127451 3752
1633	2 66 66 89	4 354 703 137	410395 12375	7·788888 39133	775935 2403	6123699 3748
1634	2 66 99 56	4 362 708 104	422766 12371	7·828009 39121	778338 2402	6119951 3743
1635	2 67 32 25	4 370 722 875	435133 12367	7·867119 39110	780740 2402	6116208 3739
1636	2 67 64 96	4 378 747 456	447497 12364	7·906216 39097	783142 2400	6112469 3734
1637	2 67 97 69	4 386 781 853	459857 12360	7·945301 39085	785542 2399	6108735 3729
1638	2 68 30 44	4 394 826 072	472213 12356	7·984374 39073	787941 2399	6105006 3725
1639	2 68 63 21	4 402 880 119	484565 12352	8·023435 39061	790340 2397	6101281 3720
1640	2 68 96 00	4 410 944 000	496913 12348	8·062485 39050	792737 2396	6097561 3716
1641	2 69 28 81	4 419 017 721	509258 12345	8·101522 39037	795133 2396	6093845 3711
1642	2 69 61 64	4 427 101 288	521599 12341	8·140548 39026	797529 2394	6090134 3707
1643	2 69 94 49	4 435 194 707	533936 12337	8·179562 39014	799923 2394	6086427 3702
1644	2 70 27 36	4 443 297 984	546270 12334	8·218563 39001	802317 2392	6082725 3698
1645	2 70 60 25	4 451 411 125	558600 12330	8·257553 38990	804709 2392	6079027 3693
1646	2 70 93 16	4 459 534 136	570926 12326	8·296532 38979	807101 2391	6075334 3689
1647	2 71 26 09	4 467 667 023	583248 12322	8·335498 38966	809492 2389	6071645 3684
1648	2 71 59 04	4 475 809 792	595566 12318	8·374452 38954	811881 2389	6067961 3680
1649	2 71 92 01	4 483 962 449	607881 12315	8·413395 38943	814270 2388	6064281 3675
1650	2 72 25 00	4 492 125 000	620192	8·452326	816658	6060606
			40·	120 +	11·	0·000

No. n	Square n²	Cube n³	Square root √n	Sq. rt. of 10n √10n	Cube root ∛n	Reciprocal 1/n
			40·	120 +	11·	0·000
1650	2 72 25 00	4 492 125 000	620192 12307	8·452326 38919	816658 2386	6060606 3671
1651	2 72 58 01	4 500 297 451	632499 12304	8·491245 38907	819044 2386	6056935 3666
1652	2 72 91 04	4 508 479 808	644803 12300	8·530152 38896	821430 2385	6053269 3662
1653	2 73 24 09	4 516 672 077	657103 12296	8·569048 38883	823815 2384	6049607 3658
1654	2 73 57 16	4 524 874 264	669399 12292	8·607931 38872	826199 2382	6045949 3653
1655	2 73 90 25	4 533 086 375	681691 12289	8·646803 38861	828581 2382	6042296 3649
1656	2 74 23 36	4 541 308 416	693980 12285	8·685664 38848	830963 2381	6038647 3644
1657	2 74 56 49	4 549 540 393	706265 12281	8·724512 38837	833344 2380	6035003 3640
1658	2 74 89 64	4 557 782 312	718546 12278	8·763349 38825	835724 2379	6031363 3635
1659	2 75 22 81	4 566 034 179	730824 12274	8·802174 38813	838103 2378	6027728 3632
1660	2 75 56 00	4 574 296 000	743098 12270	8·840987 38802	840481 2378	6024096 3626
1661	2 75 89 21	4 582 567 781	755368 12266	8·879789 38790	842859 2376	6020470 3623
1662	2 76 22 44	4 590 849 528	767634 12263	8·918579 38778	845235 2375	6016847 3618
1663	2 76 55 69	4 599 141 247	779897 12259	8·957357 38767	847610 2374	6013229 3614
1664	2 76 88 96	4 607 442 944	792156 12256	8·996124 38755	849984 2374	6009615 3609
1665	2 77 22 25	4 615 754 625	804412 12251	9·034879 38743	852358 2372	6006006 3605
1666	2 77 55 56	4 624 076 296	816663 12248	9·073622 38732	854730 2372	6002401 3601
1667	2 77 88 89	4 632 407 963	828911 12245	9·112354 38720	857101 2371	5998800 3596
1668	2 78 22 24	4 640 749 632	841156 12240	9·151074 38709	859472 2369	5995204 3592
1669	2 78 55 61	4 649 101 309	853396 12237	9·189783 38697	861841 2369	5991612 3588
1670	2 78 89 00	4 657 463 000	865633 12234	9·228480 38685	864210 2368	5988024 3584
1671	2 79 22 41	4 665 834 711	877867 12230	9·267165 38674	866578 2366	5984440 3579
1672	2 79 55 84	4 674 216 448	890097 12226	9·305839 38662	868944 2366	5980861 3575
1673	2 79 89 29	4 682 608 217	902323 12222	9·344501 38651	871310 2365	5977286 3570
1674	2 80 22 76	4 691 010 024	914545 12219	9·383152 38639	873675 2364	5973716 3567
1675	2 80 56 25	4 699 421 875	926764 12215	9·421791 38628	876039 2363	5970149 3562
1676	2 80 89 76	4 707 843 776	938979 12211	9·460419 38616	878402 2362	5966587 3558
1677	2 81 23 29	4 716 275 733	951190 12208	9·499035 38604	880764 2361	5963029 3553
1678	2 81 56 84	4 724 717 752	963398 12204	9·537639 38593	883125 2361	5959476 3550
1679	2 81 90 41	4 733 169 839	975602 12201	9·576232 38582	885485 2360	5955926 3545
1680	2 82 24 00	4 741 632 000	*987803 12197	9·614814 38570	887844 2358	5952381 3541
1681	2 82 57 61	4 750 104 241	*000000 12193	9·653384 38559	890202 2358	5948840 3537
1682	2 82 91 24	4 758 586 568	012193 12190	9·691943 38547	892559 2357	5945303 3532
1683	2 83 24 89	4 767 078 987	024383 12186	9·730490 38536	894916 2357	5941771 3529
1684	2 83 58 56	4 775 581 504	036569 12183	9·769026 38524	897271 2355	5938242 3524
1685	2 83 92 25	4 784 094 125	048752 12178	9·807550 38513	899626 2353	5934718 3520
1686	2 84 25 96	4 792 616 856	060930 12176	9·846063 38501	901979 2353	5931198 3516
1687	2 84 59 69	4 801 149 703	073106 12171	9·884564 38490	904332 2352	5927682 3511
1688	2 84 93 44	4 809 692 672	085277 12168	9·923054 38479	906684 2352	5924171 3508
1689	2 85 27 21	4 818 245 769	097445 12165	9·961533 38467	909034 2350	5920663 3503
1690	2 85 61 00	4 826 809 000	109610 12160	*0·000000 38456	911384 2349	5917160 3499
1691	2 85 94 81	4 835 382 371	121770 12158	0·038456 38444	913733 2349	5913661 3496
1692	2 86 28 64	4 843 965 888	133928 12153	0·076900 38433	916081 2348	5910165 3490
1693	2 86 62 49	4 852 559 557	146081 12150	0·115333 38422	918428 2347	5906675 3487
1694	2 86 96 36	4 861 163 384	158231 12147	0·153755 38411	920774 2346	5903188 3483
1695	2 87 30 25	4 869 777 375	170378 12143	0·192166 38399	923120 2344	5899705 3479
1696	2 87 64 16	4 878 401 536	182521 12139	0·230565 38388	925464 2343	5896226 3474
1697	2 87 98 09	4 887 025 873	194660 12136	0·268953 38376	927807 2343	5892752 3470
1698	2 88 32 04	4 895 680 392	206796 12132	0·307329 38365	930150 2341	5889282 3467
1699	2 88 66 01	4 904 335 099	218928 12128	0·345694 38354	932491 2341	5885815 3462
1700	2 89 00 00	4 913 000 000	231056	0·384048	934832	5882353
			41·	130 +	11·	0·000

35

No. n	Square n^2	Cube n^3	Square root $\sqrt{n}$	Sq. rt. of 10n $\sqrt{10n}$	Cube root $\sqrt[3]{n}$	Reciprocal $\frac{1}{n}$
			41·	130 +	11·	0·000
1700	2 89 00 00	4 913 000 000	231056	0·384048	934832	5882353
1701	2 89 34 01	4 921 675 101	243181 (12125)	0·422391 (38343)	937172 (2340)	5878895 (3458)
1702	2 89 68 04	4 930 360 408	255303 (12122)	0·460722 (38331)	939510 (2338)	5875441 (3454)
1703	2 90 02 09	4 939 055 927	267421 (12118)	0·499042 (38320)	941848 (2338)	5871991 (3450)
1704	2 90 36 16	4 947 761 664	279535 (12114) (12111)	0·537351 (38309) (38298)	944185 (2337) (2336)	5868545 (3446) (3442)
1705	2 90 70 25	4 956 477 625	291646	0·575649	946521	5865103
1706	2 91 04 36	4 965 203 816	303753 (12107)	0·613935 (38286)	948856 (2335)	5861665 (3438)
1707	2 91 38 49	4 973 940 243	315857 (12104)	0·652210 (38275)	951191 (2335)	5858231 (3434)
1708	2 91 72 64	4 982 686 912	327957 (12100)	0·690474 (38264)	953524 (2333)	5854801 (3430)
1709	2 92 06 81	4 991 443 829	340053 (12096) (12093)	0·728727 (38253) (38241)	955856 (2332) (2332)	5851375 (3426) (3422)
1710	2 92 41 00	5 000 211 000	352146	0·766968	958188	5847953
1711	2 92 75 21	5 008 988 431	364236 (12090)	0·805199 (38231)	960518 (2330)	5844535 (3418)
1712	2 93 09 44	5 017 776 128	376322 (12086)	0·843418 (38219)	962848 (2330)	5841121 (3414)
1713	2 93 43 69	5 026 574 097	388404 (12082)	0·881626 (38208)	965177 (2329)	5837712 (3409)
1714	2 93 77 96	5 035 382 344	400483 (12079) (12075)	0·919823 (38197) (38186)	967505 (2328) (2327)	5834306 (3406) (3402)
1715	2 94 12 25	5 044 200 875	412558	0·958009	969832	5830904
1716	2 94 46 56	5 053 029 696	424630 (12072)	0·996183 (38174)	972158 (2326)	5827506 (3398)
1717	2 94 80 89	5 061 868 813	436699 (12069)	1·034347 (38164)	974483 (2325)	5824112 (3394)
1718	2 95 15 24	5 070 718 232	448764 (12065)	1·072499 (38152)	976807 (2324)	5820722 (3390)
1719	2 95 49 61	5 079 577 959	460825 (12061) (12058)	1·110640 (38141) (38130)	979130 (2323) (2323)	5817336 (3386) (3383)
1720	2 95 84 00	5 088 448 000	472883	1·148770	981453	5813953
1721	2 96 18 41	5 097 328 361	484937 (12054)	1·186890 (38120)	983774 (2321)	5810575 (3378)
1722	2 96 52 84	5 106 219 048	496988 (12051)	1·224998 (38108)	986095 (2321)	5807201 (3374)
1723	2 96 87 29	5 115 120 067	509035 (12047)	1·263095 (38097)	988415 (2320)	5803831 (3370)
1724	2 97 21 76	5 124 031 424	521079 (12044) (12040)	1·301180 (38085) (38075)	990734 (2319) (2318)	5800464 (3367) (3363)
1725	2 97 56 25	5 132 953 125	533119	1·339255	993052	5797101
1726	2 97 90 76	5 141 885 176	545156 (12037)	1·377319 (38064)	995369 (2317)	5793743 (3358)
1727	2 98 25 29	5 150 827 583	557190 (12034)	1·415372 (38053)	997685 (2316)	5790388 (3355)
1728	2 98 59 84	5 159 780 352	569219 (12029)	1·453414 (38042)	*000000 (2315)	5787037 (3351)
1729	2 98 94 41	5 168 743 489	581246 (12027) (12023)	1·491445 (38031) (38019)	002314 (2314) (2314)	5783690 (3347) (3343)
1730	2 99 29 00	5 177 717 000	593269	1·529464	004628	5780347
1731	2 99 63 61	5 186 700 891	605288 (12019)	1·567473 (38009)	006940 (2312)	5777008 (3339)
1732	2 99 98 24	5 195 695 168	617304 (12016)	1·605471 (37998)	009252 (2312)	5773672 (3336)
1733	3 00 32 89	5 204 699 837	629317 (12013)	1·643458 (37987)	011563 (2311)	5770340 (3332)
1734	3 00 67 56	5 213 714 904	641326 (12009) (12005)	1·681434 (37976) (37965)	013873 (2310) (2309)	5767013 (3327) (3324)
1735	3 01 02 25	5 222 740 375	653331	1·719399	016182	5763689
1736	3 01 36 96	5 231 776 256	665333 (12002)	1·757353 (37954)	018490 (2308)	5760369 (3320)
1737	3 01 71 69	5 240 822 553	677332 (11999)	1·795296 (37943)	020797 (2307)	5757052 (3317)
1738	3 02 06 44	5 249 879 272	689327 (11995)	1·833228 (37932)	023104 (2307)	5753740 (3312)
1739	3 02 41 21	5 258 946 419	701319 (11992) (11988)	1·871149 (37921) (37911)	025409 (2305) (2305)	5750431 (3309) (3305)
1740	3 02 76 00	5 268 024 000	713307	1·909060	027714	5747126
1741	3 03 10 81	5 277 112 021	725292 (11985)	1·946959 (37899)	030017 (2303)	5743825 (3301)
1742	3 03 45 64	5 286 210 488	737274 (11982)	1·984848 (37889)	032320 (2303)	5740528 (3297)
1743	3 03 80 49	5 295 319 407	749251 (11977)	2·022725 (37877)	034622 (2302)	5737235 (3293)
1744	3 04 15 36	5 304 438 784	761226 (11975) (11971)	2·060592 (37867) (37856)	036923 (2301) (2301)	5733945 (3290) (3286)
1745	3 04 50 25	5 313 568 625	773197	2·098448	039224	5730659
1746	3 04 85 16	5 322 708 936	785165 (11968)	2·136293 (37845)	041523 (2299)	5727377 (3282)
1747	3 05 20 09	5 331 859 723	797129 (11964)	2·174128 (37835)	043821 (2298)	5724098 (3279)
1748	3 05 55 04	5 341 020 992	809090 (11961)	2·211951 (37823)	046119 (2298)	5720824 (3274)
1749	3 05 90 01	5 350 192 749	821047 (11957) (11954)	2·249764 (37813) (37802)	048416 (2297) (2295)	5717553 (3271) (3267)
1750	3 06 25 00	5 359 375 000	833001	2·287566	050711	5714286
			41·	130 +	12·	0·000

No. n	Square n^2	Cube n^3	Square root $\sqrt{n}$	Sq. rt. of $10n$ $\sqrt{10n}$	Cube root $\sqrt[3]{n}$	Reciprocal $\dfrac{1}{n}$
			41·	130 +	12·	0·000
1750	3 06 25 00	5 359 375 000	833001 11951	2·287566 37791	050711 2295	5714286 3264
1751	3 06 60 01	5 368 567 751	844952 11947	2·325357 37780	053006 2294	5711022 3259
1752	3 06 95 04	5 377 771 008	856899 11944	2·363137 37769	055300 2294	5707763 3256
1753	3 07 30 09	5 386 984 777	868843 11940	2·400906 37759	057594 2292	5704507 3253
1754	3 07 65 16	5 396 209 064	880783 11937	2·438665 37748	059886 2291	5701254 3248
1755	3 08 00 25	5 405 443 875	892720 11934	2·476413 37737	062177 2291	5698006 3245
1756	3 08 35 36	5 414 689 216	904654 11930	2·514150 37727	064468 2290	5694761 3241
1757	3 08 70 49	5 423 945 093	916584 11927	2·551877 37715	066758 2288	5691520 3238
1758	3 09 05 64	5 433 211 512	928511 11923	2·589592 37705	069046 2288	5688282 3234
1759	3 09 40 81	5 442 488 479	940434 11920	2·627297 37695	071334 2287	5685048 3230
1760	3 09 76 00	5 451 776 000	952354 11917	2·664992 37683	073621	5681818
1761	3 10 11 21	5 461 074 081	964271 11913	2·702675 37673	075908 2287	5678592 3226
1762	3 10 46 44	5 470 382 728	976184 11910	2·740348 37662	078193 2285	5675369 3223
1763	3 10 81 69	5 479 701 947	988094 11906	2·778010 37652	080478 2285	5672150 3219
1764	3 11 16 96	5 489 031 744	*000000 11903	2·815662 37641	082761 2283	5668934 3216
1765	3 11 52 25	5 498 372 125	011903 11900	2·853303 37630	085044 2283	5665722 3212
1766	3 11 87 56	5 507 723 096	023803 11896	2·890933 37619	087326 2282	5662514 3208
1767	3 12 22 89	5 517 084 663	035699 11893	2·928552 37609	089607 2281	5659310 3204
1768	3 12 58 24	5 526 456 832	047592 11890	2·966161 37598	091887 2280	5656109 3201
1769	3 12 93 61	5 535 839 609	059482 11886	3·003759 37588	094167 2280	5652911 3198
1770	3 13 29 00	5 545 233 000	071368 11883	3·041347 37577	096445 2278	5649718 3193
1771	3 13 64 41	5 554 637 011	083251 11879	3·078924 37566	098723 2278	5646527 3191
1772	3 13 99 84	5 564 051 648	095130 11877	3·116490 37556	100999 2276	5643341 3186
1773	3 14 35 29	5 573 476 917	107007 11872	3·154046 37545	103275 2276	5640158 3183
1774	3 14 70 76	5 582 912 824	118879 11870	3·191591 37535	105550 2275	5636979 3179
1775	3 15 06 25	5 592 359 375	130749 11866	3·229126 37524	107825 2273	5633803 3176
1776	3 15 41 76	5 601 816 576	142615 11863	3·266650 37513	110098 2272	5630631 3172
1777	3 15 77 29	5 611 284 433	154478 11859	3·304163 37503	112370 2272	5627462 3169
1778	3 16 12 84	5 620 762 952	166337 11856	3·341666 37493	114642 2271	5624297 3165
1779	3 16 48 41	5 630 252 139	178193 11853	3·379159 37482	116913 2270	5621135 3162
1780	3 16 84 00	5 639 752 000	190046 11850	3·416641 37471	119183 2269	5617978 3157
1781	3 17 19 61	5 649 262 541	201896 11846	3·454112 37461	121452 2268	5614823 3155
1782	3 17 55 24	5 658 783 768	213742 11843	3·491573 37450	123720 2267	5611672 3151
1783	3 17 90 89	5 668 315 687	225585 11839	3·529023 37440	125987 2267	5608525 3147
1784	3 18 26 56	5 677 858 304	237424 11836	3·566463 37429	128254 2266	5605381 3140
1785	3 18 62 25	5 687 411 625	249260 11833	3·603892 37419	130520 2265	5602241 3137
1786	3 18 97 96	5 696 975 656	261093 11830	3·641311 37408	132785 2264	5599104 3133
1787	3 19 33 69	5 706 550 403	272923 11826	3·678719 37398	135049 2263	5595971 3130
1788	3 19 69 44	5 716 135 872	284749 11823	3·716117 37388	137312 2262	5592841 3126
1789	3 20 05 21	5 725 732 069	296572 11820	3·753505 37377	139574 2261	5589715 3123
1790	3 20 41 00	5 735 339 000	308392 11816	3·790882 37366	141835 2261	5586592 3119
1791	3 20 76 81	5 744 956 671	320208 11813	3·828248 37356	144096 2260	5583473 3116
1792	3 21 12 64	5 754 585 088	332021 11810	3·865604 37346	146356 2259	5580357 3112
1793	3 21 48 49	5 764 224 257	343831 11806	3·902950 37335	148615 2258	5577245 3109
1794	3 21 84 36	5 773 874 184	355637 11803	3·940285 37325	150873 2257	5574136 3105
1795	3 22 20 25	5 783 534 875	367440 11800	3·977610 37315	153130 2257	5571031 3102
1796	3 22 56 16	5 793 206 336	379240 11797	4·014925 37304	155387 2255	5567929 3099
1797	3 22 92 09	5 802 888 573	391037 11793	4·052229 37293	157642 2255	5564830 3095
1798	3 23 28 04	5 812 581 592	402830 11790	4·089522 37284	159897 2254	5561735 3091
1799	3 23 64 01	5 822 285 399	414620 11787	4·126806 37273	162151 2253	5558644 3088
1800	3 24 00 00	5 832 000 000	426407 42·	4·164079 130 +	164404 12·	5555556 0·000

37

No. n	Square n^2	Cube n^3	Square root $\sqrt{n}$	Sq. rt. of 10n $\sqrt{10n}$	Cube root $\sqrt[3]{n}$	Reciprocal $\frac{1}{n}$
			42·	130 +	12·	0·000
1800	3 24 00 00	5 832 000 000	426407 (11783)	4·164079 (37262)	164404 (2252)	5555556 (3085)
1801	3 24 36 01	5 841 725 401	438190 (11781)	4·201341 (37253)	166656 (2252)	5552471 (3081)
1802	3 24 72 04	5 851 461 608	449971 (11776)	4·238594 (37242)	168908 (2250)	5549390 (3078)
1803	3 25 08 09	5 861 208 627	461747 (11774)	4·275836 (37231)	171158 (2250)	5546312 (3075)
1804	3 25 44 16	5 870 966 464	473521 (11771)	4·313067 (37221)	173408 (2249)	5543237 (3071)
1805	3 25 80 25	5 880 735 125	485292 (11767)	4·350288 (37211)	175657 (2248)	5540166 (3067)
1806	3 26 16 36	5 890 514 616	497059 (11764)	4·387499 (37201)	177905 (2247)	5537099 (3065)
1807	3 26 52 49	5 900 304 943	508823 (11760)	4·424700 (37191)	180152 (2247)	5534034 (3061)
1808	3 26 88 64	5 910 106 112	520583 (11758)	4·461891 (37180)	182399 (2245)	5530973 (3057)
1809	3 27 24 81	5 919 918 129	532341 (11754)	4·499071 (37169)	184644 (2245)	5527916 (3054)
1810	3 27 61 00	5 929 741 000	544095 (11751)	4·536240 (37160)	186889 (2244)	5524862 (3051)
1811	3 27 97 21	5 939 574 731	555846 (11747)	4·573400 (37149)	189133 (2243)	5521811 (3047)
1812	3 28 33 44	5 949 419 328	567593 (11745)	4·610549 (37139)	191376 (2242)	5518764 (3044)
1813	3 28 69 69	5 959 274 797	579338 (11741)	4·647688 (37129)	193618 (2242)	5515720 (3041)
1814	3 29 05 96	5 969 141 144	591079 (11738)	4·684817 (37119)	195860 (2241)	5512679 (3037)
1815	3 29 42 25	5 979 018 375	602817 (11735)	4·721936 (37108)	198101 (2239)	5509642 (3034)
1816	3 29 78 56	5 988 906 496	614552 (11731)	4·759044 (37098)	200340 (2239)	5506608 (3031)
1817	3 30 14 89	5 998 805 513	626283 (11728)	4·796142 (37088)	202579 (2239)	5503577 (3027)
1818	3 30 51 24	6 008 715 432	638011 (11725)	4·833230 (37078)	204818 (2237)	5500550 (3024)
1819	3 30 87 61	6 018 636 259	649736 (11722)	4·870308 (37068)	207055 (2236)	5497526 (3021)
1820	3 31 24 00	6 028 568 000	661458 (11719)	4·907376 (37057)	209291 (2236)	5494505 (3017)
1821	3 31 60 41	6 038 510 661	673177 (11715)	4·944433 (37047)	211527 (2235)	5491488 (3014)
1822	3 31 96 84	6 048 464 248	684892 (11712)	4·981480 (37037)	213762 (2234)	5488474 (3010)
1823	3 32 33 29	6 058 428 767	696604 (11709)	5·018517 (37027)	215996 (2233)	5485464 (3008)
1824	3 32 69 76	6 068 404 224	708313 (11706)	5·055544 (37017)	218229 (2233)	5482456 (3004)
1825	3 33 06 25	6 078 390 625	720019 (11702)	5·092561 (37006)	220462 (2232)	5479452 (3001)
1826	3 33 42 76	6 088 387 976	731721 (11700)	5·129567 (36997)	222694 (2230)	5476451 (2997)
1827	3 33 79 29	6 098 396 283	743421 (11696)	5·166564 (36986)	224924 (2230)	5473454 (2994)
1828	3 34 15 84	6 108 415 552	755117 (11693)	5·203550 (36976)	227154 (2230)	5470460 (2991)
1829	3 34 52 41	6 118 445 789	766810 (11689)	5·240526 (36967)	229384 (2228)	5467469 (2988)
1830	3 34 89 00	6 128 487 000	778499 (11687)	5·277493 (36956)	231612 (2228)	5464481 (2985)
1831	3 35 25 61	6 138 539 191	790186 (11683)	5·314449 (36946)	233840 (2226)	5461496 (2981)
1832	3 35 62 24	6 148 602 368	801869 (11680)	5·351395 (36935)	236066 (2226)	5458515 (2978)
1833	3 35 98 89	6 158 676 537	813549 (11677)	5·388330 (36926)	238292 (2225)	5455537 (2974)
1834	3 36 35 56	6 168 761 704	825226 (11674)	5·425256 (36916)	240517 (2225)	5452563 (2972)
1835	3 36 72 25	6 178 857 875	836900 (11671)	5·462172 (36905)	242742 (2223)	5449591 (2968)
1836	3 37 08 96	6 188 965 056	848571 (11667)	5·499077 (36896)	244965 (2223)	5446623 (2965)
1837	3 37 45 69	6 199 083 253	860238 (11664)	5·535973 (36886)	247188 (2222)	5443658 (2962)
1838	3 37 82 44	6 209 212 472	871902 (11661)	5·572859 (36875)	249410 (2221)	5440696 (2958)
1839	3 38 19 21	6 219 352 719	883563 (11658)	5·609734 (36866)	251631 (2221)	5437738 (2955)
1840	3 38 56 00	6 229 504 000	895221 (11655)	5·646600 (36855)	253851 (2220)	5434783 (2952)
1841	3 38 92 81	6 239 666 321	906876 (11651)	5·683455 (36846)	256071 (2219)	5431831 (2949)
1842	3 39 29 64	6 249 839 688	918527 (11649)	5·720301 (36835)	258290 (2219)	5428882 (2946)
1843	3 39 66 49	6 260 024 107	930176 (11645)	5·757136 (36826)	260507 (2218)	5425936 (2943)
1844	3 40 03 36	6 270 219 584	941821 (11642)	5·793962 (36815)	262725 (2216)	5422993 (2939)
1845	3 40 40 25	6 280 426 125	953463 (11639)	5·830777 (36806)	264941 (2215)	5420054 (2936)
1846	3 40 77 16	6 290 643 736	965102 (11636)	5·867583 (36795)	267156 (2215)	5417118 (2933)
1847	3 41 14 09	6 300 872 423	976738 (11633)	5·904378 (36786)	269371 (2214)	5414185 (2930)
1848	3 41 51 04	6 311 112 192	988371 (11629)	5·941164 (36775)	271585 (2213)	5411255 (2926)
1849	3 41 88 01	6 321 363 049	*000000 (11626)	5·977939 (36766)	273798 (2212)	5408329 (2924)
1850	3 42 25 00	6 331 625 000	011626 / 43·	6·014705 / 130 +	276010 / 12·	5405405 / 0·000

38

No. n	Square n²	Cube n³	Square root √n	Sq. rt. of 10n √10n	Cube root ∛n	Reciprocal 1/n
			43·	**130 +**	**12·**	**0·000**
1850	3 42 25 00	6 331 625 000	011626 11624	6·014705 36756	276010 2212	5405405 2920
1851	3 42 62 01	6 341 898 051	023250 11620	6·051461 36746	278222 2210	5402485 2917
1852	3 42 99 04	6 352 182 208	034870 11617	6·088207 36736	280432 2210	5399568 2914
1853	3 43 36 09	6 362 477 477	046487 11613	6·124943 36726	282642 2209	5396654 2911
1854	3 43 73 16	6 372 783 864	058100 11611	6·161669 36716	284851 2209	5393743 2907
1855	3 44 10 25	6 383 101 375	069711 11607	6·198385 36706	287060 2207	5390836 2905
1856	3 44 47 36	6 393 430 016	081318 11605	6·235091 36696	289267 2207	5387931 2901
1857	3 44 84 49	6 403 769 793	092923 11601	6·271787 36687	291474 2206	5385030 2899
1858	3 45 21 64	6 414 120 712	104524 11598	6·308474 36676	293680 2205	5382131 2895
1859	3 45 58 81	6 424 482 779	116122 11595	6·345150 36667	295885 2204	5379236 2892
1860	3 45 96 00	6 434 856 000	127717 11592	6·381817 36657	298089 2204	5376344 2889
1861	3 46 33 21	6 445 240 381	139309 11589	6·418474 36647	300293 2203	5373455 2886
1862	3 46 70 44	6 455 635 928	150898 11586	6·455121 36637	302496 2202	5370569 2882
1863	3 47 07 69	6 466 042 647	162484 11582	6·491758 36627	304698 2201	5367687 2880
1864	3 47 44 96	6 476 460 544	174066 11580	6·528385 36618	306899 2200	5364807 2877
1865	3 47 82 25	6 486 889 625	185646 11576	6·565003 36608	309099 2200	5361930 2873
1866	3 48 19 56	6 497 329 896	197222 11573	6·601611 36597	311299 2199	5359057 2871
1867	3 48 56 89	6 507 781 363	208795 11571	6·638208 36589	313498 2198	5356186 2867
1868	3 48 94 24	6 518 244 032	220366 11567	6·674797 36578	315696 2197	5353319 2864
1869	3 49 31 61	6 528 717 909	231933 11564	6·711375 36568	317893 2197	5350455 2861
1870	3 49 69 00	6 539 203 000	243497 11561	6·747943 36559	320090 2195	5347594 2859
1871	3 50 06 41	6 549 699 311	255058 11557	6·784502 36549	322285 2195	5344735 2855
1872	3 50 43 84	6 560 206 848	266615 11555	6·821051 36539	324480 2194	5341880 2852
1873	3 50 81 29	6 570 725 617	278170 11552	6·857590 36530	326674 2194	5339028 2849
1874	3 51 18 76	6 581 255 624	289722 11548	6·894120 36519	328868 2192	5336179 2846
1875	3 51 56 25	6 591 796 875	301270 11546	6·930639 36510	331060 2192	5333333 2843
1876	3 51 93 76	6 602 349 376	312816 11542	6·967149 36501	333252 2191	5330490 2839
1877	3 52 31 29	6 612 913 133	324358 11539	7·003650 36490	335443 2190	5327651 2837
1878	3 52 68 84	6 623 488 152	335897 11537	7·040140 36481	337633 2190	5324814 2834
1879	3 53 06 41	6 634 074 439	347434 11533	7·076621 36471	339823 2189	5321980 2831
1880	3 53 44 00	6 644 672 000	358967 11530	7·113092 36461	342012 2187	5319149 2828
1881	3 53 81 61	6 655 280 841	370497 11527	7·149553 36452	344199 2188	5316321 2825
1882	3 54 19 24	6 665 900 968	382024 11524	7·186005 36442	346387 2186	5313496 2822
1883	3 54 56 89	6 676 532 387	393548 11521	7·222447 36432	348573 2186	5310674 2818
1884	3 54 94 56	6 687 175 104	405069 11518	7·258879 36423	350759 2184	5307856 2816
1885	3 55 32 25	6 697 829 125	416587 11515	7·295302 36413	352943 2184	5305040 2813
1886	3 55 69 96	6 708 494 456	428102 11511	7·331715 36404	355127 2184	5302227 2810
1887	3 56 07 69	6 719 171 103	439613 11509	7·368119 36393	357311 2182	5299417 2807
1888	3 56 45 44	6 729 859 072	451122 11506	7·404512 36384	359493 2182	5296610 2804
1889	3 56 83 21	6 740 558 369	462628 11502	7·440896 36375	361675 2181	5293806 2801
1890	3 57 21 00	6 751 269 000	474130 11500	7·477271 36365	363856 2180	5291005 2798
1891	3 57 58 81	6 761 990 971	485630 11496	7·513636 36355	366036 2180	5288207 2795
1892	3 57 96 64	6 772 724 288	497126 11494	7·549991 36346	368216 2178	5285412 2792
1893	3 58 34 49	6 783 468 957	508620 11490	7·586337 36336	370394 2178	5282620 2789
1894	3 58 72 36	6 794 224 984	520110 11488	7·622673 36326	372572 2177	5279831 2786
1895	3 59 10 25	6 804 992 375	531598 11484	7·658999 36317	374749 2177	5277045 2783
1896	3 59 48 16	6 815 771 136	543082 11481	7·695316 36307	376926 2175	5274262 2781
1897	3 59 86 09	6 826 561 273	554563 11479	7·731623 36298	379101 2175	5271481 2777
1898	3 60 24 04	6 837 362 792	566042 11475	7·767921 36288	381276 2174	5268704 2775
1899	3 60 62 01	6 848 175 699	577517 11472	7·804209 36279	383450 2173	5265929 2771
1900	3 61 00 00	6 859 000 000	588989	7·840488	385623	5263158
			43·	**130 +**	**12·**	**0·000**

No. n	Square n^2	Cube n^3	Square root $\sqrt{n}$	Sq. rt. of 10n $\sqrt{10n}$	Cube root $\sqrt[3]{n}$	Reciprocal $\dfrac{1}{n}$
			43·	130 +	12·	0·000
1900	3 61 00 00	6 859 000 000	588989 11470	7·840488 36269	385623 2173	5263158 2769
1901	3 61 38 01	6 869 835 701	600459 11466	7·876757 36259	387796 2172	5260389 2765
1902	3 61 76 04	6 880 682 808	611925 11463	7·913016 36250	389968 2171	5257624 2763
1903	3 62 14 09	6 891 541 327	623388 11460	7·949266 36240	392139 2170	5254861 2760
1904	3 62 52 16	6 902 411 264	634848 11458	7·985506 36231	394309 2169	5252101 2757
1905	3 62 90 25	6 913 292 625	646306 11454	8·021737 36222	396478 2169	5249344 2754
1906	3 63 28 36	6 924 185 416	657760 11451	8·057959 36212	398647 2168	5246590 2752
1907	3 63 66 49	6 935 089 643	669211 11448	8·094171 36202	400815 2167	5243838 2748
1908	3 64 04 64	6 946 005 312	680659 11446	8·130373 36193	402982 2167	5241090 2745
1909	3 64 42 81	6 956 932 429	692105 11442	8·166566 36184	405149 2165	5238345 2743
1910	3 64 81 00	6 967 871 000	703547 11439	8·202750 36174	407314 2165	5235602 2740
1911	3 65 19 21	6 978 821 031	714986 11436	8·238924 36164	409479 2165	5232862 2736
1912	3 65 57 44	6 989 782 528	726422 11433	8·275088 36155	411644 2163	5230126 2734
1913	3 65 95 69	7 000 755 497	737855 11431	8·311243 36146	413807 2163	5227392 2732
1914	3 66 33 96	7 011 739 944	749286 11427	8·347389 36136	415970 2162	5224660 2728
1915	3 66 72 25	7 022 735 875	760713 11424	8·383525 36127	418132 2161	5221932 2725
1916	3 67 10 56	7 033 743 296	772137 11422	8·419652 36117	420293 2160	5219207 2723
1917	3 67 48 89	7 044 762 213	783559 11418	8·455769 36108	422453 2160	5216484 2720
1918	3 67 87 24	7 055 792 632	794977 11415	8·491877 36099	424613 2159	5213764 2717
1919	3 68 25 61	7 066 834 559	806392 11413	8·527976 36089	426772 2158	5211047 2714
1920	3 68 64 00	7 077 888 000	817805 11409	8·564065 36079	428930 2157	5208333 2711
1921	3 69 02 41	7 088 952 961	829214 11406	8·600144 36071	431087 2157	5205622 2708
1922	3 69 40 84	7 100 029 448	840620 11404	8·636215 36061	433244 2156	5202914 2706
1923	3 69 79 29	7 111 117 467	852024 11400	8·672276 36051	435400 2155	5200208 2703
1924	3 70 17 76	7 122 217 024	863424 11398	8·708327 36042	437555 2155	5197505 2700
1925	3 70 56 25	7 133 328 125	874822 11395	8·744369 36033	439710 2153	5194805 2697
1926	3 70 94 76	7 144 450 776	886217 11391	8·780402 36024	441863 2153	5192108 2694
1927	3 71 33 29	7 155 584 983	897608 11389	8·816426 36014	444016 2153	5189414 2692
1928	3 71 71 84	7 166 730 752	908997 11386	8·852440 36004	446169 2151	5186722 2689
1929	3 72 10 41	7 177 888 089	920383 11382	8·888444 35996	448320 2151	5184033 2686
1930	3 72 49 00	7 189 057 000	931765 11380	8·924440 35986	450471 2150	5181347 2683
1931	3 72 87 61	7 200 237 491	943145 11377	8·960426 35977	452621 2149	5178664 2681
1932	3 73 26 24	7 211 429 568	954522 11374	8·996403 35967	454770 2148	5175983 2677
1933	3 73 64 89	7 222 633 237	965896 11371	9·032370 35959	456918 2148	5173306 2675
1934	3 74 03 56	7 233 848 504	977267 11368	9·068329 35948	459066 2147	5170631 2672
1935	3 74 42 25	7 245 075 375	*988635 11365	9·104277 35940	461213 2146	5167959 2670
1936	3 74 80 96	7 256 313 856	000000 11362	9·140217 35930	463359 2146	5165289 2666
1937	3 75 19 69	7 267 563 953	011362 11359	9·176147 35921	465505 2145	5162623 2664
1938	3 75 58 44	7 278 825 672	022721 11357	9·212068 35912	467650 2144	5159959 2661
1939	3 75 97 21	7 290 099 019	034078 11353	9·247980 35903	469794 2143	5157298 2659
1940	3 76 36 00	7 301 384 000	045431 11351	9·283883 35893	471937 2143	5154639 2655
1941	3 76 74 81	7 312 680 621	056782 11347	9·319776 35884	474080 2141	5151984 2653
1942	3 77 13 64	7 323 988 888	068129 11345	9·355660 35875	476221 2142	5149331 2651
1943	3 77 52 49	7 335 308 807	079474 11341	9·391535 35865	478363 2140	5146680 2647
1944	3 77 91 36	7 346 640 384	090815 11339	9·427400 35857	480503 2140	5144033 2645
1945	3 78 30 25	7 357 983 625	102154 11336	9·463257 35847	482643 2138	5141388 2642
1946	3 78 69 16	7 369 338 536	113490 11333	9·499104 35838	484781 2139	5138746 2639
1947	3 79 08 09	7 380 705 123	124823 11330	9·534942 35829	486920 2137	5136107 2637
1948	3 79 47 04	7 392 083 392	136153 11327	9·570771 35819	489057 2137	5133470 2634
1949	3 79 86 01	7 403 473 349	147480 11324	9·606590 35810	491194 2136	5130836 2631
1950	3 80 25 00	7 414 875 000	158804	9·642400	493330	5128205
			44·	130 +	12·	0·000

No. n	Square n²	Cube n³	Square root √n	Sq. rt. of 10n √10n	Cube root ∛n	Reciprocal 1/n
			44·	130 +	12·	0·000
1950	3 80 25 00	7 414 875 000	158804 [11322]	9·642400 [35802]	493330 [2135]	5128205 [2628]
1951	3 80 64 01	7 426 288 351	170126 [11318]	9·678202 [35792]	495465 [2135]	5125577 [2626]
1952	3 81 03 04	7 437 713 408	181444 [11316]	9·713994 [35782]	497600 [2133]	5122951 [2623]
1953	3 81 42 09	7 449 150 177	192760 [11312]	9·749776 [35774]	499733 [2133]	5120328 [2621]
1954	3 81 81 16	7 460 598 664	204072 [11310]	9·785550 [35765]	501866 [2133]	5117707 [2617]
1955	3 82 20 25	7 472 058 875	215382 [11307]	9·821315 [35755]	503999 [2131]	5115090 [2616]
1956	3 82 59 36	7 483 530 816	226689 [11304]	9·857070 [35746]	506130 [2131]	5112474 [2612]
1957	3 82 98 49	7 495 014 493	237993 [11301]	9·892816 [35737]	508261 [2130]	5109862 [2610]
1958	3 83 37 64	7 506 509 912	249294 [11298]	9·928553 [35728]	510391 [2130]	5107252 [2607]
1959	3 83 76 81	7 518 017 079	260592 [11295]	9·964281 [35719]	512521 [2128]	5104645 [2604]
1960	3 84 16 00	7 529 536 000	271887 [11293]	*0·000000 [35710]	514649 [2128]	5102041 [2602]
1961	3 84 55 21	7 541 066 681	283180 [11289]	0·035710 [35700]	516777 [2128]	5099439 [2599]
1962	3 84 94 44	7 552 609 128	294469 [11287]	0·071410 [35692]	518905 [2126]	5096840 [2596]
1963	3 85 33 69	7 564 163 347	305756 [11284]	0·107102 [35682]	521031 [2126]	5094244 [2594]
1964	3 85 72 96	7 575 729 344	317040 [11281]	0·142784 [35674]	523157 [2125]	5091650 [2591]
1965	3 86 12 25	7 587 307 125	328321 [11278]	0·178458 [35664]	525282 [2125]	5089059 [2589]
1966	3 86 51 56	7 598 896 696	339599 [11275]	0·214122 [35655]	527407 [2123]	5086470 [2586]
1967	3 86 90 89	7 610 498 063	350874 [11272]	0·249777 [35646]	529530 [2123]	5083884 [2583]
1968	3 87 30 24	7 622 111 232	362146 [11269]	0·285423 [35637]	531653 [2122]	5081301 [2581]
1969	3 87 69 61	7 633 736 209	373415 [11267]	0·321060 [35628]	533775 [2122]	5078720 [2578]
1970	3 88 09 00	7 645 373 000	384682 [11264]	0·356688 [35619]	535897 [2121]	5076142 [2575]
1971	3 88 48 41	7 657 021 611	395946 [11261]	0·392307 [35610]	538018 [2120]	5073567 [2573]
1972	3 88 87 84	7 668 682 048	407207 [11258]	0·427917 [35601]	540138 [2119]	5070994 [2570]
1973	3 89 27 29	7 680 354 317	418465 [11255]	0·463518 [35592]	542257 [2119]	5068424 [2568]
1974	3 89 66 76	7 692 038 424	429720 [11252]	0·499110 [35583]	544376 [2118]	5065856 [2565]
1975	3 90 06 25	7 703 734 375	440972 [11250]	0·534693 [35574]	546494 [2117]	5063291 [2562]
1976	3 90 45 76	7 715 442 176	452222 [11246]	0·570267 [35565]	548611 [2116]	5060729 [2560]
1977	3 90 85 29	7 727 161 833	463468 [11244]	0·605832 [35556]	550727 [2116]	5058169 [2557]
1978	3 91 24 84	7 738 893 352	474712 [11241]	0·641388 [35547]	552843 [2115]	5055612 [2555]
1979	3 91 64 41	7 750 636 739	485953 [11238]	0·676935 [35538]	554958 [2114]	5053057 [2552]
1980	3 92 04 00	7 762 392 000	497191 [11235]	0·712473 [35529]	557072 [2114]	5050505 [2549]
1981	3 92 43 61	7 774 159 141	508426 [11233]	0·748002 [35520]	559186 [2113]	5047956 [2547]
1982	3 92 83 24	7 785 938 168	519659 [11229]	0·783522 [35511]	561299 [2112]	5045409 [2545]
1983	3 93 22 89	7 797 729 087	530888 [11227]	0·819033 [35502]	563411 [2112]	5042864 [2541]
1984	3 93 62 56	7 809 531 904	542115 [11224]	0·854535 [35493]	565523 [2110]	5040323 [2540]
1985	3 94 02 25	7 821 346 625	553339 [11221]	0·890028 [35484]	567633 [2110]	5037783 [2536]
1986	3 94 41 96	7 833 173 256	564560 [11218]	0·925512 [35476]	569743 [2110]	5035247 [2534]
1987	3 94 81 69	7 845 011 803	575778 [11216]	0·960988 [35466]	571853 [2109]	5032713 [2532]
1988	3 95 21 44	7 856 862 272	586994 [11212]	0·996454 [35457]	573962 [2107]	5030181 [2529]
1989	3 95 61 21	7 868 724 669	598206 [11210]	1·031911 [35449]	576069 [2108]	5027652 [2526]
1990	3 96 01 00	7 880 599 000	609416 [11207]	1·067360 [35439]	578177 [2106]	5025126 [2524]
1991	3 96 40 81	7 892 485 271	620623 [11204]	1·102799 [35431]	580283 [2106]	5022602 [2522]
1992	3 96 80 64	7 904 383 488	631827 [11202]	1·138230 [35422]	582389 [2105]	5020080 [2519]
1993	3 97 20 49	7 916 293 657	643029 [11198]	1·173652 [35413]	584494 [2105]	5017561 [2516]
1994	3 97 60 36	7 928 215 784	654227 [11196]	1·209065 [35404]	586599 [2103]	5015045 [2514]
1995	3 98 00 25	7 940 149 875	665423 [11193]	1·244469 [35395]	588702 [2103]	5012531 [2511]
1996	3 98 40 16	7 952 095 936	676616 [11190]	1·279864 [35386]	590805 [2103]	5010020 [2509]
1997	3 98 80 09	7 964 053 973	687806 [11187]	1·315250 [35378]	592908 [2101]	5007511 [2506]
1998	3 99 20 04	7 976 023 992	698993 [11185]	1·350628 [35368]	595009 [2101]	5005005 [2504]
1999	3 99 60 01	7 988 005 999	710178 [11182]	1·385996 [35360]	597110 [2100]	5002501 [2501]
2000	4 00 00 00	8 000 000 000	721360	1·421356	599210	5000000
			44·	140 +	12·	0·000

No. n	Square n²	Cube n³	Square root √n	Sq. rt. of 10n √10n	Cube root ∛n	Reciprocal 1/n
			44·	**140 +**	**12·**	**0·000**
2000	4 00 00 00	8 000 000 000	721360 [11178]	1·421356 [35351]	599210 [2100]	5000000 [2499]
2001	4 00 40 01	8 012 006 001	732538 [11177]	1·456707 [35342]	601310 [2099]	4997501 [2496]
2002	4 00 80 04	8 024 024 008	743715 [11173]	1·492049 [35334]	603409 [2098]	4995005 [2494]
2003	4 01 20 09	8 036 054 027	754888 [11171]	1·527383 [35324]	605507 [2097]	4992511 [2491]
2004	4 01 60 16	8 048 096 064	766059 [11167]	1·562707 [35316]	607604 [2097]	4990020 [2489]
2005	4 02 00 25	8 060 150 125	777226 [11165]	1·598023 [35306]	609701 [2096]	4987531 [2486]
2006	4 02 40 36	8 072 216 216	788391 [11163]	1·633329 [35298]	611797 [2095]	4985045 [2484]
2007	4 02 80 49	8 084 294 343	799554 [11159]	1·668627 [35290]	613892 [2095]	4982561 [2481]
2008	4 03 20 64	8 096 384 512	810713 [11157]	1·703917 [35280]	615987 [2094]	4980080 [2479]
2009	4 03 60 81	8 108 486 729	821870 [11154]	1·739197 [35272]	618081 [2093]	4977601 [2477]
2010	4 04 01 00	8 120 601 000	833024 [11151]	1·774469 [35263]	620174 [2093]	4975124 [2474]
2011	4 04 41 21	8 132 727 331	844175 [11148]	1·809732 [35254]	622267 [2092]	4972650 [2471]
2012	4 04 81 44	8 144 865 728	855323 [11146]	1·844986 [35245]	624359 [2091]	4970179 [2469]
2013	4 05 21 69	8 157 016 197	866469 [11142]	1·880231 [35237]	626450 [2090]	4967710 [2467]
2014	4 05 61 96	8 169 178 744	877611 [11140]	1·915468 [35228]	628540 [2090]	4965243 [2464]
2015	4 06 02 25	8 181 353 375	888751 [11138]	1·950696 [35219]	630630 [2089]	4962779 [2462]
2016	4 06 42 56	8 193 540 096	899889 [11134]	1·985915 [35210]	632719 [2089]	4960317 [2459]
2017	4 06 82 89	8 205 738 913	911023 [11132]	2·021125 [35202]	634808 [2087]	4957858 [2457]
2018	4 07 23 24	8 217 949 832	922155 [11129]	2·056327 [35193]	636895 [2087]	4955401 [2454]
2019	4 07 63 61	8 230 172 859	933284 [11126]	2·091520 [35184]	638982 [2087]	4952947 [2452]
2020	4 08 04 00	8 242 408 000	944410 [11124]	2·126704 [35176]	641069 [2085]	4950495 [2449]
2021	4 08 44 41	8 254 655 261	955534 [11120]	2·161880 [35166]	643154 [2085]	4948046 [2448]
2022	4 08 84 84	8 266 914 648	966654 [11118]	2·197046 [35159]	645239 [2085]	4945598 [2444]
2023	4 09 25 29	8 279 186 167	977772 [11116]	2·232205 [35149]	647324 [2083]	4943154 [2443]
2024	4 09 65 76	8 291 469 824	988888 [11112]	2·267354 [35141]	649407 [2083]	4940711 [2439]
2025	4 10 06 25	8 303 765 625	*000000 [11110]	2·302495 [35132]	651490 [2082]	4938272 [2438]
2026	4 10 46 76	8 316 073 576	011110 [11107]	2·337627 [35123]	653572 [2082]	4935834 [2435]
2027	4 10 87 29	8 328 393 683	022217 [11104]	2·372750 [35115]	655654 [2081]	4933399 [2433]
2028	4 11 27 84	8 340 725 952	033321 [11102]	2·407865 [35106]	657735 [2080]	4930966 [2430]
2029	4 11 68 41	8 353 070 389	044423 [11098]	2·442971 [35097]	659815 [2079]	4928536 [2428]
2030	4 12 09 00	8 365 427 000	055521 [11096]	2·478068 [35089]	661894 [2079]	4926108 [2425]
2031	4 12 49 61	8 377 795 791	066617 [11094]	2·513157 [35080]	663973 [2078]	4923683 [2423]
2032	4 12 90 24	8 390 176 768	077711 [11090]	2·548237 [35072]	666051 [2077]	4921260 [2421]
2033	4 13 30 89	8 402 569 937	088801 [11088]	2·583309 [35063]	668128 [2077]	4918839 [2418]
2034	4 13 71 56	8 414 975 304	099889 [11085]	2·618372 [35054]	670205 [2076]	4916421 [2416]
2035	4 14 12 25	8 427 392 875	110974 [11083]	2·653426 [35046]	672281 [2076]	4914005 [2414]
2036	4 14 52 96	8 439 822 656	122057 [11079]	2·688472 [35037]	674357 [2074]	4911591 [2411]
2037	4 14 93 69	8 452 264 653	133136 [11077]	2·723509 [35028]	676431 [2074]	4909180 [2411]
2038	4 15 34 44	8 464 718 872	144213 [11075]	2·758537 [35020]	678505 [2074]	4906771 [2409]
2039	4 15 75 21	8 477 185 319	155288 [11071]	2·793557 [35012]	680579 [2072]	4904365 [2406]
2040	4 16 16 00	8 489 664 000	166359 [11069]	2·828569 [35002]	682651 [2072]	4901961 [2404]
2041	4 16 56 81	8 502 154 921	177428 [11066]	2·863571 [35002]	684723 [2072]	4899559 [2402]
2042	4 16 97 64	8 514 658 088	188494 [11064]	2·898565 [34994]	686795 [2072]	4897160 [2399]
2043	4 17 38 49	8 527 173 507	199558 [11060]	2·933551 [34986]	688865 [2070]	4894763 [2397]
2044	4 17 79 36	8 539 701 184	210618 [11058]	2·968528 [34977]	690935 [2070]	4892368 [2395]
2045	4 18 20 25	8 552 241 125	221676 [11056]	3·003496 [34968]	693005 [2068]	4889976 [2392]
2046	4 18 61 16	8 564 793 336	232732 [11052]	3·038456 [34960]	695073 [2068]	4887586 [2390]
2047	4 19 02 09	8 577 357 823	243784 [11050]	3·073408 [34952]	697141 [2067]	4885198 [2388]
2048	4 19 43 04	8 589 934 592	254834 [11047]	3·108351 [34943]	699208 [2067]	4882813 [2385]
2049	4 19 84 01	8 602 523 649	265881 [11045]	3·143285 [34934]	701275 [2066]	4880429 [2384]
2050	4 20 25 00	8 615 125 000	276926	3·178211	703341	4878049 [2380]
			45·	**140 +**	**12·**	**0·000**

No. n	Square n²	Cube n³	Square root √n	Sq. rt. of 10n √10n	Cube root ∛n	Reciprocal 1/n
			45·	140 +	12·	0·000
2050	4 20 25 00	8 615 125 000	276926 ₁₁₀₄₁	3·178211 ₃₄₉₁₇	703341 ₂₀₆₅	4878049 ₂₃₇₉
2051	4 20 66 01	8 627 738 651	287967 ₁₁₀₄₀	3·213128 ₃₄₉₀₉	705406 ₂₀₆₅	4875670 ₂₃₇₆
2052	4 21 07 04	8 640 364 608	299007 ₁₁₀₃₆	3·248037 ₃₄₉₀₀	707471 ₂₀₆₄	4873294 ₂₃₇₃
2053	4 21 48 09	8 653 002 877	310043 ₁₁₀₃₄	3·282937 ₃₄₈₉₂	709535 ₂₀₆₃	4870921 ₂₃₇₂
2054	4 21 89 16	8 665 653 464	321077 ₁₁₀₃₁	3·317829 ₃₄₈₈₃	711598 ₂₀₆₂	4868549 ₂₃₆₉
2055	4 22 30 25	8 678 316 375	332108 ₁₁₀₂₈	3·352712 ₃₄₈₇₅	713660 ₂₀₆₂	4866180 ₂₃₆₇
2056	4 22 71 36	8 690 991 616	343136 ₁₁₀₂₆	3·387587 ₃₄₈₆₆	715722 ₂₀₆₂	4863813 ₂₃₆₄
2057	4 23 12 49	8 703 679 193	354162 ₁₁₀₂₃	3·422453 ₃₄₈₅₈	717784 ₂₀₆₀	4861449 ₂₃₆₃
2058	4 23 53 64	8 716 379 112	365185 ₁₁₀₂₀	3·457311 ₃₄₈₄₉	719844 ₂₀₆₀	4859086 ₂₃₅₉
2059	4 23 94 81	8 729 091 379	376205 ₁₁₀₁₈	3·492160 ₃₄₈₄₁	721904 ₂₀₅₉	4856727 ₂₃₅₈
2060	4 24 36 00	8 741 816 000	387223 ₁₁₀₁₅	3·527001 ₃₄₈₃₂	723963 ₂₀₅₉	4854369 ₂₃₅₅
2061	4 24 77 21	8 754 552 981	398238 ₁₁₀₁₂	3·561833 ₃₄₈₂₄	726022 ₂₀₅₈	4852014 ₂₃₅₅
2062	4 25 18 44	8 767 302 328	409250 ₁₁₀₁₀	3·596657 ₃₄₈₁₆	728080 ₂₀₅₇	4849661 ₂₃₅₃
2063	4 25 59 69	8 780 064 047	420260 ₁₁₀₀₇	3·631473 ₃₄₈₀₇	730137 ₂₀₅₇	4847310 ₂₃₅₁
2064	4 26 00 96	8 792 838 144	431267 ₁₁₀₀₄	3·666280 ₃₄₇₉₉	732194 ₂₀₅₅	4844961 ₂₃₄₉
2065	4 26 42 25	8 805 624 625	442271 ₁₁₀₀₂	3·701079 ₃₄₇₉₀	734249 ₂₀₅₆	4842615 ₂₃₄₆
2066	4 26 83 56	8 818 423 496	453273 ₁₀₉₉₉	3·735869 ₃₄₇₈₂	736305 ₂₀₅₄	4840271 ₂₃₄₄
2067	4 27 24 89	8 831 234 763	464272 ₁₀₉₉₆	3·770651 ₃₄₇₇₃	738359 ₂₀₅₄	4837929 ₂₃₄₂
2068	4 27 66 24	8 844 058 432	475268 ₁₀₉₉₄	3·805424 ₃₄₇₆₅	740413 ₂₀₅₃	4835590 ₂₃₃₉
2069	4 28 07 61	8 856 894 509	486262 ₁₀₉₉₁	3·840189 ₃₄₇₅₇	742466 ₂₀₅₃	4833253 ₂₃₃₇
2070	4 28 49 00	8 869 743 000	497253 ₁₀₉₈₈	3·874946 ₃₄₇₄₈	744519 ₂₀₅₂	4830918 ₂₃₃₅
2071	4 28 90 41	8 882 603 911	508241 ₁₀₉₈₆	3·909694 ₃₄₇₄₀	746571 ₂₀₅₂	4828585 ₂₃₃₃
2072	4 29 31 84	8 895 477 248	519227 ₁₀₉₈₃	3·944434 ₃₄₇₃₁	748622 ₂₀₅₁	4826255 ₂₃₃₀
2073	4 29 73 29	8 908 363 017	530210 ₁₀₉₈₀	3·979165 ₃₄₇₂₃	750673 ₂₀₅₁	4823927 ₂₃₂₈
2074	4 30 14 76	8 921 261 224	541190 ₁₀₉₇₈	4·013888 ₃₄₇₁₅	752723 ₂₀₅₀	4821601 ₂₃₂₆
2075	4 30 56 25	8 934 171 875	552168 ₁₀₉₇₅	4·048603 ₃₄₇₀₆	754772 ₂₀₄₉	4819277 ₂₃₂₄
2076	4 30 97 76	8 947 094 976	563143 ₁₀₉₇₂	4·083309 ₃₄₆₉₈	756821 ₂₀₄₈	4816956 ₂₃₂₁
2077	4 31 39 29	8 960 030 533	574115 ₁₀₉₇₀	4·118007 ₃₄₆₉₀	758869 ₂₀₄₇	4814636 ₂₃₂₀
2078	4 31 80 84	8 972 978 552	585085 ₁₀₉₆₇	4·152697 ₃₄₆₈₁	760916 ₂₀₄₇	4812320 ₂₃₁₆
2079	4 32 22 41	8 985 939 039	596052 ₁₀₉₆₅	4·187378 ₃₄₆₇₃	762963 ₂₀₄₆	4810005 ₂₃₁₅
2080	4 32 64 00	8 998 912 060	607017 ₁₀₉₆₂	4·222051 ₃₄₆₆₅	765009 ₂₀₄₅	4807692 ₂₃₁₃
2081	4 33 05 61	9 011 897 441	617979 ₁₀₉₅₉	4·256716 ₃₄₆₅₆	767054 ₂₀₄₅	4805382 ₂₃₁₀
2082	4 33 47 24	9 024 895 368	628938 ₁₀₉₅₇	4·291372 ₃₄₆₄₈	769099 ₂₀₄₄	4803074 ₂₃₀₈
2083	4 33 88 89	9 037 905 787	639895 ₁₀₉₅₄	4·326020 ₃₄₆₃₉	771143 ₂₀₄₃	4800768 ₂₃₀₆
2084	4 34 30 56	9 050 928 704	650849 ₁₀₉₅₁	4·360659 ₃₄₆₃₂	773186 ₂₀₄₃	4798464 ₂₃₀₄
2085	4 34 72 25	9 063 964 125	661800 ₁₀₉₄₉	4·395291 ₃₄₆₂₃	775229 ₂₀₄₂	4796163 ₂₃₀₁
2086	4 35 13 96	9 077 012 056	672749 ₁₀₉₄₆	4·429914 ₃₄₆₁₅	777271 ₂₀₄₁	4793864 ₂₂₉₉
2087	4 35 55 69	9 090 072 503	683695 ₁₀₉₄₄	4·464529 ₃₄₆₀₆	779312 ₂₀₄₁	4791567 ₂₂₉₇
2088	4 35 97 44	9 103 145 472	694639 ₁₀₉₄₁	4·499135 ₃₄₅₉₈	781353 ₂₀₄₀	4789272 ₂₂₉₅
2089	4 36 39 21	9 116 230 969	705580 ₁₀₉₃₈	4·533733 ₃₄₅₉₀	783393 ₂₀₄₀	4786979 ₂₂₉₃
2090	4 36 81 00	9 129 329 000	716518 ₁₀₉₃₅	4·568323 ₃₄₅₈₂	785433 ₂₀₃₈	4784689 ₂₂₉₀
2091	4 37 22 81	9 142 439 571	727453 ₁₀₉₃₄	4·602905 ₃₄₅₇₃	787471 ₂₀₃₉	4782401 ₂₂₈₈
2092	4 37 64 64	9 155 562 688	738387 ₁₀₉₃₀	4·637478 ₃₄₅₆₅	789510 ₂₀₃₇	4780115 ₂₂₈₆
2093	4 38 06 49	9 168 698 357	749317 ₁₀₉₂₈	4·672043 ₃₄₅₅₇	791547 ₂₀₃₇	4777831 ₂₂₈₄
2094	4 38 48 36	9 181 846 584	760245 ₁₀₉₂₅	4·706600 ₃₄₅₄₈	793584 ₂₀₃₆	4775549 ₂₂₈₂
2095	4 38 90 25	9 195 007 375	771170 ₁₀₉₂₃	4·741148 ₃₄₅₄₁	795620 ₂₀₃₆	4773270 ₂₂₇₉
2096	4 39 32 16	9 208 180 736	782093 ₁₀₉₂₀	4·775689 ₃₄₅₃₂	797656 ₂₀₃₅	4770992 ₂₂₇₈
2097	4 39 74 09	9 221 366 673	793013 ₁₀₉₁₇	4·810221" ₃₄₅₂₃	799691 ₂₀₃₄	4768717 ₂₂₇₅
2098	4 40 16 04	9 234 565 192	803930 ₁₀₉₁₅	4·844744 ₃₄₅₁₆	801725 ₂₀₃₄	4766444 ₂₂₇₃
2099	4 40 58 01	9 247 776 299	814845 ₁₀₉₁₂	4·879260 ₃₄₅₀₇	803759 ₂₀₃₃	4764173 ₂₂₇₁
2100	4 41 00 00	9 261 000 000	825757 45·	4·913767 140 +	805792 12·	4761905 0·000

No. n	Square n^2	Cube n^3	Square root $\sqrt{n}$	Sq. rt. of 10n $\sqrt{10n}$	Cube root $\sqrt[3]{n}$	Reciprocal $\dfrac{1}{n}$
			45·	140 +	12·	0·000
2100	4 41 00 00	9 261 000 000	825757 10910	4·913767 34500	805792 2032	4761905 2267
2101	4 41 42 01	9 274 236 301	836667 10907	4·948267 34491	807824 2032	4759638 2264
2102	4 41 84 04	9 287 485 208	847574 10904	4·982758 34482	809856 2031	4757374 2262
2103	4 42 26 09	9 300 746 727	858478 10902	5·017240 34475	811887 2030	4755112 2260
2104	4 42 68 16	9 314 020 864	869380 10899	5·051715 34466	813917 2030	4752852 2258
2105	4 43 10 25	9 327 307 625	880279 10897	5·086181 34458	815947 2029	4750594 2256
2106	4 43 52 36	9 340 607 016	891176 10894	5·120639 34450	817976 2029	4748338 2254
2107	4 43 94 49	9 353 919 043	902070 10891	5·155089 34442	820005 2027	4746084 2251
2108	4 44 36 64	9 367 243 712	912961 10889	5·189531 34434	822032 2028	4743833 2249
2109	4 44 78 81	9 380 581 029	923850 10886	5·223965 34425	824060 2026	4741584 2248
2110	4 45 21 00	9 393 931 000	934736 10884	5·258390 34418	826086 2026	4739336 2245
2111	4 45 63 21	9 407 293 631	945620 10881	5·292808 34409	828112 2025	4737091 2243
2112	4 46 05 44	9 420 668 928	956501 10879	5·327217 34401	830137 2025	4734848 2240
2113	4 46 47 69	9 434 056 897	967380 10876	5·361618 34393	832162 2024	4732608 2239
2114	4 46 89 96	9 447 457 544	978256 10873	5·396011 34385	834186 2023	4730369 2237
2115	4 47 32 25	9 460 870 875	989129 10871	5·430396 34376	836209 2023	4728132 2234
2116	4 47 74 56	9 474 296 896	*000000 10868	5·464772 34369	838232 2022	4725898 2234
2117	4 48 16 89	9 487 735 613	010868 10866	5·499141 34360	840254 2022	4723666 2232
2118	4 48 59 24	9 501 187 032	021734 10863	5·533501 34353	842276 2022	4721435 2231
2119	4 49 01 61	9 514 651 159	032597 10861	5·567854 34344	844296 2021	4719207 2228
2120	4 49 44 00	9 528 128 000	043458 10858	5·602198 34336	846317 2019	4716981 2226
2121	4 49 86 41	9 541 617 561	054316 10855	5·636534 34328	848336 2019	4714757 2224
2122	4 50 28 84	9 555 119 848	065171 10853	5·670862 34320	850355 2018	4712535 2222
2123	4 50 71 29	9 568 634 867	076024 10850	5·705182 34312	852373 2018	4710316 2219
2124	4 51 13 76	9 582 162 624	086874 10848	5·739494 34303	854391 2017	4708098 2218
2125	4 51 56 25	9 595 703 125	097722 10846	5·773797 34296	856408 2016	4705882 2216
2126	4 51 98 76	9 609 256 376	108568 10842	5·808093 34288	858424 2016	4703669 2213
2127	4 52 41 29	9 622 822 383	119410 10840	5·842381 34279	860440 2015	4701457 2212
2128	4 52 83 84	9 636 401 152	130250 10838	5·876660 34272	862455 2015	4699248 2209
2129	4 53 26 41	9 649 992 689	141088 10835	5·910932 34263	864470 2014	4697041 2207
2130	4 53 69 00	9 663 597 000	151923 10833	5·945195 34256	866484 2013	4694836 2205
2131	4 54 11 61	9 677 214 091	162756 10830	5·979451 34247	868497 2012	4692633 2203
2132	4 54 54 24	9 690 843 968	173586 10827	6·013698 34239	870509 2012	4690432 2201
2133	4 54 96 89	9 704 486 637	184413 10825	6·047937 34232	872521 2012	4688233 2199
2134	4 55 39 56	9 718 142 104	195238 10822	6·082169 34223	874533 2010	4686036 2197
2135	4 55 82 25	9 731 810 375	206060 10820	6·116392 34215	876543 2010	4683841 2195
2136	4 56 24 96	9 745 491 456	216880 10817	6·150607 34208	878553 2010	4681648 2193
2137	4 56 67 69	9 759 185 353	227697 10815	6·184815 34199	880563 2009	4679457 2191
2138	4 57 10 44	9 772 892 072	238512 10812	6·219014 34191	882572 2008	4677268 2189
2139	4 57 53 21	9 786 611 619	249324 10810	6·253205 34183	884580 2007	4675082 2186
2140	4 57 96 00	9 800 344 000	260134 10807	6·287388 34176	886587 2007	4672897 2185
2141	4 58 38 81	9 814 089 221	270941 10805	6·321564 34167	888594 2007	4670715 2182
2142	4 58 81 64	9 827 847 288	281746 10802	6·355731 34159	890601 2005	4668534 2181
2143	4 59 24 49	9 841 618 207	292548 10800	6·389890 34152	892606 2005	4666356 2178
2144	4 59 67 36	9 855 401 984	303348 10797	6·424042 34143	894611 2005	4664179 2177
2145	4 60 10 25	9 869 198 625	314145 10794	6·458185 34136	896616 2004	4662005 2173
2146	4 60 53 16	9 883 008 136	324939 10792	6·492321 34127	898620 2003	4659832 2170
2147	4 60 96 09	9 896 830 523	335731 10790	6·526448 34120	900623 2003	4657662 2169
2148	4 61 39 04	9 910 665 792	346521 10787	6·560568 34111	902626 2001	4655493 2166
2149	4 61 82 01	9 924 513 949	357308 10784	6·594679 34104	904627 2002	4653327 2164
2150	4 62 25 00	9 938 375 000	368092 46·	6·628783 140 +	906629 12·	4651163 0·000

No. n	Square n²	Cube n³	Square root √n	Sq. rt. of 10n √10n	Cube root ∛n	Reciprocal 1/n
			46·	140 +	12·	0·000
2150	4 62 25 00	9 938 375 000	368092 10783	6·628783 34096	906629 2001	4651163 2163
2151	4 62 68 01	9 952 248 951	378875 10779	6·662879 34088	908630 2000	4649000 2160
2152	4 63 11 04	9 966 135 808	389654 10777	6·696967 34079	910630 1999	4646840 2158
2153	4 63 54 09	9 980 035 577	400431 10775	6·731046 34072	912629 1999	4644682 2156
2154	4 63 97 16	9 993 948 264	411206 10772	6·765118 34065	914628 1998	4642526 2155
2155	4 64 40 25	10 007 873 875	421978 10769	6·799183 34056	916626 1998	4640371 2152
2156	4 64 83 36	10 021 812 416	432747 10767	6·833239 34048	918624 1997	4638219 2150
2157	4 65 26 49	10 035 763 893	443514 10765	6·867287 34040	920621 1996	4636069 2149
2158	4 65 69 64	10 049 728 312	454279 10762	6·901327 34033	922617 1996	4633920 2146
2159	4 66 12 81	10 063 705 679	465041 10759	6·935360 34025	924613 1995	4631774 2144
2160	4 66 56 00	10 077 696 000	475800 10757	6·969385 34016	926608 1995	4629630 2143
2161	4 66 99 21	10 091 699 281	486557 10755	7·003401 34009	928603 1994	4627487 2140
2162	4 67 42 44	10 105 715 528	497312 10752	7·037410 34001	930597 1993	4625347 2138
2163	4 67 85 69	10 119 744 747	508064 10749	7·071411 33993	932590 1993	4623209 2137
2164	4 68 28 96	10 133 786 944	518813 10747	7·105404 33986	934583 1992	4621072 2134
2165	4 68 72 25	10 147 842 125	529560 10745	7·139390 33977	936575 1991	4618938 2133
2166	4 69 15 56	10 161 910 296	540305 10742	7·173367 33970	938566 1991	4616805 2130
2167	4 69 58 89	10 175 991 463	551047 10740	7·207337 33962	940557 1990	4614675 2129
2168	4 70 02 24	10 190 085 632	561787 10737	7·241299 33954	942547 1990	4612546 2126
2169	4 70 45 61	10 204 192 809	572524 10735	7·275253 33946	944537 1989	4610420 2125
2170	4 70 89 00	10 218 313 000	583259 10732	7·309199 33938	946526 1988	4608295 2123
2171	4 71 32 41	10 232 446 211	593991 10730	7·343137 33930	948514 1988	4606172 2120
2172	4 71 75 84	10 246 592 448	604721 10727	7·377067 33923	950502 1987	4604052 2119
2173	4 72 19 29	10 260 751 717	615448 10725	7·410990 33915	952489 1987	4601933 2117
2174	4 72 62 76	10 274 924 024	626173 10722	7·444905 33907	954476 1986	4599816 2115
2175	4 73 06 25	10 289 109 375	636895 10720	7·478812 33899	956462 1985	4597701 2113
2176	4 73 49 76	10 303 307 776	647615 10718	7·512711 33892	958447 1985	4595588 2111
2177	4 73 93 29	10 317 519 233	658333 10715	7·546603 33884	960432 1984	4593477 2109
2178	4 74 36 84	10 331 743 752	669048 10712	7·580487 33875	962416 1984	4591368 2107
2179	4 74 80 41	10 345 981 339	679760 10710	7·614362 33869	964400 1983	4589261 2105
2180	4 75 24 00	10 360 232 000	690470 10708	7·648231 33860	966383 1982	4587156 2103
2181	4 75 67 61	10 374 495 741	701178 10705	7·682091 33853	968365 1982	4585053 2102
2182	4 76 11 24	10 388 772 568	711883 10703	7·715944 33844	970347 1981	4582951 2099
2183	4 76 54 89	10 403 062 487	722586 10700	7·749788 33838	972328 1980	4580852 2097
2184	4 76 98 56	10 417 365 504	733286 10698	7·783626 33829	974308 1980	4578755 2096
2185	4 77 42 25	10 431 681 625	743984 10695	7·817455 33822	976288 1979	4576659 2094
2186	4 77 85 96	10 446 010 856	754679 10693	7·851277 33814	978267 1979	4574565 2091
2187	4 78 29 69	10 460 353 203	765372 10690	7·885091 33806	980246 1978	4572474 2090
2188	4 78 73 44	10 474 708 672	776062 10688	7·918897 33798	982224 1978	4570384 2088
2189	4 79 17 21	10 489 077 269	786750 10686	7·952695 33791	984202 1977	4568296 2086
2190	4 79 61 00	10 503 459 000	797436 10683	7·986486 33783	986179 1976	4566210 2084
2191	4 80 04 81	10 517 853 871	808119 10681	8·020269 33775	988155 1976	4564126 2082
2192	4 80 48 64	10 532 261 888	818800 10678	8·054044 33768	990131 1975	4562044 2080
2193	4 80 92 49	10 546 683 057	829478 10676	8·087812 33760	992106 1975	4559964 2079
2194	4 81 36 36	10 561 117 384	840154 10673	8·121572 33752	994080 1974	4557885 2076
2195	4 81 80 25	10 575 564 875	850827 10671	8·155324 33744	996054 1973	4555809 2075
2196	4 82 24 16	10 590 025 536	861498 10669	8·189068 33737	998027 1973	4553734 2073
2197	4 82 68 09	10 604 499 373	872167 10666	8·222805 33729	*000000 1972	4551661 2070
2198	4 83 12 04	10 618 986 392	882833 10663	8·256534 33722	001972 1972	4549591 2069
2199	4 83 56 01	10 633 486 599	893496 10662	8·290256 33714	003944 1970	4547522 2067
2200	4 84 00 00	10 648 000 000	904158 46·	8·323970 140 +	005914 13·	4545455 0·000

No. n	Square n^2	Cube n^3	Square root $\sqrt{n}$	Sq. rt. of $10n$ $\sqrt{10n}$	Cube root $\sqrt[3]{n}$	Reciprocal $\dfrac{1}{n}$
			46·	140 +	13·	0·000
2200	4 84 00 00	10 648 000 000	904158	8·323970	005914	4545455
2201	4 84 44 01	10 662 526 601	914816 10658	8·357676 33706	007885 1971	4543380 2066
2202	4 84 88 04	10 677 066 408	925473 10657	8·391374 33698	009854 1969	4541326 2063
2203	4 85 32 09	10 691 619 427	936127 10654	8·425065 33691	011824 1970	4539265 2061
2204	4 85 76 16	10 706 185 664	946778 10651	8·458748 33683	013792 1968	4537205 2060
			10650	33676	1968	2058
2205	4 86 20 25	10 720 765 125	957428	8·492424 33668	015760 1967	4535147
2206	4 86 64 36	10 735 357 816	968074 10646	8·526092 33660	017727 1967	4533092 2055
2207	4 87 08 49	10 749 963 743	978719 10645	8·559752 33653	019694 1966	4531038 2054
2208	4 87 52 64	10 764 582 912	989360 10641	8·593405 33645	021660 1966	4528986 2052
2209	4 87 96 81	10 779 215 329	*000000 10640	8·627050 33637	023626 1965	4526935 2051
			10637			2048
2210	4 88 41 00	10 793 861 000	010637	8·660687 33630	025591 1964	4524887
2211	4 88 85 21	10 808 519 931	021272 10635	8·694317 33623	027555 1964	4522840 2047
2212	4 89 29 44	10 823 192 128	031904 10632	8·727940 33614	029519 1963	4520796 2044
2213	4 89 73 69	10 837 877 597	042534 10630	8·761554 33607	031482 1962	4518753 2043
2214	4 90 17 96	10 852 576 344	053161 10627	8·795161 33600	033444 1962	4516712 2041
			10626			2039
2215	4 90 62 25	10 867 288 375	063787	8·828761 33592	035406 1962	4514673
2216	4 91 06 56	10 882 013 696	074409 10622	8·862353 33584	037368 1961	4512635 2038
2217	4 91 50 89	10 896 752 313	085029 10620	8·895937 33577	039329 1960	4510600 2035
2218	4 91 95 24	10 911 504 232	095647 10618	8·929514 33569	041289 1960	4508566 2034
2219	4 92 39 61	10 926 269 459	106263 10616	8·963083 33561	043248 1959	4506534 2032
			10613			2029
2220	4 92 84 00	10 941 048 000	116876	8·996644 33554	045208 1958	4504505
2221	4 93 28 41	10 955 839 861	127487 10611	9·030198 33547	047166 1958	4502476 2029
2222	4 93 72 84	10 970 645 048	138095 10608	9·063745 33539	049124 1957	4500450 2026
2223	4 94 17 29	10 985 463 567	148701 10606	9·097284 33531	051081 1957	4498426 2024
2224	4 94 61 76	11 000 295 424	159304 10603	9·130815 33524	053038 1956	4496403 2023
			10602			2021
2225	4 95 06 25	11 015 140 625	169906	9·164339 33516	054994 1955	4494382
2226	4 95 50 76	11 029 999 176	180504 10598	9·197855 33509	056949 1955	4492363 2019
2227	4 95 95 29	11 044 871 083	191101 10597	9·231364 33501	058904 1955	4490346 2017
2228	4 96 39 84	11 059 756 352	201695 10594	9·264865 33494	060859 1953	4488330 2016
2229	4 96 84 41	11 074 654 989	212287 10592	9·298359 33486	062812 1954	4486317 2013
			10589			2012
2230	4 97 29 00	11 089 567 000	222876	9·331845 33479	064766 1952	4484305
2231	4 97 73 61	11 104 492 391	233463 10587	9·365324 33471	066718 1952	4482295 2010
2232	4 98 18 24	11 119 431 168	244047 10584	9·398795 33464	068670 1952	4480287 2008
2233	4 98 62 89	11 134 383 337	254629 10582	9·432259 33456	070622 1950	4478280 2007
2234	4 99 07 56	11 149 348 904	265209 10580	9·465715 33449	072572 1951	4476276 2004
			10578			2003
2235	4 99 52 25	11 164 327 875	275787	9·499164 33441	074523 1949	4474273
2236	4 99 96 96	11 179 320 256	286362 10575	9·532605 33434	076472 1949	4472272 2001
2237	5 00 41 69	11 194 326 053	296934 10572	9·566039 33426	078421 1949	4470273 1999
2238	5 00 86 44	11 209 345 272	307505 10571	9·599465 33419	080370 1948	4468275 1998
2239	5 01 31 21	11 224 377 919	318073 10568	9·632884 33411	082318 1947	4466280 1995
			10565			1994
2240	5 01 76 00	11 239 424 000	328638	9·666295 33404	084265 1947	4464286
2241	5 02 20 81	11 254 483 521	339202 10564	9·699699 33397	086212 1946	4462294 1992
2242	5 02 65 64	11 269 556 488	349762 10560	9·733059 33389	088158 1946	4460303 1991
2243	5 03 10 49	11 284 642 907	360321 10559	9·766485 33381	090104 1945	4458315 1988
2244	5 03 55 36	11 299 742 784	370877 10556	9·799866 33375	092049 1944	4456328 1987
			10554			1985
2245	5 04 00 25	11 314 856 125	381431	9·833241 33366	093993 1944	4454343
2246	5 04 45 16	11 329 982 936	391982 10551	9·866607 33360	095937 1944	4452360 1983
2247	5 04 90 09	11 345 123 223	402532 10550	9·899967 33352	097881 1942	4450378 1982
2248	5 05 35 04	11 360 276 992	413078 10546	9·933319 33344	099823 1942	4448399 1979
2249	5 05 80 01	11 375 444 249	423623 10545	9·966663 33337	101765 1942	4446421 1978
			10542			1977
2250	5 06 25 00	11 390 625 000	434165	10·000000	103707	4444444
			47·	140 +	13·	0·000

No. n	Square n^2	Cube n^3	Square root $\sqrt{n}$	Sq. rt. of 10n $\sqrt{10n}$	Cube root $\sqrt[3]{n}$	Reciprocal $\dfrac{1}{n}$
			47·	150 +	13·	0·000
2250	5 06 25 00	11 390 625 000	434165 10540	0·000000 33330	103707 1941	4444444 1974
2251	5 06 70 01	11 405 819 251	444705 10537	0·033330 33322	105648 1940	4442470 1973
2252	5 07 15 04	11 421 027 008	455242 10535	0·066652 33315	107588 1940	4440497 1971
2253	5 07 60 09	11 436 248 277	465777 10533	0·099967 33307	109528 1940	4438526 1969
2254	5 08 05 16	11 451 483 064	476310 10530	0·133274 33300	111468 1938	4436557 1967
2255	5 08 50 25	11 466 731 375	486840 10528	0·166574 33293	113406 1938	4434590 1966
2256	5 08 95 36	11 481 993 216	497368 10526	0·199867 33285	115344 1938	4432624 1964
2257	5 09 40 49	11 497 268 593	507894 10523	0·233152 33278	117282 1937	4430660 1962
2258	5 09 85 64	11 512 557 512	518417 10522	0·266430 33271	119219 1936	4428698 1961
2259	5 10 30 81	11 527 859 979	528939 10518	0·299701 33263	121155 1936	4426737 1958
2260	5 10 76 00	11 543 176 000	539457 10517	0·332964 33256	123091 1935	4424779 1957
2261	5 11 21 21	11 558 505 581	549974 10514	0·366220 33248	125026 1935	4422822 1956
2262	5 11 66 44	11 573 848 728	560488 10512	0·399468 33241	126961 1934	4420866 1953
2263	5 12 11 69	11 589 205 447	571000 10509	0·432709 33234	128895 1934	4418913 1952
2264	5 12 56 96	11 604 575 744	581509 10507	0·465943 33226	130829 1933	4416961 1950
2265	5 13 02 25	11 619 959 625	592016 10505	0·499169 33220	132762 1932	4415011 1948
2266	5 13 47 56	11 635 357 096	602521 10502	0·532389 33211	134694 1932	4413063 1947
2267	5 13 92 89	11 650 768 163	613023 10501	0·565600 33205	136626 1931	4411116 1947
2268	5 14 38 24	11 666 192 832	623524 10497	0·598805 33197	138557 1931	4409171 1943
2269	5 14 83 61	11 681 631 109	634021 10496	0·632002 33190	140488 1930	4407228 1942
2270	5 15 29 00	11 697 083 000	644517 10493	0·665192 33182	142418 1930	4405286 1939
2271	5 15 74 41	11 712 548 511	655010 10491	0·698374 33175	144348 1929	4403347 1939
2272	5 16 19 84	11 728 027 648	665501 10489	0·731549 33168	146277 1928	4401408 1936
2273	5 16 65 29	11 743 520 417	675990 10486	0·764717 33161	148205 1928	4399472 1935
2274	5 17 10 76	11 759 026 824	686476 10484	0·797878 33153	150133 1928	4397537 1933
2275	5 17 56 25	11 774 546 875	696960 10482	0·831031 33146	152061 1926	4395604 1931
2276	5 18 01 76	11 790 080 576	707442 10479	0·864177 33139	153987 1927	4393673 1929
2277	5 18 47 29	11 805 627 933	717921 10477	0·897316 33132	155914 1925	4391744 1928
2278	5 18 92 84	11 821 188 952	728398 10475	0·930448 33124	157839 1925	4389816 1927
2279	5 19 38 41	11 836 763 639	738873 10473	0·963572 33117	159764 1925	4387889 1924
2280	5 19 84 00	11 852 352 000	749346 10470	0·996689 33109	161689 1924	4385965 1923
2281	5 20 29 61	11 867 954 041	759816 10468	1·029798 33103	163613 1923	4384042 1921
2282	5 20 75 24	11 883 569 768	770284 10465	1·062901 33095	165536 1923	4382121 1920
2283	5 21 20 89	11 899 199 187	780749 10464	1·095996 33088	167459 1922	4380201 1917
2284	5 21 66 56	11 914 842 304	791213 10461	1·129084 33081	169381 1922	4378284 1916
2285	5 22 12 25	11 930 499 125	801674 10458	1·162165 33073	171303 1921	4376368 1915
2286	5 22 57 96	11 946 169 656	812132 10457	1·195238 33066	173224 1921	4374453 1913
2287	5 23 03 69	11 961 853 903	822589 10454	1·228304 33059	175145 1920	4372540 1911
2288	5 23 49 44	11 977 551 872	833043 10452	1·261363 33052	177065 1919	4370629 1909
2289	5 23 95 21	11 993 263 569	843495 10449	1·294415 33045	178984 1919	4368720 1908
2290	5 24 41 00	12 008 989 000	853944 10448	1·327460 33037	180903 1918	4366812 1906
2291	5 24 86 81	12 024 728 171	864392 10445	1·360497 33030	182821 1918	4364906 1904
2292	5 25 32 64	12 040 481 088	874837 10443	1·393527 33023	184739 1917	4363002 1903
2293	5 25 78 49	12 056 247 757	885280 10440	1·426550 33016	186656 1917	4361099 1901
2294	5 26 24 36	12 072 028 184	895720 10438	1·459566 33008	188573 1916	4359198 1900
2295	5 26 70 25	12 087 822 375	906158 10436	1·492574 33001	190489 1916	4357298 1897
2296	5 27 16 16	12 103 630 336	916594 10434	1·525575 32995	192405 1915	4355401 1896
2297	5 27 62 09	12 119 452 073	927028 10431	1·558570 32986	194320 1914	4353505 1895
2298	5 28 08 04	12 135 287 592	937459 10429	1·591556 32980	196234 1914	4351610 1893
2299	5 28 54 01	12 151 136 899	947888 10427	1·624536 32973	198148 1913	4349717 1891
2300	5 29 00 00	12 167 000 000	958315	1·657509	200061	4347826
			47·	150 +	13·	0·000

No. n	Square n^2	Cube n^3	Square root $\sqrt{n}$	Sq. rt. of 10n $\sqrt{10n}$	Cube root $\sqrt[3]{n}$	Reciprocal $\dfrac{1}{n}$
			47·	150 +	13·	0·000
2300	5 29 00 00	12 167 000 000	958315	1·657509	200061	4347826
2301	5 29 46 01	12 182 876 901	968740 10425	1·690474 32965	201974 1913	4345937 1889
2302	5 29 92 04	12 198 767 608	979162 10422	1·723433 32959	203886 1912	4344049 1888
2303	5 30 38 09	12 214 672 127	989582 10420	1·756384 32951	205798 1912	4342162 1887
2304	5 30 84 16	12 230 590 464	*000000 10418	1·789328 32944	207709 1911	4340278 1884
			10416	32937	1911	1883
2305	5 31 30 25	12 246 522 625	010416 10413	1·822265 32929	209620 1910	4338395 1882
2306	5 31 76 36	12 262 468 616	020829 10411	1·855194 32923	211530 1909	4336513 1879
2307	5 32 22 49	12 278 428 443	031240 10409	1·888117 32915	213439 1909	4334634 1878
2308	5 32 68 64	12 294 402 112	041649 10406	1·921032 32908	215348 1908	4332756 1877
2309	5 33 14 81	12 310 389 629	052055 10404	1·953940 32902	217256 1908	4330879 1875
2310	5 33 61 00	12 326 391 000	062459 10402	1·986842 32894	219164 1907	4329004 1873
2311	5 34 07 21	12 342 406 231	072861 10400	2·019736 32886	221071 1907	4327131 1871
2312	5 34 53 44	12 358 435 328	083261 10398	2·052622 32880	222978 1906	4325260 1870
2313	5 34 99 69	12 374 478 297	093659 10395	2·085502 32873	224884 1906	4323390 1869
2314	5 35 45 96	12 390 535 144	104054 10393	2·118375 32866	226790 1905	4321521 1867
2315	5 35 92 25	12 406 605 875	114447 10391	2·151241 32858	228695 1904	4319654 1865
2316	5 36 38 56	12 422 690 496	124838 10388	2·184099 32851	230599 1904	4317789 1863
2317	5 36 84 89	12 438 789 013	135226 10386	2·216950 32845	232503 1904	4315926 1862
2318	5 37 31 24	12 454 901 432	145612 10385	2·249795 32837	234407 1903	4314064 1860
2319	5 37 77 61	12 471 027 759	155997 10381	2·282632 32830	236310 1902	4312204 1859
2320	5 38 24 00	12 487 168 000	166378 10380	2·315462 32823	238212 1902	4310345 1857
2321	5 38 70 41	12 503 322 161	176758 10377	2·348285 32816	240114 1901	4308488 1856
2322	5 39 16 84	12 519 490 248	187135 10375	2·381101 32809	242015 1901	4306632 1854
2323	5 39 63 29	12 535 672 267	197510 10373	2·413910 32802	243916 1900	4304778 1852
2324	5 40 09 76	12 551 868 224	207883 10371	2·446712 32795	245816 1899	4302926 1851
2325	5 40 56 25	12 568 078 125	218254 10368	2·479507 32788	247715 1899	4301075 1849
2326	5 41 02 76	12 584 301 976	228622 10366	2·512295 32780	249614 1899	4299226 1847
2327	5 41 49 29	12 600 539 783	238988 10364	2·545075 32774	251513 1898	4297379 1846
2328	5 41 95 84	12 616 791 552	249352 10362	2·577849 32767	253411 1897	4295533 1845
2329	5 42 42 41	12 633 057 289	259714 10360	2·610616 32759	255308 1897	4293688 1843
2330	5 42 89 00	12 649 337 000	270074 10357	2·643375 32753	257205 1896	4291845 1841
2331	5 43 35 61	12 665 630 691	280431 10355	2·676128 32745	259101 1896	4290004 1839
2332	5 43 82 24	12 681 938 368	290786 10353	2·708873 32739	260997 1895	4288165 1838
2333	5 44 28 89	12 698 260 037	301139 10350	2·741612 32731	262892 1895	4286327 1837
2334	5 44 75 56	12 714 595 704	311489 10349	2·774343 32725	264787 1894	4284490 1835
2335	5 45 22 25	12 730 945 375	321838 10346	2·807068 32717	266681 1894	4282655 1833
2336	5 45 68 96	12 747 309 056	332184 10344	2·839785 32711	268575 1893	4280822 1832
2337	5 46 15 69	12 763 686 753	342528 10342	2·872496 32703	270468 1892	4278990 1830
2338	5 46 62 44	12 780 078 472	352870 10339	2·905199 32697	272360 1892	4277160 1829
2339	5 47 09 21	12 796 484 219	363209 10337	2·937896 32689	274252 1892	4275331 1827
2340	5 47 56 00	12 812 904 000	373546 10336	2·970585 32683	276144 1891	4273504 1825
2341	5 48 02 81	12 829 337 821	383882 10333	3·003268 32675	278035 1890	4271679 1824
2342	5 48 49 64	12 845 785 688	394215 10330	3·035943 32669	279925 1890	4269855 1823
2343	5 48 96 49	12 862 247 607	404545 10329	3·068612 32662	281815 1889	4268032 1820
2344	5 49 43 36	12 878 723 584	414874 10326	3·101274 32654	283704 1889	4266212 1820
2345	5 49 90 25	12 895 213 625	425200 10324	3·133928 32648	285593 1888	4264392 1817
2346	5 50 37 16	12 911 717 736	435524 10322	3·166576 32641	287481 1888	4262575 1817
2347	5 50 84 09	12 928 235 923	445846 10320	3·199217 32633	289369 1887	4260758 1814
2348	5 51 31 04	12 944 768 192	456166 10317	3·231850 32627	291256 1887	4258944 1813
2349	5 51 78 01	12 961 314 549	466483 10316	3·264477 32620	293143 1886	4257131 1812
2350	5 52 25 00	12 977 875 000	476799	3·297097	295029	4255319
			48·	150 +	13·	0·000

48

No. n	Square n²	Cube n³	Square root √n	Sq. rt. of 10n √10n	Cube root ∛n	Reciprocal 1/n
			48·	150 +	13·	0·000
2350	5 52 25 00	12 977 875 000	476799 [10313]	3·297097 [32613]	295029 [1886]	4255319 [1810]
2351	5 52 72 01	12 994 449 551	487112 [10311]	3·329710 [32606]	296915 [1885]	4253509 [1808]
2352	5 53 19 04	13 011 038 208	497423 [10308]	3·362316 [32599]	298800 [1884]	4251701 [1807]
2353	5 53 66 09	13 027 640 977	507731 [10307]	3·394915 [32592]	300684 [1884]	4249894 [1806]
2354	5 54 13 16	13 044 257 864	518038 [10304]	3·427507 [32586]	302568 [1883]	4248088 [1803]
2355	5 54 60 25	13 060 888 875	528342 [10302]	3·460093 [32578]	304451 [1883]	4246285 [1803]
2356	5 55 07 36	13 077 534 016	538644 [10300]	3·492671 [32571]	306334 [1883]	4244482 [1801]
2357	5 55 54 49	13 094 193 293	548944 [10298]	3·525242 [32565]	308217 [1881]	4242681 [1799]
2358	5 56 01 64	13 110 866 712	559242 [10296]	3·557807 [32557]	310098 [1882]	4240882 [1798]
2359	5 56 48 81	13 127 554 279	569538 [10293]	3·590364 [32551]	311980 [1880]	4239084 [1796]
2360	5 56 96 00	13 144 256 000	579831 [10291]	3·622915 [32544]	313860 [1881]	4237288 [1795]
2361	5 57 43 21	13 160 971 881	590122 [10290]	3·655459 [32537]	315741 [1879]	4235493 [1793]
2362	5 57 90 44	13 177 701 928	600412 [10286]	3·687996 [32530]	317620 [1880]	4233700 [1791]
2363	5 58 37 69	13 194 446 147	610698 [10285]	3·720526 [32523]	319500 [1878]	4231909 [1791]
2364	5 58 84 96	13 211 204 544	620983 [10283]	3·753049 [32516]	321378 [1878]	4230118 [1788]
2365	5 59 32 25	13 227 977 125	631266 [10280]	3·785565 [32509]	323256 [1878]	4228330 [1787]
2366	5 59 79 56	13 244 763 896	641546 [10278]	3·818074 [32503]	325134 [1877]	4226543 [1786]
2367	5 60 26 89	13 261 564 863	651824 [10276]	3·850577 [32495]	327011 [1876]	4224757 [1784]
2368	5 60 74 24	13 278 380 032	662100 [10274]	3·883072 [32489]	328887 [1876]	4222973 [1783]
2369	5 61 21 61	13 295 209 409	672374 [10272]	3·915561 [32482]	330763 [1876]	4221190 [1781]
2370	5 61 69 00	13 312 053 000	682646 [10269]	3·948043 [32475]	332639 [1875]	4219409 [1779]
2371	5 62 16 41	13 328 910 811	692915 [10268]	3·980518 [32468]	334514 [1874]	4217630 [1778]
2372	5 62 63 84	13 345 782 848	703183 [10265]	4·012986 [32462]	336388 [1874]	4215852 [1777]
2373	5 63 11 29	13 362 669 117	713448 [10263]	4·045448 [32454]	338262 [1873]	4214075 [1775]
2374	5 63 58 76	13 379 569 624	723711 [10261]	4·077902 [32448]	340135 [1873]	4212300 [1774]
2375	5 64 06 25	13 396 484 375	733972 [10258]	4·110350 [32441]	342008 [1873]	4210526 [1772]
2376	5 64 53 76	13 413 413 376	744230 [10257]	4·142791 [32434]	343881 [1871]	4208754 [1770]
2377	5 65 01 29	13 430 356 633	754487 [10254]	4·175225 [32427]	345752 [1872]	4206984 [1770]
2378	5 65 48 84	13 447 314 152	764741 [10253]	4·207652 [32421]	347624 [1870]	4205214 [1767]
2379	5 65 96 41	13 464 285 939	774994 [10250]	4·240073 [32413]	349494 [1870]	4203447 [1766]
2380	5 66 44 00	13 481 272 000	785244 [10248]	4·272486 [32407]	351364 [1870]	4201681 [1765]
2381	5 66 91 61	13 498 272 341	795492 [10245]	4·304893 [32400]	353234 [1869]	4199916 [1763]
2382	5 67 39 24	13 515 286 968	805737 [10244]	4·337293 [32393]	355103 [1869]	4198153 [1762]
2383	5 67 86 89	13 532 315 887	815981 [10241]	4·369686 [32387]	356972 [1868]	4196391 [1760]
2384	5 68 34 56	13 549 359 104	826222 [10240]	4·402073 [32379]	358840 [1868]	4194631 [1759]
2385	5 68 82 25	13 566 416 625	836462 [10237]	4·434452 [32373]	360708 [1867]	4192872 [1757]
2386	5 69 29 96	13 583 488 456	846699 [10235]	4·466825 [32366]	362575 [1866]	4191115 [1756]
2387	5 69 77 69	13 600 574 603	856934 [10233]	4·499191 [32359]	364441 [1866]	4189359 [1754]
2388	5 70 25 44	13 617 675 072	867167 [10231]	4·531550 [32353]	366307 [1866]	4187605 [1753]
2389	5 70 73 21	13 634 789 869	877398 [10228]	4·563903 [32345]	368173 [1865]	4185852 [1752]
2390	5 71 21 00	13 651 919 000	887626 [10227]	4·596248 [32339]	370038 [1864]	4184100 [1750]
2391	5 71 68 81	13 669 062 471	897853 [10224]	4·628587 [32332]	371902 [1864]	4182350 [1748]
2392	5 72 16 64	13 686 220 288	908077 [10222]	4·660919 [32326]	373766 [1864]	4180602 [1747]
2393	5 72 64 49	13 703 392 457	918299 [10220]	4·693245 [32318]	375630 [1862]	4178855 [1746]
2394	5 73 12 36	13 720 578 984	928519 [10218]	4·725563 [32312]	377492 [1863]	4177109 [1744]
2395	5 73 60 25	13 737 779 875	938737 [10216]	4·757875 [32306]	379355 [1862]	4175365 [1742]
2396	5 74 08 16	13 754 995 136	948953 [10214]	4·790181 [32298]	381217 [1861]	4173623 [1741]
2397	5 74 56 09	13 772 224 773	959167 [10211]	4·822479 [32292]	383078 [1861]	4171882 [1740]
2398	5 75 04 04	13 789 468 792	969378 [10210]	4·854771 [32285]	384939 [1860]	4170142 [1738]
2399	5 75 52 01	13 806 727 199	979588 [10207]	4·887056 [32278]	386799 [1860]	4168404 [1737]
2400	5 76 00 00	13 824 000 000	989795	4·919334	388659	4166667
			48·	150 +	13·	0·000

No. n	Square n²	Cube n³	Square root √n (48·)	Sq. rt. of 10n √10n (150 +)	Cube root ∛n (13·)	Reciprocal 1/n (0·000)
2400	5 76 00 00	13 824 000 000	989795	4·919334 32271	388659 1859	4166667
2401	5 76 48 01	13 841 287 201	*000000 10205	4·951605 32265	390518 1859	4164931 1736
2402	5 76 96 04	13 858 588 808	010203 10203	4·983870 32258	392377 1858	4163197 1734
2403	5 77 44 09	13 875 904 827	020404 10201	5·016128 32252	394235 1858	4161465 1732
2404	5 77 92 16	13 893 235 264	030603 10199	5·048380 32244	396093 1857	4159734 1731
			10196			1730
2405	5 78 40 25	13 910 580 125	040799 10195	5·080624 32238	397950 1857	4158004 1728
2406	5 78 88 36	13 927 939 416	050994 10192	5·112862 32231	399807 1856	4156276 1727
2407	5 79 36 49	13 945 313 143	061186 10191	5·145093 32225	401663 1856	4154549 1725
2408	5 79 84 64	13 962 701 312	071377 10188	5·177318 32218	403519 1855	4152824 1724
2409	5 80 32 81	13 980 103 929	081565 10186	5·209536 32211	405374 1855	4151100 1722
2410	5 80 81 00	13 997 521 000	091751 10184	5·241747 32204	407229 1854	4149378 1721
2411	5 81 29 21	14 014 952 531	101935 10182	5·273951 32198	409083 1853	4147657 1720
2412	5 81 77 44	14 032 398 528	112117 10179	5·306149 32191	410936 1853	4145937 1718
2413	5 82 25 69	14 049 858 997	122296 10178	5·338340 32185	412789 1853	4144219 1717
2414	5 82 73 96	14 067 333 944	132474 10176	5·370525 32178	414642 1852	4142502 1715
2415	5 83 22 25	14 084 823 375	142650 10173	5·402703 32171	416494 1852	4140787 1714
2416	5 83 70 56	14 102 327 296	152823 10171	5·434874 32164	418346 1851	4139073 1713
2417	5 84 18 89	14 119 845 713	162994 10169	5·467038 32158	420197 1850	4137360 1711
2418	5 84 67 24	14 137 378 632	173163 10168	5·499196 32151	422047 1850	4135649 1709
2419	5 85 15 61	14 154 926 059	183331 10165	5·531347 32145	423897 1850	4133940 1709
2420	5 85 64 00	14 172 488 000	193496 10162	5·563492 32138	425747 1849	4132231 1706
2421	5 86 12 41	14 190 064 461	203658 10161	5·595630 32131	427596 1848	4130525 1706
2422	5 86 60 84	14 207 655 448	213819 10159	5·627761 32125	429444 1848	4128819 1704
2423	5 87 09 29	14 225 260 967	223978 10157	5·659886 32118	431292 1848	4127115 1702
2424	5 87 57 76	14 242 881 024	234135 10154	5·692004 32111	433140 1847	4125413 1702
2425	5 88 06 25	14 260 515 625	244289 10152	5·724115 32105	434987 1846	4123711 1699
2426	5 88 54 76	14 278 164 776	254441 10151	5·756220 32098	436833 1846	4122012 1699
2427	5 89 03 29	14 295 828 483	264592 10148	5·788318 32091	438679 1846	4120313 1697
2428	5 89 51 84	14 313 506 752	274740 10146	5·820409 32085	440525 1845	4118616 1695
2429	5 90 00 41	14 331 199 589	284886 10144	5·852494 32079	442370 1844	4116921 1695
2430	5 90 49 00	14 348 907 000	295030 10142	5·884573 32071	444214 1844	4115226 1692
2431	5 90 97 61	14 366 628 991	305172 10140	5·916644 32066	446058 1844	4113534 1692
2432	5 91 46 24	14 384 365 568	315312 10138	5·948710 32058	447902 1843	4111842 1690
2433	5 91 94 89	14 402 116 737	325450 10136	5·980768 32052	449745 1842	4110152 1689
2434	5 92 43 56	14 419 882 504	335586 10133	6·012820 32045	451587 1842	4108463 1687
2435	5 92 92 25	14 437 662 875	345719 10132	6·044865 32039	453429 1841	4106776 1686
2436	5 93 40 96	14 455 457 856	355851 10129	6·076904 32032	455270 1841	4105090 1684
2437	5 93 89 69	14 473 267 453	365980 10128	6·108936 32026	457111 1841	4103406 1683
2438	5 94 38 44	14 491 091 672	376108 10125	6·140962 32019	458952 1840	4101723 1682
2439	5 94 87 21	14 508 930 519	386233 10123	6·172981 32013	460792 1839	4100041 1680
2440	5 95 36 00	14 526 784 000	396356 10121	6·204994 32005	462631 1839	4098361 1679
2441	5 95 84 81	14 544 652 121	406477 10119	6·236999 32000	464470 1838	4096682 1678
2442	5 96 33 64	14 562 534 888	416596 10117	6·268999 31993	466308 1838	4095004 1676
2443	5 96 82 49	14 580 432 307	426713 10115	6·300992 31986	468146 1838	4093328 1675
2444	5 97 31 36	14 598 344 384	436828 10113	6·332978 31980	469984 1837	4091653 1673
2445	5 97 80 25	14 616 271 125	446941 10111	6·364958 31973	471821 1836	4089980 1673
2446	5 98 29 16	14 634 212 536	457052 10109	6·396931 31967	473657 1836	4088307 1670
2447	5 98 78 09	14 652 168 623	467161 10107	6·428898 31960	475493 1835	4086637 1670
2448	5 99 27 04	14 670 139 392	477268 10104	6·460858 31953	477328 1835	4084967 1668
2449	5 99 76 01	14 688 124 849	487372 10103	6·492811 31947	479163 1834	4083299 1666
2450	6 00 25 00	14 706 125 000	497475 49·	6·524758 150 +	480997 13·	4081633 0·000

No. n	Square n^2	Cube n^3	Square root $\sqrt{n}$	Sq. rt. of 10n $\sqrt{10n}$	Cube root $\sqrt[3]{n}$	Reciprocal $\frac{1}{n}$
			49·	150 +	13·	0·000
2450	6 00 25 00	14 706 125 000	497475 10100	6·524758 31941	480997 1834	4081633 1666
2451	6 00 74 01	14 724 139 851	507575 10099	6·556699 31934	482831 1834	4079967 1664
2452	6 01 23 04	14 742 169 408	517674 10099	6·588633 31928	484665 1833	4078303 1662
2453	6 01 72 09	14 760 213 677	527770 10096	6·620561 31921	486498 1832	4076641 1661
2454	6 02 21 16	14 778 272 664	537864 10094	6·652482 31914	488330 1832	4074980 1660
2455	6 02 70 25	14 796 346 375	547957 10090	6·684396 31908	490162 1831	4073320 1659
2456	6 03 19 36	14 814 434 816	558047 10088	6·716304 31902	491993 1831	4071661 1657
2457	6 03 68 49	14 832 537 993	568135 10086	6·748206 31895	493824 1831	4070004 1656
2458	6 04 17 64	14 850 655 912	578221 10084	6·780101 31888	495655 1830	4068348 1654
2459	6 04 66 81	14 868 788 579	588305 10082	6·811989 31882	497485 1829	4066694 1653
2460	6 05 16 00	14 886 936 000	598387 10080	6·843871 31876	499314 1829	4065041 1652
2461	6 05 65 21	14 905 098 181	608467 10078	6·875747 31869	501143 1828	4063389 1651
2462	6 06 14 44	14 923 275 128	618545 10076	6·907616 31863	502971 1828	4061738 1649
2463	6 06 63 69	14 941 466 847	628621 10074	6·939479 31856	504799 1828	4060089 1647
2464	6 07 12 96	14 959 673 344	638695 10071	6·971335 31850	506627 1827	4058442 1647
2465	6 07 62 25	14 977 894 625	648766 10070	7·003185 31843	508454 1826	4056795 1645
2466	6 08 11 56	14 996 130 696	658836 10068	7·035028 31837	510280 1826	4055150 1644
2467	6 08 60 89	15 014 381 563	668904 10065	7·066865 31830	512106 1826	4053506 1642
2468	6 09 10 24	15 032 647 232	678969 10064	7·098695 31824	513932 1825	4051864 1641
2469	6 09 59 61	15 050 927 709	689033 10062	7·130519 31817	515757 1824	4050223 1640
2470	6 10 09 00	15 069 223 000	699095 10059	7·162336 31811	517581 1824	4048583 1638
2471	6 10 58 41	15 087 533 111	709154 10058	7·194147 31805	519405 1824	4046945 1638
2472	6 11 07 84	15 105 858 048	719212 10055	7·225952 31798	521229 1823	4045307 1635
2473	6 11 57 29	15 124 197 817	729267 10053	7·257750 31792	523052 1822	4043672 1635
2474	6 12 06 76	15 142 552 424	739320 10052	7·289542 31785	524874 1822	4042037 1633
2475	6 12 56 25	15 160 921 875	749372 10049	7·321327 31779	526696 1822	4040404 1632
2476	6 13 05 76	15 179 306 176	759421 10048	7·353106 31773	528518 1821	4038772 1630
2477	6 13 55 29	15 197 705 333	769469 10045	7·384879 31766	530339 1820	4037142 1629
2478	6 14 04 84	15 216 119 352	779514 10043	7·416645 31759	532159 1820	4035513 1628
2479	6 14 54 41	15 234 548 239	789557 10041	7·448404 31753	533979 1820	4033885 1627
2480	6 15 04 00	15 252 992 000	799598 10040	7·480157 31747	535799 1819	4032258 1625
2481	6 15 53 61	15 271 450 641	809638 10037	7·511904 31741	537618 1819	4030633 1624
2482	6 16 03 24	15 289 924 168	819675 10035	7·543645 31734	539437 1818	4029009 1623
2483	6 16 52 89	15 308 412 587	829710 10033	7·575379 31727	541255 1817	4027386 1621
2484	6 17 02 56	15 326 915 904	839743 10031	7·607106 31722	543072 1817	4025765 1620
2485	6 17 52 25	15 345 434 125	849774 10029	7·638828 31715	544889 1817	4024145 1619
2486	6 18 01 96	15 363 967 256	859803 10028	7·670543 31708	546706 1816	4022526 1617
2487	6 18 51 69	15 382 515 303	869831 10025	7·702251 31702	548522 1816	4020909 1616
2488	6 19 01 44	15 401 078 272	879856 10023	7·733953 31696	550338 1815	4019293 1615
2489	6 19 51 21	15 419 656 169	889879 10021	7·765649 31689	552153 1815	4017678 1614
2490	6 20 01 00	15 438 249 000	899900 10019	7·797338 31683	553968 1814	4016064 1612
2491	6 20 50 81	15 456 856 771	909919 10017	7·829021 31677	555782 1814	4014452 1611
2492	6 21 00 64	15 475 479 488	919936 10015	7·860698 31670	557596 1813	4012841 1610
2493	6 21 50 49	15 494 117 157	929951 10013	7·892368 31664	559409 1813	4011231 1608
2494	6 22 00 36	15 512 769 784	939964 10011	7·924032 31658	561222 1812	4009623 1607
2495	6 22 50 25	15 531 437 375	949975 10009	7·955690 31651	563034 1812	4008016 1606
2496	6 23 00 16	15 550 119 936	959984 10007	7·987341 31645	564846 1811	4006410 1604
2497	6 23 50 09	15 568 817 473	969991 10005	8·018986 31639	566657 1811	4004806 1603
2498	6 24 00 04	15 587 529 992	979996 10003	8·050625 31632	568468 1810	4003203 1602
2499	6 24 50 01	15 606 257 499	989999 10001	8·082257 31626	570278 1810	4001601 1601
2500	6 25 00 00	15 625 000 000	*000000 50·	8·113883 150 +	572088 13·	4000000 0·000

No. n	Square n^2	Cube n^3	Square root $\sqrt{n}$	Sq. rt. of 10n $\sqrt{10n}$	Cube root $\sqrt[3]{n}$	Reciprocal $\dfrac{1}{n}$
			50·	150 +	13·	0·000
2500	6 25 00 00	15 625 000 000	000000	8·113883	572088	4000000
2501	6 25 50 01	15 643 757 501	009999 (9999)	8·145503 (31620)	573897 (1809)	3998401 (1599)
2502	6 26 00 04	15 662 530 008	019996 (9997)	8·177116 (31613)	575706 (1809)	3996803 (1598)
2503	6 26 50 09	15 681 317 527	029991 (9995)	8·208723 (31607)	577515 (1808)	3995206 (1597)
2504	6 27 00 16	15 700 120 064	039984 (9993)	8·240324 (31601)	579323 (1807)	3993610 (1596)
2505	6 27 50 25	15 718 937 625	049975 (9991)	8·271918 (31594)	581130 (1807)	3992016 (1594)
2506	6 28 00 36	15 737 770 216	059964 (9989)	8·303506 (31588)	582937 (1807)	3990423 (1593)
2507	6 28 50 49	15 756 617 843	069951 (9987)	8·335088 (31582)	584744 (1806)	3988831 (1592)
2508	6 29 00 64	15 775 480 512	079936 (9985)	8·366663 (31575)	586550 (1805)	3987241 (1590)
2509	6 29 50 81	15 794 358 229	089919 (9983)	8·398232 (31569)	588355 (1805)	3985652 (1589)
2510	6 30 01 00	15 813 251 000	099900 (9981)	8·429795 (31563)	590160 (1805)	3984064 (1588)
2511	6 30 51 21	15 832 158 831	109879 (9979)	8·461352 (31557)	591965 (1804)	3982477 (1587)
2512	6 31 01 44	15 851 081 728	119856 (9977)	8·492902 (31550)	593769 (1803)	3980892 (1585)
2513	6 31 51 69	15 870 019 697	129831 (9975)	8·524446 (31544)	595572 (1804)	3979308 (1584)
2514	6 32 01 96	15 888 972 744	139805 (9974)	8·555984 (31538)	597376 (1802)	3977725 (1583)
2515	6 32 52 25	15 907 940 875	149776 (9971)	8·587515 (31531)	599178 (1802)	3976143 (1582)
2516	6 33 02 56	15 926 924 096	159745 (9969)	8·619040 (31525)	600980 (1802)	3974563 (1580)
2517	6 33 52 89	15 945 922 413	169712 (9967)	8·650559 (31519)	602782 (1801)	3972984 (1579)
2518	6 34 03 24	15 964 935 832	179677 (9965)	8·682072 (31513)	604583 (1801)	3971406 (1578)
2519	6 34 53 61	15 983 964 359	189640 (9963)	8·713578 (31506)	606384 (1800)	3969829 (1577)
2520	6 35 04 00	16 003 008 000	199602 (9962)	8·745079 (31501)	608184 (1800)	3968254 (1575)
2521	6 35 54 41	16 022 066 761	209561 (9959)	8·776573 (31494)	609984 (1799)	3966680 (1574)
2522	6 36 04 84	16 041 140 648	219518 (9957)	8·808060 (31487)	611783 (1799)	3965107 (1573)
2523	6 36 55 29	16 060 229 667	229473 (9955)	8·839542 (31482)	613582 (1799)	3963535 (1572)
2524	6 37 05 76	16 079 333 824	239427 (9954)	8·871017 (31475)	615381 (1797)	3961965 (1570)
2525	6 37 56 25	16 098 453 125	249378 (9951)	8·902486 (31469)	617178 (1798)	3960396 (1569)
2526	6 38 06 76	16 117 587 576	259327 (9949)	8·933949 (31463)	618976 (1797)	3958828 (1568)
2527	6 38 57 29	16 136 737 183	269275 (9948)	8·965405 (31456)	620773 (1796)	3957262 (1566)
2528	6 39 07 84	16 155 901 952	279220 (9945)	8·996855 (31450)	622569 (1796)	3955696 (1566)
2529	6 39 58 41	16 175 081 889	289164 (9944)	9·028299 (31444)	624365 (1796)	3954132 (1564)
2530	6 40 09 00	16 194 277 000	299105 (9941)	9·059737 (31438)	626161 (1795)	3952569 (1563)
2531	6 40 59 61	16 213 487 291	309045 (9940)	9·091169 (31432)	627956 (1794)	3951008 (1561)
2532	6 41 10 24	16 232 712 768	318983 (9938)	9·122594 (31425)	629750 (1794)	3949447 (1561)
2533	6 41 60 89	16 251 953 437	328918 (9935)	9·154013 (31419)	631544 (1794)	3947888 (1559)
2534	6 42 11 56	16 271 209 304	338852 (9934)	9·185426 (31413)	633338 (1793)	3946330 (1558)
2535	6 42 62 25	16 290 480 375	348784 (9932)	9·216833 (31407)	635131 (1793)	3944773 (1557)
2536	6 43 12 96	16 309 766 656	358713 (9929)	9·248234 (31401)	636924 (1792)	3943218 (1555)
2537	6 43 63 69	16 329 068 153	368641 (9928)	9·279628 (31394)	638716 (1792)	3941663 (1555)
2538	6 44 14 44	16 348 384 872	378567 (9926)	9·311017 (31389)	640508 (1791)	3940110 (1553)
2539	6 44 65 21	16 367 716 819	388491 (9924)	9·342399 (31382)	642299 (1791)	3938558 (1552)
2540	6 45 16 00	16 387 064 000	398413 (9922)	9·373775 (31376)	644090 (1790)	3937008 (1550)
2541	6 45 66 81	16 406 426 421	408333 (9920)	9·405144 (31369)	645880 (1790)	3935458 (1550)
2542	6 46 17 64	16 425 804 088	418251 (9918)	9·436508 (31364)	647670 (1789)	3933910 (1548)
2543	6 46 68 49	16 445 197 007	428167 (9916)	9·467865 (31357)	649459 (1789)	3932363 (1547)
2544	6 47 19 36	16 464 605 184	438081 (9914)	9·499216 (31351)	651248 (1789)	3930818 (1545)
2545	6 47 70 25	16 484 028 625	447993 (9912)	9·530561 (31345)	653037 (1788)	3929273 (1545)
2546	6 48 21 16	16 503 467 336	457903 (9910)	9·561900 (31339)	654825 (1787)	3927730 (1543)
2547	6 48 72 09	16 522 921 323	467812 (9909)	9·593233 (31333)	656612 (1787)	3926188 (1542)
2548	6 49 23 04	16 542 390 592	477718 (9906)	9·624560 (31327)	658399 (1787)	3924647 (1541)
2549	6 49 74 01	16 561 875 149	487622 (9904)	9·655880 (31320)	660186 (1786)	3923107 (1540)
2550	6 50 25 00	16 581 375 000	497525 (9903)	9·687194 (31314)	661972	3921569 (1538)
			50·	150 +	13·	0·000

No. n	Square n²	Cube n³	Square root √n	Sq. rt. of 10n √10n	Cube root ∛n	Reciprocal 1/n
			50·	150 +	13·	0·000
2550	6 50 25 00	16 581 375 000	497525	9·687194 31308	661972 1786	3921569
2551	6 50 76 01	16 600 890 151	507425 9900	9·718502 31302	663758 1785	3920031 1538
2552	6 51 27 04	16 620 420 608	517324 9899	9·749804 31296	665543 1785	3918495 1536
2553	6 51 78 09	16 639 966 377	527220 9896	9·781100 31290	667328 1784	3916960 1535
2554	6 52 29 16	16 659 527 464	537115 9895	9·812390 31284	669112 1784	3915427 1533
			9893			1533
2555	6 52 80 25	16 679 103 875	547008 9891	9·843674 31277	670896 1783	3913894 1531
2556	6 53 31 36	16 698 695 616	556899 9889	9·874951 31272	672679 1783	3912363 1530
2557	6 53 82 49	16 718 302 693	566788 9886	9·906223 31265	674462 1782	3910833 1529
2558	6 54 33 64	16 737 925 112	576674 9885	9·937488 31259	676244 1782	3909304 1528
2559	6 54 84 81	16 757 562 879	586559 9884	9·968747 31253	678026 1782	3907776 1526
2560	6 55 36 00	16 777 216 000	596443 9881	*0·000000 31247	679808 1781	3906250 1525
2561	6 55 87 21	16 796 884 481	606324 9879	0·031247 31241	681589 1780	3904725 1524
2562	6 56 38 44	16 816 568 328	616203 9877	0·062488 31235	683369 1780	3903201 1523
2563	6 56 89 69	16 836 267 547	626080 9876	0·093723 31228	685149 1780	3901678 1522
2564	6 57 40 96	16 855 982 144	635956 9873	0·124951 31223	686929 1779	3900156 1521
2565	6 57 92 25	16 875 712 125	645829 9872	0·156174 31216	688708 1779	3898635 1519
2566	6 58 43 56	16 895 457 496	655701 9869	0·187390 31211	690487 1778	3897116 1518
2567	6 58 94 89	16 915 218 263	665570 9868	0·218601 31204	692265 1778	3895598 1517
2568	6 59 46 24	16 934 994 432	675438 9866	0·249805 31198	694043 1777	3894081 1516
2569	6 59 97 61	16 954 786 009	685304 9863	0·281003 31192	695820 1777	3892565 1514
2570	6 60 49 00	16 974 593 000	695167 9862	0·312195 31187	697597 1776	3891051 1514
2571	6 61 00 41	16 994 415 411	705029 9860	0·343382 31180	699373 1776	3889537 1512
2572	6 61 51 84	17 014 253 248	714889 9858	0·374562 31174	701149 1775	3888025 1511
2573	6 62 03 29	17 034 106 517	724747 9857	0·405736 31167	702924 1775	3886514 1510
2574	6 62 54 76	17 053 975 224	734604 9854	0·436903 31162	704699 1775	3885004 1509
2575	6 63 06 25	17 073 859 375	744458 9852	0·468065 31156	706474 1774	3883495 1507
2576	6 63 57 76	17 093 758 976	754310 9851	0·499221 31150	708248 1774	3881988 1507
2577	6 64 09 29	17 113 674 033	764161 9848	0·530371 31144	710022 1773	3880481 1505
2578	6 64 60 84	17 133 604 552	774009 9847	0·561515 31137	711795 1772	3878976 1504
2579	6 65 12 41	17 153 550 539	783856 9844	0·592652 31132	713567 1773	3877472 1503
2580	6 65 64 00	17 173 512 000	793700 9843	0·623784 31126	715340 1771	3875969 1502
2581	6 66 15 61	17 193 488 941	803543 9841	0·654910 31119	717111 1772	3874467 1500
2582	6 66 67 24	17 213 481 368	813384 9839	0·686029 31114	718883 1771	3872967 1500
2583	6 67 18 89	17 233 489 287	823223 9837	0·717143 31107	720654 1770	3871467 1498
2584	6 67 70 56	17 253 512 704	833060 9835	0·748250 31102	722424 1770	3869969 1497
2585	6 68 22 25	17 273 551 625	842895 9834	0·779352 31095	724194 1770	3868472 1496
2586	6 68 73 96	17 293 606 056	852729 9831	0·810447 31090	725964 1769	3866976 1495
2587	6 69 25 69	17 313 676 003	862560 9829	0·841537 31083	727733 1768	3865481 1493
2588	6 69 77 44	17 333 761 472	872389 9828	0·872620 31078	729501 1768	3863988 1493
2589	6 70 29 21	17 353 862 469	882217 9826	0·903698 31071	731269 1768	3862495 1491
2590	6 70 81 00	17 373 979 000	892043 9823	0·934769 31066	733037 1767	3861004 1490
2591	6 71 32 81	17 394 111 071	901866 9822	0·965835 31059	734804 1767	3859514 1489
2592	6 71 84 64	17 414 258 688	911688 9820	0·996894 31054	736571 1766	3858025 1488
2593	6 72 36 49	17 434 421 857	921508 9818	1·027948 31047	738337 1766	3856537 1487
2594	6 72 88 36	17 454 600 584	931326 9817	1·058995 31042	740103 1765	3855050 1485
2595	6 73 40 25	17 474 794 875	941143 9814	1·090037 31035	741868 1765	3853565 1485
2596	6 73 92 16	17 495 004 736	950957 9812	1·121072 31030	743633 1765	3852080 1483
2597	6 74 44 09	17 515 230 173	960769 9811	1·152102 31024	745398 1764	3850597 1482
2598	6 74 96 04	17 535 471 192	970580 9808	1·183126 31017	747162 1764	3849115 1481
2599	6 75 48 01	17 555 727 799	980388 9807	1·214143 31012	748926 1763	3847634 1480
2600	6 76 00 00	17 576 000 000	990195	1·245155	750689	3846154
			50·	160 +	13·	0·000

No. n	Square n^2	Cube n^3	Square root $\sqrt{n}$	Sq. rt. of $10n$ $\sqrt{10n}$	Cube root $\sqrt[3]{n}$	Reciprocal $\frac{1}{n}$
			50·	160 +	13·	0·000
2600	6 76 00 00	17 576 000 000	990195 9805	1·245155 31006	750689 1762	3846154 1479
2601	6 76 52 01	17 596 287 801	*000000 9803	1·276161 30999	752451 1763	3844675 1477
2602	6 77 04 04	17 616 591 208	009803 9801	1·307160 30994	754214 1761	3843198 1477
2603	6 77 56 09	17 636 910 227	019604 9799	1·338154 30988	755975 1762	3841721 1475
2604	6 78 08 16	17 657 244 864	029403 9798	1·369142 30982	757737 1761	3840246 1474
2605	6 78 60 25	17 677 595 125	039201 9795	1·400124 30976	759498 1760	3838772 1473
2606	6 79 12 36	17 697 961 016	048996 9794	1·431100 30970	761258 1760	3837299 1472
2607	6 79 64 49	17 718 342 543	058790 9791	1·462070 30964	763018 1760	3835827 1471
2608	6 80 16 64	17 738 739 712	068581 9790	1·493034 30958	764778 1759	3834356 1470
2609	6 80 68 81	17 759 152 529	078371 9788	1·523992 30952	766537 1758	3832886 1468
2610	6 81 21 00	17 779 581 000	088159 9786	1·554944 30946	768295 1758	3831418 1468
2611	6 81 73 21	17 800 025 131	097945 9784	1·585890 30941	770053 1758	3829950 1466
2612	6 82 25 44	17 820 484 928	107729 9783	1·616831 30934	771811 1757	3828484 1465
2613	6 82 77 69	17 840 960 397	117512 9780	1·647765 30929	773568 1757	3827019 1464
2614	6 83 29 96	17 861 451 544	127292 9779	1·678694 30922	775325 1757	3825555 1463
2615	6 83 82 25	17 881 958 375	137071 9776	1·709616 30917	777082 1756	3824092 1462
2616	6 84 34 56	17 902 480 896	146847 9775	1·740533 30911	778838 1756	3822630 1461
2617	6 84 86 89	17 923 019 113	156622 9773	1·771444 30905	780593 1755	3821169 1459
2618	6 85 39 24	17 943 573 032	166395 9771	1·802349 30899	782348 1755	3819710 1459
2619	6 85 91 61	17 964 142 659	176166 9770	1·833248 30893	784103 1754	3818251 1457
2620	6 86 44 00	17 984 728 000	185936 9767	1·864141 30887	785857 1754	3816794 1456
2621	6 86 96 41	18 005 329 061	195703 9765	1·895028 30881	787611 1753	3815338 1455
2622	6 87 48 84	18 025 945 848	205468 9764	1·925909 30875	789364 1753	3813883 1454
2623	6 88 01 29	18 046 578 367	215232 9762	1·956784 30870	791117 1752	3812429 1453
2624	6 88 53 76	18 067 226 624	224994 9760	1·987654 30863	792869 1752	3810976 1452
2625	6 89 06 25	18 087 890 625	234754 9758	2·018517 30858	794621 1751	3809524 1451
2626	6 89 58 76	18 108 570 376	244512 9756	2·049375 30852	796372 1751	3808073 1451
2627	6 90 11 29	18 129 265 883	254268 9754	2·080227 30846	798123 1751	3806624 1449
2628	6 90 63 84	18 149 977 152	264022 9753	2·111073 30840	799874 1750	3805175 1449
2629	6 91 16 41	18 170 704 189	273775 9751	2·141913 30834	801624 1750	3803728 1447
2630	6 91 69 00	18 191 447 000	283526 9748	2·172747 30829	803374 1749	3802281 1445
2631	6 92 21 61	18 212 205 591	293274 9747	2·203576 30822	805123 1749	3800836 1444
2632	6 92 74 24	18 232 979 968	303021 9745	2·234398 30817	806872 1748	3799392 1443
2633	6 93 26 89	18 253 770 137	312766 9744	2·265215 30811	808620 1748	3797949 1442
2634	6 93 79 56	18 274 576 104	322510 9741	2·296026 30805	810368 1748	3796507 1441
2635	6 94 32 25	18 295 397 875	332251 9740	2·326831 30799	812116 1747	3795066 1439
2636	6 94 84 96	18 316 235 456	341991 9737	2·357630 30793	813863 1746	3793627 1439
2637	6 95 37 69	18 337 088 853	351728 9736	2·388423 30788	815609 1746	3792188 1437
2638	6 95 90 44	18 357 958 072	361464 9734	2·419211 30781	817355 1746	3790751 1437
2639	6 96 43 21	18 378 843 119	371198 9732	2·449992 30776	819101 1745	3789314 1435
2640	6 96 96 00	18 399 744 000	380930 9731	2·480768 30770	820846 1745	3787879 1434
2641	6 97 48 81	18 420 660 721	390661 9728	2·511538 30764	822591 1745	3786445 1434
2642	6 98 01 64	18 441 593 288	400389 9727	2·542302 30758	824336 1744	3785011 1432
2643	6 98 54 49	18 462 541 707	410116 9725	2·573060 30753	826080 1743	3783579 1431
2644	6 99 07 36	18 483 505 984	419841 9722	2·603813 30747	827823 1743	3782148 1430
2645	6 99 60 25	18 504 486 125	429563 9722	2·634560 30741	829566 1743	3780718 1429
2646	7 00 13 16	18 525 482 136	439285 9719	2·665301 30735	831309 1742	3779289 1427
2647	7 00 66 09	18 546 494 023	449004 9717	2·696036 30729	833051 1742	3777862 1427
2648	7 01 19 04	18 567 521 792	458721 9716	2·726765 30723	834793 1741	3776435 1426
2649	7 01 72 01	18 588 565 449	468437 9714	2·757488 30718	836534 1741	3775009 1424
2650	7 02 25 00	18 609 625 000	478151 51·	2·788206 160 +	838275 13·	3773585 0·000

54

No. n	Square n^2	Cube n^3	Square root $\sqrt{n}$	Sq. rt. of $10n$ $\sqrt{10n}$	Cube root $\sqrt[3]{n}$	Reciprocal $\dfrac{1}{n}$
			51·	160 +	13·	0·000
2650	7 02 25 00	18 609 625 000	478151	2·788206	838275	3773585
2651	7 02 78 01	18 630 700 451	487863 9712	2·818918 30712	840015 1740	3772161 1424
2652	7 03 31 04	18 651 791 808	497573 9710	2·849624 30706	841755 1740	3770739 1422
2653	7 03 84 09	18 672 899 077	507281 9708	2·880324 30700	843495 1740	3769318 1421
2654	7 04 37 16	18 694 022 264	516987 9706	2·911019 30695	845234 1739	3767898 1420
			9705	30688	1739	1420
2655	7 04 90 25	18 715 161 375	526692 9703	2·941707 30683	846973 1738	3766478 1418
2656	7 05 43 36	18 736 316 416	536395 9701	2·972390 30677	848711 1738	3765060 1417
2657	7 05 96 49	18 757 487 393	546096 9699	3·003067 30672	850449 1737	3763643 1416
2658	7 06 49 64	18 778 674 312	555795 9697	3·033739 30665	852186 1737	3762227 1415
2659	7 07 02 81	18 799 877 179	565492 9696	3·064404 30660	853923 1737	3760812 1414
2660	7 07 56 00	18 821 096 000	575188	3·095064	855660	3759398
2661	7 08 09 21	18 842 330 781	584882 9694	3·125718 30654	857396 1736	3757986 1412
2662	7 08 62 44	18 863 581 528	594573 9691	3·156367 30649	859132 1736	3756574 1412
2663	7 09 15 69	18 884 848 247	604263 9690	3·187009 30642	860867 1735	3755163 1411
2664	7 09 68 96	18 906 130 944	613952 9689	3·217646 30637	862602 1735	3753754 1409
			9686	30631	1734	1409
2665	7 10 22 25	18 927 429 625	623638 9685	3·248277 30625	864336 1734	3752345 1407
2666	7 10 75 56	18 948 744 296	633323 9682	3·278902 30620	866070 1733	3750938 1407
2667	7 11 28 89	18 970 074 963	643005 9681	3·309522 30614	867803 1733	3749531 1405
2668	7 11 82 24	18 991 421 632	652686 9679	3·340136 30608	869536 1733	3748126 1404
2669	7 12 35 61	19 012 784 309	662365 9678	3·370744 30602	871269 1732	3746722 1404
2670	7 12 89 00	19 034 163 000	672043	3·401346	873001	3745318
2671	7 13 42 41	19 055 557 711	681718 9675	3·431943 30597	874733 1732	3743916 1402
2672	7 13 95 84	19 076 968 448	691392 9674	3·462534 30591	876464 1731	3742515 1401
2673	7 14 49 29	19 098 395 217	701064 9672	3·493119 30585	878195 1731	3741115 1400
2674	7 15 02 76	19 119 838 024	710734 9670	3·523699 30580	879925 1730	3739716 1399
			9668	30573	1730	1398
2675	7 15 56 25	19 141 296 875	720402 9667	3·554272 30568	881655 1730	3738318 1397
2676	7 16 09 76	19 162 771 776	730069 9664	3·584840 30563	883385 1729	3736921 1396
2677	7 16 63 29	19 184 262 733	739733 9663	3·615403 30556	885114 1729	3735525 1395
2678	7 17 16 84	19 205 769 752	749396 9661	3·645959 30551	886843 1728	3734130 1394
2679	7 17 70 41	19 227 292 839	759057 9659	3·676510 30545	888571 1728	3732736 1393
2680	7 18 24 00	19 248 832 000	768716	3·707055	890299	3731343
2681	7 18 77 61	19 270 387 241	778374 9658	3·737595 30540	892027 1728	3729952 1391
2682	7 19 31 24	19 291 958 568	788030 9656	3·768129 30534	893754 1727	3728561 1391
2683	7 19 84 89	19 313 545 987	797683 9653	3·798657 30528	895480 1726	3727171 1390
2684	7 20 38 56	19 335 149 504	807335 9652	3·829179 30522	897206 1726	3725782 1389
			9651	30517	1726	1387
2685	7 20 92 25	19 356 769 125	816986 9648	3·859696 30511	898932 1725	3724395 1387
2686	7 21 45 96	19 378 404 856	826634 9647	3·890207 30506	900657 1725	3723008 1385
2687	7 21 99 69	19 400 056 703	836281 9645	3·920713 30499	902382 1725	3721623 1385
2688	7 22 53 44	19 421 724 672	845926 9643	3·951212 30494	904107 1724	3720238 1383
2689	7 23 07 21	19 443 408 769	855569 9641	3·981706 30489	905831 1723	3718855 1383
2690	7 23 61 00	19 465 109 000	865210	4·012195	907554	3717472
2691	7 24 14 81	19 486 825 371	874849 9639	4·042677 30482	909277 1723	3716091 1381
2692	7 24 68 64	19 508 557 888	884487 9638	4·073154 30477	911000 1723	3714710 1381
2693	7 25 22 49	19 530 306 557	894123 9636	4·103626 30472	912722 1722	3713331 1379
2694	7 25 76 36	19 552 071 384	903757 9634	4·134092 30466	914444 1722	3711952 1379
			9632	30460	1722	1377
2695	7 26 30 25	19 573 852 375	913389 9631	4·164552 30454	916166 1721	3710575 1376
2696	7 26 84 16	19 595 649 536	923020 9629	4·195006 30449	917887 1720	3709199 1375
2697	7 27 38 09	19 617 462 873	932649 9627	4·225455 30443	919607 1720	3707824 1375
2698	7 27 92 04	19 639 292 392	942276 9625	4·255898 30437	921327 1720	3706449 1373
2699	7 28 46 01	19 661 138 099	951901 9623	4·286335 30432	923047 1720	3705076 1372
2700	7 29 00 00	19 683 000 000	961524 51·	4·316767 160 +	924767 13·	3703704 0·000

55

No. n	Square n^2	Cube n^3	Square root $\sqrt{n}$	Sq. rt. of 10n $\sqrt{10n}$	Cube root $\sqrt[3]{n}$	Reciprocal $\frac{1}{n}$
			51·	160 +	13·	0·000
2700	7 29 00 00	19 683 000 000	961524 (9622)	4·316767 (30426)	924767 (1718)	3703704 (1372)
2701	7 29 54 01	19 704 878 101	971146 (9620)	4·347193 (30421)	926485 (1719)	3702332 (1370)
2702	7 30 08 04	19 726 772 408	980766 (9618)	4·377614 (30415)	928204 (1718)	3700962 (1370)
2703	7 30 62 09	19 748 682 927	*990384 (9616)	4·408029 (30409)	929922 (1718)	3699593 (1369)
2704	7 31 16 16	19 770 609 664	*000000 (9614)	4·438438 (30404)	931640 (1717)	3698225 (1368)
						(1367)
2705	7 31 70 25	19 792 552 625	009614 (9613)	4·468842 (30398)	933357 (1717)	3696858 (1366)
2706	7 32 24 36	19 814 511 816	019227 (9611)	4·499240 (30393)	935074 (1716)	3695492 (1366)
2707	7 32 78 49	19 836 487 243	028838 (9609)	4·529633 (30386)	936790 (1716)	3694126 (1364)
2708	7 33 32 64	19 858 478 912	038447 (9608)	4·560019 (30382)	938506 (1715)	3692762 (1363)
2709	7 33 86 81	19 880 486 829	048055 (9605)	4·590401 (30375)	940221 (1715)	3691399 (1362)
2710	7 34 41 00	19 902 511 000	057660 (9604)	4·620776 (30370)	941936 (1715)	3690037 (1361)
2711	7 34 95 21	19 924 551 431	067264 (9602)	4·651146 (30365)	943651 (1715)	3688676 (1361)
2712	7 35 49 44	19 946 608 128	076866 (9601)	4·681511 (30359)	945365 (1714)	3687316 (1360)
2713	7 36 03 69	19 968 681 097	086467 (9598)	4·711870 (30353)	947079 (1714)	3685957 (1359)
2714	7 36 57 96	19 990 770 344	096065 (9597)	4·742223 (30348)	948793 (1712)	3684598 (1359)
2715	7 37 12 25	20 012 875 875	105662 (9595)	4·772571 (30342)	950505 (1713)	3683241 (1357)
2716	7 37 66 56	20 034 997 696	115257 (9593)	4·802913 (30336)	952218 (1712)	3681885 (1356)
2717	7 38 20 89	20 057 135 813	124850 (9592)	4·833249 (30331)	953930 (1712)	3680530 (1355)
2718	7 38 75 24	20 079 290 232	134442 (9589)	4·863580 (30325)	955642 (1711)	3679176 (1355)
2719	7 39 29 61	20 101 460 959	144031 (9588)	4·893905 (30320)	957353 (1711)	3677823 (1354)
						(1353)
2720	7 39 84 00	20 123 648 000	153619 (9586)	4·924225 (30314)	959064 (1711)	3676471 (1352)
2721	7 40 38 41	20 145 851 361	163205 (9585)	4·954539 (30309)	960775 (1710)	3675119 (1352)
2722	7 40 92 84	20 168 071 048	172790 (9583)	4·984848 (30303)	962485 (1710)	3673769 (1350)
2723	7 41 47 29	20 190 307 067	182373 (9580)	5·015151 (30297)	964194 (1709)	3672420 (1349)
2724	7 42 01 76	20 212 559 424	191953 (9580)	5·045448 (30292)	965903 (1709)	3671072 (1348)
						(1347)
2725	7 42 56 25	20 234 828 125	201533 (9577)	5·075740 (30287)	967612 (1709)	3669725 (1346)
2726	7 43 10 76	20 257 113 176	211110 (9576)	5·106027 (30280)	969321 (1708)	3668379 (1346)
2727	7 43 65 29	20 279 414 583	220686 (9573)	5·136307 (30276)	971029 (1707)	3667033 (1344)
2728	7 44 19 84	20 301 732 352	230259 (9573)	5·166583 (30269)	972736 (1707)	3665689 (1344)
2729	7 44 74 41	20 324 066 489	239832 (9570)	5·196852 (30264)	974443 (1707)	3664346 (1343)
						(1342)
2730	7 45 29 00	20 346 417 000	249402 (9569)	5·227116 (30259)	976150 (1706)	3663004 (1342)
2731	7 45 83 61	20 368 783 891	258971 (9566)	5·257375 (30253)	977856 (1706)	3661662 (1342)
2732	7 46 38 24	20 391 167 168	268537 (9565)	5·287628 (30248)	979562 (1705)	3660322 (1340)
2733	7 46 92 89	20 413 566 837	278102 (9564)	5·317876 (30242)	981267 (1705)	3658983 (1339)
2734	7 47 47 56	20 435 982 904	287666 (9561)	5·348118 (30236)	982972 (1705)	3657644 (1339)
						(1337)
2735	7 48 02 25	20 458 415 375	297227 (9560)	5·378354 (30231)	984677 (1704)	3656307 (1336)
2736	7 48 56 96	20 480 864 256	306787 (9558)	5·408585 (30225)	986381 (1704)	3654971 (1336)
2737	7 49 11 69	20 503 329 553	316345 (9557)	5·438810 (30220)	988085 (1703)	3653635 (1334)
2738	7 49 66 44	20 525 811 272	325902 (9554)	5·469030 (30215)	989788 (1703)	3652301 (1334)
2739	7 50 21 21	20 548 309 419	335456 (9553)	5·499245 (30209)	991491 (1703)	3650968 (1333)
2740	7 50 76 00	20 570 824 000	345009 (9551)	5·529454 (30203)	993194 (1702)	3649635 (1333)
2741	7 51 30 81	20 593 355 021	354560 (9550)	5·559657 (30198)	994896 (1702)	3648304 (1331)
2742	7 51 85 64	20 615 902 488	364110 (9548)	5·589855 (30192)	996598 (1701)	3646973 (1331)
2743	7 52 40 49	20 638 466 407	373658 (9545)	5·620047 (30187)	998299 (1701)	3645643 (1330)
2744	7 52 95 36	20 661 046 784	383203 (9545)	5·650234 (30181)	*000000 (1700)	3644315 (1328)
						(1328)
2745	7 53 50 25	20 683 643 625	392748 (9542)	5·680415 (30176)	001700 (1701)	3642987 (1326)
2746	7 54 05 16	20 706 256 936	402290 (9541)	5·710591 (30170)	003401 (1699)	3641661 (1326)
2747	7 54 60 09	20 728 886 723	411831 (9539)	5·740761 (30165)	005100 (1699)	3640335 (1325)
2748	7 55 15 04	20 751 532 992	421370 (9537)	5·770926 (30160)	006799 (1699)	3639010 (1324)
2749	7 55 70 01	20 774 195 749	430907 (9535)	5·801086 (30154)	008498 (1699)	3637686 (1322)
2750	7 56 25 00	20 796 875 000	440442	5·831240	010197	3636364
			52·	160 +	14·	0·000

No. n	Square n^2	Cube n^3	Square root $\sqrt{n}$	Sq. rt. of 10n $\sqrt{10n}$	Cube root $\sqrt[3]{n}$	Reciprocal $\dfrac{1}{n}$
			52·	160 +	14·	0·000
2750	7 56 25 00	20 796 875 000	440442 9534	5·831240 30148	010197 1698	3636364 1322
2751	7 56 80 01	20 819 570 751	449976 9532	5·861388 30143	011895 1697	3635042 1321
2752	7 57 35 04	20 842 283 008	459508 9530	5·891531 30137	013592 1697	3633721 1320
2753	7 57 90 09	20 865 011 777	469038 9529	5·921668 30132	015289 1697	3632401 1319
2754	7 58 45 16	20 887 757 064	478567 9527	5·951800 30127	016986 1697	3631082 1318
2755	7 59 00 25	20 910 518 875	488094 9525	5·981927 30121	018683 1695	3629764 1317
2756	7 59 55 36	20 933 297 216	497619 9523	6·012048 30121	020378 1696	3628447 1317
2757	7 60 10 49	20 956 092 093	507142 9522	6·042163 30115	022074 1695	3627131 1316
2758	7 60 65 64	20 978 903 512	516664 9520	6·072273 30110	023769 1695	3625816 1315
2759	7 61 20 81	21 001 731 479	526184 9518	6·102378 30105	025464 1694	3624502 1314
2760	7 61 76 00	21 024 576 000	535702 9517	6·132477 30099	027158 1694	3623188 1314
2761	7 62 31 21	21 047 437 081	545219 9514	6·162571 30094	028852 1694	3621876 1312
2762	7 62 86 44	21 070 314 728	554733 9513	6·192659 30088	030546 1693	3620565 1311
2763	7 63 41 69	21 093 208 947	564246 9512	6·222742 30083	032239 1692	3619254 1311
2764	7 63 96 96	21 116 119 744	573758 9509	6·252820 30078	033931 1692	3617945 1309
2765	7 64 52 25	21 139 047 125	583267 9508	6·282891 30071	035624 1691	3616637 1308
2766	7 65 07 56	21 161 991 096	592775 9506	6·312958 30067	037315 1692	3615329 1308
2767	7 65 62 89	21 184 951 663	602281 9505	6·343019 30061	039007 1691	3614022 1307
2768	7 66 18 24	21 207 928 832	611786 9502	6·373075 30056	040698 1691	3612717 1305
2769	7 66 73 61	21 230 922 609	621288 9501	6·403125 30050	042389 1690	3611412 1305
2770	7 67 29 00	21 253 933 000	630789 9500	6·433170 30045	044079 1690	3610108 1304
2771	7 67 84 41	21 276 960 011	640289 9497	6·463209 30039	045769 1689	3608805 1303
2772	7 68 39 84	21 300 003 648	649786 9496	6·493243 30034	047458 1689	3607504 1301
2773	7 68 95 29	21 323 063 917	659282 9494	6·523272 30029	049147 1689	3606203 1301
2774	7 69 50 76	21 346 140 824	668776 9493	6·553295 30023	050836 1688	3604903 1300
2775	7 70 06 25	21 369 234 375	678269 9490	6·583312 30017	052524 1688	3603604 1299
2776	7 70 61 76	21 392 344 576	687759 9490	6·613325 30013	054212 1687	3602305 1299
2777	7 71 17 29	21 415 471 433	697249 9487	6·643332 30007	055899 1687	3601008 1297
2778	·7 71 72 84	21 438 614 952	706736 9485	6·673333 30001	057586 1687	3599712 1296
2779	7 72 28 41	21 461 775 139	716221 9484	6·703329 29996	059273 1686	3598417 1295
2780	7 72 84 00	21 484 952 000	725705 9482	6·733320 29991	060959 1685	3597122 1295
2781	7 73 39 61	21 508 145 541	735187 9481	6·763305 29985	062644 1686	3595829 1293
2782	7 73 95 24	21 531 355 768	744668 9479	6·793285 29980	064330 1685	3594536 1293
2783	7 74 50 89	21 554 582 687	754147 9477	6·823260 29975	066015 1684	3593245 1291
2784	7 75 06 56	21 577 826 304	763624 9475	6·853229 29969	067699 1684	3591954 1291
2785	7 75 62 25	21 601 086 625	773099 9474	6·883193 29964	069383 1684	3590664 1290
2786	7 76 17 96	21 624 363 656	782573 9472	6·913151 29958	071067 1684	3589375 1289
2787	7 76 73 69	21 647 657 403	792045 9470	6·943104 29953	072751 1682	3588088 1287
2788	7 77 29 44	21 670 967 872	801515 9469	6·973052 29948	074433 1683	3586801 1287
2789	7 77 85 21	21 694 295 069	810984 9467	7·002994 29942	076116 1682	3585515 1286
2790	7 78 41 00	21 717 639 000	820451 9465	7·032931 29937	077798 1682	3584229 1286
2791	7 78 96 81	21 740 999 671	829916 9463	7·062862 29931	079480 1681	3582945 1284
2792	7 79 52 64	21 764 377 088	839379 9462	7·092789 29927	081161 1681	3581662 1283
2793	7 80 08 49	21 787 771 257	848841 9460	7·122709 29920	082842 1681	3580380 1282
2794	7 80 64 36	21 811 182 184	858301 9459	7·152625 29916	084523 1680	3579098 1282
2795	7 81 20 25	21 834 609 875	867760 9456	7·182535 29910	086203 1680	3577818 1280
2796	7 81 76 16	21 858 054 336	877216 9455	7·212440 29905	087883 1679	3576538 1280
2797	7 82 32 09	21 881 515 573	886671 9454	7·242339 29899	089562 1679	3575259 1279
2798	7·82 88 04	21 904 993 592	896125 9451	7·272233 29894	091241 1678	3573981 1278
2799	7 83 44 01	21 928 488 399	905576 9450	7·302122 29889	092919 1678	3572705 1276
2800	7 84 00 00	21 952 000 000	915026	7·332005	094597	3571429
			52·	160 +	14·	0·000

No. n	Square n²	Cube n³	Square root √n	Sq. rt. of 10n √10n	Cube root ∛n	Reciprocal 1/n
			52·	160 +	14·	0·000
2800	7 84 00 00	21 952 000 000	915026 ₉₄₄₈	7·332005 ₂₉₈₇₈	094597 ₁₆₇₈	3571429 ₁₂₇₅
2801	7 84 56 01	21 975 528 401	924474 ₉₄₄₇	7·361883 ₂₉₈₇₃	096275 ₁₆₇₈	3570154 ₁₂₇₅
2802	7 85 12 04	21 999 073 608	933921 ₉₄₄₅	7·391756 ₂₉₈₆₇	097953 ₁₆₇₆	3568879 ₁₂₇₃
2803	7 85 68 09	22 022 635 627	943366 ₉₄₄₃	7·421623 ₂₉₈₆₃	099629 ₁₆₇₇	3567606 ₁₂₇₂
2804	7 86 24 16	22 046 214 464	952809 ₉₄₄₂	7·451486 ₂₉₈₅₆	101306 ₁₆₇₆	3566334 ₁₂₇₂
2805	7 86 80 25	22 069 810 125	962251 ₉₄₄₀	7·481342 ₂₉₈₅₂	102982 ₁₆₇₆	3565062 ₁₂₇₀
2806	7 87 36 36	22 093 422 616	971691 ₉₄₃₈	7·511194 ₂₉₈₄₆	104658 ₁₆₇₅	3563792 ₁₂₇₀
2807	7 87 92 49	22 117 051 943	981129 ₉₄₃₆	7·541040 ₂₉₈₄₁	106333 ₁₆₇₅	3562522 ₁₂₆₈
2808	7 88 48 64	22 140 698 112	990565 ₉₄₃₅	7·570881 ₂₉₈₃₅	108008 ₁₆₇₅	3561254 ₁₂₆₈
2809	7 89 04 81	22 164 361 129	*000000 ₉₄₃₃	7·600716 ₂₉₈₃₀	109683 ₁₆₇₄	3559986 ₁₂₆₇
2810	7 89 61 00	22 188 041 000	009433 ₉₄₃₂	7·630546 ₂₉₈₂₅	111357 ₁₆₇₄	3558719 ₁₂₆₆
2811	7 90 17 21	22 211 737 731	018865 ₉₄₂₉	7·660371 ₂₉₈₂₀	113031 ₁₆₇₃	3557453 ₁₂₆₅
2812	7 90 73 44	22 235 451 328	028294 ₉₄₂₈	7·690191 ₂₉₈₁₄	114704 ₁₆₇₃	3556188 ₁₂₆₄
2813	7 91 29 69	22 259 181 797	037722 ₉₄₂₇	7·720005 ₂₉₈₀₉	116377 ₁₆₇₂	3554924 ₁₂₆₄
2814	7 91 85 96	22 282 929 144	047149 ₉₄₂₅	7·749814 ₂₉₈₀₃	118049 ₁₆₇₃	3553660 ₁₂₆₂
2815	7 92 42 25	22 306 693 375	056574 ₉₄₂₃	7·779617 ₂₉₇₉₉	119722 ₁₆₇₁	3552398 ₁₂₆₂
2816	7 92 98 56	22 330 474 496	065997 ₉₄₂₁	7·809416 ₂₉₇₉₃	121393 ₁₆₇₂	3551136 ₁₂₆₀
2817	7 93 54 89	22 354 272 513	075418 ₉₄₂₀	7·839209 ₂₉₇₈₈	123065 ₁₆₇₁	3549876 ₁₂₆₀
2818	7 94 11 24	22 378 087 432	084838 ₉₄₁₈	7·868997 ₂₉₇₈₂	124736 ₁₆₇₀	3548616 ₁₂₅₉
2819	7 94 67 61	22 401 919 259	094256 ₉₄₁₆	7·898779 ₂₉₇₇₇	126406 ₁₆₇₀	3547357 ₁₂₅₈
2820	7 95 24 00	22 425 768 000	103672 ₉₄₁₅	7·928556 ₂₉₇₇₂	128076 ₁₆₇₀	3546099 ₁₂₅₇
2821	7 95 80 41	22 449 633 661	113087 ₉₄₁₃	7·958328 ₂₉₇₆₇	129746 ₁₆₇₀	3544842 ₁₂₅₆
2822	7 96 36 84	22 473 516 248	122500 ₉₄₁₁	7·988095 ₂₉₇₆₁	131416 ₁₆₆₉	3543586 ₁₂₅₅
2823	7 96 93 29	22 497 415 767	131911 ₉₄₁₀	8·017856 ₂₉₇₅₆	133085 ₁₆₆₈	3542331 ₁₂₅₅
2824	7 97 49 76	22 521 332 224	141321 ₉₄₀₈	8·047612 ₂₉₇₅₁	134753 ₁₆₆₈	3541076 ₁₂₅₃
2825	7 98 06 25	22 545 265 625	150729 ₉₄₀₆	8·077363 ₂₉₇₄₆	136421 ₁₆₆₈	3539823 ₁₂₅₃
2826	7 98 62 76	22 569 215 976	160135 ₉₄₀₅	8·107109 ₂₉₇₄₀	138089 ₁₆₆₈	3538570 ₁₂₅₁
2827	7 99 19 29	22 593 183 283	169540 ₉₄₀₃	8·136849 ₂₉₇₃₅	139757 ₁₆₆₇	3537319 ₁₂₅₁
2828	7 99 75 84	22 617 167 552	178943 ₉₄₀₂	8·166584 ₂₉₇₃₀	141424 ₁₆₆₆	3536068 ₁₂₅₀
2829	8 00 32 41	22 641 168 789	188345 ₉₃₉₉	8·196314 ₂₉₇₂₄	143090 ₁₆₆₇	3534818 ₁₂₄₉
2830	8 00 89 00	22 665 187 000	197744 ₉₃₉₈	8·226038 ₂₉₇₂₀	144757 ₁₆₆₅	3533569 ₁₂₄₈
2831	8 01 45 61	22 689 222 191	207142 ₉₃₉₇	8·255758 ₂₉₇₁₄	146422 ₁₆₆₅	3532321 ₁₂₄₈
2832	8 02 02 24	22 713 274 368	216539 ₉₃₉₅	8·285472 ₂₉₇₀₉	148088 ₁₆₆₅	3531073 ₁₂₄₆
2833	8 02 58 89	22 737 343 537	225934 ₉₃₉₃	8·315181 ₂₉₇₀₃	149753 ₁₆₆₅	3529827 ₁₂₄₅
2834	8 03 15 56	22 761 429 704	235327 ₉₃₉₁	8·344884 ₂₉₆₉₈	151418 ₁₆₆₄	3528582 ₁₂₄₅
2835	8 03 72 25	22 785 532 875	244718 ₉₃₉₀	8·374582 ₂₉₆₉₃	153082 ₁₆₆₄	3527337 ₁₂₄₄
2836	8 04 28 96	22 809 653 056	254108 ₉₃₈₈	8·404275 ₂₉₆₈₈	154746 ₁₆₆₃	3526093 ₁₂₄₃
2837	8 04 85 69	22 833 790 253	263496 ₉₃₈₆	8·433963 ₂₉₆₈₃	156409 ₁₆₆₃	3524850 ₁₂₄₂
2838	8 05 42 44	22 857 944 472	272882 ₉₃₈₅	8·463646 ₂₉₆₇₇	158072 ₁₆₆₃	3523608 ₁₂₄₁
2839	8 05 99 21	22 882 115 719	282267 ₉₃₈₃	8·493323 ₂₉₆₇₂	159735 ₁₆₆₃	3522367 ₁₂₄₀
2840	8 06 56 00	22 906 304 000	291650 ₉₃₈₂	8·522995 ₂₉₆₆₇	161398 ₁₆₆₁	3521127 ₁₂₄₀
2841	8 07 12 81	22 930 509 321	301032 ₉₃₈₀	8·552662 ₂₉₆₆₂	163059 ₁₆₆₂	3519887 ₁₂₄₀
2842	8 07 69 64	22 954 731 688	310412 ₉₃₇₈	8·582324 ₂₉₆₅₇	164721 ₁₆₆₁	3518649 ₁₂₃₈
2843	8 08 26 49	22 978 971 107	319790 ₉₃₇₇	8·611981 ₂₉₆₅₁	166382 ₁₆₆₁	3517411 ₁₂₃₇
2844	8 08 83 36	23 003 227 584	329167 ₉₃₇₄	8·641632 ₂₉₆₄₆	168043 ₁₆₆₀	3516174 ₁₂₃₆
2845	8 09 40 25	23 027 501 125	338541 ₉₃₇₄	8·671278 ₂₉₆₄₁	169703 ₁₆₆₀	3514938 ₁₂₃₅
2846	8 09 97 16	23 051 791 736	347915 ₉₃₇₁	8·700919 ₂₉₆₃₅	171363 ₁₆₆₀	3513703 ₁₂₃₄
2847	8 10 54 09	23 076 099 423	357286 ₉₃₇₀	8·730554 ₂₉₆₃₁	173023 ₁₆₅₉	3512469 ₁₂₃₃
2848	8 11 11 04	23 100 424 192	366656 ₉₃₆₉	8·760185 ₂₉₆₂₅	174682 ₁₆₅₉	3511236 ₁₂₃₂
2849	8 11 68 01	23 124 766 049	376025 ₉₃₆₆	8·789810 ₂₉₆₂₀	176341 ₁₆₅₈	3510004 ₁₂₃₂
2850	8 12 25 00	23 149 125 000	385391	8·819430	177999	3508772
			53·	160 +	14·	0·000

No. n	Square n^2	Cube n^3	Square root $\sqrt{n}$	Sq. rt. of $10n$ $\sqrt{10n}$	Cube root $\sqrt[3]{n}$	Reciprocal $\dfrac{1}{n}$
			53·	160 +	14·	0·000
2850	8 12 25 00	23 149 125 000	385391 9365	8·819430 29615	177999 1658	3508772 1231
2851	8 12 82 01	23 173 501 051	394756 9364	8·849045 29610	179657 1658	3507541 1230
2852	8 13 39 04	23 197 894 208	404120 9361	8·878655 29604	181315 1657	3506311 1229
2853	8 13 96 09	23 222 304 477	413481 9361	8·908259 29599	182972 1657	3505082 1228
2854	8 14 53 16	23 246 731 864	422842 9358	8·937858 29594	184629 1657	3503854 1227
2855	8 15 10 25	23 271 176 375	432200 9357	8·967452 29589	186286 1656	3502627 1226
2856	8 15 67 36	23 295 638 016	441557 9355	8·997041 29584	187942 1656	3501401 1226
2857	8 16 24 49	23 320 116 793	450912 9354	9·026625 29579	189598 1655	3500175 1225
2858	8 16 81 64	23 344 612 712	460266 9352	9·056204 29573	191253 1655	3498950 1224
2859	8 17 38 81	23 369 125 779	469618 9350	9·085777 29568	192908 1654	3497726 1223
2860	8 17 96 00	23 393 656 000	478968 9348	9·115345 29563	194562 1655	3496503 1222
2861	8 18 53 21	23 418 203 381	488316 9348	9·144908 29558	196217 1653	3495281 1221
2862	8 19 10 44	23 442 767 928	497664 9345	9·174466 29553	197870 1654	3494060 1220
2863	8 19 67 69	23 467 349 647	507009 9344	9·204019 29547	199524 1653	3492840 1220
2864	8 20 24 96	23 491 948 544	516353 9342	9·233566 29543	201177 1653	3491620 1219
2865	8 20 82 25	23 516 564 625	525695 9340	9·263109· 29537	202830 1652	3490401 1217
2866	8 21 39 56	23 541 197 896	535035 9339	9·292646 29532	204482 1652	3489184 1217
2867	8 21 96 89	23 565 848 363	544374 9337	9·322178 29527	206134 1651	3487967 1217
2868	8 22 54 24	23 590 516 032	553711 9336	9·351705 29521	207785 1651	3486750 1215
2869	8 23 11 61	23 615 200 909	563047 9334	9·381227 29516	209436 1651	3485535 1214
2870	8 23 69 00	23 639 903 000	572381 9332	9·410743 29512	211087 1650	3484321 1214
2871	8 24 26 41	23 664 622 311	581713 9331	9·440255 29506	212737 1650	3483107 1213
2872	8 24 83 84	23 689 358 848	591044 9329	9·469761 29502	214387 1650	3481894 1212
2873	8 25 41 29	23 714 112 617	600373 9328	9·499263 29496	216037 1649	3480682 1211
2874	8 25 98 76	23 738 883 624	609701 9325	9·528759 29491	217686 1649	3479471 1210
2875	8 26 56 25	23 763 671 875	619026 9325	9·558250 29485	219335 1648	3478261 1210
2876	8 27 13 76	23 788 477 376	628351 9322	9·587735 29481	220983 1648	3477051 1208
2877	8 27 71 29	23 813 300 133	637673 9321	9·617216 29476	222631 1648	3475843 1208
2878	8 28 28 84	23 838 140 152	646994 9320	9·646692 29470	224279 1647	3474635 1207
2879	8 28 86 41	23 862 997 439	656314 9317	9·676162 29465	225926 1647	3473428 1206
2880	8 29 44 00	23 887 872 000	665631 9317	9·705627 29461	227573 1647	3472222 1205
2881	8 30 01 61	23 912 763 841	674948 9314	9·735088 29455	229220 1646	3471017 1204
2882	8 30 59 24	23 937 672 968	684262 9313	9·764543 29450	230866 1646	3469813 1204
2883	8 31 16 89	23 962 599 387	693575 9311	9·793993 29445	232512 1645	3468609 1203
2884	8 31 74 56	23 987 543 104	702886 9310	9·823438 29440	234157 1645	3467406 1201
2885	8 32 32 25	24 012 504 125	712196 9308	9·852878 29434	235802 1645	3466205 1202
2886	8 32 89 96	24 037 482 456	721504 9307	9·882312 29430	237447 1644	3465003 1200
2887	8 33 47 69	24 062 478 103	730811 9304	9·911742 29424	239091 1644	3463803 1199
2888	8 34 05 44	24 087 491 072	740115 9304	9·941166 29420	240735 1643	3462604 1199
2889	8 34 63 21	24 112 521 369	749419 9301	9·970586 29414	242378 1643	3461405 1197
2890	8 35 21 00	24 137 569 000	758720 9300	*0·000000 29409	244021 1643	3460208 1197
2891	8 35 78 81	24 162 633 971	768020 9299	0·029409 29404	245664 1642	3459011 1196
2892	8 36 36 64	24 187 716 288	777319 9296	0·058813 29399	247306 1642	3457815 1196
2893	8 36 94 49	24 212 815 957	786615 9296	0·088212 29394	248948 1642	3456619 1194
2894	8 37 52 36	24 237 932 984	795911 9293	0·117606 29389	250590 1641	3455425 1194
2895	8 38 10 25	24 263 067 375	805204 9292	0·146995 29384	252231 1641	3454231 1192
2896	8 38 68 16	24 288 219 136	814496 9291	0·176379 29379	253872 1640	3453039 1192
2897	8 39 26 09	24 313 388 273	823787 9288	0·205758 29374	255512 1640	3451847 1191
2898	8 39 84 04	24 338 574 792	833075 9288	0·235132 29368	257152 1640	3450656 1191
2899	8 40 42 01	24 363 778 699	842363 9285	0·264500 29364	258792 1639	3449465 1189
2900	8 41 00 00	24 389 000 000	851648 53·	0·293864 170 +	260431 14·	3448276 0·000

No. n	Square n²	Cube n³	Square root √n		Sq. rt. of 10n √10n		Cube root ∛n		Reciprocal 1/n	
			53·		**170 +**		**14·**		**0·000**	
2900	8 41 00 00	24 389 000 000	851648	9284	0·293864	29358	260431	1639	3448276	1189
2901	8 41 58 01	24 414 238 701	860932	9282	0·323222	29354	262070	1639	3447087	1188
2902	8 42 16 04	24 439 494 808	870214	9281	0·352576	29348	263709	1638	3445899	1187
2903	8 42 74 09	24 464 768 327	879495	9279	0·381924	29343	265347	1638	3444712	1186
2904	8 43 32 16	24 490 059 264	888774	9278	0·411267	29338	266985	1637	3443526	1185
2905	8 43 90 25	24 515 367 625	898052	9276	0·440605	29334	268622	1637	3442341	1185
2906	8 44 48 36	24 540 693 416	907328	9274	0·469939	29328	270259	1637	3441156	1184
2907	8 45 06 49	24 566 036 643	916602	9273	0·499267	29323	271896	1636	3439972	1182
2908	8 45 64 64	24 591 397 312	925875	9271	0·528590	29318	273532	1636	3438790	1183
2909	8 46 22 81	24 616 775 429	935146	9270	0·557908	29313	275168	1636	3437607	1181
2910	8 46 81 00	24 642 171 000	944416	9268	0·587221	29308	276804	1635	3436426	1180
2911	8 47 39 21	24 667 584 031	953684	9266	0·616529	29303	278439	1635	3435246	1180
2912	8 47 97 44	24 693 014 528	962950	9265	0·645832	29298	280074	1634	3434066	1179
2913	8 48 55 69	24 718 462 497	972215	9263	0·675130	29293	281708	1634	3432887	1178
2914	8 49 13 96	24 743 927 944	981478	9262	0·704423	29288	283342	1634	3431709	1177
2915	8 49 72 25	24 769 410 875	·990740	9260	0·733711	29283	284976	1633	3430532	1177
2916	8 50 30 56	24 794 911 296	*000000	9258	0·762994	29277	286609	1633	3429355	1175
2917	8 50 88 89	24 820 429 213	009258	9257	0·792271	29273	288242	1633	3428180	1175
2918	8 51 47 24	24 845 964 632	018515	9256	0·821544	29268	289875	1632	3427005	1174
2919	8 52 05 61	24 871 517 559	027771	9253	0·850812	29263	291507	1632	3425831	1173
2920	8 52 64 00	24 897 088 000	037024	9252	0·880075	29258	293139	1631	3424658	1173
2921	8 53 22 41	24 922 675 961	046276	9251	0·909333	29252	294770	1632	3423485	1172
2922	8 53 80 84	24 948 281 448	055527	9249	0·938585	29248	296402	1630	3422313	1170
2923	8 54 39 29	24 973 904 467	064776	9247	0·967833	29243	298032	1631	3421143	1170
2924	8 54 97 76	24 999 545 024	074023	9246	0·997076	29238	299663	1630	3419973	1170
2925	8 55 56 25	25 025 203 125	083269	9244	1·026314	29233	301293	1629	3418803	1168
2926	8 56 14 76	25 050 878 776	092513	9243	1·055547	29227	302922	1629	3417635	1168
2927	8 56 73 29	25 076 571 983	101756	9241	1·084774	29223	304551	1629	3416467	1166
2928	8 57 31 84	25 102 282 752	110997	9240	1·113997	29218	306180	1629	3415301	1166
2929	8 57 90 41	25 128 011 089	120237	9237	1·143215	29213	307809	1628	3414135	1166
2930	8 58 49 00	25 153 757 000	129474	9237	1·172428	29208	309437	1628	3412969	1164
2931	8 59 07 61	25 179 520 491	138711	9234	1·201636	29202	311065	1627	3411805	1164
2932	8 59 66 24	25 205 301 568	147945	9234	1·230838	29198	312692	1627	3410641	1163
2933	8 60 24 89	25 231 100 237	157179	9231	1·260036	29193	314319	1627	3409478	1162
2934	8 60 83 56	25 256 916 504	166410	9230	1·289229	29188	315946	1626	3408316	1161
2935	8 61 42 25	25 282 750 375	175640	9229	1·318417	29183	317572	1626	3407155	1160
2936	8 62 00 96	25 308 601 856	184869	9227	1·347600	29178	319198	1625	3405995	1160
2937	8 62 59 69	25 334 470 953	194096	9225	1·376778	29173	320823	1625	3404835	1159
2938	8 63 18 44	25 360 357 672	203321	9224	1·405951	29168	322448	1625	3403676	1158
2939	8 63 77 21	25 386 262 019	212545	9222	1·435119	29163	324073	1625	3402518	1157
2940	8 64 36 00	25 412 184 000	221767	9220	1·464282	29158	325698	1624	3401361	1157
2941	8 64 94 81	25 438 123 621	230987	9219	1·493440	29153	327322	1623	3400204	1156
2942	8 65 53 64	25 464 080 888	240206	9218	1·522593	29148	328945	1624	3399048	1155
2943	8 66 12 49	25 490 055 807	249424	9216	1·551741	29144	330569	1622	3397893	1154
2944	8 66 71 36	25 516 048 384	258640	9214	1·580885	29138	332191	1623	3396739	1153
2945	8 67 30 25	25 542 058 625	267854	9213	1·610023	29133	333814	1622	3395586	1153
2946	8 67 89 16	25 568 086 536	277067	9211	1·639156	29129	335436	1622	3394433	1152
2947	8 68 48 09	25 594 132 123	286278	9210	1·668285	29123	337058	1622	3393281	1151
2948	8 69 07 04	25 620 195 392	295488	9208	1·697408	29119	338680	1621	3392130	1150
2949	8 69 66 01	25 646 276 349	304696	9206	1·726527	29113	340301	1620	3390980	1149
2950	8 70 25 00	25 672 375 000	313902		1·755640		341921		3389831	
			54·		**170 +**		**14·**		**0·000**	

No. n	Square n²	Cube n³	Square root √n	Sq. rt. of 10n √(10n)	Cube root ∛n	Reciprocal 1/n
			54·	170 +	14·	0·000
2950	8 70 25 00	25 672 375 000	313902 9205	1·755640 29109	341921 1621	3389831 1149
2951	8 70 84 01	25 698 491 351	323107 9204	1·784749 29104	343542 1620	3388682 1148
2952	8 71 43 04	25 724 625 408	332311 9202	1·813853 29099	345162 1619	3387534 1147
2953	8 72 02 09	25 750 777 177	341513 9200	1·842952 29093	346781 1620	3386387 1147
2954	8 72 61 16	25 776 946 664	350713 9199	1·872045 29089	348401 1619	3385240 1145
2955	8 73 20 25	25 803 133 875	359912 9197	1·901134 29084	350020 1618	3384095 1145
2956	8 73 79 36	25 829 338 816	369109 9195	1·930218 29080	351638 1618	3382950 1144
2957	8 74 38 49	25 855 561 493	378304 9195	1·959298 29074	353256 1618	3381806 1143
2958	8 74 97 64	25 881 801 912	387499 9192	1·988372 29069	354874 1618	3380663 1143
2959	8 75 56 81	25 908 060 079	396691 9191	2·017441 29064	356492 1617	3379520 1142
2960	8 76 16 00	25 934 336 000	405882 9189	2·046505 29060	358109 1616	3378378 1141
2961	8 76 75 21	25 960 629 681	415071 9188	2·075565 29054	359725 1617	3377237 1140
2962	8 77 34 44	25 986 941 128	424259 9187	2·104619 29050	361342 1616	3376097 1139
2963	8 77 93 69	26 013 270 347	433446 9184	2·133669 29045	362958 1615	3374958 1139
2964	8 78 52 96	26 039 617 344	442630 9184	2·162714 29040	364573 1616	3373819 1138
2965	8 79 12 25	26 065 982 125	451814 9181	2·191754 29035	366189 1615	3372681 1137
2966	8 79 71 56	26 092 364 696	460995 9180	2·220789 29030	367804 1614	3371544 1136
2967	8 80 30 89	26 118 765 063	470175 9179	2·249819 29025	369418 1614	3370408 1136
2968	8 80 90 24	26 145 183 232	479354 9177	2·278844 29020	371032 1614	3369272 1135
2969	8 81 49 61	26 171 619 209	488531 9175	2·307864 29015	372646 1614	3368137 1134
2970	8 82 09 00	26 198 073 000	497706 9174	2·336879 29011	374260 1613	3367003 1133
2971	8 82 68 41	26 224 544 611	506880 9173	2·365890 29006	375873 1612	3365870 1132
2972	8 83 27 84	26 251 034 048	516053 9171	2·394896 29000	377485 1613	3364738 1132
2973	8 83 87 29	26 277 541 317	525224 9169	2·423896 28996	379098 1612	3363606 1131
2974	8 84 46 76	26 304 066 424	534393 9168	2·452892 28991	380710 1611	3362475 1130
2975	8 85 06 25	26 330 609 375	543561 9166	2·481883 28986	382321 1612	3361345 1130
2976	8 85 65 76	26 357 170 176	552727 9164	2·510869 28981	383933 1611	3360215 1129
2977	8 86 25 29	26 383 748 833	561891 9164	2·539850 28977	385544 1610	3359086 1128
2978	8 86 84 84	26 410 345 352	571055 9161	2·568827 28971	387154 1610	3357958 1127
2979	8 87 44 41	26 436 959 739	580216 9160	2·597798 28967	388764 1610	3356831 1126
2980	8 88 04 00	26 463 592 000	589376 9159	2·626765 28962	390374 1610	3355705 1126
2981	8 88 63 61	26 490 242 141	598535 9157	2·655727 28957	391984 1609	3354579 1125
2982	8 89 23 24	26 516 910 168	607692 9155	2·684684 28952	393593 1609	3353454 1124
2983	8 89 82 89	26 543 596 087	616847 9154	2·713636 28947	395202 1608	3352330 1124
2984	8 90 42 56	26 570 299 904	626001 9153	2·742583 28942	396810 1608	3351206 1122
2985	8 91 02 25	26 597 021 625	635154 9150	2·771525 28938	398418 1608	3350084 1122
2986	8 91 61 96	26 623 761 256	644304 9150	2·800463 28933	400026 1607	3348962 1121
2987	8 92 21 69	26 650 518 803	653454 9147	2·829396 28927	401633 1607	3347841 1121
2988	8 92 81 44	26 677 294 272	662601 9147	2·858323 28923	403240 1607	3346720 1119
2989	8 93 41 21	26 704 087 669	671748 9144	2·887246 28919	404847 1606	3345601 1119
2990	8 94 01 00	26 730 899 000	680892 9144	2·916165 28913	406453 1606	3344482 1119
2991	8 94 60 81	26 757 728 271	690036 9141	2·945078 28908	408059 1605	3343363 1117
2992	8 95 20 64	26 784 575 488	699177 9140	2·973986 28904	409664 1605	3342246 1117
2993	8 95 80 49	26 811 440 657	708317 9139	3·002890 28899	411269 1605	3341129 1116
2994	8 96 40 36	26 838 323 784	717456 9137	3·031789 28894	412874 1605	3340013 1115
2995	8 97 00 25	26 865 224 875	726593 9136	3·060683 28889	414479 1604	3338898 1114
2996	8 97 60 16	26 892 143 936	735729 9134	3·089572 28885	416083 1604	3337784 1114
2997	8 98 20 09	26 919 080 973	744863 9132	3·118457 28879	417687 1603	3336670 1113
2998	8 98 80 04	26 946 035 992	753995 9131	3·147336 28875	419290 1603	3335557 1112
2999	8 99 40 01	26 973 008 999	763126 9130	3·176211 28870	420893 1603	3334445 1112
3000	9 00 00 00	27 000 000 000	772256 54·	3·205081 170 +	422496 14·	3333333 0·000

No. n	Square n²	Cube n³	Square root √n	Sq. rt. of 10n √10n	Cube root ∛n	Reciprocal 1/n
			54·	170 +	14·	0·000
3000	9 00 00 00	27 000 000 000	772256 (9128)	3·205081 (28865)	422496 (1602)	3333333 (1110)
3001	9 00 60 01	27 027 009 001	781384 (9126)	3·233946 (28860)	424098 (1602)	3332223 (1110)
3002	9 01 20 04	27 054 036 008	790510 (9125)	3·262806 (28856)	425700 (1602)	3331113 (1110)
3003	9 01 80 09	27 081 081 027	799635 (9123)	3·291662 (28850)	427302 (1601)	3330003 (1108)
3004	9 02 40 16	27 108 144 064	808758 (9122)	3·320512 (28846)	428903 (1601)	3328895 (1108)
3005	9 03 00 25	27 135 225 125	817880 (9121)	3·349358 (28841)	430504 (1600)	3327787 (1107)
3006	9 03 60 36	27 162 324 216	827001 (9118)	3·378199 (28837)	432104 (1600)	3326680 (1106)
3007	9 04 20 49	27 189 441 343	836119 (9118)	3·407036 (28831)	433704 (1600)	3325574 (1106)
3008	9 04 80 64	27 216 576 512	845237 (9116)	3·435867 (28827)	435304 (1600)	3324468 (1105)
3009	9 05 40 81	27 243 729 729	854353 (9114)	3·464694 (28822)	436904 (1599)	3323363 (1104)
3010	9 06 01 00	27 270 901 000	863467 (9113)	3·493516 (28817)	438503 (1599)	3322259 (1103)
3011	9 06 61 21	27 298 090 331	872580 (9111)	3·522333 (28812)	440102 (1599)	3321156 (1103)
3012	9 07 21 44	27 325 297 728	881691 (9110)	3·551145 (28808)	441700 (1598)	3320053 (1102)
3013	9 07 81 69	27 352 523 197	890801 (9108)	3·579953 (28803)	443298 (1598)	3318951 (1101)
3014	9 08 41 96	27 379 766 744	899909 (9107)	3·608756 (28798)	444896 (1597)	3317850 (1100)
3015	9 09 02 25	27 407 028 375	909016 (9105)	3·637554 (28793)	446493 (1597)	3316750 (1100)
3016	9 09 62 56	27 434 308 096	918121 (9104)	3·666347 (28788)	448090 (1597)	3315650 (1099)
3017	9 10 22 89	27 461 605 913	927225 (9102)	3·695135 (28784)	449687 (1596)	3314551 (1099)
3018	9 10 83 24	27 488 921 832	936327 (9100)	3·723919 (28779)	451283 (1596)	3313453 (1098)
3019	9 11 43 61	27 516 255 859	945427 (9100)	3·752698 (28774)	452879 (1596)	3312355 (1098)
3020	9 12 04 00	27 543 608 000	954527 (9097)	3·781472 (28769)	454475 (1595)	3311258 (1096)
3021	9 12 64 41	27 570 978 261	963624 (9097)	3·810241 (28765)	456070 (1595)	3310162 (1096)
3022	9 13 24 84	27 598 366 648	972721 (9094)	3·839006 (28760)	457665 (1594)	3309067 (1095)
3023	9 13 85 29	27 625 773 167	981815 (9093)	3·867766 (28755)	459259 (1595)	3307972 (1095)
3024	9 14 45 76	27 653 197 824	990908 (9092)	3·896521 (28750)	460854 (1595)	3306878 (1094)
3025	9 15 06 25	27 680 640 625	*000000 (9090)	3·925271 (28746)	462447 (1594)	3305785 (1092)
3026	9 15 66 76	27 708 101 576	009090 (9089)	3·954017 (28741)	464041 (1593)	3304693 (1092)
3027	9 16 27 29	27 735 580 683	018179 (9087)	3·982758 (28736)	465634 (1593)	3303601 (1091)
3028	9 16 87 84	27 763 077 952	027266 (9086)	4·011494 (28731)	467227 (1592)	3302510 (1091)
3029	9 17 48 41	27 790 593 389	036352 (9084)	4·040225 (28727)	468819 (1592)	3301420 (1090)
3030	9 18 09 00	27 818 127 000	045436 (9082)	4·068952 (28722)	470411 (1592)	3300330 (1089)
3031	9 18 69 61	27 845 678 791	054518 (9082)	4·097674 (28717)	472003 (1591)	3299241 (1089)
3032	9 19 30 24	27 873 248 768	063600 (9079)	4·126391 (28712)	473594 (1591)	3298153 (1088)
3033	9 19 90 89	27 900 836 937	072679 (9078)	4·155103 (28708)	475185 (1591)	3297066 (1087)
3034	9 20 51 56	27 928 443 304	081757 (9077)	4·183811 (28703)	476776 (1590)	3295979 (1087)
3035	9 21 12 25	27 956 067 875	090834 (9075)	4·212514 (28698)	478366 (1590)	3294893 (1086)
3036	9 21 72 96	27 983 710 656	099909 (9074)	4·241212 (28694)	479956 (1590)	3293808 (1085)
3037	9 22 33 69	28 011 371 653	108983 (9072)	4·269906 (28688)	481546 (1589)	3292723 (1085)
3038	9 22 94 44	28 039 050 872	118055 (9071)	4·298594 (28684)	483135 (1589)	3291639 (1084)
3039	9 23 55 21	28 066 748 319	127126 (9069)	4·327278 (28680)	484724 (1589)	3290556 (1083)
3040	9 24 16 00	28 094 464 000	136195 (9068)	4·355958 (28674)	486313 (1588)	3289474 (1082)
3041	9 24 76 81	28 122 197 921	145263 (9066)	4·384632 (28670)	487901 (1588)	3288392 (1082)
3042	9 25 37 64	28 149 950 088	154329 (9065)	4·413302 (28665)	489489 (1588)	3287311 (1081)
3043	9 25 98 49	28 177 720 507	163394 (9063)	4·441967 (28661)	491077 (1587)	3286231 (1080)
3044	9 26 59 36	28 205 509 184	172457 (9062)	4·470628 (28656)	492664 (1587)	3285151 (1080)
3045	9 27 20 25	28 233 316 125	181519 (9060)	4·499284 (28651)	494251 (1586)	3284072 (1079)
3046	9 27 81 16	28 261 141 336	190579 (9059)	4·527935 (28646)	495837 (1586)	3282994 (1078)
3047	9 28 42 09	28 288 984 823	199638 (9057)	4·556581 (28642)	497423 (1586)	3281917 (1077)
3048	9 29 03 04	28 316 846 592	208695 (9056)	4·585223 (28637)	499009 (1586)	3280840 (1077)
3049	9 29 64 01	28 344 726 649	217751 (9054)	4·613860 (28632)	500595 (1585)	3279764 (1076)
3050	9 30 25 00	28 372 625 000	226805	4·642492	502180	3278689
			55·	170 +	14·	0·000

No. n	Square n^2	Cube n^3	Square root $\sqrt{n}$	Sq. rt. of 10n $\sqrt{10n}$	Cube root $\sqrt[3]{n}$	Reciprocal $\frac{1}{n}$
			55·	170 +	14·	0·000
3050	9 30 25 00	28 372 625 000	226805 9053	4·642492 28628	502180 1584	3278689 1075
3051	9 30 86 01	28 400 541 651	235858 9051	4·671120 28622	503764 1585	3277614 1074
3052	9 31 47 04	28 428 476 608	244909 9050	4·699742 28619	505349 1584	3276540 1073
3053	9 32 08 09	28 456 429 877	253959 9049	4·728361 28613	506933 1584	3275467 1073
3054	9 32 69 16	28 484 401 464	263008 9046	4·756974 28609	508517 1583	3274394 1072
3055	9 33 30 25	28 512 391 375	272054 9046	4·785583 28604	510100 1583	3273322 1071
3056	9 33 91 36	28 540 399 616	281100 9044	4·814187 28600	511683 1583	3272251 1070
3057	9 34 52 49	28 568 426 193	290144 9042	4·842787 28594	513266 1582	3271181 1070
3058	9 35 13 64	28 596 471 112	299186 9041	4·871381 28590	514848 1582	3270111 1069
3059	9 35 74 81	28 624 534 379	308227 9040	4·899971 28586	516430 1582	3269042 1068
3060	9 36 36 00	28 652 616 000	317267 9038	4·928557 28581	518012 1581	3267974 1068
3061	9 36 97 21	28 680 715 981	326305 9036	4·957138 28576	519593 1581	3266906 1067
3062	9 37 58 44	28 708 834 328	335341 9035	4·985714 28571	521174 1581	3265839 1066
3063	9 38 19 69	28 736 971 047	344376 9034	5·014285 28567	522755 1580	3264773 1065
3064	9 38 80 96	28 765 126 144	353410 9032	5·042852 28562	524335 1580	3263708 1065
3065	9 39 42 25	28 793 299 625	362442 9031	5·071414 28557	525915 1579	3262643 1064
3066	9 40 03 56	28 821 491 496	371473 9029	5·099971 28553	527494 1580	3261579 1064
3067	9 40 64 89	28 849 701 763	380502 9028	5·128524 28548	529074 1579	3260515 1063
3068	9 41 26 24	28 877 930 432	389530 9026	5·157072 28544	530653 1578	3259452 1062
3069	9 41 87 61	28 906 177 509	398556 9025	5·185616 28539	532231 1578	3258390 1061
3070	9 42 49 00	28 934 443 000	407581 9023	5·214155 28534	533809 1578	3257329 1061
3071	9 43 10 41	28 962 726 911	416604 9022	5·242689 28529	535387 1578	3256268 1060
3072	9 43 71 84	28 991 029 248	425626 9020	5·271218 28525	536965 1577	3255208 1059
3073	9 44 33 29	29 019 350 017	434646 9019	5·299743 28521	538542 1577	3254149 1059
3074	9 44 94 76	29 047 689 224	443665 9018	5·328264 28515	540119 1576	3253090 1057
3075	9 45 56 25	29 076 046 875	452683 9015	5·356779 28511	541695 1576	3252033 1058
3076	9 46 17 76	29 104 422 976	461698 9015	5·385290 28506	543271 1576	3250975 1056
3077	9 46 79 29	29 132 817 533	470713 9013	5·413796 28502	544847 1576	3249919 1056
3078	9 47 40 84	29 161 230 552	479726 9012	5·442298 28497	546423 1575	3248863 1055
3079	9 48 02 41	29 189 662 039	488738 9010	5·470795 28493	547998 1575	3247808 1055
3080	9 48 64 00	29 218 112 000	497748 9008	5·499288 28488	549573 1574	3246753 1054
3081	9 49 25 61	29 246 580 441	506756 9008	5·527776 28483	551147 1574	3245699 1053
3082	9 49 87 24	29 275 067 368	515764 9005	5·556259 28478	552721 1574	3244646 1052
3083	9 50 48 89	29 303 572 787	524769 9005	5·584737 28474	554295 1573	3243594 1052
3084	9 51 10 56	29 332 096 704	533774 9002	5·613211 28470	555868 1574	3242542 1051
3085	9 51 72 25	29 360 639 125	542776 9002	5·641681 28464	557442 1572	3241491 1050
3086	9 52 33 96	29 389 200 056	551778 9000	5·670145 28461	559014 1573	3240441 1050
3087	9 52 95 69	29 417 779 503	560778 8998	5·698606 28455	560587 1572	3239391 1049
3088	9 53 57 44	29 446 377 472	569776 8997	5·727061 28451	562159 1572	3238342 1048
3089	9 54 19 21	29 474 993 969	578773 8995	5·755512 28446	563731 1571	3237294 1048
3090	9 54 81 00	29 503 629 000	587768 8994	5·783958 28442	565302 1571	3236246 1047
3091	9 55 42 81	29 532 282 571	596762 8993	5·812400 28437	566873 1571	3235199 1046
3092	9 56 04 64	29 560 954 688	605755 8991	5·840837 28433	568444 1570	3234153 1046
3093	9 56 66 49	29 589 645 357	614746 8990	5·869270 28428	570014 1570·	3233107 1045
3094	9 57 28 36	29 618 354 584	623736 8988	5·897698 28423	571584 1570	3232062 1044
3095	9 57 90 25	29 647 082 375	632724 8987	5·926121 28419	573154 1569	3231018 1044
3096	9 58 52 16	29 675 828 736	641711 8985	5·954540 28414	574723 1569	3229974 1043
3097	9 59 14 09	29 704 593 673	650696 8984	5·982954 28409	576292 1569	3228931 1042
3098	9 59 76 04	29 733 377 192	659680 8983	6·011363 28405	577861 1568	3227889 1042
3099	9 60 38 01	29 762 179 299	668663 8981	6·039768 28401	579429 1568	3226847 1041
3100	9 61 00 00	29 791 000 000	677644	6·068169	580997	3225806
			55·	170 +	14·	0·000

No. n	Square n²	Cube n³	Square root √n		Sq. rt. of 10n √10n		Cube root ∛n		Reciprocal 1/n	
			55·		170 +		14·		0·000	
3100	9 61 00 00	29 791 000 000	677644	8979	6·068169	28395	580997	1568	3225806	1040
3101	9 61 62 01	29 819 839 301	686623	8978	6·096564	28392	582565	1567	3224766	1040
3102	9 62 24 04	29 848 697 208	695601	8977	6·124956	28386	584132	1567	3223727	1039
3103	9 62 86 09	29 877 573 727	704578	8975	6·153342	28382	585699	1567	3222688	1039
3104	9 63 48 16	29 906 468 864	713553	8974	6·181724	28378	587266	1566	3221649	1039
3105	9 64 10 25	29 935 382 625	722527	8972	6·210102	28373	588832	1566	3220612	1037
3106	9 64 72 36	29 964 315 016	731499	8971	6·238475	28368	590398	1566	3219575	1037
3107	9 65 34 49	29 993 266 043	740470	8969	6·266843	28364	591964	1565	3218539	1036
3108	9 65 96 64	30 022 235 712	749439	8968	6·295207	28359	593529	1565	3217503	1036
3109	9 66 58 81	30 051 224 029	758407	8967	6·323566	28355	595094·	1565	3216468	1035
3110	9 67 21 00	30 080 231 000	767374	8965	6·351921	28350	596659	1564	3215434	1034
3111	9 67 83 21	30 109 256 631	776339	8964	6·380271	28346	598223	1564	3214401	1033
3112	9 68 45 44	30 138 300 928	785303	8962	6·408617	28341	599787	1564	3213368	1033
3113	9 69 07 69	30 167 363 897	794265	8961	6·436958	28336	601351	1563	3212335	1033
3114	9 69 69 96	30 196 445 544	803226	8959	6·465294	28332	602914	1563	3211304	1031
3115	9 70 32 25	30 225 545 875	812185	8958	6·493626	28327	604477	1563	3210273	1031
3116	9 70 94 56	30 254 664 896	821143	8956	6·521953	28323	606040	1562	3209243	1030
3117	9 71 56 89	30 283 802 613	830099	8955	6·550276	28318	607602	1562	3208213	1030
3118	9 72 19 24	30 312 959 032	839054	8954	6·578594	28314	609164	1562	3207184	1029
3119	9 72 81 61	30 342 134 159	848008	8952	6·606908	28309	610726	1561	3206156	1028
3120	9 73 44 00	30 371 328 000	856960	8951	6·635217	28305	612287	1561	3205128	1028
3121	9 74 06 41	30 400 540 561	865911	8949	6·663522	28300	613848	1561	3204101	1027
3122	9 74 68 84	30 429 771 848	874860	8948	6·691822	28296	615409	1560	3203075	1026
3123	9 75 31 29	30 459 021 867	883808	8946	6·720118	28291	616969	1560	3202049	1026
3124	9 75 93 76	30 488 290 624	892754	8945	6·748409	28286	618529	1560	3201024	1025
3125	9 76 56 25	30 517 578 125	901699	8944	6·776695	28282	620089	1559	3200000	1024
3126	9 77 18 76	30 546 884 376	910643	8942	6·804977	28278	621648	1559	3198976	1024
3127	9 77 81 29	30 576 209 383	919585	8941	6·833255	28273	623207	1559	3197953	1023
3128	9 78 43 84	30 605 553 152	928526	8939	6·861528	28268	624766	1558	3196931	1022
3129	9 79 06 41	30 634 915 689	937465	8938	6·889796	28264	626324	1558	3195909	1022
3130	9 79 69 00	30 664 297 000	946403	8936	6·918060	28260	627882	1558	3194888	1021
3131	9 80 31 61	30 693 697 091	955339	8935	6·946320	28254	629440	1557	3193868	1020
3132	9 80 94 24	30 723 115 968	964274	8934	6·974574	28251	630997	1557	3192848	1020
3133	9 81 56 89	30 752 553 637	973208	8932	7·002825	28246	632554	1557	3191829	1019
3134	9 82 19 56	30 782 010 104	982140	8931	7·031071	28241	634111	1556	3190810	1017
3135	9 82 82 25	30 811 485 375	*991071	8929	7·059312	28237	635667	1556	3189793	1017
3136	9 83 44 96	30 840 979 456	*000000	8928	7·087549	28232	637223	1556	3188776	1017
3137	9 84 07 69	30 870 492 353	008928	8926	7·115781	28228	638779	1555	3187759	1016
3138	9 84 70 44	30 900 024 072	017854	8925	7·144009	28224	640334	1555	3186743	1015
3139	9 85 33 21	30 929 574 619	026779	8924	7·172233	28218	641889	1555	3185728	1015
3140	9 85 96 00	30 959 144 000	035703	8922	7·200451	28215	643444	1554	3184713	1014
3141	9 86 58 81	30 988 732 221	044625	8921	7·228666	28210	644998	1554	3183699	1013
3142	9 87 21 64	31 018 339 288	053546	8919	7·256876	28205	646552	1554	3182686	1012
3143	9 87 84 49	31 047 965 207	062465	8918	7·285081	28201	648106	1553	3181674	1012
3144	9 88 47 36	31 077 609 984	071383	8917	7·313282	28197	649659	1553	3180662	1012
3145	9 89 10 25	31 107 273 625	080300	8915	7·341479	28191	651212	1553	3179650	1010
3146	9 89 73 16	31 136 956 136	089215	8913	7·369670	28188	652765	1552	3178640	1011
3147	9 90 36 09	31 166 657 523	098128	8913	7·397858	28183	654317	1552	3177629	1009
3148	9 90 99 04	31 196 377 792	107041	8910	7·426041	28178	655869	1552	3176620	1009
3149	9 91 62 01	31 226 116 949	115951	8910	7·454219	28174	657421	1551	3175611	1008
3150	9 92 25 00	31 255 875 000	124861		7·482393		658972		3174603	
			56·		170 +		14·		0·000	

No. n	Square n²	Cube n³	Square root √n	Sq. rt. of 10n √10n	Cube root ∛n	Reciprocal 1/n
			56·	170+	14·	0·000
3150	9 92 25 00	31 255 875 000	124861 8908	7·482393 28170	658972 1551	3174603 1007
3151	9 92 88 01	31 285 651 951	133769 8906	7·510563 28165	660523 1551	3173596 1007
3152	9 93 51 04	31 315 447 808	142675 8906	7·538728 28161	662074 1551	3172589 1006
3153	9 94 14 09	31 345 262 577	151581 8903	7·566889 28156	663624 1550	3171583 1006
3154	9 94 77 16	31 375 096 264	160484 8903	7·595045 28152	665174 1550	3170577 1005
3155	9 95 40 25	31 404 948 875	169387 8901	7·623197 28147	666724 1549	3169572 1004
3156	9 96 03 36	31 434 820 416	178288 8899	7·651344 28143	668273 1550	3168568 1004
3157	9 96 66 49	31 464 710 893	187187 8898	7·679487 28138	669823 1548	3167564 1003
3158	9 97 29 64	31 494 620 312	196085 8897	7·707625 28134	671371 1549	3166561 1003
3159	9 97 92 81	31 524 548 679	204982 8895	7·735759 28129	672920 1548	3165559 1002
3160	9 98 56 00	31 554 496 000	213877 8894	7·763888 28125	674468 1548	3164557 1002
3161	9 99 19 21	31 584 462 281	222771 8893	7·792013 28121	676016 1547	3163556 1001
3162	9 99 82 44	31 614 447 528	231664 8891	7·820134 28116	677563 1547	3162555 1001
3163	10 00 45 69	31 644 451 747	240555 8889	7·848250 28112	679110 1547	3161555 1000
3164	10 01 08 96	31 674 474 944	249444 8889	7·876362 28107	680657 1546	3160556 999
3165	10 01 72 25	31 704 517 125	258333 8887	7·904469 28102	682203 1547	3159558 998
3166	10 02 35 56	31 734 578 296	267220 8885	7·932571 28099	683750 1545	3158560 998
3167	10 02 98 89	31 764 658 463	276105 8884	7·960670 28094	685295 1546	3157562 998
3168	10 03 62 24	31 794 757 632	284989 8883	7·988764 28089	686841 1545	3156566 996
3169	10 04 25 61	31 824 875 809	293872 8881	8·016853 28085	688386 1545	3155570 996
3170	10 04 89 00	31 855 013 000	302753 8880	8·044938 28081	689931 1544	3154574 996
3171	10 05 52 41	31 885 169 211	311633 8878	8·073019 28076	691475 1545	3153579 995
3172	10 06 15 84	31 915 344 448	320511 8877	8·101095 28072	693020 1544	3152585 994
3173	10 06 79 29	31 945 538 717	329388 8876	8·129167 28067	694564 1543	3151592 993
3174	10 07 42 76	31 975 752 024	338264 8874	8·157234 28063	696107 1543	3150599 993
3175	10 08 06 25	32 005 984 375	347138 8873	8·185297 28058	697650 1543	3149606 991
3176	10 08 69 76	32 036 235 776	356011 8872	8·213355 28054	699193 1543	3148615 991
3177	10 09 33 29	32 066 506 233	364883 8870	8·241409 28050	700736 1542	3147624 991
3178	10 09 96 84	32 096 795 752	373753 8868	8·269459 28045	702278 1542	3146633 990
3179	10 10 60 41	32 127 104 339	382621 8868	8·297504 28041	703820 1542	3145643 989
3180	10 11 24 00	32 157 432 000	391489 8866	8·325545 28036	705362 1541	3144654 988
3181	10 11 87 61	32 187 778 741	400355 8864	8·353581 28032	706903 1541	3143666 988
3182	10 12 51 24	32 218 144 568	409219 8863	8·381613 28028	708444 1541	3142678 988
3183	10 13 14 89	32 248 529 487	418082 8862	8·409641 28023	709984 1540	3141690 986
3184	10 13 78 56	32 278 933 504	426944 8860	8·437664 28019	711525 1540	3140704 987
3185	10 14 42 25	32 309 356 625	435804 8859	8·465683 28014	713065 1539	3139717 985
3186	10 15 05 96	32 339 798 856	444663 8858	8·493697 28010	714604 1540	3138732 985
3187	10 15 69 69	32 370 260 203	453521 8856	8·521707 28006	716144 1539	3137747 984
3188	10 16 33 44	32 400 740 672	462377 8855	8·549713 28001	717683 1538	3136763 984
3189	10 16 97 21	32 431 240 269	471232 8853	8·577714 27997	719221 1539	3135779 983
3190	10 17 61 00	32 461 759 000	480085 8852	8·605711 27992	720760 1538	3134796 982
3191	10 18 24 81	32 492 296 871	488937 8851	8·633703 27988	722298 1538	3133814 982
3192	10 18 88 64	32 522 853 888	497788 8849	8·661691 27984	723836 1537	3132832 981
3193	10 19 52 49	32 553 430 057	506637 8848	8·689675 27979	725373 1537	3131851 981
3194	10 20 16 36	32 584 025 384	515485 8846	8·717654 27976	726910 1537	3130870 980
3195	10 20 89 25	32 614 639 875	524331 8845	8·745630 27970	728447 1536	3129890 979
3196	10 21 44 16	32 645 273 536	533176 8844	8·773600 27966	729983 1537	3128911 979
3197	10 22 08 09	32 675 926 373	542020 8842	8·801566 27962	731520 1535	3127932 978
3198	10 22 72 04	32 706 598 392	550862 8841	8·829528 27957	733055 1536	3126954 977
3199	10 23 36 01	32 737 289 599	559703 8839	8·857485 27953	734591 1535	3125977 977
3200	10 24 00 00	32 768 000 000	568542	8·885438	736126	3125000
			56·	170 +	14·	0·000

No. n	Square n^2	Cube n^3	Square root $\sqrt{n}$	Sq. rt. of 10n $\sqrt{10n}$	Cube root $\sqrt[3]{n}$	Reciprocal $\frac{1}{n}$
			56·	170 +	14·	0·000
3200	10 24 00 00	32 768 000 000	568542 8839	8·885438 27949	736126 1535	3125000 976
3201	10 24 64 01	32 798 729 601	577381 8836	8·913387 27944	737661 1534	3124024 976
3202	10 25 28 04	32 829 478 408	586217 8836	8·941331 27940	739195 1535	3123048 975
3203	10 25 92 09	32 860 246 427	595053 8834	8·969271 27936	740730 1533	3122073 974
3204	10 26 56 16	32 891 033 664	603887 8832	8·997207 27931	742263 1534	3121099 974
3205	10 27 20 25	32 921 840 125	612719 8832	9·025138 27927	743797 1533	3120125 973
3206	10 27 84 36	32 952 665 816	621551 8830	9·053065 27922	745330 1533	3119152 973
3207	10 28 48 49	32 983 510 743	630381 8828	9·080987 27918	746863 1533	3118179 972
3208	10 29 12 64	33 014 374 912	639209 8827	9·108905 27914	748396 1532	3117207 971
3209	10 29 76 81	33 045 258 329	648036 8826	9·136819 27910	749928 1532	3116236 971
3210	10 30 41 00	33 076 161 000	656862 8824	9·164729 27905	751460 1532	3115265 970
3211	10 31 05 21	33 107 082 931	665686 8823	9·192634 27901	752992 1531	3114295 970
3212	10 31 69 44	33 138 024 128	674509 8822	9·220535 27896	754523 1531	3113325 969
3213	10 32 33 69	33 168 984 597	683331 8820	9·248431 27892	756054 1531	3112356 968
3214	10 32 97 96	33 199 964 344	692151 8819	9·276323 27888	757585 1530	3111388 968
3215	10 33 62 25	33 230 963 375	700970 8818	9·304211 27883	759115 1530	3110420 967
3216	10 34 26 56	33 261 981 696	709788 8816	9·332094 27879	760645 1530	3109453 967
3217	10 34 90 89	33 293 019 313	718604 8814	9·359973 27875	762175 1530	3108486 966
3218	10 35 55 24	33 324 076 232	727418 8814	9·387848 27870	763705 1529	3107520 966
3219	10 36 19 61	33 355 152 459	736232 8812	9·415718 27866	765234 1529	3106555 965
3220	10 36 84 00	33 386 248 000	745044 8810	9·443584 27862	766763 1528	3105590 964
3221	10 37 48 41	33 417 362 861	753854 8810	9·471446 27858	768291 1528	3104626 964
3222	10 38 12 84	33 448 497 048	762664 8808	9·499304 27853	769819 1528	3103662 963
3223	10 38 77 29	33 479 650 567	771472 8806	9·527157 27848	771347 1528	3102699 962
3224	10 39 41 76	33 510 823 424	780278 8805	9·555005 27845	772875 1527	3101737 962
3225	10 40 06 25	33 542 015 625	789083 8804	9·582850 27840	774402 1527	3100775 961
3226	10 40 70 76	33 573 227 176	797887 8803	9·610690 27836	775929 1526	3099814 961
3227	10 41 35 29	33 604 458 083	806690 8801	9·638526 27831	777455 1527	3098853 960
3228	10 41 99 84	33 635 708 352	815491 8800	9·666357 27828	778982 1526	3097893 960
3229	10 42 64 41	33 666 977 989	824291 8798	9·694185 27823	780508 1525	3096934 959
3230	10 43 29 00	33 698 267 000	833089 8797	9·722008 27818	782033 1526	3095975 959
3231	10 43 93 61	33 729 575 391	841886 8796	9·749826 27814	783559 1525	3095017 958
3232	10 44 58 24	33 760 903 168	850682 8794	9·777640 27810	785084 1524	3094059 958
3233	10 45 22 89	33 792 250 337	859476 8793	9·805450 27806	786608 1525	3093102 957
3234	10 45 87 56	33 823 616 904	868269 8791	9·833256 27801	788133 1524	3092146 956
3235	10 46 52 25	33 855 002 875	877060 8791	9·861057 27798	789657 1524	3091190 955
3236	10 47 16 96	33 886 408 256	885851 8788	9·888855 27792	791181 1523	3090235 955
3237	10 47 81 69	33 917 833 053	894639 8788	9·916647 27789	792704 1523	3089280 954
3238	10 48 46 44	33 949 277 272	903427 8786	9·944439 27784	794227 1523	3088326 953
3239	10 49 11 21	33 980 740 919	912213 8785	9·972220 27780	795750 1522	3087373 953
3240	10 49 76 00	34 012 224 000	920998 8783	*0·000000 27776	797272 1523	3086420 953
3241	10 50 40 81	34 043 726 521	929781 8782	0·027776 27771	798795 1522	3085467 951
3242	10 51 05 64	34 075 248 488	938563 8781	●0·055547 27767	800317 1521	3084516 951
3243	10 51 70 49	34 106 789 907	947344 8779	0·083314 27763	801838 1521	3083565 951
3244	10 52 35 36	34 138 350 784	956123 8778	0·111077 27758	803359 1521	3082614 950
3245	10 53 00 25	34 169 931 125	964901 8777	0·138835 27755	804880 1521	3081664 949
3246	10 53 65 16	34 201 530 936	973678 8775	0·166590 27750	806401 1520	3080715 949
3247	10 54 30 09	34 233 150 223	982453 8774	0·194340 27745	807921 1520	3079766 948
3248	10 54 95 04	34 264 788 992	991227 8773	0·222085 27742	809441 1520	3078818 948
3249	10 55 60 01	34 296 447 249	*000000 8771	0·249827 27737	810961 1519	3077870 947
3250	10 56 25 00	34 328 125 000	008771 57·	0·277564 180 +	812480 14·	3076923 0·000

66

No. n	Square n²	Cube n³	Square root √n	Sq. rt. of 10n √10n	Cube root ∛n	Reciprocal 1/n
			57·	180 +	14·	0·000
3250	10 56 25 00	34 328 125 000	008771 8770	0·277564 27733	812480 1519	3076923 946
3251	10 56 90 01	34 359 822 251	017541 8769	0·305297 27728	813999 1519	3075977 946
3252	10 57 55 04	34 391 539 008	026310 8767	0·333025 27725	815518 1519	3075031 946
3253	10 58 20 09	34 423 275 277	035077 8766	0·360750 27720	817037 1518	3074085 944
3254	10 58 85 16	34 455 031 064	043843 8764	0·388470 27716	818555 1518	3073141 944
3255	10 59 50 25	34 486 806 375	052607 8763	0·416186 27711	820073 1517	3072197 944
3256	10 60 15 36	34 518 601 216	061370 8762	0·443897 27707	821590 1517	3071253 944
3257	10 60 80 49	34 550 415 593	070132 8761	0·471604 27703	823107 1517	3070310 943
3258	10 61 45 64	34 582 249 512	078893 8759	0·499307 27699	824624 1517	3069368 942
3259	10 62 10 81	34 614 102 979	087652 8758	0·527006 27695	826141 1516	3068426 942 941
3260	10 62 76 00	34 645 976 000	096410 8756	0·554701 27690	827657 1516	3067485 941
3261	10 63 41 21	34 677 868 581	105166 8755	0·582391 27686	829173 1516	3066544 941 940
3262	10 64 06 44	34 709 780 728	113921 8754	0·610077 27682	830689 1515	3065604 940
3263	10 64 71 69	34 741 712 447	122675 8752	0·637759 27678	832204 1515	3064664 940 939
3264	10 65 36 96	34 773 663 744	131427 8752	0·665437 27673	833719 1515	3063725 939 938
3265	10 66 02 25	34 805 634 625	140179 8749	0·693110 27669	835234 1514	3062787 938
3266	10 66 67 56	34 837 625 096	148928 8749	0·720779 27665	836748 1514	3061849 938 937
3267	10 67 32 89	34 869 635 163	157677 8747	0·748444 27661	838262 1514	3060912 937
3268	10 67 98 24	34 901 664 832	166424 8745	0·776105 27656	839776 1514	3059976 936
3269	10 68 63 61	34 933 714 109	175169 8745	0·803761 27652	841290 1513	3059039 937 935
3270	10 69 29 00	34 965 783 000	183914 8743	0·831413 27648	842803 1513	3058104
3271	10 69 94 41	34 997 871 511	192657 8742	0·859061 27644	844316 1512	3057169 935
3272	10 70 59 84	35 029 979 648	201399 8740	0·886705 27639	845828 1512	3056235 934
3273	10 71 25 29	35 062 107 417	210139 8739	0·914344 27636	847340 1512	3055301 934 933
3274	10 71 90 76	35 094 254 824	218878 8738	0·941980 27631	848852 1512	3054368 933 933
3275	10 72 56 25	35 126 421 875	227616 8736	0·969611 27627	850364 1511	3053435 932
3276	10 73 21 76	35 158 608 576	236352 8735	0·997238 27622	851875 1511	3052503 932 931
3277	10 73 87 29	35 190 814 933	245087 8734	1·024860 27619	853386 1511	3051572 931
3278	10 74 52 84	35 223 040 952	253821 8732	1·052479 27614	854897 1511	3050641 931
3279	10 75 18 41	35 255 286 639	262553 8731	1·080093 27610	856408 1510	3049710 931 930
3280	10 75 84 00	35 287 552 000	271284 8730	1·107703 27606	857918 1509	3048780
3281	10 76 49 61	35 319 837 041	280014 8728	1·135309 27601	859427 ·510	3047851 929
3282	10 77 15 24	35 352 141 768	288742 8727	1·162910 27597	860937 1509	3046923 928
3283	10 77 80 89	35 384 466 187	297469 8726	1·190507 27594	862446 1509	3045995 928
3284	10 78 46 56	35 416 810 304	306195 8725	1·218101 27589	863955 1509	3045067 927
3285	10 79 12 25	35 449 174 125	314920 8723	1·245690 27584	865464 1508	3044140 926
3286	10 79 77 96	35 481 557 656	323643 8721	1·273274 27581	866972 1508	3043214 926
3287	10 80 43 69	35 513 960 903	332364 8721	1·300855 27576	868480 1508	3042288 926 925
3288	10 81 09 44	35 546 383 872	341085 8719	1·328431 27572	869987 1507	3041363 925
3289	10 81 75 21	35 578 826 569	349804 8718	1·356003 27568	871495 1508	3040438 925 924
3290	10 82 41 00	35 611 289 000	358522 8716	1·383571 27564	873002 1507	3039514 924
3291	10 83 06 81	35 643 771 171	367238 8715	1·411135 27560	874509 1507	3038590 924 923
3292	10 83 72 64	35 676 273 088	375953 8714	1·438695 27555	876015 1506	3037667 923 922
3293	10 84 38 49	35 708 794 757	384667 8712	1·466250 27552	877521 1506	3036745 922
3294	10 85 04 36	35 741 336 184	393379 8712	1·493802 27547	879027 1506	3035823 922
3295	10 85 70 25	35 773 897 375	402091 8709	1·521349 27542	880533 1505	3034901 920
3296	10 86 36 16	35 806 478 336	410800 8709	1·548891 27539	882038 1505	3033981 921
3297	10 87 02 09	35 839 079 073	419509 8707	1·576430 27535	883543 1504	3033060 921
3298	10 87 68 04	35 871 699 592	428216 8706	1·603965 27530	885047 1505	3032141 919
3299	10 88 34 01	35 904 339 899	436922 8704	1·631495 27526	886552 1504	3031222 919 919
3300	10 89 00 00	35 937 000 000	445626	1·659021	888056	3030303
			57·	180 +	14·	0·000

No. n	Square n²	Cube n³	Square root √n	Sq. rt. of 10n √10n	Cube root ∛n	Reciprocal 1/n
			57·	180 +	14·	0·000
3300	10 89 00 00	35 937 000 000	445626 8704	1·659021 27522	888056 1503	3030303
3301	10 89 66 01	35 969 679 901	454330 8702	1·686543 27518	889559 1504	3029385 918
3302	10 90 32 04	36 002 379 608	463032 8700	1·714061 27514	891063 1503	3028468 917
3303	10 90 98 09	36 035 099 127	471732 8699	1·741575 27509	892566 1502	3027551 917
3304	10 91 64 16	36 067 838 464	480431 8698	1·769084 27506	894068 1503	3026634 915
3305	10 92 30 25	36 100 597 625	489129 8697	1·796590 27501	895571 1502	3025719 916
3306	10 92 96 36	36 133 376 616	497826 8695	1·824091 27497	897073 1502	3024803 914
3307	10 93 62 49	36 166 175 443	506521 8694	1·851588 27493	898575 1502	3023889 914
3308	10 94 28 64	36 198 994 112	515215 8693	1·879081 27488	900077 1501	3022975 914
3309	10 94 94 81	36 231 832 629	523908 8691	1·906569 27485	901578 1501	3022061 913
3310	10 95 61 00	36 264 691 000	532599 8691	1·934054 27480	903079 1500	3021148 912
3311	10 96 27 21	36 297 569 231	541290 8688	1·961534 27477	904579 1501	3020236 912
3312	10 96 93 44	36 330 467 328	549978 8688	1·989011 27472	906080 1501	3019324 912
3313	10 97 59 69	36 363 385 297	558666 8686	2·016483 27468	907580 1500	3018412 910
3314	10 98 25 96	36 396 323 144	567352 8685	2·043951 27464	909080 1500	3017502 911
3315	10 98 92 25	36 429 280 875	576037 8683	2·071415 27459	910579 1499	3016591 909
3316	10 99 58 56	36 462 258 496	584720 8682	2·098874 27456	912078 1499	3015682 910
3317	11 00 24 89	36 495 256 013	593402 8681	2·126330 27451	913577 1499	3014772 910
3318	11 00 91 24	36 528 273 432	602083 8680	2·153781 27447	915076 1498	3013864 908
3319	11 01 57 61	36 561 310 759	610763 8678	2·181228 27444	916574 1498	3012956 908
3320	11 02 24 00	36 594 368 000	619441 8677	2·208672 27439	918072 1497	3012048 908
3321	11 02 90 41	36 627 445 161	628118 8676	2·236111 27434	919569 1498	3011141 907
3322	11 03 56 84	36 660 542 248	636794 8674	2·263545 27431	921067 1497	3010235 906
3323	11 04 23 29	36 693 659 267	645468 8673	2·290976 27427	922564 1497	3009329 906
3324	11 04 89 76	36 726 796 224	654141 8672	2·318403 27422	924061 1496	3008424 905
3325	11 05 56 25	36 759 953 125	662813 8670	2·345825 27419	925557 1496	3007519 904
3326	11 06 22 76	36 793 129 976	671483 8670	2·373244 27414	927053 1496	3006615 904
3327	11 06 89 29	36 826 326 783	680153 8667	2·400658 27410	928549 1496	3005711 903
3328	11 07 55 84	36 859 543 552	688820 8667	2·428068 27406	930045 1496	3004808 903
3329	11 08 22 41	36 892 780 289	697487 8665	2·455474 27402	931540 1495	3003905 902
3330	11 08 89 00	36 926 037 000	706152 8664	2·482876 27398	933035 1494	3003003 902
3331	11 09 55 61	36 959 313 691	714816 8663	2·510274 27393	934529 1495	3002101 902
3332	11 10 22 24	36 992 610 368	723479 8661	2·537667 27390	936024 1494	3001200 901
3333	11 10 88 89	37 025 927 037	732140 8660	2·565057 27385	937518 1494	3000300 900
3334	11 11 55 56	37 059 263 704	740800 8659	2·592442 27382	939012 1493	2999400 900
3335	11 12 22 25	37 092 620 375	749459 8657	2·619824 27377	940505 1493	2998501 899
3336	11 12 88 96	37 125 997 056	758116 8656	2·647201 27373	941998 1493	2997602 899
3337	11 13 55 69	37 159 393 753	766772 8655	2·674574 27369	943491 1493	2996704 898
3338	11 14 22 44	37 192 810 472	775427 8654	2·701943 27365	944984 1492	2995806 898
3339	11 14 89 21	37 226 247 219	784081 8652	2·729308 27361	946476 1492	2994909 897
3340	11 15 56 00	37 259 704 000	792733 8651	2·756669 27357	947968 1492	2994012 897
3341	11 16 22 81	37 293 180 821	801384 8650	2·784026 27352	949460 1491	2993116 896
3342	11 16 89 64	37 326 677 688	810034 8648	2·811378 27349	950951 1491	2992220 896
3343	11 17 56 49	37 360 194 607	818682 8647	2·838727 27344	952442 1491	2991325 895
3344	11 18 23 36	37 393 731 584	827329 8646	2·866071 27341	953933 1490	2990431 894
3345	11 18 90 25	37 427 288 625	835975 8644	2·893412 27336	955423 1490	2989537 894
3346	11 19 57 16	37 460 865 736	844619 8644	2·920748 27332	956913 1490	2988643 893
3347	11 20 24 09	37 494 462 923	853263 8642	2·948080 27328	958403 1490	2987750 892
3348	11 20 91 04	37 528 080 192	861905 8640	2·975408 27324	959893 1489	2986858 892
3349	11 21 58 01	37 561 717 549	870545 8640	3·002732 27320	961382 1489	2985966 891
3350	11 22 25 00	37 595 375 000	879185	3·030052	962871	2985075
			57·	180 +	14·	0·000

No. n	Square n^2	Cube n^3	Square root $\sqrt{n}$	Sq. rt. of $10n$ $\sqrt{10n}$	Cube root $\sqrt[3]{n}$	Reciprocal $\dfrac{1}{n}$
			57·	180 +	14·	0·000
3350	11 22 25 00	37 595 375 000	879185 $_{8638}$	3·030052 $_{27316}$	962871 $_{1489}$	2985075 $_{891}$
3351	11 22 92 01	37 629 052 551	887823 $_{8636}$	3·057368 $_{27312}$	964360 $_{1488}$	2984184 $_{890}$
3352	11 23 59 04	37 662 750 208	896459 $_{8636}$	3·084680 $_{27308}$	965848 $_{1488}$	2983294 $_{890}$
3353	11 24 26 09	37 696 467 977	905095 $_{8634}$	3·111988 $_{27303}$	967336 $_{1488}$	2982404 $_{889}$
3354	11 24 93 16	37 730 205 864	913729 $_{8633}$	3·139291 $_{27300}$	968824 $_{1488}$	2981515 $_{889}$
3355	11 25 60 25	37 763 963 875	922362 $_{8631}$	3·166591 $_{27295}$	970312 $_{1487}$	2980626 $_{888}$
3356	11 26 27 36	37 797 742 016	930993 $_{8631}$	3·193886 $_{27292}$	971799 $_{1487}$	2979738 $_{888}$
3357	11 26 94 49	37 831 540 293	939624 $_{8629}$	3·221178 $_{27287}$	973286 $_{1486}$	2978850 $_{887}$
3358	11 27 61 64	37 865 358 712	948253 $_{8628}$	3·248465 $_{27284}$	974772 $_{1487}$	2977963 $_{886}$
3359	11 28 28 81	37 899 197 279	956881 $_{8626}$	3·275749 $_{27279}$	976259 $_{1486}$	2977077 $_{887}$
3360	11 28 96 00	37 933 056 000	965507 $_{8625}$	3·303028 $_{27275}$	977745 $_{1486}$	2976190 $_{885}$
3361	11 29 63 21	37 966 934 881	974132 $_{8624}$	3·330303 $_{27271}$	979231 $_{1485}$	2975305 $_{885}$
3362	11 30 30 44	38 000 833 928	982756 $_{8623}$	3·357574 $_{27267}$	980716 $_{1485}$	2974420 $_{884}$
3363	11 30 97 69	38 034 753 147	991379 $_{8621}$	3·384841 $_{27263}$	982201 $_{1485}$	2973536 $_{884}$
3364	11 31 64 96	38 068 692 544	*000000 $_{8620}$	3·412104 $_{27259}$	983686 $_{1485}$	2972652 $_{884}$
3365	11 32 32 25	38 102 652 125	008620 $_{8619}$	3·439363 $_{27255}$	985171 $_{1484}$	2971768 $_{883}$
3366	11 32 99 56	38 136 631 896	017239 $_{8617}$	3·466618 $_{27251}$	986655 $_{1484}$	2970885 $_{882}$
3367	11 33 66 89	38 170 631 863	025856 $_{8617}$	3·493869 $_{27247}$	988139 $_{1483}$	2970003 $_{882}$
3368	11 34 34 24	38 204 652 032	034473 $_{8614}$	3·521116 $_{27243}$	989622 $_{1484}$	2969121 $_{881}$
3369	11 35 01 61	38 238 692 409	043087 $_{8614}$	3·548359 $_{27239}$	991106 $_{1483}$	2968240 $_{881}$
3370	11 35 69 00	38 272 753 000	051701 $_{8612}$	3·575598 $_{27234}$	992589 $_{1483}$	2967359 $_{880}$
3371	11 36 36 41	38 306 833 811	060313 $_{8612}$	3·602832 $_{27231}$	994072 $_{1482}$	2966479 $_{880}$
3372	11 37 03 84	38 340 934 848	068925 $_{8609}$	3·630063 $_{27227}$	995554 $_{1482}$	2965599 $_{879}$
3373	11 37 71 29	38 375 056 117	077534 $_{8609}$	3·657290 $_{27222}$	997036 $_{1482}$	2964720 $_{879}$
3374	11 38 38 76	38 409 197 624	086143 $_{8607}$	3·684512 $_{27219}$	998518 $_{1482}$	2963841 $_{878}$
3375	11 39 06 25	38 443 359 375	094750 $_{8606}$	3·711731 $_{27214}$	*000000 $_{1481}$	2962963 $_{878}$
3376	11 39 73 76	38 477 541 376	103356 $_{8605}$	3·738945 $_{27211}$	001481 $_{1481}$	2962085 $_{877}$
3377	11 40 41 29	38 511 743 633	111961 $_{8603}$	3·766156 $_{27206}$	002962 $_{1481}$	2961208 $_{876}$
3378	11 41 08 84	38 545 966 152	120564 $_{8603}$	3·793362 $_{27203}$	004443 $_{1481}$	2960332 $_{877}$
3379	11 41 76 41	38 580 208 939	129167 $_{8600}$	3·820565 $_{27198}$	005924 $_{1480}$	2959455 $_{875}$
3380	11 42 44 00	38 614 472 000	137767 $_{8600}$	3·847763 $_{27195}$	007404 $_{1480}$	2958580 $_{875}$
3381	11 43 11 61	38 648 755 341	146367 $_{8598}$	3·874958 $_{27190}$	008884 $_{1479}$	2957705 $_{875}$
3382	11 43 79 24	38 683 058 968	154965 $_{8597}$	3·902148 $_{27186}$	010363 $_{1479}$	2956830 $_{874}$
3383	11 44 46 89	38 717 382 887	163562 $_{8596}$	3·929334 $_{27183}$	011842 $_{1479}$	2955956 $_{873}$
3384	11 45 14 56	38 751 727 104	172158 $_{8595}$	3·956517 $_{27178}$	013321 $_{1479}$	2955083 $_{873}$
3385	11 45 82 25	38 786 091 625	180753 $_{8593}$	3·983695 $_{27174}$	014800 $_{1479}$	2954210 $_{873}$
3386	11 46 49 96	38 820 476 456	189346 $_{8592}$	4·010869 $_{27171}$	016279 $_{1478}$	2953337 $_{872}$
3387	11 47 17 69	38 854 881 603	197938 $_{8591}$	4·038040 $_{27166}$	017757 $_{1478}$	2952465 $_{871}$
3388	11 47 85 44	38 889 307 072	206529 $_{8589}$	4·065206 $_{27162}$	019235 $_{1477}$	2951594 $_{871}$
3389	11 48 53 21	38 923 752 869	215118 $_{8589}$	4·092368 $_{27158}$	020712 $_{1477}$	2950723 $_{870}$
3390	11 49 21 00	38 958 219 000	223707 $_{8586}$	4·119526 $_{27155}$	022189 $_{1477}$	2949853 $_{870}$
3391	11 49 88 81	38 992 705 471	232293 $_{8586}$	4·146681 $_{27150}$	023666 $_{1477}$	2948983 $_{870}$
3392	11 50 56 64	39 027 212 288	240879 $_{8585}$	4·173331 $_{27146}$	025143 $_{1476}$	2948113 $_{869}$
3393	11 51 24 49	39 061 739 457	249464 $_{8583}$	4·200977 $_{27142}$	026619 $_{1476}$	2947244 $_{868}$
3394	11 51 92 36	39 096 286 984	258047 $_{8582}$	4·228119 $_{27139}$	028095 $_{1476}$	2946376 $_{868}$
3395	11 52 60 25	39 130 854 875	266629 $_{8580}$	4·255258 $_{27134}$	029571 $_{1476}$	2945508 $_{867}$
3396	11 53 28 16	39 165 443 136	275209 $_{8579}$	4·282392 $_{27130}$	031047 $_{1475}$	2944641 $_{867}$
3397	11 53 96 09	39 200 051 773	283788 $_{8579}$	4·309522 $_{27127}$	032522 $_{1475}$	2943774 $_{866}$
3398	11 54 64 04	39 234 680 792	292367 $_{8576}$	4·336649 $_{27122}$	033997 $_{1475}$	2942908 $_{866}$
3399	11 55 32 01	39 269 330 199	300943 $_{8576}$	4·363771 $_{27118}$	035472 $_{1474}$	2942042 $_{866}$
3400	11 56 00 00	39 304 000 000	309519 $_{58·}$	4·390889 $_{180 +}$	036946 $_{15·}$	2941176 $_{0·000}$

No. n	Square n²	Cube n³	Square root √n	Sq. rt. of 10n √10n	Cube root ∛n	Reciprocal 1/n
			58·	180 +	15·	0·000
3400	11 56 00 00	39 304 000 000	309519 8574	4·390889 27114	036946 1474	2941176 864
3401	11 56 68 01	39 338 690 201	318093 8573	4·418003 27111	038420 1474	2940312 865
3402	11 57 36 04	39 373 400 808	326666 8572	4·445114 27106	039894 1473	2939447 863
3403	11 58 04 09	39 408 131 827	335238 8571	4·472220 27102	041367 1473	2938584 864
3404	11 58 72 16	39 442 883 264	343809 8569	4·499322 27099	042840 1473	2937720 862
3405	11 59 40 25	39 477 655 125	352378 8568	4·526421 27094	044313 1473	2936858 863
3406	11 60 08 36	39 512 447 416	360946 8567	4·553515 27091	045786 1472	2935995 861
3407	11 60 76 49	39 547 260 143	369513 8565	4·580606 27086	047258 1472	2935134 862
3408	11 61 44 64	39 582 093 312	378078 8564	4·607692 27083	048730 1472	2934272 860
3409	11 62 12 81	39 616 946 929	386642 8563	4·634775 27078	050202 1472	2933412 861
3410	11 62 81 00	39 651 821 000	395205 8562	4·661853 27075	051674 1471	2932551 859
3411	11 63 49 21	39 686 715 531	403767 8560	4·688928 27070	053145 1471	2931692 860
3412	11 64 17 44	39 721 630 528	412327 8560	4·715998 27067	054616 1471	2930832 858
3413	11 64 85 69	39 756 565 997	420887 8558	4·743065 27062	056086 1470	2929974 859
3414	11 65 53 96	39 791 521 944	429445 8556	4·770127 27059	057557 1470	2929115 857
3415	11 66 22 25	39 826 498 375	438001 8556	4·797186 27055	059027 1469	2928258 858
3416	11 66 90 56	39 861 495 296	446557 8554	4·824241 27051	060496 1470	2927400 856
3417	11 67 58 89	39 896 512 713	455111 8553	4·851292 27046	061966 1469	2926544 856
3418	11 68 27 24	39 931 550 632	463664 8552	4·878338 27043	063435 1469	2925688 856
3419	11 68 95 61	39 966 609 059	472216 8550	4·905381 27039	064904 1469	2924832 855
3420	11 69 64 00	40 001 688 000	480766 8549	4·932420 27035	066373 1468	2923977 855
3421	11 70 32 41	40 036 787 461	489315 8548	4·959455 27031	067841 1468	2923122 854
3422	11 71 00 84	40 071 907 448	497863 8547	4·986486 27027	069309 1468	2922268 854
3423	11 71 69 29	40 107 047 967	506410 8545	5·013513 27023	070777 1467	2921414 853
3424	11 72 37 76	40 142 209 024	514955 8545	5·040536 27019	072244 1467	2920561 853
3425	11 73 06 25	40 177 390 625	523500 8543	5·067555 27015	073711 1467	2919708 852
3426	11 73 74 76	40 212 592 776	532043 8541	5·094570 27012	075178 1467	2918856 852
3427	11 74 43 29	40 247 815 483	540584 8541	5·121582 27007	076645 1466	2918004 851
3428	11 75 11 84	40 283 058 752	549125 8539	5·148589 27003	078111 1466	2917153 851
3429	11 75 80 41	40 318 322 589	557664 8538	5·175592 27000	079577 1466	2916302 850
3430	11 76 49 00	40 353 607 000	566202 8537	5·202592 26995	081043 1465	2915452 850
3431	11 77 17 61	40 388 911 991	574739 8535	5·229587 26992	082508 1465	2914602 849
3432	11 77 86 24	40 424 237 568	583274 8534	5·256579 26987	083973 1465	2913753 849
3433	11 78 54 89	40 459 583 737	591808 8533	5·283566 26984	085438 1465	2912904 848
3434	11 79 23 56	40 494 950 504	600341 8532	5·310550 26980	086903 1464	2912056 848
3435	11 79 92 25	40 530 337 875	608873 8531	5·337530 26976	088367 1464	2911208 847
3436	11 80 60 96	40 565 745 856	617404 8529	5·364506 26972	089831 1464	2910361 847
3437	11 81 29 69	40 601 174 453	625933 8528	5·391478 26968	091295 1464	2909514 846
3438	11 81 98 44	40 636 623 672	634461 8527	5·418446 26964	092759 1463	2908668 846
3439	11 82 67 21	40 672 093 519	642988 8525	5·445410 26960	094222 1463	2907822 845
3440	11 83 36 00	40 707 584 000	651513 8525	5·472370 26956	095685 1462	2906977 845
3441	11 84 04 81	40 743 095 121	660038 8523	5·499326 26952	097147 1463	2906132 845
3442	11 84 73 64	40 778 626 888	668561 8521	5·526278 26949	098610 1462	2905288 844
3443	11 85 42 49	40 814 179 307	677082 8521	5·553227 26944	100072 1461	2904444 844
3444	11 86 11 36	40 849 752 384	685603 8519	5·580171 26941	101533 1462	2903600 842
3445	11 86 80 25	40 885 346 125	694122 8518	5·607112 26937	102995 1461	2902758 843
3446	11 87 49 16	40 920 960 536	702640 8517	5·634049 26932	104456 1461	2901915 842
3447	11 88 18 09	40 956 595 623	711157 8516	5·660981 26929	105917 1461	2901073 842
3448	11 88 87 04	40 992 251 392	719673 8514	5·687910 26925	107378 1460	2900232 841
3449	11 89 56 01	41 027 927 849	728187 8514	5·714835 26921	108838 1460	2899391 841
3450	11 90 25 00	41 063 625 000	736701 58·	5·741756 180 +	110298 15·	2898551 0·000

70

No. n	Square n^2	Cube n^3	Square root $\sqrt{n}$	Sq. rt. of $10n$ $\sqrt{10n}$	Cube root $\sqrt[3]{n}$	Reciprocal $\dfrac{1}{n}$
			58·	180 +	15·	0·000
3450	11 90 25 00	41 063 625 000	736701 $_{8512}$	5·741756 $_{26917}$	110298 $_{1460}$	2898551 $_{840}$
3451	11 90 94 01	41 099 342 851	745213 $_{8510}$	5·768673 $_{26914}$	111758 $_{1459}$	2897711 $_{840}$
3452	11 91 63 04	41 135 081 408	753723 $_{8510}$	5·795587 $_{26909}$	113217 $_{1460}$	2896871 $_{839}$
3453	11 92 32 09	41 170 840 677	762233 $_{8508}$	5·822496 $_{26905}$	114677 $_{1459}$	2896032 $_{838}$
3454	11 93 01 16	41 206 620 664	770741 $_{8507}$	5·849401 $_{26902}$	116136 $_{1458}$	2895194 $_{838}$
3455	11 93 70 25	41 242 421 375	779248 $_{8506}$	5·876303 $_{26898}$	117594 $_{1459}$	2894356 $_{837}$
3456	11 94 39 36	41 278 242 816	787754 $_{8504}$	5·903201 $_{26893}$	119053 $_{1458}$	2893519 $_{837}$
3457	11 95 08 49	41 314 084 993	796258 $_{8504}$	5·930094 $_{26890}$	120511 $_{1458}$	2892682 $_{837}$
3458	11 95 77 64	41 349 947 912	804762 $_{8502}$	5·956984 $_{26886}$	121969 $_{1457}$	2891845 $_{836}$
3459	11 96 46 81	41 385 831 579	813264 $_{8501}$	5·983870 $_{26882}$	123426 $_{1457}$	2891009 $_{836}$
3460	11 97 16 00	41 421 736 000	821765 $_{8499}$	6·010752 $_{26879}$	124883 $_{1457}$	2890173 $_{835}$
3461	11 97 85 21	41 457 661 181	830264 $_{8499}$	6·037631 $_{26874}$	126340 $_{1457}$	2889338 $_{835}$
3462	11 98 54 44	41 493 607 128	838763 $_{8497}$	6·064505 $_{26870}$	127797 $_{1456}$	2888504 $_{834}$
3463	11 99 23 69	41 529 573 847	847260 $_{8496}$	6·091375 $_{26867}$	129253 $_{1457}$	2887670 $_{834}$
3464	11 99 92 96	41 565 561 344	855756 $_{8495}$	6·118242 $_{26863}$	130710 $_{1455}$	2886836 $_{834}$
3465	12 00 62 25	41 601 569 625	864251 $_{8493}$	6·145105 $_{26859}$	132165 $_{1456}$	2886003 $_{833}$
3466	12 01 31 56	41 637 598 696	872744 $_{8492}$	6·171964 $_{26854}$	133621 $_{1455}$	2885170 $_{833}$
3467	12 02 00 89	41 673 648 563	881236 $_{8491}$	6·198818 $_{26852}$	135076 $_{1455}$	2884338 $_{832}$
3468	12 02 70 24	41 709 719 232	889727 $_{8490}$	6·225670 $_{26847}$	136531 $_{1455}$	2883506 $_{832}$
3469	12 03 39 61	41 745 810 709	898217 $_{8489}$	6·252517 $_{26843}$	137986 $_{1454}$	2882675 $_{831}$
3470	12 04 09 00	41 781 923 000	906706 $_{8487}$	6·279360 $_{26840}$	139440 $_{1455}$	2881844 $_{830}$
3471	12 04 78 41	41 818 056 111	915193 $_{8486}$	6·306200 $_{26835}$	140895 $_{1455}$	2881014 $_{830}$
3472	12 05 47 84	41 854 210 048	923679 $_{8485}$	6·333035 $_{26832}$	142349 $_{1453}$	2880184 $_{829}$
3473	12 06 17 29	41 890 384 817	932164 $_{8484}$	6·359867 $_{26828}$	143802 $_{1454}$	2879355 $_{829}$
3474	12 06 86 76	41 926 580 424	940648 $_{8483}$	6·386695 $_{26824}$	145256 $_{1453}$	2878526 $_{828}$
3475	12 07 56 25	41 962 796 875	949131 $_{8481}$	6·413519 $_{26820}$	146709 $_{1452}$	2877698 $_{828}$
3476	12 08 25 76	41 999 034 176	957612 $_{8480}$	6·440339 $_{26816}$	148161 $_{1453}$	2876870 $_{827}$
3477	12 08 95 29	42 035 292 333	966092 $_{8479}$	6·467155 $_{26813}$	149614 $_{1452}$	2876043 $_{827}$
3478	12 09 64 84	42 071 571 352	974571 $_{8477}$	6·493968 $_{26808}$	151066 $_{1452}$	2875216 $_{827}$
3479	12 10 34 41	42 107 871 239	983048 $_{8477}$	6·520776 $_{26805}$	152518 $_{1452}$	2874389 $_{826}$
3480	12 11 04 00	42 144 192 000	·991525 $_{8475}$	6·547581 $_{26801}$	153970 $_{1451}$	2873563 $_{825}$
3481	12 11 73 61	42 180 533 641	*000000 $_{8474}$	6·574382 $_{26797}$	155421 $_{1451}$	2872738 $_{825}$
3482	12 12 43 24	42 216 896 168	008474 $_{8473}$	6·601179 $_{26793}$	156872 $_{1451}$	2871913 $_{825}$
3483	12 13 12 89	42 253 279 587	016947 $_{8471}$	6·627972 $_{26790}$	158323 $_{1451}$	2871088 $_{824}$
3484	12 13 82 56	42 289 683 904	025418 $_{8471}$	6·654762 $_{26785}$	159774 $_{1450}$	2870264 $_{824}$
3485	12 14 52 25	42 326 109 125	033889 $_{8469}$	6·681547 $_{26782}$	161224 $_{1450}$	2869440 $_{823}$
3486	12 15 21 96	42 362 555 256	042358 $_{8468}$	6·708329 $_{26778}$	162674 $_{1450}$	2868617 $_{822}$
3487	12 15 91 69	42 399 022 303	050826 $_{8466}$	6·735107 $_{26773}$	164124 $_{1449}$	2867795 $_{823}$
3488	12 16 61 44	42 435 510 272	059292 $_{8466}$	6·761880 $_{26771}$	165573 $_{1449}$	2866972 $_{821}$
3489	12 17 31 21	42 472 019 169	067758 $_{8464}$	6·788651 $_{26766}$	167022 $_{1449}$	2866151 $_{821}$
3490	12 18 01 00	42 508 549 000	076222 $_{8463}$	6·815417 $_{26762}$	168471 $_{1449}$	2865330 $_{821}$
3491	12 18 70 81	42 545 099 771	084685 $_{8462}$	6·842179 $_{26759}$	169920 $_{1448}$	2864509 $_{821}$
3492	12 19 40 64	42 581 671 488	093147 $_{8460}$	6·868938 $_{26755}$	171368 $_{1448}$	2863688 $_{819}$
3493	12 20 10 49	42 618 264 157	101607 $_{8460}$	6·895693 $_{26751}$	172816 $_{1448}$	2862869 $_{820}$
3494	12 20 80 36	42 654 877 784	110067 $_{8458}$	6·922444 $_{26747}$	174264 $_{1447}$	2862049 $_{819}$
3495	12 21 50 25	42 691 512 375	118525 $_{8457}$	6·949191 $_{26743}$	175711 $_{1448}$	2861230 $_{818}$
3496	12 22 20 16	42 728 167 936	126982 $_{8456}$	6·975934 $_{26740}$	177159 $_{1447}$	2860412 $_{818}$
3497	12 22 90 09	42 764 844 473	135438 $_{8454}$	7·002674 $_{26735}$	178606 $_{1446}$	2859594 $_{818}$
3498	12 23 60 04	42 801 541 992	143892 $_{8454}$	7·029409 $_{26732}$	180052 $_{1447}$	2858776 $_{817}$
3499	12 24 30 01	42 838 260 499	152346 $_{8452}$	7·056141 $_{26728}$	181499 $_{1446}$	2857959 $_{816}$
3500	12 25 00 00	42 875 000 000	160798	7·082869	182945	2857143
			59·	180 +	15·	0·000

No. n	Square n^2	Cube n^3	Square root $\sqrt{n}$	Sq. rt. of 10n $\sqrt{10n}$	Cube root $\sqrt[3]{n}$	Reciprocal $\frac{1}{n}$
			59·	180 +	15·	0·000
3500	12 25 00 00	42 875 000 000	160798 ₈₄₅₁	7·082869 ₂₆₇₂₅	182945 ₁₄₄₆	2857143 ₈₁₆
3501	12 25 70 01	42 911 760 501	169249 ₈₄₅₀	7·109594 ₂₆₇₂₀	184391 ₁₄₄₅	2856327 ₈₁₆
3502	12 26 40 04	42 948 542 008	177699 ₈₄₄₈	7·136314 ₂₆₇₁₇	185836 ₁₄₄₅	2855511 ₈₁₆
3503	12 27 10 09	42 985 344 527	186147 ₈₄₄₇	7·163031 ₂₆₇₁₂	187282 ₁₄₄₅	2854696 ₈₁₅
3504	12 27 80 16	43 022 168 064	194594 ₈₄₄₆	7·189743 ₂₆₇₀₉	188727 ₁₄₄₄	2853881 ₈₁₅
3505	12 28 50 25	43 059 012 625	203040 ₈₄₄₅	7·216452 ₂₆₇₀₅	190171 ₁₄₄₅	2853067 ₈₁₄
3506	12 29 20 36	43 095 878 216	211485 ₈₄₄₄	7·243157 ₂₆₇₀₂	191616 ₁₄₄₄	2852253 ₈₁₃
3507	12 29 90 49	43 132 764 843	219929 ₈₄₄₃	7·269859 ₂₆₆₉₇	193060 ₁₄₄₄	2851440 ₈₁₃
3508	12 30 60 64	43 169 672 512	228372 ₈₄₄₁	7·296556 ₂₆₆₉₄	194504 ₁₄₄₄	2850627 ₈₁₃
3509	12 31 30 81	43 206 601 229	236813 ₈₄₄₀	7·323250 ₂₆₆₉₀	195948 ₁₄₄₃	2849815 ₈₁₂
3510	12 32 01 00	43 243 551 000	245253 ₈₄₃₉	7·349940 ₂₆₆₈₆	197391 ₁₄₄₃	2849003 ₈₁₂
3511	12 32 71 21	43 280 521 831	253692 ₈₄₃₈	7·376626 ₂₆₆₈₂	198834 ₁₄₄₃	2848191 ₈₁₂
3512	12 33 41 44	43 317 513 728	262130 ₈₄₃₆	7·403308 ₂₆₆₇₉	200277 ₁₄₄₃	2847380 ₈₁₁
3513	12 34 11 69	43 354 526 697	270566 ₈₄₃₅	7·429987 ₂₆₆₇₅	201720 ₁₄₄₂	2846570 ₈₁₀
3514	12 34 81 96	43 391 560 744	279001 ₈₄₃₄	7·456662 ₂₆₆₇₁	203162 ₁₄₄₂	2845760 ₈₁₀
3515	12 35 52 25	43 428 615 875	287435 ₈₄₃₃	7·483333 ₂₆₆₆₇	204604 ₁₄₄₂	2844950 ₈₀₉
3516	12 36 22 56	43 465 692 096	295868 ₈₄₃₂	7·510000 ₂₆₆₆₃	206046 ₁₄₄₁	2844141 ₈₀₉
3517	12 36 92 89	43 502 789 413	304300 ₈₄₃₁	7·536663 ₂₆₆₆₀	207487 ₁₄₄₁	2843332 ₈₀₈
3518	12 37 63 24	43 539 907 832	312731 ₈₄₂₉	7·563323 ₂₆₆₅₅	208928 ₁₄₄₁	2842524 ₈₀₈
3519	12 38 33 61	43 577 047 359	321160 ₈₄₂₈	7·589978 ₂₆₆₅₂	210369 ₁₄₄₁	2841716 ₈₀₇
3520	12 39 04 00	43 614 208 000	329588 ₈₄₂₇	7·616630 ₂₆₆₄₉	211810 ₁₄₄₀	2840909 ₈₀₇
3521	12 39 74 41	43 651 389 761	338015 ₈₄₂₅	7·643279 ₂₆₆₄₄	213250 ₁₄₄₀	2840102 ₈₀₆
3522	12 40 44 84	43 688 592 648	346440 ₈₄₂₅	7·669923 ₂₆₆₄₁	214690 ₁₄₄₀	2839296 ₈₀₆
3523	12 41 15 29	43 725 816 667	354865 ₈₄₂₃	7·696564 ₂₆₆₃₆	216130 ₁₄₄₀	2838490 ₈₀₆
3524	12 41 85 76	43 763 061 824	363288 ₈₄₂₂	7·723200 ₂₆₆₃₄	217570 ₁₄₃₉	2837684 ₈₀₅
3525	12 42 56 25	43 800 328 125	371710 ₈₄₂₁	7·749834 ₂₆₆₂₉	219009 ₁₄₃₉	2836879 ₈₀₄
3526	12 43 26 76	43 837 615 576	380131 ₈₄₂₀	7·776463 ₂₆₆₂₅	220448 ₁₄₃₉	2836075 ₈₀₄
3527	12 43 97 29	43 874 924 183	388551 ₈₄₁₉	7·803088 ₂₆₆₂₂	221887 ₁₄₃₈	2835271 ₈₀₄
3528	12 44 67 84	43 912 253 952	396970 ₈₄₁₇	7·829710 ₂₆₆₁₈	223325 ₁₄₃₈	2834467 ₈₀₃
3529	12 45 38 41	43 949 604 889	405387 ₈₄₁₆	7·856328 ₂₆₆₁₄	224763 ₁₄₃₈	2833664 ₈₀₃
3530	12 46 09 00	43 986 977 000	413803 ₈₄₁₅	7·882942 ₂₆₆₁₁	226201 ₁₄₃₈	2832861 ₈₀₂
3531	12 46 79 61	44 024 370 291	422218 ₈₄₁₄	7·909553 ₂₆₆₀₆	227639 ₁₄₃₇	2832059 ₈₀₂
3532	12 47 50 24	44 061 784 768	430632 ₈₄₁₂	7·936159 ₂₆₆₀₃	229076 ₁₄₃₇	2831257 ₈₀₂
3533	12 48 20 89	44 099 220 437	439044 ₈₄₁₂	7·962762 ₂₆₅₉₉	230513 ₁₄₃₇	2830456 ₈₀₁
3534	12 48 91 56	44 136 677 304	447456 ₈₄₁₀	7·989361 ₂₆₅₉₆	231950 ₁₄₃₇	2829655 ₈₀₁
3535	12 49 62 25	44 174 155 375	455866 ₈₄₀₉	8·015957 ₂₆₅₉₁	233387 ₁₄₃₆	2828854 ₈₀₀
3536	12 50 32 96	44 211 654 656	464275 ₈₄₀₈	8·042548 ₂₆₅₈₈	234823 ₁₄₃₆	2828054 ₈₀₀
3537	12 51 03 69	44 249 175 153	472683 ₈₄₀₆	8·069136 ₂₆₅₈₄	236259 ₁₄₃₆	2827255 ₇₉₉
3538	12 51 74 44	44 286 716 872	481089 ₈₄₀₆	8·095720 ₂₆₅₈₁	237695 ₁₄₃₅	2826456 ₇₉₉
3539	12 52 45 21	44 324 279 819	489495 ₈₄₀₄	8·122301 ₂₆₅₇₆	239130 ₁₄₃₆	2825657 ₇₉₉
3540	12 53 16 00	44 361 864 000	497899 ₈₄₀₃	8·148877 ₂₆₅₇₃	240566 ₁₄₃₅	2824859 ₇₉₈
3541	12 53 86 81	44 399 469 421	506302 ₈₄₀₂	8·175450 ₂₆₅₆₉	242001 ₁₄₃₄	2824061 ₇₉₈
3542	12 54 57 64	44 437 096 088	514704 ₈₄₀₁	8·202019 ₂₆₅₆₅	243435 ₁₄₃₅	2823264 ₇₉₇
3543	12 55 28 49	44 474 744 007	523105 ₈₃₉₉	8·228584 ₂₆₅₆₂	244870 ₁₄₃₄	2822467 ₇₉₇
3544	12 55 99 36	44 512 413 184	531504 ₈₃₉₉	8·255146 ₂₆₅₅₈	246304 ₁₄₃₄	2821670 ₇₉₇
3545	12 56 70 25	44 550 103 625	539903 ₈₃₉₇	8·281704 ₂₆₅₅₄	247738 ₁₄₃₃	2820874 ₇₉₅
3546	12 57 41 16	44 587 815 336	548300 ₈₃₉₇	8·308258 ₂₆₅₅₀	249171 ₁₄₃₄	2820079 ₇₉₅
3547	12 58 12 09	44 625 548 323	556696 ₈₃₉₆	8·334808 ₂₆₅₄₇	250605 ₁₄₃₄	2819284 ₇₉₅
3548	12 58 83 04	44 663 302 592	565090 ₈₃₉₄	8·361355 ₂₆₅₄₃	252038 ₁₄₃₂	2818489 ₇₉₅
3549	12 59 54 01	44 701 078 149	573484 ₈₃₉₂	8·387898 ₂₆₅₃₉	253470 ₁₄₃₃	2817695 ₇₉₄
3550	12 60 25 00	44 738 875 000	581876	8·414437	254903	2816901
			59·	180 +	15·	0·000

No. n	Square n^2	Cube n^3	Square root $\sqrt{n}$ 59·	Sq. rt. of 10n $\sqrt{10n}$ 180 +	Cube root $\sqrt[3]{n}$ 15·	Reciprocal $\frac{1}{n}$ 0·000
3550	12 60 25 00	44 738 875 000	581876 8392	8·414437 26535	254903 1432	2816901 793
3551	12 60 96 01	44 776 693 151	590268 8390	8·440972 26532	256335 1432	2816108 793
3552	12 61 67 04	44 814 532 608	598658 8389	8·467504 26528	257767 1432	2815315 792
3553	12 62 38 09	44 852 393 377	607047 8387	8·494032 26524	259199 1431	2814523 792
3554	12 63 09 16	44 890 275 464	615434 8387	8·520556 26520	260630 1431 1432	2813731 791
3555	12 63 80 25	44 928 178 875	623821 8385	8·547076 26517	262062 1430	2812940
3556	12 64 51 36	44 966 103 616	632206 8384	8·573593 26513	263492 1431	2812148 792
3557	12 65 22 49	45 004 049 693	640590 8383	8·600106 26509	264923 1431	2811358 790
3558	12 65 93 64	45 042 017 112	648973 8382	8·626615 26506	266354 1430	2810568 790
3559	12 66 64 81	45 080 005 879	657355 8381	8·653121 26502	267784 1429	2809778 790
3560	12 67 36 00	45 118 016 000	665736 8379	8·679623 26498	269213 1430	2808989 789
3561	12 68 07 21	45 156 047 481	674115 8378	8·706121 26494	270643 1429	2808200 788
3562	12 68 78 44	45 194 100 328	682493 8377	8·732615 26491	272072 1429	2807412 788
3563	12 69 49 69	45 232 174 547	690870 8376	8·759106 26487	273501 1429	2806624 788
3564	12 70 20 96	45 270 270 144	699246 8375	8·785593 26483	274930 1429	2805836 787
3565	12 70 92 25	45 308 387 125	707621 8374	8·812076 26479	276359 1428	2805049 787
3566	12 71 63 56	45 346 525 496	715995 8372	8·838555 26476	277787 1428	2804262 786
3567	12 72 34 89	45 384 685 263	724367 8371	8·865031 26472	279215 1428	2803476 786
3568	12 73 06 24	45 422 866 432	732738 8370	8·891503 26469	280642 1427	2802691 785
3569	12 73 77 61	45 461 069 009	741108 8369	8·917972 26464	282070 1427	2801905 785
3570	12 74 49 00	45 499 293 000	749477 8368	8·944436 26461	283497 1427	2801120 784
3571	12 75 20 41	45 537 538 411	757845 8366	8·970897 26457	284924 1427	2800336 784
3572	12 75 91 84	45 575 805 248	766211 8366	8·997354 26454	286351 1426	2799552 783
3573	12 76 63 29	45 614 093 517	774577 8364	9·023808 26450	287777 1426	2798769 784
3574	12 77 34 76	45 652 403 224	782941 8363	9·050258 26446	289203 1426	2797985 782
3575	12 78 06 25	45 690 734 375	791304 8362	9·076704 26442	290629 1425	2797203 782
3576	12 78 77 76	45 729 086 976	799666 8360	9·103146 26439	292054 1426	2796421 782
3577	12 79 49 29	45 767 461 033	808026 8360	9·129585 26435	293480 1425	2795639 782
3578	12 80 20 84	45 805 856 552	816386 8358	9·156020 26432	294905 1425	2794857 780
3579	12 80 92 41	45 844 273 539	824744 8357	9·182452 26427	296330 1424	2794077 781
3580	12 81 64 00	45 882 712 000	833101 8356	9·208879 26424	297754 1424	2793296 780
3581	12 82 35 61	45 921 171 941	841457 8355	9·235303 26421	299178 1424	2792516 780
3582	12 83 07 24	45 959 653 368	849812 8354	9·261724 26416	300602 1424	2791736 779
3583	12 83 78 89	45 998 156 287	858166 8352	9·288140 26413	302026 1423	2790957 778
3584	12 84 50 56	46 036 680 704	866518 8352	9·314553 26409	303449 1424	2790179 779
3585	12 85 22 25	46 075 226 625	874870 8350	9·340962 26406	304873 1423	2789400 778
3586	12 85 93 96	46 113 794 056	883220 8349	9·367368 26402	306296 1422	2788622 777
3587	12 86 65 69	46 152 383 003	891569 8348	9·393770 26398	307718 1423	2787845 777
3588	12 87 37 44	46 190 993 472	899917 8346	9·420168 26394	309141 1422	2787068 777
3589	12 88 09 21	46 229 625 469	908263 8346	9·446562 26391	310563 1422	2786291 776
3590	12 88 81 00	46 268 279 000	916609 8344	9·472953 26387	311985 1421	2785515 775
3591	12 89 52 81	46 306 954 071	924953 8343	9·499340 26384	313406 1421	2784740 776
3592	12 90 24 64	46 345 650 688	933296 8342	9·525724 26380	314827 1422	2783964 774
3593	12 90 96 49	46 384 368 857	941638 8341	9·552104 26376	316249 1420	2783190 775
3594	12 91 68 36	46 423 108 584	949979 8340	9·578480 26372	317669 1421	2782415 774
3595	12 92 40 25	46 461 869 875	958319 8338	9·604852 26369	319090 1420	2781641 773
3596	12 93 12 16	46 500 652 736	966657 8338	9·631221 26365	320510 1420	2780868 773
3597	12 93 84 09	46 539 457 173	974995 8336	9·657586 26362	321930 1420	2780095 773
3598	12 94 56 04	46 578 283 192	983331 8335	9·683948 26357	323350 1419	2779322 772
3599	12 95 28 01	46 617 130 799	991666 8334	9·710305 26355	324769 1420	2778550 772
3600	12 96 00 00	46 656 000 000	*000000 60·	9·736660 180 +	326189 15·	2777778 0·000

73

No. n	Square n^2	Cube n^3	Square root $\sqrt{n}$	Sq. rt. of 10n $\sqrt{10n}$	Cube root $\sqrt[3]{n}$	Reciprocal $\frac{1}{n}$
			60·	180 +		0·000
3600	12 96 00 00	46 656 000 000	000000 8333	9·736660 26350	3261·59 1419	2777778 772
3601	12 96 72 01	46 694 890 801	008333 8331	9·763010 26347	327608 1418	2777006 771
3602	12 97 44 04	46 733 803 208	016664 8331	9·789357 26343	329026 1419	2776235 770
3603	12 98 16 09	46 772 737 227	024995 8329	9·815700 26340	330445 1418	2775465 770
3604	12 98 88 16	46 811 692 864	033324 8328	9·842040 26335	331863 1418	2774695 770
3605	12 99 60 25	46 850 670 125	041652 8327	9·868375 26333	333281 1417	2773925 769
3606	13 00 32 36	46 889 669 016	049979 8326	9·894708 26328	334698 1418	2773156 769
3607	13 01 04 49	46 928 689 543	058305 8325	9·921036 26325	336116 1417	2772387 768
3608	13 01 76 64	46 967 731 712	066630 8323	9·947361 26321	337533 1417	2771619 768
3609	13 02 48 81	47 006 795 529	074953 8323	9·973682 26318	338950 1416	2770851 768
3610	13 03 21 00	47 045 881 000	083276 8321	*0·000000 26314	340366 1417	2770083 767
3611	13 03 93 21	47 084 988 131	091597 8320	0·026314 26310	341783 1416	2769316 767
3612	13 04 65 44	47 124 116 928	099917 8319	0·052624 26307	343199 1416	2768549 766
3613	13 05 37 69	47 163 267 397	108236 8317	0·078931 26303	344615 1415	2767783 766
3614	13 06 09 96	47 202 439 544	116553 8317	0·105234 26299	346030 1416	2767017 765
3615	13 06 82 25	47 241 633 375	124870 8316	0·131533 26296	347446 1415	2766252 765
3616	13 07 54 56	47 280 848 896	133186 8314	0·157829 26292	348861 1414	2765487 765
3617	13 08 26 89	47 320 086 113	141500 8313	0·184121 26289	350275 1415	2764722 765
3618	13 08 99 24	47 359 345 032	149813 8312	0·210410 26285	351690 1414	2763958 764
3619	13 09 71 61	47 398 625 659	158125 8311	0·236695 26281	353104 1414	2763194 764
3620	13 10 44 00	47 437 928 000	166436 8310	0·262976 26278	354518 1414	2762431 763
3621	13 11 16 41	47 477 252 061	174746 8308	0·289254 26273	355932 1413	2761668 763
3622	13 11 88 84	47 516 597 848	183054 8308	0·315527 26271	357345 1413	2760906 762
3623	13 12 61 29	47 555 965 367	191362 8306	0·341798 26267	358758 1413	2760144 762
3624	13 13 33 76	47 595 354 624	199668 8305	0·368065 26263	360171 1413	2759382 761
3625	13 14 06 25	47 634 765 625	207973 8304	0·394328 26259	361584 1413	2758621 761
3626	13 14 78 76	47 674 198 376	216277 8303	0·420587 26256	362997 1412	2757860 761
3627	13 15 51 29	47 713 652 883	224580 8301	0·446843 26252	364409 1412	2757100 760
3628	13 16 23 84	47 753 129 152	232881 8301	0·473095 26249	365821 1411	2756340 760
3629	13 16 96 41	47 792 627 189	241182 8299	0·499344 26245	367232 1412	2755580 760
3630	13 17 69 00	47 832 147 000	249481 8299	0·525589 26241	368644 1411	2754821 759
3631	13 18 41 61	47 871 688 591	257780 8297	0·551830 26238	370055 1411	2754062 759
3632	13 19 14 24	47 911 251 968	266077 8296	0·578068 26234	371466 1410	2753304 758
3633	13 19 86 89	47 950 837 137	274373 8294	0·604302 26231	372876 1411	2752546 757
3634	13 20 59 56	47 990 444 104	282667 8294	0·630533 26227	374287 1410	2751789 757
3635	13 21 32 25	48 030 072 875	290961 8293	0·656760 26223	375697 1410	2751032 757
3636	13 22 04 96	48 069 723 456	299254 8291	0·682983 26220	377107 1409	2750275 756
3637	13 22 77 69	48 109 395 853	307545 8290	0·709203 26216	378516 1409	2749519 756
3638	13 23 50 44	48 149 090 072	315835 8290	0·735419 26212	379925 1410	2748763 755
3639	13 24 23 21	48 188 806 119	324125 8288	0·761631 26209	381335 1408	2748008 755
3640	13 24 96 00	48 228 544 000	332413 8286	0·787840 26206	382743 1409	2747253 755
3641	13 25 68 81	48 268 303 721	340699 8286	0·814046 26201	384152 1408	2746498 755
3642	13 26 41 64	48 308 085 288	348985 8285	0·840247 26198	385560 1408	2745744 754
3643	13 27 14 49	48 347 888 707	357270 8283	0·866445 26195	386968 1408	2744990 754
3644	13 27 87 36	48 387 713 984	365553 8282	0·892640 26191	388376 1408	2744237 753
3645	13 28 60 25	48 427 561 125	373835 8282	0·918831 26187	389784 1407	2743484 753
3646	13 29 33 16	48 467 430 136	382117 8280	0·945018 26184	391191 1407	2742732 752
3647	13 30 06 09	48 507 321 023	390397 8278	0·971202 26180	392598 1407	2741980 752
3648	13 30 79 04	48 547 233 792	398675 8278	0·997382 26177	394005 1406	2741228 752
3649	13 31 52 01	48 587 168 449	406953 8277	1·023559 26173	395411 1406	2740477 751
3650	13 32 25 00	48 627 125 000	415230 60·	1·049732 190 +	396817 15·	2739726 0·000

No. n	Square n²	Cube n³	Square root √n	Sq. rt. of 10n √10n	Cube root ∛n	Reciprocal 1/n
			60·	190 +	15·	0·000
3650	13 32 25 00	48 627 125 000	415230 _8275_	1·049732 _26169_	396817 _1406_	2739726 _750_
3651	13 32 98 01	48 667 103 451	423505 _8275_	1·075901 _26166_	398223 _1406_	2738976 _750_
3652	13 33 71 04	48 707 103 808	431780 _8273_	1·102067 _26162_	399629 _1405_	2738226 _750_
3653	13 34 44 09	48 747 126 077	440053 _8272_	1·128229 _26159_	401034 _1406_	2737476 _749_
3654	13 35 17 16	48 787 170 264	448325 _8271_	1·154388 _26155_	402440 _1405_	2736727 _749_
3655	13 35 90 25	48 827 236 375	456596 _8270_	1·180543 _26151_	403845 _1404_	2735978 _748_
3656	13 36 63 36	48 867 324 416	464866 _8269_	1·206694 _26148_	405249 _1405_	2735230 _748_
3657	13 37 36 49	48 907 434 393	473135 _8267_	1·232842 _26145_	406654 _1404_	2734482 _748_
3658	13 38 09 64	48 947 566 312	481402 _8267_	1·258987 _26145_	408058 _1404_	2733734 _748_
3659	13 38 82 81	48 987 720 179	489669 _8265_	1·285127 _26140_	409462 _1403_	2732987 _747_
3660	13 39 56 00	49 027 896 000	497934 _8264_	1·311265 _26138_	410865 _1404_	2732240 _747_
3661	13 40 29 21	49 068 093 781	506198 _8263_	1·337398 _26133_	412269 _1403_	2731494 _746_
3662	13 41 02 44	49 108 313 528	514461 _8262_	1·363528 _26130_	413672 _1403_	2730748 _746_
3663	13 41 75 69	49 148 555 247	522723 _8261_	1·389655 _26127_	415075 _1403_	2730003 _745_
3664	13 42 48 96	49 188 818 944	530984 _8259_	1·415778 _26123_	416478 _1402_	2729258 _745_
3665	13 43 22 25	49 229 104 625	539243 _8259_	1·441897 _26119_	417880 _1402_	2728513 _745_
3666	13 43 95 56	49 269 412 296	547502 _8257_	1·468013 _26116_	419282 _1402_	2727769 _744_
3667	13 44 68 89	49 309 741 963	555759 _8257_	1·494125 _26112_	420684 _1402_	2727025 _744_
3668	13 45 42 24	49 350 093 632	564016 _8255_	1·520234 _26109_	422086 _1401_	2726281 _744_
3669	13 46 15 61	49 390 467 309	572271 _8254_	1·546339 _26105_	423487 _1401_	2725538 _743_
3670	13 46 89 00	49 430 863 000	580525 _8253_	1·572441 _26102_	424888 _1401_	2724796 _743_
3671	13 47 62 41	49 471 280 711	588778 _8252_	1·598539 _26098_	426289 _1401_	2724053 _742_
3672	13 48 35 84	49 511 720 448	597030 _8250_	1·624633 _26094_	427690 _1400_	2723312 _741_
3673	13 49 09 29	49 552 182 217	605280 _8250_	1·650724 _26091_	429090 _1400_	2722570 _741_
3674	13 49 82 76	49 592 666 024	613530 _8248_	1·676811 _26087_	430490 _1400_	2721829 _741_
3675	13 50 56 25	49 633 171 875	621778 _8248_	1·702895 _26084_	431890 _1399_	2721088 _740_
3676	13 51 29 76	49 673 699 776	630026 _8246_	1·728975 _26080_	433289 _1400_	2720348 _740_
3677	13 52 03 29	49 714 249 733	638272 _8245_	1·755052 _26077_	434689 _1399_	2719608 _740_
3678	13 52 76 84	49 754 821 752	646517 _8244_	1·781125 _26073_	436088 _1399_	2718869 _739_
3679	13 53 50 41	49 795 415 839	654761 _8243_	1·807195 _26070_	437487 _1398_	2718130 _739_
3680	13 54 24 00	49 836 032 000	663004 _8241_	1·833261 _26066_	438885 _1399_	2717391 _739_
3681	13 54 97 61	49 876 670 241	671245 _8241_	1·859323 _26062_	440284 _1398_	2716653 _738_
3682	13 55 71 24	49 917 330 568	679486 _8239_	1·885382 _26059_	441682 _1397_	2715915 _738_
3683	13 56 44 89	49 958 012 987	687725 _8239_	1·911438 _26056_	443079 _1398_	2715178 _737_
3684	13 57 18 56	49 998 717 504	695964 _8237_	1·937490 _26052_	444477 _1397_	2714441 _737_
3685	13 57 92 25	50 039 444 125	704201 _8236_	1·963538 _26048_	445874 _1397_	2713704 _736_
3686	13 58 65 96	50 080 192 856	712437 _8235_	1·989583 _26045_	447271 _1397_	2712968 _736_
3687	13 59 39 69	50 120 963 703	720672 _8234_	2·015624 _26041_	448668 _1397_	2712232 _737_
3688	13 60 13 44	50 161 756 672	728906 _8233_	2·041662 _26038_	450065 _1396_	2711497 _735_
3689	13 60 87 21	50 202 571 769	737139 _8231_	2·067696 _26031_	451461 _1396_	2710762 _735_
3690	13 61 61 00	50 243 409 000	745370 _8231_	2·093727 _26027_	452857 _1396_	2710027 _734_
3691	13 62 34 81	50 284 268 371	753601 _8229_	2·119754 _26024_	454253 _1395_	2709293 _734_
3692	13 63 08 64	50 325 149 888	761830 _8228_	2·145778 _26020_	455648 _1396_	2708559 _733_
3693	13 63 82 49	50 366 053 557	770058 _8228_	2·171798 _26017_	457044 _1395_	2707826 _733_
3694	13 64 56 36	50 406 979 384	778286 _8226_	2·197815 _26013_	458439 _1395_	2707093 _733_
3695	13 65 30 25	50 447 927 375	786512 _8225_	2·223828 _26009_	459834 _1394_	2706360 _732_
3696	13 66 04 16	50 488 897 536	794737 _8223_	2·249837 _26007_	461228 _1394_	2705628 _732_
3697	13 66 78 09	50 529 889 873	802960 _8223_	2·275844 _26002_	462622 _1394_	2704896 _732_
3698	13 67 52 04	50 570 904 392	811183 _8222_	2·301846 _25999_	464016 _1394_	2704164 _731_
3699	13 68 26 01	50 611 941 099	819405 _8220_	2·327845 _25996_	465410 _1394_	2703433 _730_
3700	13 69 00 00	50 653 000 000	827625	2·353841	466804	2702703
			60·	190 +	15·	0·000

75

No. n	Square n²	Cube n³	Square root √n	Sq. rt. of 10n √10n	Cube root ∛n	Reciprocal 1/n
			60·	190 +	15·	0·000
3700	13 69 00 00	50 653 000 000	827625 8220	2·353841 25992	466804 1393	2702703 731
3701	13 69 74 01	50 694 081 101	835845 8218	2·379833 25988	468197 1393	2701972 729
3702	13 70 48 04	50 735 184 408	844063 8217	2·405821 25985	469590 1393	2701243 730
3703	13 71 22 09	50 776 309 927	852280 8216	2·431806 25982	470983 1392	2700513 729
3704	13 71 96 16	50 817 457 664	860496 8215	2·457788 25978	472375 1393	2699784 729
3705	13 72 70 25	50 858 627 625	868711 8214	2·483766 25974	473768 1392	2699055 728
3706	13 73 44 36	50 899 819 816	876925 8213	2·509740 25971	475160 1391	2698327 728
3707	13 74 18 49	50 941 034 243	885138 8211	2·535711 25967	476551 1391	2697599 727
3708	13 74 92 64	50 982 270 912	893349 8211	2·561678 25964	477943 1391	2696872 727
3709	13 75 66 81	51 023 529 829	901560 8209	2·587642 25961	479334 1391	2696145 727
3710	13 76 41 00	51 064 811 000	909769 8209	2·613603 25957	480725 1391	2695418 727
3711	13 77 15 21	51 106 114 431	917978 8207	2·639560 25953	482116 1391	2694691 725
3712	13 77 89 44	51 147 440 128	926185 8206	2·665513 25950	483507 1390	2693966 725
3713	13 78 63 69	51 188 788 097	934391 8205	2·691463 25947	484897 1390	2693240 726
3714	13 79 37 96	51 230 158 344	942596 8204	2·717410 25943	486287 1390	2692515 725
3715	13 80 12 25	51 271 550 875	950800 8203	2·743353 25939	487677 1389	2691790 724
3716	13 80 86 56	51 312 965 696	959003 8201	2·769292 25936	489066 1389	2691066 724
3717	13 81 60 89	51 354 402 813	967204 8201	2·795228 25933	490455 1389	2690342 724
3718	13 82 35 24	51 395 862 232	975405 8199	2·821161 25929	491844 1389	2689618 723
3719	13 83 09 61	51 437 343 959	983604 8199	2·847090 25925	493233 1389	2688895 723
3720	13 83 84 00	51 478 848 000	991803 8197	2·873015 25922	494622 1388	2688172 722
3721	13 84 58 41	51 520 374 361	*000000 8196	2·898937 25919	496010 1388	2687450 722
3722	13 85 32 84	51 561 923 048	008196 8195	2·924856 25915	497398 1388	2686728 722
3723	13 86 07 29	51 603 404 067	016391 8194	2·950771 25912	498786 1387	2686006 722
3724	13 86 81 76	51 645 087 424	024585 8193	2·976683 25908	500173 1388	2685285 721
3725	13 87 56 25	51 686 703 125	032778 8192	3·002591 25904	501561 1387	2684564 721
3726	13 88 30 76	51 728 341 176	040970 8191	3·028495 25901	502948 1387	2683843 721
3727	13 89 05 29	51 770 001 583	049161 8189	3·054396 25898	504335 1386	2683123 720
3728	13 89 79 84	51 811 684 352	057350 8189	3·080294 25894	505721 1386	2682403 719
3729	13 90 54 41	51 853 389 489	065539 8187	3·106188 25891	507107 1386	2681684 719
3730	13 91 29 00	51 895 117 000	073726 8186	3·132079 25887	508493 1386	2680965 718
3731	13 92 03 61	51 936 866 891	081912 8185	3·157966 25884	509879 1386	2680247 719
3732	13 92 78 24	51 978 639 168	090097 8184	3·183850 25881	511265 1385	2679528 717
3733	13 93 52 89	52 020 433 837	098281 8183	3·209731 25876	512650 1385	2678811 718
3734	13 94 27 56	52 062 250 904	106464 8182	3·235607 25874	514035 1385	2678093 717
3735	13 95 02 25	52 104 090 375	114646 8181	3·261481 25870	515420 1385	2677376 716
3736	13 95 76 96	52 145 952 256	122827 8180	3·287351 25866	516805 1384	2676660 717
3737	13 96 51 69	52 187 836 553	131007 8178	3·313217 25863	518189 1384	2675943 716
3738	13 97 26 44	52 229 743 272	139185 8178	3·339080 25860	519573 1384	2675227 715
3739	13 98 01 21	52 271 672 419	147363 8176	3·364940 25856	520957 1383	2674512 715
3740	13 98 76 00	52 313 624 000	155539 8176	3·390796 25853	522340 1384	2673797 715
3741	13 99 50 81	52 355 598 021	163715 8174	3·416649 25849	523724 1383	2673082 714
3742	14 00 25 64	52 397 594 488	171889 8173	3·442498 25846	525107 1383	2672368 714
3743	14 01 00 49	52 439 613 407	180062 8172	3·468344 25842	526490 1382	2671654 714
3744	14 01 75 36	52 481 654 784	188234 8171	3·494186 25839	527872 1382	2670940 713
3745	14 02 50 25	52 523 718 625	196405 8170	3·520025 25835	529254 1383	2670227 713
3746	14 03 25 16	52 565 804 936	204575 8169	3·545860 25832	530637 1381	2669514 712
3747	14 04 00 09	52 607 913 723	212744 8167	3·571692 25829	532018 1382	2668802 712
3748	14 04 75 04	52 650 044 992	220911 8167	3·597521 25825	533400 1381	2668090 712
3749	14 05 50 01	52 692 198 749	229078 8166	3·623346 25821	534781 1382	2667378 711
3750	14 06 25 00	52 734 375 000	237244 61·	3·649167 190 +	536163 15·	2666667 0·000

76

No. n	Square n²	Cube n³	Square root √n	Sq. rt. of 10n √10n	Cube root ∛n	Reciprocal 1/n
			61·	**190 +**	**15·**	**0·000**
3750	14 06 25 00	52 734 375 000	237244 ₈₁₆₄	3·649167 ₂₅₈₁₈	536163 ₁₃₈₀	2666667 ₇₁₁
3751	14 07 00 01	52 776 573 751	245408 ₈₁₆₃	3·674985 ₂₅₈₁₅	537543 ₁₃₈₁	2665956 ₇₁₁
3752	14 07 75 04	52 818 795 008	253571 ₈₁₆₃	3·700800 ₂₅₈₁₁	538924 ₁₃₈₀	2665245 ₇₁₀
3753	14 08 50 09	52 861 038 777	261734 ₈₁₆₁	3·726611 ₂₅₈₀₈	540304 ₁₃₈₁	2664535 ₇₁₀
3754	14 09 25 16	52 903 305 064	269895 ₈₁₆₀	3·752419 ₂₅₈₀₅	541685 ₁₃₇₉	2663825 ₇₀₉
3755	14 10 00 25	52 945 593 875	278055 ₈₁₅₉	3·778224 ₂₅₈₀₁	543064 ₁₃₈₀	2663116 ₇₀₉
3756	14 10 75 36	52 987 905 216	286214 ₈₁₅₈	3·804025 ₂₅₇₉₇	544444 ₁₃₇₉	2662407 ₇₀₉
3757	14 11 50 49	53 030 239 093	294372 ₈₁₅₆	3·829822 ₂₅₇₉₄	545823 ₁₃₈₀	2661698 ₇₀₈
3758	14 12 25 64	53 072 595 512	302528 ₈₁₅₆	3·855616 ₂₅₇₉₁	547203 ₁₃₇₉	2660990 ₇₀₈
3759	14 13 00 81	53 114 974 479	310684 ₈₁₅₅	3·881407 ₂₅₇₈₇	548582 ₁₃₇₈	2660282 ₇₀₈
3760	14 13 76 00	53 157 376 000	318839 ₈₁₅₃	3·907194 ₂₅₇₈₄	549960 ₁₃₇₉	265957+ ₇₀₇
3761	14 14 51 21	53 199 800 081	326992 ₈₁₅₃	3·932978 ₂₅₇₈₁	551339 ₁₃₇₈	2658867 ₇₀₆
3762	14 15 26 44	53 242 246 728	335145 ₈₁₅₁	3·958759 ₂₅₇₇₆	552717 ₁₃₇₈	2658161 ₇₀₇
3763	14 16 01 69	53 284 715 947	343296 ₈₁₅₁	3·984535 ₂₅₇₇₄	554095 ₁₃₇₇	2657454 ₇₀₆
3764	14 16 76 96	53 327 207 744	351447 ₈₁₄₉	4·010309 ₂₅₇₇₀	555472 ₁₃₇₈	2656748 ₇₀₆
3765	14 17 52 25	53 369 722 125	359596 ₈₁₄₈	4·036079 ₂₅₇₆₇	556850 ₁₃₇₇	2656042 ₇₀₅
3766	14 18 27 56	53 412 259 096	367744 ₈₁₄₇	4·061846 ₂₅₇₆₃	558227 ₁₃₇₇	2655337 ₇₀₅
3767	14 19 02 89	53 454 818 663	375891 ₈₁₄₆	4·087609 ₂₅₇₆₀	559604 ₁₃₇₇	2654632 ₇₀₄
3768	14 19 78 24	53 497 400 832	384037 ₈₁₄₅	4·113369 ₂₅₇₅₆	560981 ₁₃₇₆	2653928 ₇₀₄
3769	14 20 53 61	53 540 005 609	392182 ₈₁₄₄	4·139125 ₂₅₇₅₃	562357 ₁₃₇₆	2653224 ₇₀₄
3770	14 21 29 00	53 582 633 000	400326 ₈₁₄₂	4·164878 ₂₅₇₅₀	563733 ₁₃₇₆	2652520 ₇₀₄
3771	14 22 04 41	53 625 283 011	408468 ₈₁₄₂	4·190628 ₂₅₇₄₆	565109 ₁₃₇₆	2651816 ₇₀₃
3772	14 22 79 84	53 667 955 648	416610 ₈₁₄₁	4·216374 ₂₅₇₄₃	566485 ₁₃₇₆	2651113 ₇₀₂
3773	14 23 55 29	53 710 650 917	424751 ₈₁₃₉	4·242117 ₂₅₇₃₉	567861 ₁₃₇₅	2650411 ₇₀₂
3774	14 24 30 76	53 753 368 824	432890 ₈₁₃₉	4·267856 ₂₅₇₃₆	569236 ₁₃₇₅	2649709 ₇₀₂
3775	14 25 06 25	53 796 109 375	441029 ₈₁₃₇	4·293592 ₂₅₇₃₃	570611 ₁₃₇₅	2649007 ₇₀₂
3776	14 25 81 76	53 838 872 576	449166 ₈₁₃₆	4·319325 ₂₅₇₂₉	571986 ₁₃₇₅	2648305 ₇₀₁
3777	14 26 57 29	53 881 658 433	457302 ₈₁₃₅	4·345054 ₂₅₇₂₆	573360 ₁₃₇₄	2647604 ₇₀₁
3778	14 27 32 84	53 924 466 952	465437 ₈₁₃₅	4·370780 ₂₅₇₂₂	574734 ₁₃₇₅	2646903 ₇₀₀
3779	14 28 08 41	53 967 298 139	473572 ₈₁₃₃	4·396502 ₂₅₇₁₉	576109 ₁₃₇₃	2646203 ₇₀₀
3780	14 28 84 00	54 010 152 000	481705 ₈₁₃₂	4·422221 ₂₅₇₁₅	577482 ₁₃₇₄	2645503 ₇₀₀
3781	14 29 59 61	54 053 028 541	489837 ₈₁₃₀	4·447936 ₂₅₇₁₃	578856 ₁₃₇₃	2644803 ₇₀₀
3782	14 30 35 24	54 095 927 768	497967 ₈₁₃₀	4·473649 ₂₅₇₀₈	580229 ₁₃₇₃	2644104 ₆₉₉
3783	14 31 10 89	54 138 849 687	506097 ₈₁₂₉	4·499357 ₂₅₇₀₆	581602 ₁₃₇₃	2643405 ₆₉₉
3784	14 31 86 56	54 181 794 304	514226 ₈₁₂₈	4·525063 ₂₅₇₀₂	582975 ₁₃₇₃	2642706 ₆₉₈
3785	14 32 62 25	54 224 761 625	522354 ₈₁₂₆	4·550765 ₂₅₆₉₈	584348 ₁₃₇₂	2642008 ₆₉₈
3786	14 33 37 96	54 267 751 656	530480 ₈₁₂₆	4·576463 ₂₅₆₉₅	585720 ₁₃₇₂	2641310 ₆₉₇
3787	14 34 13 69	54 310 764 403	538606 ₈₁₂₄	4·602158 ₂₅₆₉₂	587092 ₁₃₇₂	2640613 ₆₉₇
3788	14 34 89 44	54 353 799 872	546730 ₈₁₂₄	4·627850 ₂₅₆₈₈	588464 ₁₃₇₂	2639916 ₆₉₇
3789	14 35 65 21	54 396 858 069	554854 ₈₁₂₂	4·653538 ₂₅₆₈₅	589836 ₁₃₇₁	2639219 ₆₉₇
3790	14 36 41 00	54 439 939 000	562976 ₈₁₂₁	4·679223 ₂₅₆₈₂	591207 ₁₃₇₁	2638522 ₆₉₆
3791	14 37 16 81	54 483 042 671	571097 ₈₁₂₀	4·704905 ₂₅₆₇₈	592578 ₁₃₇₁	2637826 ₆₉₅
3792	14 37 92 64	54 526 169 088	579217 ₈₁₁₉	4·730583 ₂₅₆₇₅	593949 ₁₃₇₁	2637131 ₆₉₅
3793	14 38 68 49	54 569 318 257	587336 ₈₁₁₈	4·756258 ₂₅₆₇₁	595320 ₁₃₇₁	2636436 ₆₉₅
3794	14 39 44 36	54 612 490 184	595454 ₈₁₁₇	4·781929 ₂₅₆₆₈	596690 ₁₃₇₀	2635741 ₆₉₅
3795	14 40 20 25	54 655 684 875	603571 ₈₁₁₆	4·807597 ₂₅₆₆₅	598060 ₁₃₇₀	2635046 ₆₉₄
3796	14 40 96 16	54 698 902 336	611687 ₈₁₁₅	4·833262 ₂₅₆₆₁	599430 ₁₃₇₀	2634352 ₆₉₄
3797	14 41 72 09	54 742 142 573	619802 ₈₁₁₄	4·858923 ₂₅₆₅₈	600800 ₁₃₆₉	2633658 ₆₉₃
3798	14 42 48 04	54 785 405 592	627916 ₈₁₁₂	4·884581 ₂₅₆₅₅	602169 ₁₃₇₀	2632965 ₆₉₃
3799	14 43 24 01	54 828 691 399	636028 ₈₁₁₂	4·910236 ₂₅₆₅₁	603539 ₁₃₆₉	2632272 ₆₉₃
3800	14 44 00 00	54 872 000 000	644140	4·935887	604908	2631579
			61·	**190 +**	**15·**	**0·000**

No. n	Square n²	Cube n³	Square root √n	Sq. rt. of 10n √10n	Cube root ∛n	Reciprocal 1/n
			61·	190 +	15·	0·000
3800	14 44 00 00	54 872 000 000	644140 8111	4·935887 25648	604908 1368	2631579 692
3801	14 44 76 01	54 915 331 401	652251 8109	4·961535 25644	606276 1369	2630887 692
3802	14 45 52 04	54 958 685 608	660360 8108	4·987179 25641	607645 1368	2630195 692
3803	14 46 28 09	55 002 062 627	668468 8108	5·012820 25638	609013 1368	2629503 691
3804	14 47 04 16	55 045 462 464	676576 8106	5·038458 25634	610381 1368	2628812 691
3805	14 47 80 25	55 088 885 125	684682 8105	5·064092 25631	611749 1367	2628121 691
3806	14 48 56 36	55 132 330 616	692787 8104	5·089723 25627	613116 1368	2627430 690
3807	14 49 32 49	55 175 798 943	700891 8103	5·115350 25625	614484 1367	2626740 690
3808	14 50 08 64	55 219 290 112	708994 8102	5·140975 25621	615851 1366	2626050 689
3809	14 50 84 81	55 262 804 129	717096 8101	5·166596 25617	617217 1367	2625361 689
3810	14 51 61 00	55 306 341 000	725197 8100	5·192213 25614	618584 1366	2624672 689
3811	14 52 37 21	55 349 900 731	733297 8099	5·217827 25611	619950 1366	2623983 688
3812	14 53 13 44	55 393 483 328	741396 8098	5·243438 25607	621316 1366	2623295 688
3813	14 53 89 69	55 437 088 797	749494 8097	5·269045 25604	622682 1366	2622607 688
3814	14 54 65 96	55 480 717 144	757591 8095	5·294649 25601	624048 1365	2621919 687
3815	14 55 42 25	55 524 368 375	765686 8095	5·320250 25597	625413 1365	2621232 687
3816	14 56 18 56	55 568 042 496	773781 8093	5·345847 25594	626778 1365	2620545 686
3817	14 56 94 89	55 611 739 513	781874 8093	5·371441 25591	628143 1365	2619859 687
3818	14 57 71 24	55 655 459 432	789967 8091	5·397032 25587	629508 1365	2619172 685
3819	14 58 47 61	55 699 202 259	798058 8091	5·422619 25584	630872 1364	2618487 686
3820	14 59 24 00	55 742 968 000	806149 8089	5·448203 25580	632237 1364	2617801 685
3821	14 60 00 41	55 786 756 661	814238 8088	5·473783 25578	633601 1364	2617116 685
3822	14 60 76 84	55 830 568 248	822326 8087	5·499361 25573	634964 1363	2616431 684
3823	14 61 53 29	55 874 402 767	830413 8086	5·524934 25571	636328 1363	2615747 684
3824	14 62 29 76	55 918 260 224	838499 8085	5·550505 25567	637691 1363	2615063 684
3825	14 63 06 25	55 962 140 625	846584 8084	5·576072 25564	639054 1363	2614379 683
3826	14 63 82 76	56 006 043 976	854668 8083	5·601636 25560	640417 1362	2613696 683
3827	14 64 59 29	56 049 970 283	862751 8082	5·627196 25558	641779 1363	2613013 683
3828	14 65 35 84	56 093 919 552	870833 8081	5·652754 25553	643142 1362	2612330 682
3829	14 66 12 41	56 137 891 789	878914 8080	5·678307 25551	644504 1361	2611648 682
3830	14 66 89 00	56 181 887 000	886994 8079	5·703858 25547	645865 1362	2610966 681
3831	14 67 65 61	56 225 905 191	895073 8079	5·729405 25544	647227 1361	2610285 682
3832	14 68 42 24	56 269 946 368	903150 8077	5·754949 25540	648588 1361	2609603 680
3833	14 69 18 89	56 314 010 537	911227 8075	5·780489 25537	649949 1361	2608923 681
3834	14 69 95 56	56 358 097 704	919302 8075	5·806026 25534	651310 1361	2608242 680
3835	14 70 72 25	56 402 207 875	927377 8073	5·831560 25531	652671 1360	2607562 680
3836	14 71 48 96	56 446 341 056	935450 8073	5·857091 25527	654031 1361	2606882 680
3837	14 72 25 69	56 490 497 253	943523 8071	5·882618 25524	655392 1359	2606203 679
3838	14 73 02 44	56 534 676 472	951594 8070	5·908142 25520	656751 1360	2605524 679
3839	14 73 79 21	56 578 878 719	959664 8070	5·933662 25517	658111 1360	2604845 679
3840	14 74 56 00	56 623 104 000	967734 8068	5·959179 25514	659471 1359	2604167 678
3841	14 75 32 81	56 667 352 321	975802 8067	5·984693 25511	660830 1359	2603489 678
3842	14 76 09 64	56 711 623 688	983869 8066	6·010204 25507	662189 1359	2602811 678
3843	14 76 86 49	56 755 918 107	991935 8065	6·035711 25504	663547 1358	2602134 677
3844	14 77 63 36	56 800 235 584	*000000 8064	6·061215 25501	664906 1359	2601457 677
3845	14 78 40 25	56 844 576 125	008064 8063	6·086716 25497	666264 1358	2600780 676
3846	14 79 17 16	56 888 939 736	016127 8062	6·112213 25494	667622 1358	2600104 676
3847	14 79 94 09	56 933 326 423	024189 8061	6·137707 25490	668980 1358	2599428 676
3848	14 80 71 04	56 977 736 192	032250 8059	6·163197 25488	670338 1357	2598753 676
3849	14 81 48 01	57 022 169 049	040309 8059	6·188685 25484	671695 1357	2598077 674
3850	14 82 25 00	57 066 625 000	048368	6·214169	673052	2597403
			62·	190 +	15·	0·000

No. n	Square n^2	Cube n^3	Square root $\sqrt{n}$	Sq. rt. of 10n $\sqrt{10n}$	Cube root $\sqrt[3]{n}$	Reciprocal $\frac{1}{n}$
			62·	190 +	15·	0·000
3850	14 82 25 00	57 066 625 000	048368 8058	6·214169 25480	673052 1357	2597403 675
3851	14 83 02 01	57 111 104 051	056426 8057	6·239649 25478	674409 1357	2596728 675
3852	14 83 79 04	57 155 606 208	064483 8055	6·265127 25474	675766 1357	2596054 674
3853	14 84 56 09	57 200 131 477	072538 8055	6·290601 25471	677122 1356	2595380 674
3854	14 85 33 16	57 244 679 864	080593 8053	6·316072 25467	678478 1356	2594707 673
3855	14 86 10 25	57 289 251 375	088646 8053	6·341539 25464	679834 1356	2594034 673
3856	14 86 87 36	57 333 846 016	096699 8051	6·367003 25461	681190 1355	2593361 672
3857	14 87 64 49	57 378 463 793	104750 8051	6·392464 25458	682545 1355	2592689 672
3858	14 88 41 64	57 423 104 712	112801 8049	6·417922 25454	683900 1355	2592017 672
3859	14 89 18 81	57 467 768 779	120850 8048	6·443376 25451	685255 1355	2591345 671
3860	14 89 96 00	57 512 456 000	128898 8048	6·468827 25448	686610 1355	2590674 671
3861	14 90 73 21	57 557 166 381	136946 8046	6·494275 25444	687965 1355	2590003 671
3862	14 91 50 44	57 601 899 928	144992 8045	6·519719 25441	689319 1354	2589332 670
3863	14 92 27 69	57 646 656 647	153037 8044	6·545160 25438	690673 1354	2588662 670
3864	14 93 04 96	57 691 436 544	161081 8043	6·570598 25435	692027 1353	2587992 670
3865	14 93 82 25	57 736 239 625	169124 8042	6·596033 25431	693380 1354	2587322 669
3866	14 94 59 56	57 781 065 896	177166 8041	6·621464 25428	694734 1353	2586653 669
3867	14 95 36 89	57 825 915 363	185207 8040	6·646892 25424	696087 1353	2585984 669
3868	14 96 14 24	57 870 788 032	193247 8039	6·672316 25422	697440 1352	2585315 668
3869	14 96 91 61	57 915 683 909	201286 8038	6·697738 25418	698792 1353	2584647 668
3870	14 97 69 00	57 960 603 000	209324 8037	6·723156 25415	700145 1352	2583979 667
3871	14 98 46 41	58 005 545 311	217361 8036	6·748571 25411	701497 1352	2583312 667
3872	14 99 23 84	58 050 510 848	225397 8035	6·773982 25408	702849 1352	2582645 667
3873	15 00 01 29	58 095 499 617	233432 8033	6·799390 25405	704201 1351	2581978 667
3874	15 00 78 76	58 140 511 624	241465 8033	6·824795 25402	705552 1351	2581311 666
3875	15 01 56 25	58 185 546 875	249498 8032	6·850197 25398	706903 1351	2580645 666
3876	15 02 33 76	58 230 605 376	257530 8030	6·875595 25395	708254 1351	2579979 665
3877	15 03 11 29	58 275 687 133	265560 8030	6·900990 25392	709605 1351	2579314 665
3878	15 03 88 84	58 320 792 152	273590 8028	6·926382 25389	710956 1350	2578649 665
3879	15 04 66 41	58 365 920 439	281618 8028	6·951771 25385	712306 1350	2577984 664
3880	15 05 44 00	58 411 072 000	289646 8027	6·977156 25382	713656 1350	2577320 664
3881	15 06 21 61	58 456 246 841	297673 8025	7·002538 25379	715006 1350	2576656 664
3882	15 06 99 24	58 501 444 968	305698 8024	7·027917 25375	716355 1349	2575992 664
3883	15 07 76 89	58 546 666 387	313722 8024	7·053292 25372	717705 1350	2575328 663
3884	15 08 54 56	58 591 911 104	321746 8022	7·078664 25369	719054 1349	2574665 662
3885	15 09 32 25	58 637 179 125	329768 8022	7·104033 25366	720403 1349	2574003 663
3886	15 10 09 96	58 682 470 456	337790 8020	·7·129399 25363	721752 1348	2573340 662
3887	15 10 87 69	58 727 785 103	345810 8019	7·154762 25359	723100 1348	2572678 662
3888	15 11 65 44	58 773 123 072	353829 8018	7·180121 25356	724448 1348	2572016 661
3889	15 12 43 21	58 818 484 369	361847 8018	7·205477 25352	725796 1348	2571355 661
3890	15 13 21 00	58 863 869 000	369865 8016	7·230829 25350	727144 1348	2570694 661
3891	15 13 98 81	58 909 276 971	377881 8015	7·256179 25346	728492 1347	2570033 660
3892	15 14 76 64	58 954 708 288	385896 8014	7·281525 25343	729839 1347	2569373 660
3893	15 15 54 49	59 000 162 957	393910 8013	7·306868 25339	731186 1347	2568713 660
3894	15 16 32 36	59 045 640 984	401923 8012	7·332207 25337	732533 1347	2568053 659
3895	15 17 10 25	59 091 142 375	409935 8011	7·357544 25333	733880 1346	2567394 659
3896	15 17 88 16	59 136 667 136	417946 8010	7·382877 25330	735226 1346	2566735 659
3897	15 18 66 09	59 182 215 273	425956 8009	7·408207 25326	736572 1346	2566076 658
3898	15 19 44 04	59 227 786 792	433965 8008	7·433533 25323	737918 1346	2565418 658
3899	15 20 22 01	59 273 381 699	441973 8007	7·458856 25321	739264 1345	2564760 657
3900	15 21 00 00	59 319 000 000	449980	7·484177	740609	2564103
			62·	190 +	15·	0·000

No. n	Square n^2	Cube n^3	Square root $\sqrt{n}$	Sq. rt. of 10n $\sqrt{10n}$	Cube root $\sqrt[3]{n}$	Reciprocal $\frac{1}{n}$
			62·	190 +	15·	0·000
3900	15 21 00 00	59 319 000 000	449980 8006	7·484177 25316	740609 1345	2564103 658
3901	15 21 78 01	59 364 641 701	457986 8005	7·509493 25314	741954 1345	2563445 657
3902	15 22 56 04	59 410 306 808	465991 8004	7·534807 25310	743299 1345	2562788 656
3903	15 23 34 09	59 455 995 327	473995 8002	7·560117 25308	744644 1345	2562132 657
3904	15 24 12 16	59 501 707 264	481997 8002	7·585425 25303	745989 1344	2561475 656
3905	15 24 90 25	59 547 442 625	489999 8001	7·610728 25301	747333 1344	2560819 655
3906	15 25 68 36	59 593 201 416	498000 8000	7·636029 25298	748677 1344	2560164 655
3907	15 26 46 49	59 638 983 643	506000 7998	7·661327 25294	750021 1344	2559509 655
3908	15 27 24 64	59 684 789 312	513998 7998	7·686621 25291	751365 1343	2558854 655
3909	15 28 02 81	59 730 618 429	521996 7997	7·711912 25287	752708 1343	2558199 654
3910	15 28 81 00	59 776 471 000	529993 7995	7·737199 25285	754051 1343	2557545 654
3911	15 29 59 21	59 822 347 031	537988 7995	7·762484 25281	755394 1343	2556891 654
3912	15 30 37 44	59 868 246 528	545983 7994	7·787765 25278	756737 1342	2556237 653
3913	15 31 15 69	59 914 169 497	553977 7992	7·813043 25275	758079 1343	2555584 653
3914	15 31 93 96	59 960 115 944	561969 7992	7·838318 25271	759422 1342	2554931 653
3915	15 32 72 25	60 006 085 875	569961 7990	7·863589 25269	760764 1341	2554278 652
3916	15 33 50 56	60 052 079 296	577951 7990	7·888858 25265	762105 1341	2553626 652
3917	15 34 28 89	60 098 096 213	585941 7988	7·914123 25262	763447 1341	2552974 651
3918	15 35 07 24	60 144 136 632	593929 7988	7·939385 25258	764788 1341	2552323 652
3919	15 35 85 61	60 190 200 559	601917 7986	7·964643 25256	766129 1341	2551671 651
3920	15 36 64 00	60 236 288 000	609903 7986	7·989899 25252	767470 1341	2551020 650
3921	15 37 42 41	60 282 398 961	617889 7984	8·015151 25249	768811 1340	2550370 650
3922	15 38 20 84	60 328 533 448	625873 7984	8·040400 25246	770151 1341	2549720 650
3923	15 38 99 29	60 374 691 467	633857 7982	8·065646 25242	771492 1340	2549070 650
3924	15 39 77 76	60 420 873 024	641839 7981	8·090888 25240	772832 1339	2548420 649
3925	15 40 56 25	60 467 078 125	649820 7981	8·116128 25236	774171 1340	2547771 649
3926	15 41 34 76	60 513 306 776	657801 7979	8·141364 25233	775511 1339	2547122 649
3927	15 42 13 29	60 559 558 983	665780 7978	8·166597 25229	776850 1339	2546473 648
3928	15 42 91 84	60 605 834 752	673758 7978	8·191826 25227	778189 1339	2545825 648
3929	15 43 70 41	60 652 134 089	681736 7976	8·217053 25223	779528 1339	2545177 648
3930	15 44 49 00	60 698 457 000	689712 7975	8·242276 25220	780867 1338	2544529 647
3931	15 45 27 61	60 744 803 491	697687 7975	8·267496 25217	782205 1338	2543882 647
3932	15 46 06 24	60 791 173 568	705662 7973	8·292713 25214	783543 1338	2543235 647
3933	15 46 84 89	60 837 567 237	713635 7972	8·317927 25210	784881 1338	2542588 646
3934	15 47 63 56	60 883 984 504	721607 7971	8·343137 25207	786219 1337	2541942 646
3935	15 48 42 25	60 930 425 375	729578 7971	8·368344 25204	787556 1338	2541296 646
3936	15 49 20 96	60 976 889 856	737549 7969	8·393548 25201	788894 1337	2540650 645
3937	15 49 99 69	61 023 377 953	745518 7968	8·418749 25198	790231 1336	2540005 645
3938	15 50 78 44	61 069 889 672	753486 7967	8·443947 25194	791567 1337	2539360 645
3939	15 51 57 21	61 116 425 019	761453 7966	8·469141 25191	792904 1336	2538715 644
3940	15 52 36 00	61 162 984 000	769419 7965	8·494332 25188	794240 1336	2538071 644
3941	15 53 14 81	61 209 566 621	777384 7965	8·519520 25185	795576 1336	2537427 644
3942	15 53 93 64	61 256 172 888	785349 7963	8·544705 25182	796912 1336	2536783 643
3943	15 54 72 49	61 302 802 807	793312 7962	8·569887 25178	798248 1335	2536140 643
3944	15 55 51 36	61 349 456 384	801274 7961	8·595065 25176	799583 1336	2535497 643
3945	15 56 30 25	61 396 133 625	809235 7960	8·620241 25172	800919 1335	2534854 642
3946	15 57 09 16	61 442 834 536	817195 7959	8·645413 25169	802254 1334	2534212 642
3947	15 57 88 09	61 489 559 123	825154 7958	8·670582 25165	803588 1335	2533570 642
3948	15 58 67 04	61 536 307 392	833112 7957	8·695747 25163	804923 1334	2532928 642
3949	15 59 46 01	61 583 079 349	841069 7956	8·720910 25159	806257 1334	2532287 641
3950	15 60 25 00	61 629 875 000	849025	8·746069	807591	2531646
			62·	190 +	15·	0·000

No. n	Square n^2	Cube n^3	Square root $\sqrt{n}$	Sq. rt. of $10n$ $\sqrt{10n}$	Cube root $\sqrt[3]{n}$	Reciprocal $\dfrac{1}{n}$
			62·	190 +	15·	0·000
3950	15 60 25 00	61 629 875 000	840025 7956	8·746069 25156	807591 1334	2531646 641
3951	15 61 04 01	61 676 694 351	856981 7954	8·771225 25153	808925 1334	2531005 641
3952	15 61 83 04	61 723 537 408	864935 7953	8·796378 25150	810259 1334	2530364 640
3953	15 62 62 09	61 770 404 177	872888 7952	8·821528 25147	811592 1333	2529724 640
3954	15 63 41 16	61 817 294 664	880840 7951	8·846675 25143	812925 1333	2529084 639
3955	15 64 20 25	61 864 208 875	888791 7950	8·871818 25140	814258 1333	2528445 639
3956	15 64 99 36	61 911 146 816	896741 7949	8·896958 25137	815591 1333	2527806 639
3957	15 65 78 49	61 958 108 493	904690 7948	8·922095 25134	816924 1332	2527167 638
3958	15 66 57 64	62 005 093 912	912638 7947	8·947229 25131	818256 1332	2526529 639
3959	15 67 36 81	62 052 103 079	920585 7946	8·972360 25127	819588 1332	2525890 637
3960	15 68 16 00	62 099 136 000	928531 7945	8·997487 25125	820920 1331	2525253 638
3961	15 68 95 21	62 146 192 681	936476 7944	9·022612 25122	822251 1332	2524615 637
3962	15 69 74 44	62 193 273 128	944420 7943	9·047733 25118	823583 1331	2523978 637
3963	15 70 53 69	62 240 377 347	952363 7942	9·072851 25115	824914 1331	2523341 637
3964	15 71 32 96	62 287 505 344	960305 7941	9·097966 25112	826245 1331	2522704 636
3965	15 72 12 25	62 334 657 125	968246 7940	9·123078 25108	827576 1330	2522068 636
3966	15 72 91 56	62 381 832 696	976186 7939	9·148186 25105	828906 1330	2521432 635
3967	15 73 70 89	62 429 032 063	984125 7938	9·173291 25103	830236 1330	2520797 636
3968	15 74 50 24	62 476 255 232	992063 7937	9·198394 25099	831566 1330	2520161 635
3969	15 75 29 61	62 523 502 209	*000000 7936	9·223493 25095	832896 1330	2519526 634
3970	15 76 09 00	62 570 773 000	007936 7935	9·248588 25093	834226 1329	2518892 635
3971	15 76 88 41	62 618 067 611	015871 7934	9·273681 25090	835555 1329	2518257 634
3972	15 77 67 84	62 665 386 048	023805 7933	9·298771 25086	836884 1329	2517623 634
3973	15 78 47 29	62 712 728 317	031738 7932	9·323857 25083	838213 1329	2516990 633
3974	15 79 26 76	62 760 094 424	039670 7931	9·348940 25080	839542 1329	2516356 633
3975	15 80 06 25	62 807 484 375	047601 7930	9·374020 25077	840871 1328	2515723 632
3976	15 80 85 76	62 854 898 176	055531 7929	9·399097 25074	842199 1328	2515091 633
3977	15 81 65 29	62 902 335 833	063460 7928	9·424171 25071	843527 1328	2514458 632
3978	15 82 44 84	62 949 797 352	071388 7927	9·449242 25067	844855 1327	2513826 632
3979	15 83 24 41	62 997 282 739	079315 7926	9·474309 25064	846182 1327	2513194 631
3980	15 84 04 00	63 044 792 000	087241 7925	9·499373 25062	847510 1327	2512563 631
3981	15 84 83 61	63 092 325 141	095166 7924	9·524435 25058	848837 1327	2511932 631
3982	15 85 63 24	63 139 882 168	103090 7923	9·549493 25054	850164 1326	2511301 631
3983	15 86 42 89	63 187 463 087	111013 7922	9·574547 25052	851490 1327	2510670 631
3984	15 87 22 56	63 235 067 904	118935 7921	9·599599 25049	852817 1326	2510040 630
3985	15 88 02 25	63 282 696 625	126856 7920	9·624648 25045	854143 1326	2509410 629
3986	15 88 81 96	63 330 349 256	134776 7920	9·649693 25043	855469 1326	2508781 630
3987	15 89 61 69	63 378 025 803	142696 7918	9·674736 25039	856795 1326	2508151 628
3988	15 90 41 44	63 425 726 272	150614 7917	9·699775 25036	858121 1325	2507523 629
3989	15 91 21 21	63 473 450 669	158531 7916	9·724811 25033	859446 1325	2506894 628
3990	15 92 01 00	63 521 199 000	166447 7915	9·749844 25029	860771 1325	2506266 628
3991	15 92 80 81	63 568 971 271	174362 7914	9·774873 25027	862096 1325	2505638 628
3992	15 93 60 64	63 616 767 488	182276 7913	9·799900 25023	863421 1324	2505010 627
3993	15 94 40 49	63 664 587 657	190189 7912	9·824923 25021	864745 1325	2504383 627
3994	15 95 20 36	63 712 431 784	198101 7911	9·849944 25017	866070 1324	2503756 627
3995	15 96 00 25	63 760 299 875	206012 7911	9·874961 25014	867394 1323	2503129 626
3996	15 96 80 16	63 808 191 936	213923 7909	9·899975 25011	868717 1324	2502503 627
3997	15 97 60 09	63 856 107 973	221832 7908	9·924986 25008	870041 1323	2501876 625
3998	15 98 40 04	63 904 047 992	229740 7907	9·949994 25004	871364 1324	2501251 626
3999	15 99 20 01	63 952 011 999	237647 7906	9·974998 25002	872688 1323	2500625 625
4000	16 00 00 00	64 000 000 000	245553 03·	10·000000 190 +	874011 15·	2500000 0·000

No. n	Square n^2	Cube n^3	Square root $\sqrt{n}$	Sq. rt. of $10n$ $\sqrt{10n}$	Cube root $\sqrt[3]{n}$	Reciprocal $\frac{1}{n}$
			63·	200 +	15·	0·000
4000	16 00 00 00	64 000 000 000	245553 _7905_	0·000000 _24998_	874011 _1322_	2500000 _625_
4001	16 00 80 01	64 048 012 001	253458 _7905_	0·024998 _24996_	875333 _1323_	2499375 _624_
4002	16 01 60 04	64 096 048 008	261363 _7903_	0·049994 _24992_	876656 _1322_	2498751 _625_
4003	16 02 40 09	64 144 108 027	269266 _7902_	0·074986 _24989_	877978 _1322_	2498126 _624_
4004	16 03 20 16	64 192 192 064	277168 _7901_	0·099975 _24986_	879300 _1322_	2497502 _623_
4005	16 04 00 25	64 240 300 125	285069 _7901_	0·124961 _24983_	880622 _1322_	2496879 _623_
4006	16 04 80 36	64 288 432 216	292970 _7899_	0·149944 _24980_	881944 _1321_	2496256 _623_
4007	16 05 60 49	64 336 588 343	300869 _7898_	0·174924 _24976_	883265 _1321_	2495633 _623_
4008	16 06 40 64	64 384 768 512	308767 _7897_	0·199900 _24974_	884586 _1321_	2495010 _622_
4009	16 07 20 81	64 432 972 729	316664 _7897_	0·224874 _24970_	885907 _1321_	2494388 _622_
4010	16 08 01 00	64 481 201 000	324561 _7895_	0·249844 _24967_	887228 _1320_	2493766 _622_
4011	16 08 81 21	64 529 453 331	332456 _7894_	0·274811 _24964_	888548 _1321_	2493144 _622_
4012	16 09 61 44	64 577 729 728	340350 _7894_	0·299775 _24961_	889869 _1320_	2492522 _621_
4013	16 10 41 69	64 626 030 197	348244 _7892_	0·324736 _24958_	891189 _1320_	2491901 _620_
4014	16 11 21 96	64 674 354 744	356136 _7892_	0·349694 _24955_	892509 _1319_	2491281 _621_
4015	16 12 02 25	64 722 703 375	364028 _7890_	0·374649 _24952_	893828 _1320_	2490660 _620_
4016	16 12 82 56	64 771 076 096	371918 _7890_	0·399601 _24948_	895148 _1319_	2490040 _620_
4017	16 13 62 89	64 819 472 913	379808 _7888_	0·424549 _24946_	896467 _1319_	2489420 _620_
4018	16 14 43 24	64 867 893 832	387696 _7887_	0·449495 _24942_	897786 _1319_	2488800 _619_
4019	16 15 23 61	64 916 338 859	395583 _7887_	0·474437 _24940_	899105 _1318_	2488181 _619_
4020	16 16 04 00	64 964 808 000	403470 _7885_	0·499377 _24936_	900423 _1319_	2487562 _618_
4021	16 16 84 41	65 013 301 261	411355 _7885_	0·524313 _24933_	901742 _1318_	2486944 _619_
4022	16 17 64 84	65 061 818 648	419240 _7884_	0·549246 _24930_	903060 _1318_	2486325 _618_
4023	16 18 45 29	65 110 360 167	427124 _7882_	0·574176 _24927_	904378 _1317_	2485707 _618_
4024	16 19 25 76	65 158 925 824	435006 _7882_	0·599103 _24923_	905695 _1318_	2485089 _617_
4025	16 20 06 25	65 207 515 625	442888 _7880_	0·624026 _24921_	907013 _1317_	2484472 _617_
4026	16 20 86 76	65 256 129 576	450768 _7880_	0·648947 _24918_	908330 _1317_	2483855 _617_
4027	16 21 67 29	65 304 767 683	458648 _7879_	0·673865 _24914_	909647 _1317_	2483238 _616_
4028	16 22 47 84	65 353 429 952	466527 _7877_	0·698779 _24912_	910964 _1316_	2482622 _617_
4029	16 23 28 41	65 402 116 389	474404 _7877_	0·723691 _24908_	912280 _1317_	2482005 _615_
4030	16 24 09 00	65 450 827 000	482281 _7876_	0·748599 _24905_	913597 _1316_	2481390 _616_
4031	16 24 89 61	65 499 561 791	490157 _7874_	0·773504 _24902_	914913 _1316_	2480774 _615_
4032	16 25 70 24	65 548 320 768	498031 _7874_	0·798406 _24899_	916229 _1316_	2480159 _615_
4033	16 26 50 89	65 597 103 937	505905 _7873_	0·823305 _24896_	917545 _1315_	2479544 _615_
4034	16 27 31 56	65 645 911 304	513778 _7872_	0·848201 _24893_	918860 _1315_	2478929 _614_
4035	16 28 12 25	65 694 742 875	521650 _7871_	0·873094 _24890_	920175 _1315_	2478315 _614_
4036	16 28 92 96	65 743 598 656	529521 _7870_	0·897984 _24887_	921490 _1315_	2477701 _614_
4037	16 29 73 69	65 792 478 653	537391 _7868_	0·922871 _24883_	922805 _1315_	2477087 _613_
4038	16 30 54 44	65 841 382 872	545259 _7868_	0·947754 _24881_	924120 _1314_	2476474 _614_
4039	16 31 35 21	65 890 311 319	553127 _7867_	0·972635 _24877_	925434 _1314_	2475860 _612_
4040	16 32 16 00	65 939 264 000	560994 _7866_	0·997512 _24875_	926748 _1314_	2475248 _613_
4041	16 32 96 81	65 988 240 921	568860 _7865_	1·022387 _24871_	928062 _1314_	2474635 _612_
4042	16 33 77 64	66 037 242 088	576725 _7864_	1·047258 _24868_	929376 _1314_	2474023 _612_
4043	16 34 58 49	66 086 267·507	584589 _7863_	1·072126 _24866_	930690 _1313_	2473411 _612_
4044	16 35 39 36	66 135 317 184	592452 _7862_	1·096992 _24862_	932003 _1313_	2472799 _611_
4045	16 36 20 25	66 184 391 125	600314 _7862_	1·121854 _24859_	933316 _1313_	2472188 _611_
4046	16 37 01 16	66 233 489 336	608176 _7860_	1·146713 _24856_	934629 _1313_	2471577 _611_
4047	16 37 82 09	66 282 611 823	616036 _7859_	1·171569 _24852_	935942 _1312_	2470966 _610_
4048	16 38 63 04	66 331 758 592	623895 _7858_	1·196421 _24850_	937254 _1313_	2470356 _610_
4049	16 39 44 01	66 380 929 649	631753 _7857_	1·221271 _24847_	938567 _1312_	2469746 _610_
4050	16 40 25 00	66 430 125 000	639610	1·246118	939879	2469136
			63·	200 +	15·	0·000

No. n	Square n²	Cube n³	Square root √n	Sq. rt. of 10n √10n	Cube root ∛n	Reciprocal 1/n
			63·	200 +	15·	0·000
4050	16 40 25 00	66 430 125 000	639610 7857	1·246118 24844	939879 1311	2469136 610
4051	16 41 06 01	66 479 344 651	647467 7855	1·270962 24840	941190 1312	2468526 609
4052	16 41 87 04	66 528 588 608	655322 7854	1·295802 24838	942502 1311	2467917 609
4053	16 42 68 09	66 577 856 877	663176 7854	1·320640 24834	943813 1312	2467308 608
4054	16 43 49 16	66 627 149 464	671030 7852	1·345474 24832	945125 1310	2466700 609
4055	16 44 30 25	66 676 466 375	678882 7851	1·370306 24828	946435 1311	2466091 608
4056	16 45 11 36	66 725 807 616	686733 7851	1·395134 24825	947746 1311	2465483 608
4057	16 45 92 49	66 775 173 193	694584 7849	1·419959 24823	949057 1310	2464876 607
4058	16 46 73 64	66 824 563 112	702433 7849	1·444782 24819	950367 1310	2464268 607
4059	16 47 54 81	66 873 977 379	710282 7847	1·469601 24816	951677 1310	2463661 607
4060	16 48 36 00	66 923 416 000	718129 7847	1·494417 24813	952987 1310	2463054 606
4061	16 49 17 21	66 972 878 981	725976 7845	1·519230 24810	954297 1309	2462448 607
4062	16 49 98 44	67 022 366 328	733821 7845	1·544040 24807	955606 1309	2461841 605
4063	16 50 79 69	67 071 878 047	741666 7844	1·568847 24804	956915 1309	2461236 605
4064	16 51 60 96	67 121 414 144	749510 7843	1·593651 24801	958224 1309	2460630 606
4065	16 52 42 25	67 170 974 625	757353 7841	1·618452 24797	959533 1309	2460025 605
4066	16 53 23 56	67 220 559 496	765194 7841	1·643249 24795	960842 1309	2459420 605
4067	16 54 04 89	67 270 168 763	773035 7840	1·668044 24792	962150 1308	2458815 605
4068	16 54 86 24	67 319 802 432	780875 7839	1·692836 24788	963458 1308	2458210 604
4069	16 55 67 61	67 369 460 509	788714 7838	1·717624 24786	964766 1308	2457606 604
4070	16 56 49 00	67 419 143 000	796552 7837	1·742410 24783	966074 1307	2457002 603
4071	16 57 30 41	67 468 849 911	804389 7836	1·767193 24779	967381 1308	2456399 603
4072	16 58 11 84	67 518 581 248	812225 7835	1·791972 24777	968689 1307	2455796 603
4073	16 58 93 29	67 568 337 017	820060 7834	1·816749 24773	969996 1307	2455193 603
4074	16 59 74 76	67 618 117 224	827894 7833	1·841522 24770	971303 1306	2454590 602
4075	16 60 56 25	67 667 921 875	835727 7832	1·866292 24768	972609 1307	2453988 602
4076	16 61 37 76	67 717 750 976	843559 7831	1·891060 24764	973916 1306	2453386 602
4077	16 62 19 29	67 767 604 533	851390 7830	1·915824 24761	975222 1306	2452784 602
4078	16 63 00 84	67 817 482 552	859220 7829	1·940585 24759	976528 1306	2452182 601
4079	16 63 82 41	67 867 385 039	867049 7829	1·965344 24755	977834 1305	2451581 601
4080	16 64 64 00	67 917 312 000	874878 7827	1·990099 24752	979139 1306	2450980 600
4081	16 65 45 61	67 967 263 441	882705 7826	2·014851 24749	980445 1305	2450380 600
4082	16 66 27 24	68 017 239 368	890531 7826	2·039600 24746	981750 1305	2449780 600
4083	16 67 08 89	68 067 239 787	898357 7824	2·064346 24743	983055 1305	2449180 600
4084	16 67 90 56	68 117 264 704	906181 7824	2·089089 24740	984360 1305	2448580 600
4085	16 68 72 25	68 167 314 125	914005 7822	2·113829 24737	985664 1305	2447980 599
4086	16 69 53 96	68 217 388 056	921827 7822	2·138566 24734	986969 1304	2447381 599
4087	16 70 35 69	68 267 486 503	929649 7820	2·163300 24731	988273 1304	2446782 599
4088	16 71 17 44	68 317 609 472	937469 7820	2·188031 24728	989577 1303	2446184 598
4089	16 71 99 21	68 367 756 969	945289 7819	2·212759 24725	990880 1304	2445586 598
4090	16 72 81 00	68 417 929 000	953108 7818	2·237484 24722	992184 1303	2444988 598
4091	16 73 62 81	68 468 125 571	960926 7816	2·262206 24719	993487 1303	2444390 597
4092	16 74 44 64	68 518 346 688	968742 7816	2·286925 24716	994790 1303	2443793 597
4093	16 75 26 49	68 568 592 357	976558 7815	2·311642 24713	996093 1302	2443196 597
4094	16 76 08 36	68 618 862 584	984373 7814	2·336354 24709	997395 1303	2442599 597
4095	16 76 90 25	68 669 157 375	992187 7813	2·361063 24707	998698 1302	2442002 596
4096	16 77 72 16	68 719 476 736	*000000 7812	2·385770 24704	*000000 1302	2441406 596
4097	16 78 54 09	68 769 820 673	007812 7811	2·410474 24701	001302 1302	2440810 596
4098	16 79 36 04	68 820 189 192	015623 7810	2·435175 24698	002604 1302	2440215 595
4099	16 80 18 01	68 870 582 299	023433 7809	2·459873 24694	003905 1302	2439619 596
4100	16 81 00 00	68 921 000 000	031242	2 484567	005207	2439024
			64·	200 +	16·	0·000

No. n	Square n^2	Cube n^3	Square root $\sqrt{n}$	Sq. rt. of 10n $\sqrt{10n}$	Cube root $\sqrt[3]{n}$	Reciprocal $\frac{1}{n}$
			64·	**200 +**	**16·**	**0·000**
4100	16 81 00 00	68 921 000 000	031242 _7809_	2·484567 _24692_	005207 _1301_	2439024
4101	16 81 82 01	68 971 442 301	039051 _7807_	2·509259 _24689_	006508 _1301_	2438430 _594_
4102	16 82 64 04	69 021 909 208	046858 _7806_	2·533948 _24685_	007809 _1301_	2437835 _595_
4103	16 83 46 09	69 072 400 727	054664 _7806_	2·558633 _24683_	009109 _1300_	2437241 _594_
4104	16 84 28 16	69 122 916 864	062470 _7804_	2·583316 _24680_	010410 _1301_	2436647 _594_ _593_
4105	16 85 10 25	69 173 457 625	070274 _7803_	2·607996 _24677_	011710 _1300_	2436054 _594_
4106	16 85 92 36	69 224 023 016	078077 _7803_	2·632673 _24673_	013010 _1300_	2435460 _594_
4107	16 86 74 49	69 274 613 043	085880 _7801_	2·657346 _24671_	014310 _1300_	2434867 _593_
4108	16 87 56 64	69 325 227 712	093681 _7801_	2·682017 _24668_	015610 _1300_	2434275 _592_
4109	16 88 38 81	69 375 867 029	101482 _7800_	2·706685 _24664_	016909 _1299_	2433682 _593_ _592_
4110	16 89 21 00	69 426 531 000	109282 _7798_	2·731349 _24662_	018208 _1299_	2433090 _592_
4111	16 90 03 21	69 477 219 631	117080 _7798_	2·756011 _24659_	019507 _1299_	2432498 _591_
4112	16 90 85 44	69 527 932 928	124878 _7797_	2·780670 _24655_	020806 _1299_	2431907 _592_
4113	16 91 67 69	69 578 670 897	132675 _7796_	2·805325 _24653_	022105 _1299_	2431315 _591_
4114	16 92 49 96	69 629 433 544	140471 _7795_	2·829978 _24650_	023403 _1298_	2430724 _591_ _590_
4115	16 93 32 25	69 680 220 875	148266 _7794_	2·854628 _24646_	024701 _1298_	2430134 _591_
4116	16 94 14 56	69 731 032 896	156060 _7794_	2·879274 _24644_	025999 _1298_	2429543 _591_
4117	16 94 96 89	69 781 869 613	163853 _7793_	2·903918 _24641_	027297 _1298_	2428953 _590_
4118	16 95 79 24	69 832 731 032	171645 _7792_	2·928559 _24638_	028595 _1297_	2428363 _590_
4119	16 96 61 61	69 883 617 159	179436 _7791_	2·953197 _24634_	029892 _1297_	2427774 _589_ _590_
4120	16 97 44 00	69 934 528 000	187226 _7789_	2·977831 _24632_	031189 _1297_	2427184 _589_
4121	16 98 32 41	69 985 463 561	195015 _7789_	3·002463 _24629_	032486 _1297_	2426595 _589_ _588_
4122	16 99 08 84	70 036 423 848	202804 _7787_	3·027092 _24626_	033783 _1297_	2426007 _588_
4123	16 99 91 29	70 087 408 867	210591 _7787_	3·051718 _24622_	035079 _1296_	2425418 _589_
4124	17 00 73 76	70 138 418 624	218377 _7786_	3·076340 _24620_	036376 _1297_	2424830 _588_ _588_
4125	17 01 56 25	70 189 453 125	226163 _7784_	3·100960 _24617_	037672 _1296_	2424242 _587_
4126	17 02 38 76	70 240 512 376	233947 _7784_	3·125577 _24614_	038968 _1296_	2423655 _587_
4127	17 03 21 29	70 291 596 383	241731 _7783_	3·150191 _24611_	040263 _1295_	2423068 _587_
4128	17 04 03 84	70 342 705 152	249514 _7781_	3·174802 _24607_	041559 _1296_	2422481 _587_
4129	17 04 86 41	70 393 838 689	257295 _7781_	3·199409 _24605_	042854 _1295_	2421894 _587_ _586_
4130	17 05 69 00	70 444 997 000	265076 _7780_	3·224014 _24602_	044149 _1295_	2421308 _587_
4131	17 06 51 61	70 496 180 091	272856 _7779_	3·248616 _24599_	045444 _1294_	2420721 _585_
4132	17 07 34 24	70 547 387 968	280635 _7778_	3·273215 _24596_	046738 _1295_	2420136 _586_
4133	17 08 16 89	70 598 620 637	288413 _7777_	3·297811 _24593_	048033 _1294_	2419550 _585_
4134	17 08 99 56	70 649 878 104	296190 _7776_	3·322404 _24590_	049327 _1294_	2418965 _585_ _585_
4135	17 09 82 25	70 701 160 375	303966 _7775_	3·346994 _24587_	050621 _1294_	2418380 _585_
4136	17 10 64 96	70 752 467 456	311741 _7774_	3·371581 _24584_	051915 _1294_	2417795 _584_
4137	17 11 47 69	70 803 799 353	319515 _7773_	3·396165 _24581_	053208 _1293_	2417211 _585_
4138	17 12 30 44	70 855 156 072	327288 _7772_	3·420746 _24578_	054502 _1294_	2416626 _583_
4139	17 13 13 21	70 906 537 619	335060 _7772_	3·445324 _24575_	055795 _1293_	2416043 _584_
4140	17 13 96 00	70 957 944 000	342832 _7770_	3·469899 _24573_	057088 _1292_	2415459 _583_
4141	17 14 78 81	71 009 375 221	350602 _7770_	3·494472 _24569_	058380 _1293_	2414876 _583_
4142	17 15 61 64	71 060 831 288	358372 _7768_	3·519041 _24566_	059673 _1292_	2414293 _583_
4143	17 16 44 49	71 112 312 207	366140 _7768_	3·543607 _24563_	060965 _1292_	2413710 _583_
4144	17 17 27 36	71 163 817 984	373908 _7766_	3·568170 _24561_	062257 _1292_	2413127 _583_ _582_
4145	17 18 10 25	71 215 348 625	381674 _7766_	3·592731 _24557_	063549 _1292_	2412545 _582_
4146	17 18 93 16	71 266 904 136	389440 _7765_	3·617288 _24554_	064841 _1292_	2411963 _582_
4147	17 19 76 09	71 318 484 523	397205 _7764_	3·641842 _24552_	066133 _1291_	2411382 _581_
4148	17 20 59 04	71 370 089 792	404969 _7763_	3·666394 _24548_	067424 _1291_	2410800 _581_
4149	17 21 42 01	71 421 719 949	412732 _7762_	3·690942 _24546_	068715 _1291_	2410219 _581_ _580_
4150	17 22 25 00	71 473 375 000	420494 **64·**	3·715488 **200 +**	070006 **16·**	2409639 **0·000**

No. n	Square n²	Cube n³	Square root √n	Sq. rt. of 10n √10n	Cube root ∛n	Reciprocal 1/n
			64·	200 +	16·	0·000
4150	17 22 25 00	71 473 375 000	420494 7761	3·715488 24542	070006 1290	2409639 581
4151	17 23 08 01	71 525 054 951	428255 7760	3·740030 24540	071296 1291	2409058 580
4152	17 23 91 04	71 576 759 808	436015 7759	3·764570 24537	072587 1290	2408478 580
4153	17 24 74 09	71 628 489 577	443774 7758	3·789107 24533	073877 1290	2407898 580
4154	17 25 57 16	71 680 244 264	451532 7757	3·813640 24531	075167 1290	2407318 579
4155	17 26 40 25	71 732 023 875	459289 7757	3·838171 24528	076457 1290	2406739 579
4156	17 27 23 36	71 783 828 416	467046 7755	3·862699 24525	077747 1289	2406160 579
4157	17 28 06 49	71 835 657 893	474801 7755	3·887224 24522	079036 1289	2405581 579
4158	17 28 89 64	71 887 512 312	482556 7753	3·911746 24519	080325 1289	2405002 578
4159	17 29 72 81	71 939 391 679	490309 7753	3·936265 24516	081614 1289	2404424 578
4160	17 30 56 00	71 991 296 000	498062 7752	3·960781 24513	082903 1289	2403846 578
4161	17 31 39 21	72 043 225 281	505814 7752	3·985294 24510	084192 1288	2403268 577
4162	17 32 22 44	72 095 179 528	513564 7750	4·009804 24507	085480 1288	2402691 577
4163	17 33 05 69	72 147 158 747	521314 7749	4·034311 24504	086768 1288	2402114 577
4164	17 33 88 96	72 199 162 944	529063 7748	4·058815 24501	088056 1288	2401537 577
4165	17 34 72 25	72 251 192 125	536811 7747	4·083316 24499	089344 1287	2400960 576
4166	17 35 55 56	72 303 246 296	544558 7746	4·107815 24495	090631 1288	2400384 576
4167	17 36 38 89	72 355 325 463	552304 7746	4·132310 24492	091919 1287	2399808 576
4168	17 37 22 24	72 407 429 632	560050 7744	4·156802 24490	093206 1287	2399232 575
4169	17 38 05 61	72 459 558 809	567794 7743	4·181292 24487	094493 1287	2398657 575
4170	17 38 89 00	72 511 713 000	575537 7743	4·205779 24483	095780 1286	2398082 575
4171	17 39 72 41	72 563 892 211	583280 7741	4·230262 24481	097066 1287	2397507 575
4172	17 40 55 84	72 616 096 448	591021 7741	4·254743 24478	098353 1286	2396932 574
4173	17 41 39 29	72 668 325 717	598762 7739	4·279221 24475	099639 1286	2396358 575
4174	17 42 22 76	72 720 580 024	606501 7739	4·303696 24471	100925 1285	2395783 573
4175	17 43 06 25	72 772 859 375	614240 7738	4·328167 24469	102210 1286	2395210 574
4176	17 43 89 76	72 825 163 776	621978 7737	4·352636 24466	103496 1285	2394636 573
4177	17 44 73 29	72 877 493 233	629715 7735	4·377102 24464	104781 1285	2394063 573
4178	17 45 56 84	72 929 847 752	637450 7735	4·401566 24460	106066 1285	2393490 573
4179	17 46 40 41	72 982 227 339	645185 7735	4·426026 24457	107351 1285	2392917 573
4180	17 47 24 00	73 034 632 000	652920 7733	4·450483 24454	108636 1284	2392344 572
4181	17 48 07 61	73 087 061 741	660653 7733	4·474937 24452	109920 1284	2391772 572
4182	17 48 91 24	73 139 516 568	668385 7732	4·499389 24448	111204 1285	2391200 572
4183	17 49 74 89	73 191 996 487	676116 7731	4·523837 24446	112489 1283	2390629 571
4184	17 50 58 56	73 244 501 504	683847 7729	4·548283 24442	113772 1284	2390057 571
4185	17 51 42 25	73 297 031 625	691576 7728	4·572725 24440	115056 1284	2389486 571
4186	17 52 25 96	73 349 586 856	699304 7728	4·597165 24437	116340 1283	2388915 570
4187	17 53 09 69	73 402 167 203	707032 7727	4·621602 24434	117623 1283	2388345 570
4188	17 53 93 44	73 454 772 672	714759 7726	4·646036 24431	118906 1283	2387775 570
4189	17 54 77 21	73 507 403 269	722485 7724	4·670467 24428	120189 1282	2387205 570
4190	17 55 61 00	73 560 059 000	730209 7724	4·694895 24425	121471 1283	2386635 570
4191	17 56 44 81	73 612 739 871	737933 7723	4·719320 24422	122754 1282	2386065 569
4192	17 57 28 64	73 665 445 888	745656 7723	4·743742 24420	124036 1282	2385496 569
4193	17 58 12 49	73 718 177 057	753378 7721	4·768162 24416	125318 1282	2384927 568
4194	17 58 96 36	73 770 933 384	761099 7721	4·792578 24413	126600 1281	2384359 569
4195	17 59 80 25	73 823 714 875	768820 7719	4·816991 24411	127881 1282	2383790 568
4196	17 60 64 16	73 876 521 536	776539 7718	4·841402 24408	129163 1281	2383222 568
4197	17 61 48 09	73 929 353 373	784257 7718	4·865810 24405	130444 1281	2382654 567
4198	17 62 32 04	73 982 210 392	791975 7716	4·890215 24401	131725 1281	2382087 568
4199	17 63 16 01	74 035 092 599	799691 7716	4·914616 24399	133006 1280	2381519 567
4200	17 64 00 00	74 088 000 000	807407 64·	4·939015 200+	134286 16·	2380952 0·000

85

No. n	Square n²	Cube n³	Square root √n	Sq. rt. of 10n √10n	Cube root ∛n	Reciprocal 1/n
			64·	200 +	16·	0·000
4200	17 64 00 00	74 088 000 000	807407 7715	4·939015 24396	134286 1281	2380952 566
4201	17 64 84 01	74 140 932 601	815122 7713	4·963411 24394	135567 1280	2380386 566
4202	17 65 68 04	74 193 890 408	822835 7713	4·987805 24390	136847 1280	2379819 567
4203	17 66 52 09	74 246 873 427	830548 7712	5·012195 24387	138127 1280	2379253 566
4204	17 67 36 16	74 299 881 664	838260 7711	5·036582 24385	139407 1279	2378687 566
4205	17 68 20 25	74 352 915 125	845971 7710	5·060967 24381	140686 1280	2378121 565
4206	17 69 04 36	74 405 973 816	853681 7710	5·085348 24379	141966 1279	2377556 565
4207	17 69 88 49	74 459 057 743	861391 7708	5·109727 24375	143245 1279	2376991 565
4208	17 70 72 64	74 512 166 912	869099 7707	5·134102 24373	144524 1279	2376426 565
4209	17 71 56 81	74 565 301 329	876806 7707	5·158475 24370	145803 1278	2375861 564
4210	17 72 41 00	74 618 461 000	884513 7705	5·182845 24367	147081 1279	2375297 564
4211	17 73 25 21	74 671 645 931	892218 7705	5·207212 24365	148360 1278	2374733 564
4212	17 74 09 44	74 724 856 128	899923 7704	5·231577 24361	149638 1278	2374169 564
4213	17 74 93 69	74 778 091 597	907627 7702	5·255938 24358	150916 1278	2373606 563
4214	17 75 77 96	74 831 352 344	915329 7702	5·280296 24356	152194 1277	2373042 564
4215	17 76 62 25	74 884 638 375	923031 7701	5·304652 24352	153471 1277	2372479 562
4216	17 77 46 56	74 937 949 696	930732 7700	5·329004 24350	154748 1278	2371917 563
4217	17 78 30 89	74 991 286 313	938432 7700	5·353354 24347	156026 1277	2371354 562
4218	17 79 15 24	75 044 648 232	946132 7698	5·377701 24344	157303 1276	2370792 562
4219	17 79 99 61	75 098 035 459	953830 7697	5·402045 24341	158579 1277	2370230 562
4220	17 80 84 00	75 151 448 000	961527 7696	5·426386 24338	159856 1276	2369668 561
4221	17 81 68 41	75 204 885 861	969223 7696	5·450724 24335	161132 1276	2369107 561
4222	17 82 52 84	75 258 349 048	976919 7695	5·475059 24333	162408 1276	2368546 561
4223	17 83 37 29	75 311 837 567	984614 7693	5·499392 24329	163684 1276	2367985 561
4224	17 84 21 76	75 365 351 424	992307 7693	5·523721 24327	164960 1276	2367424 560
4225	17 85 06 25	75 418 890 625	*000000 7692	5·548048 24324	166236 1275	2366864 560
4226	17 85 90 76	75 472 455 176	007692 7691	5·572372 24321	167511 1275	2366304 560
4227	17 86 75 29	75 526 045 083	015383 7690	5·596693 24318	168786 1275	2365744 560
4228	17 87 59 84	75 579 660 352	023073 7689	5·621011 24315	170061 1275	2365184 560
4229	17 88 44 41	75 633 300 989	030762 7688	5·645326 24312	171336 1274	2364625 559
4230	17 89 29 00	75 686 967 000	038450 7687	5·669638 24309	172610 1275	2364066 559
4231	17 90 13 61	75 740 658 391	046137 7687	5·693947 24307	173885 1274	2363507 559
4232	17 90 98 24	75 794 375 168	053824 7685	5·718254 24304	175159 1274	2362949 558
4233	17 91 82 89	75 848 117 337	061509 7685	5·742558 24300	176433 1273	2362391 558
4234	17 92 67 56	75 901 884 904	069194 7684	5·766858 24298	177706 1274	2361833 558
4235	17 93 52 25	75 955 677 875	076878 7682	5·791156 24295	178980 1273	2361275 557
4236	17 94 36 96	76 009 496 256	084560 7682	5·815451 24292	180253 1273	2360718 558
4237	17 95 21 69	76 063 340 053	092242 7681	5·839743 24290	181526 1273	2360160 556
4238	17 96 06 44	76 117 209 272	099923 7680	5·864033 24286	182799 1273	2359604 557
4239	17 96 91 21	76 171 103 919	107603 7679	5·888319 24284	184072 1273	2359047 556
4240	17 97 76 00	76 225 024 000	115282 7679	5·912603 24281	185345 1272	2358491 557
4241	17 98 60 81	76 278 969 521	122961 7677	5·936884 24277	186617 1272	2357934 555
4242	17 99 45 64	76 332 940 488	130638 7676	5·961161 24275	187889 1272	2357379 555
4243	18 00 30 49	76 386 936 907	138314 7676	5·985436 24273	189161 1272	2356823 556
4244	18 01 15 36	76 440 958 784	145990 7675	6·009709 24269	190433 1271	2356268 555
4245	18 02 00 25	76 495 006 125	153665 7673	6·033978 24266	191704 1272	2355713 555
4246	18 02 85 16	76 549 078 936	161338 7673	6·058244 24264	192976 1271	2355158 555
4247	18 03 70 09	76 603 177 223	169011 7672	6·082508 24260	194247 1271	2354603 554
4248	18 04 55 04	76 657 300 992	176683 7671	6·106768 24258	195518 1270	2354049 554
4249	18 05 40 01	76 711 450 249	184354 7670	6·131026 24255	196788 1271	2353495 554
4250	18 06 25 00	76 765 625 000	192024 65:	6·155281 200 +	198059 16·	2352941 0·000

No. n	Square n^2	Cube n^3	Square root $\sqrt{n}$	Sq. rt. of 10n $\sqrt{10n}$	Cube root $\sqrt[3]{n}$	Reciprocal $\dfrac{1}{n}$
			65·	200 +	16·	0·000
4250	18 06 25 00	76 765 625 000	192024 7669	6·155281 24252	198059 1270	2352941 553
4251	18 07 10 01	76 819 825 251	199693 7669	6·179533 24250	199329 1270	2352388 553
4252	18 07 95 04	76 874 051 008	207362 7667	6·203783 24246	200599 1270	2351834 554
4253	18 08 80 09	76 928 302 277	215029 7666	6·228029 24244	201869 1270	2351281 553
4254	18 09 65 16	76 982 579 064	222695 7666	6·252273 24240	203139 1270	2350729 552
4255	18 10 50 25	77 036 881 375	230361 7665	6·276513 24238	204409 1269	2350176 552
4256	18 11 35 36	77 091 209 216	238026 7664	6·300751 24235	205678 1269	2349624 552
4257	18 12 20 49	77 145 562 593	245690 7662	6·324986 24233	206947 1269	2349072 552
4258	18 13 05 64	77 199 941 512	253352 7662	6·349219 24229	208216 1269	2348520 551
4259	18 13 90 81	77 254 345 979	261014 7661	6·373448 24226	209485 1268	2347969 551
4260	18 14 76 00	77 308 776 000	268675 7661	6·397674 24224	210753 1269	2347418 551
4261	18 15 61 21	77 363 231 581	276336 7659	6·421898 24221	212022 1268	2346867 551
4262	18 16 46 44	77 417 712 728	283995 7658	6·446119 24218	213290 1268	2346316 550
4263	18 17 31 69	77 472 219 447	291653 7658	6·470337 24215	214558 1268	2345766 550
4264	18 18 16 96	77 526 751 744	299311 7656	6·494552 24212	215826 1267	2345216 550
4265	18 19 02 25	77 581 309 625	306967 7656	6·518764 24210	217093 1268	2344666 550
4266	18 19 87 56	77 635 893 096	314623 7655	6·542974 24206	218361 1267	2344116 550
4267	18 20 72 89	77 690 502 163	322278 7654	6·567180 24204	219628 1267	2343567 549
4268	18 21 58 24	77 745 136 832	329932 7653	6·591384 24201	220895 1266	2343018 549
4269	18 22 43 61	77 799 797 109	337585 7652	6·615585 24198	222161 1267	2342469 549
4270	18 23 29 00	77 854 483 000	345237 7651	6·639783 24195	223428 1266	2341920 548
4271	18 24 14 41	77 909 194 511	352888 7651	6·663978 24193	224694 1267	2341372 548
4272	18 24 99 84	77 963 931 648	360539 7649	6·688171 24190	225961 1265	2340824 548
4273	18 25 85 29	78 018 694 417	368188 7649	6·712361 24186	227226 1266	2340276 547
4274	18 26 70 76	78 073 482 824	375837 7647	6·736547 24184	228492 1266	2339729 548
4275	18 27 56 25	78 128 296 875	383484 7647	6·760731 24181	229758 1265	2339181 547
4276	18 28 41 76	78 183 136 576	391131 7646	6·784912 24179	231023 1265	2338634 547
4277	18 29 27 29	78 238 001 933	398777 7645	6·809091 24175	232288 1265	2338087 547
4278	18 30 12 84	78 292 892 952	406422 7644	6·833266 24173	233553 1265	2337541 546
4279	18 30 98 41	78 347 809 639	414066 7643	6·857439 24170	234818 1265	2336995 546
4280	18 31 84 00	78 402 752 000	421709 7642	6·881609 24167	236083 1264	2336449 546
4281	18 32 69 61	78 457 720 041	429351 7642	6·905776 24164	237347 1264	2335903 546
4282	18 33 55 24	78 512 713 768	436993 7640	6·929940 24161	238611 1264	2335357 545
4283	18 34 40 89	78 567 733 187	444633 7640	6·954101 24159	239875 1264	2334812 545
4284	18 35 26 56	78 622 778 304	452273 7638	6·978260 24155	241139 1264	2334267 545
4285	18 36 12 25	78 677 849 125	459911 7638	7·002415 24153	242403 1263	2333722 544
4286	18 36 97 96	78 732 945 656	467549 7637	7·026568 24150	243666 1263	2333178 544
4287	18 37 83 69	78 788 067 903	475186 7636	7·050718 24148	244929 1263	2332634 544
4288	18 38 69 44	78 843 215 872	482822 7635	7·074866 24144	246192 1263	2332090 544
4289	18 39 55 21	78 898 389 569	490457 7635	7·099010 24142	247455 1263	2331546 544
4290	18 40 41 00	78 953 589 000	498092 7633	7·123152 24139	248718 1262	2331002 543
4291	18 41 26 81	79 008 814 171	505725 7632	7·147291 24136	249980 1263	2330459 543
4292	18 42 12 64	79 064 065 088	513357 7632	7·171427 24133	251243 1262	2329916 543
4293	18 42 98 49	79 119 341 757	520989 7631	7·195560 24130	252505 1261	2329373 542
4294	18 43 84 36	79 174 644 184	528620 7630	7·219690 24128	253766 1262	2328831 542
4295	18 44 70 25	79 229 972 375	536250 7628	7·243818 24125	255028 1261	2328289 542
4296	18 45 56 16	79 285 326 336	543878 7628	7·267943 24121	256289 1262	2327747 542
4297	18 46 42 09	79 340 706 073	551506 7628	7·292064 24120	257551 1261	2327205 541
4298	18 47 28 04	79 396 111 592	559134 7626	7·316184 24116	258812 1261	2326664 542
4299	18 48 14 01	79 451 542 899	566760 7625	7·340300 24114	260073 1260	2326122 541
4300	18 49 00 00	79 507 000 000	574385 65·	7·364414 200 +	261333 16·	2325581 0·000

No. n	Square n^2	Cube n^3	Square root $\sqrt{n}$	Sq. rt. of 10n $\sqrt{10n}$	Cube root $\sqrt[3]{n}$	Reciprocal $\frac{1}{n}$
			65·	200 +	16·	0·000
4300	18 49 00 00	79 507 000 000	574385 7625	7·364414 24110	261333 1261	2325581 540
4301	18 49 86 01	79 562 482 901	582010 7623	7·388524 24108	262594 1260	2325041 541
4302	18 50 72 04	79 617 991 608	589633 7623	7·412632 24105	263854 1260	2324500 540
4303	18 51 58 09	79 673 526 127	597256 7622	7·436737 24103	265114 1260	2323960 540
4304	18 52 44 16	79 729 086 464	604878 7621	7·460840 24099	266374 1260	2323420 540
4305	18 53 30 25	79 784 672 625	612499 7620	7·484939 24097	267634 1259	2322880 539
4306	18 54 16 36	79 840 284 616	620119 7619	7·509036 24094	268893 1260	2322341 539
4307	18 55 02 49	79 895 922 443	627738 7618	7·533130 24091	270153 1259	2321802 539
4308	18 55 88 64	79 951 586 112	635356 7618	7·557221 24088	271412 1259	2321263 539
4309	18 56 74 81	80 007 275 629	642974 7616	7·581309 24086	272671 1258	2320724 539 538
4310	18 57 61 00	80 062 991 000	650590 7616	7·605395 24083	273929 1259	2320186 539
4311	18 58 47 21	80 118 732 231	658206 7615	7·629478 24080	275188 1258	2319647 538
4312	18 59 33 44	80 174 499 328	665821 7614	7·653558 24077	276446 1258	2319109 538
4313	18 60 19 69	80 230 292 297	673435 7612	7·677635 24074	277704 1258	2318572 537 538
4314	18 61 05 96	80 286 111 144	681047 7613	7·701709 24072	278962 1258	2318034 537
4315	18 61 92 25	80 341 955 875	688660 7611	7·725781 24069	280220 1257	2317497 537
4316	18 62 78 56	80 397 826 496	696271 7610	7·749850 24066	281477 1258	2316960 537
4317	18 63 64 89	80 453 723 013	703881 7610	7·773916 24063	282735 1257	2316423 537
4318	18 64 51 24	80 509 645 432	711491 7608	7·797979 24060	283992 1257	2315887 536
4319	18 65 37 61	80 565 593 759	719099 7608	7·822039 24058	285249 1257	2315351 536
4320	18 66 24 00	80 621 568 000	726707 7607	7·846097 24055	286506 1256	2314815 536
4321	18 67 10 41	80 677 568 161	734314 7606	7·870152 24052	287762 1257	2314279 536 535
4322	18 67 96 84	80 733 594 248	741920 7605	7·894204 24049	289019 1256	2313744 535
4323	18 68 83 29	80 789 646 267	749525 7604	7·918253 24047	290275 1256	2313208 536 535
4324	18 69 69 76	80 845 724 224	757129 7603	7·942300 24043	291531 1256	2312673 535 534
4325	18 70 56 25	80 901 828 125	764732 7603	7·966343 24041	292787 1255	2312139 535
4326	18 71 42 76	80 957 957 976	772335 7601	7·990384 24039	294042 1256	2311604 534
4327	18 72 29 29	81 014 113 783	779936 7601	8·014423 24035	295298 1255	2311070 534
4328	18 73 15 84	81 070 295 552	787537 7600	8·038458 24033	296553 1255	2310536 534
4329	18 74 02 41	81 126 503 289	795137 7599	8·062491 24029	297808 1255	2310002 534 533
4330	18.74 89 00	81 182 737 000	802736 7598	8·086520 24028	299063 1254	2309469 533
4331	18 75 75 61	81 238 996 691	810334 7597	8·110548 24024	300317 1255	2308936 533
4332	18 76 62 24	81 295 282 368	817931 7596	8·134572 24021	301572 1254	2308403 533
4333	18 77 48 89	81 351 594 037	825527 7595	8·158593 24019	302826 1254	2307870 533
4334	18 78 35 56	81 407 931 704	833122 7595	8·182612 24016	304080 1254	2307337 533 532
4335	18 79 22 25	81 464 295 375	840717 7594	8·206628 24013	305334 1254	2306805 532
4336	18 80 08 96	81 520 685 056	848311 7592	8·230641 24011	306588 1253	2306273 532
4337	18 80 95 69	81 577 100 753	855903 7592	8·254652 24007	307841 1254	2305741 532
4338	18 81 82 44	81 633 542 472	863495 7591	8·278659 24005	309095 1253	2305210 531
4339	18 82 69 21	81 690 010 219	871086 7590	8·302664 24003	310348 1253	2304678 532 531
4340	18 83 56 00	81 746 504 000	878676 7590	8·326667 23999	311601 1252	2304147 530
4341	18 84 42 81	81 803 023 821	886266 7588	8·350666 23997	312853 1253	2303617 531
4342	18 85 29 64	81 859 569 688	893854 7588	8·374663 23993	314106 1252	2303086 531
4343	18 86 16 49	81 916 141 607	901442 7586	8·398656 23992	315358 1252	2302556 530
4344	18 87 03 36	81 972 739 584	909028 7586	8·422648 23988	316610 1252	2302026 530
4345	18 87 90 25	82 029 363 625	916614 7585	8·446636 23985	317862 1252	2301496 530
4346	18 88 77 16	82 086 013 736	924199 7584	8·470621 23983	319114 1251	2300966 530 529
4347	18 89 64 09	82 142 689 923	931783 7583	8·494604 23980	320365 1252	2300437 529
4348	18 90 51 04	82 199 392 192	939366 7582	8·518584 23978	321617 1251	2299908 529
4349	18 91 38 01	82 256 120 549	946948 7582	8·542562 23974	322868 1251	2299379 529 528
4350	18 92 25 00	82 312 875 000	954530	8·566536	324119	2298851
			65·	200 +	16·	0·000

No. n	Square n^2	Cube n^3	Square root $\sqrt{n}$	Sq. rt. of 10n $\sqrt{10n}$	Cube root $\sqrt[3]{n}$	Reciprocal $\frac{1}{n}$
			65·	200 +	16·	0·000
4350	18 92 25 00	82 312 875 000	954530 7580	8·566536 23972	324119 1251	2298851
4351	18 93 12 01	82 369 655 551	962110 7580	8·590508 23969	325370 1251	2298322 529
4352	18 93 99 04	82 426 462 208	969690 7579	8·614477 23966	326620 1250	2297794 528
4353	18 94 86 09	82 483 294 977	977269 7578	8·638443 23964	327871 1251	2297266 528
4354	18 95 73 16	82 540 153 864	984847 7577	8·662407 23961	329121 1250	2296739 527 528
4355	18 96 60 25	82 597 038 875	992424 7576	8·686368 23958	330371 1250	2296211 527
4356	18 97 47 36	82 653 950 016	*000000 7575	8·710326 23955	331621 1250	2295684 527
4357	18 98 34 49	82 710 887 293	007575 7575	8·734281 23952	332871 1249	2295157 527 526
4358	18 99 21 64	82 767 850 712	015150 7573	8·758233 23950	334120 1249	2294631 527
4359	19 00 08 81	82 824 840 279	022723 7573	8·782183 23947	335369 1249	2294104 526
4360	19 00 96 00	82 881 856 000	030296 7572	8·806130 23944	336616 1249	2293578
4361	19 01 83 21	82 938 897 881	037868 7571	8·830074 23942	337867 1249	2293052 526
4362	19 02 70 44	82 995 965 928	045439 7570	8·854016 23939	339116 1248	2292526 526
4363	19 03 57 69	83 053 060 147	053009 7569	8·877955 23936	340364 1249	2292001 525
4364	19 04 44 96	83 110 180 544	060578 7569	8·901891 23933	341613 1248	2291476 525 525
4365	19 05 32 25	83 167 327 125	068147 7567	8·925824 23931	342861 1248	2290951
4366	19 06 19 56	83 224 499 896	075714 7567	8·949755 23928	344109 1248	2290426 525
4367	19 07 06 89	83 281 698 863	083281 7566	8·973683 23925	345357 1247	2289902 524
4368	19 07 94 24	83 338 924 032	090847 7564	8·997608 23922	346604 1247	2289377 525
4369	19 08 81 61	83 396 175 409	098411 7565	9·021530 23920	347851 1248	2288853 524 523
4370	19 09 69 00	83 453 453 000	105976 7563	9·045450 23916	349099 1247	2288330
4371	19 10 56 41	83 510 756 811	113539 7562	9·069366 23915	350346 1246	2287806 524
4372	19 11 43 84	83 568 086 848	121101 7561	9·093281 23911	351592 1246	2287283 523
4373	19 12 31 29	83 625 443 117	128662 7561	9·117192 23909	352839 1247	2286760 523
4374	19 13 18 76	83 682 825 624	136223 7560	9·141101 23906	354085 1246	2286237 523 523
4375	19 14 06 25	83 740 234 375	143783 7559	9·165007 23903	355332 1246	2285714
4376	19 14 93 76	83 797 669 376	151342 7558	9·188910 23900	356578 1245	2285192 522
4377	19 15 81 29	83 855 130 633	158900 7557	9·212810 23898	357823 1246	2284670 522
4378	19 16 68 84	83 912 618 152	166457 7556	9·236708 23895	359069 1246	2284148 522
4379	19 17 56 41	83 970 131 939	174013 7555	9·260603 23892	360315 1245	2283626 522 521
4380	19 18 44 00	84 027 672 000	181568 7555	9·284495 23890	361560 1245	2283105
4381	19 19 31 61	84 085 238 341	189123 7554	9·308385 23887	362805 1245	2282584 521
4382	19 20 19 24	84 142 830 968	196677 7552	9·332272 23884	364050 1244	2282063 521
4383	19 21 06 89	84 200 449 887	204229 7552	9·356156 23881	365294 1245	2281542 521
4384	19 21 94 56	84 258 095 104	211781 7552	9·380037 23879	366539 1244	2281022 520 520
4385	19 22 82 25	84 315 766 625	219333 7550	9·403916 23876	367783 1244	2280502
4386	19 23 69 96	84 373 464 456	226883 7549	9·427792 23873	369027 1244	2279982 520
4387	19 24 57 69	84 431 188 603	234432 7549	9·451665 23871	370271 1244	2279462 520
4388	19 25 45 44	84 488 939 072	241981 7547	9·475536 23867	371515 1244	2278943 519
4389	19 26 33 21	84 546 715 869	249528 7547	9·499403 23865	372759 1243	2278423 520 519
4390	19 27 21 00	84 604 519 000	257075 7546	9·523268 23863	374002 1243	2277904
4391	19 28 08 81	84 662 348 471	264621 7545	9·547131 23859	375245 1243	2277386 518
4392	19 28 96 64	84 720 204 288	272166 7545	9·570990 23857	376488 1243	2276867 519
4393	19 29 84 49	84 778 086 457	279710 7544	9·594847 23854	377731 1242	2276349 518
4394	19 30 72 36	84 835 994 984	287254 7544	9·618701 23852	378974 1242	2275831 518 518
4395	19 31 60 25	84 893 929 875	294796 7542	9·642553 23849	380216 1242	2275313
4396	19 32 48 16	84 951 891 136	302338 7542	9·666402 23846	381458 1242	2274795 518
4397	19 33 36 09	85 009 878 773	309879 7541	9·690248 23843	382700 1242	2274278 517
4398	19 34 24 04	85 067 892 792	317419 7540	9·714091 23841	383942 1242	2273761 517
4399	19 35 12 01	85 125 933 199	324958 7539 7538	9·737932 23838	385184 1241	2273244 517 517
4400	19 36 00 00	85 184 000 000	332496 66·	9·761770 200 +	386425 16·	2272727 0·000

No. n	Square n^2	Cube n^3	Square root $\sqrt{n}$	Sq. rt. of $10n$ $\sqrt{10n}$	Cube root $\sqrt[3]{n}$	Reciprocal $\dfrac{1}{n}$
			66·	200 +	16·	0·000
4400	19 36 00 00	85 184 000 000	332496	9·761770	386425	2272727
4401	19 36 88 01	85 242 093 201	340033 7537	9·785605 23835	387667 1242	2272211 516
4402	19 37 76 04	85 300 212 808	347570 7537	9·809437 23832	388908 1241	2271695 516
4403	19 38 64 09	85 358 358 827	355105 7535	9·833267 23830	390149 1241	2271179 516
4404	19 39 52 16	85 416 531 264	362640 7535	9·857094 23827	391389 1240	2270663 516
			7534	23825	1241	515
4405	19 40 40 25	85 474 730 125	370174 7533	9·880919 23821	392630 1240	2270148 516
4406	19 41 28 36	85 532 955 416	377707 7533	9·904740 23819	393870 1241	2269632 515
4407	19 42 16 49	85 591 207 143	385239 7532	9·928559 23817	395111 1240	2269117 515
4408	19 43 04 64	85 649 485 312	392771 7532	9·952376 23813	396351 1239	2268603 514
4409	19 43 92 81	85 707 789 929	400301 7530	9·976189 23811	397590 1240	2268088 515
			7530		.1240	514
4410	19 44 81 00	85 766 121 000	407831	*0·000000	398830	2267574
4411	19 45 69 21	85 824 478 531	415360 7529	0·023808 23808	400069 1239	2267060 514
4412	19 46 57 44	85 882 862 528	422888 7528	0·047614 23806	401309 1240	2266546 514
4413	19 47 45 69	85 941 272 997	430415 7527	0·071416 23802	402548 1239	2266032 514
4414	19 48 33 96	85 999 709 944	437941 7526	0·095217 23801	403787 1239	2265519 513
			7525	23797	1238	513
4415	19 49 22 25	86 058 173 375	445466 7525	0·119014 23795	405025 1239	2265006 513
4416	19 50 10 56	86 116 663 296	452991 7525	0·142809 23792	406264 1238	2264493 513
4417	19 50 98 89	86 175 179 713	460515 7524	0·166601 23789	407502 1238	2263980 513
4418	19 51 87 24	86 233 722 632	468037 7522	0·190390 23786	408740 1238	2263468 512
4419	19 52 75 61	86 292 292 059	475559 7522	0·214176 23784	409978 1238	2262955 513
			7522			512
4420	19 53 64 00	86 350 888 000	483081	0·237960	411216	2262443
4421	19 54 52 41	86 409 510 461	490601 7520	0·261742 23782	412453 1237	2261932 511
4422	19 55 40 84	86 468 159 448	498120 7519	0·285520 23778	413691 1238	2261420 512
4423	19 56 29 29	86 526 834 967	505639 7519	0·309296 23776	414928 1237	2260909 511
4424	19 57 17 76	86 585 537 024	513157 7518	0·333069 23773	416165 1237	2260398 511
			7516	23771	1237	511
4425	19 58 06 25	86 644 265 625	520673 7517	0·356840 23767	417402 1236	2259887
4426	19 58 94 76	86 703 020 776	528190 7515	0·380607 23766	418638 1237	2259376 511
4427	19 59 83 29	86 761 802 483	535705 7514	0·404373 23762	419875 1236	2258866 510
4428	19 60 71 84	86 820 610 752	543219 7514	0·428135 23760	421111 1236	2258356 510
4429	19 61 60 41	86 879 445 589	550733 7512	0·451895 23757	422347 1236	2257846 510
						510
4430	19 62 49 00	86 938 307 000	558245	0·475652	423583	2257336
4431	19 63 37 61	86 997 194 991	565757 7512	0·499406 23754	424819 1236	2256827 509
4432	19 64 26 24	87 056 109 568	573268 7511	0·523158 23752	426054 1235	2256318 509
4433	19 65 14 89	87 115 050 737	580778 7510	0·546907 23749	427289 1235	2255809 509
4434	19 66 03 56	87 174 018 504	588287 7509	0·570653 23746	428525 1236	2255300 509
			7509	23744	1235	509
4435	19 66 92 25	87 233 012 875	595796 7507	0·594397 23741	429760 1234	2254791
4436	19 67 80 96	87 292 033 856	603303 7507	0·618138 23738	430994 1235	2254283 508
4437	19 68 69 69	87 351 081 453	610810 7506	0·641876 23736	432229 1234	2253775 508
4438	19 69 58 44	87 410 155 672	618316 7505	0·665612 23733	433463 1235	2253267 508
4439	19 70 47 21	87 469 256 519	625821 7504	0·689345 23730	434698 1234	2252760 507
						508
4440	19 71 36 00	87 528 384 000	633325	0·713075	435932	2252252
4441	19 72 24 81	87 587 538 121	640828 7503	0·736803 23728	437165 1233	2251745 507
4442	19 73 13 64	87 646 718 888	648331 7503	0·760528 23725	438399 1234	2251238 507
4443	19 74 02 49	87 705 926 307	655832 7501	0·784250 23722	439632 1234	2250731 507
4444	19 74 91 36	87 765 160 384	663333 7501	0·807969 23719	440866 1233	2250225 506
			7500	23717		506
4445	19 75 80 25	87 824 421 125	670833 7499	0·831686 23715	442099 1233	2249719
4446	19 76 69 16	87 883 708 536	678332 7499	0·855401 23711	443332 1232	2249213 506
4447	19 77 58 09	87 943 022 623	685831 7497	0·879112 23709	444564 1233	2248707 506
4448	19 78 47 04	88 002 363 392	693328 7497	0·902821 23706	445797 1232	2248201 506
4449	19 79 36 01	88 061 730 849	700825 7495	0·926527 23704	447029 1233	2247696 505
						505
4450	19 80 25 00	88 121 125 000	708320 66·	0·950231 210 +	448262 16·	2247191 0·000

No. n	Square n²	Cube n³	Square root √n	Sq. rt. of 10n √10n	Cube root ∛n	Reciprocal 1/n
			66·	210 +	16·	0·000
4450	19 80 25 00	88 121 125 000	708320 7495	0·950231 23701	448262 1232	2247191 505
4451	19 81 14 01	88 180 545 851	715815 7494	0·973932 23698	449494 1231	2246686 505
4452	19 82 03 04	88 239 993 408	723309 7493	0·997630 23696	450725 1232	2246181 505
4453	19 82 92 09	88 299 467 677	730802 7493	1·021326 23693	451957 1231	2245677 504
4454	19 83 81 16	88 358 968 664	738295 7491	1·045019 23690	453188 1232	2245173 504
4455	19 84 70 25	88 418 496 375	745786 7491	1·068709 23688	454420 1231	2244669 504
4456	19 85 59 36	88 478 050 816	753277 7490	1·092397 23685	455651 1231	2244165 504
4457	19 86 48 49	88 537 631 993	760767 7489	1·116082 23682	456882 1230	2243662 503
4458	19 87 37 64	88 597 239 912	768256 7488	1·139764 23680	458112 1231	2243158 503
4459	19 88 26 81	88 656 874 579	775744 7487	1·163444 23677	459343 1230	2242655 503
4460	19 89 16 00	88 716 536 000	783231 7487	1·187121 23674	460573 1230	2242152 502
4461	19 90 05 21	88 776 224 181	790718 7486	1·210795 23672	461803 1230	2241650 503
4462	19 90 94 44	88 835 939 128	798204 7484	1·234467 23669	463033 1230	2241147 502
4463	19 91 83 69	88 895 680 847	805688 7484	1·258136 23666	464263 1230	2240645 502
4464	19 92 72 96	88 955 449 344	813172 7483	1·281802 23664	465493 1229	2240143 501
4465	19 93 62 25	89 015 244 625	820655 7483	1·305466 23661	466722 1229	2239642 502
4466	19 94 51 56	89 075 066 696	828138 7481	1·329127 23659	467951 1229	2239140 501
4467	19 95 40 89	89 134 915 563	835619 7481	1·352786 23655	469180 1229	2238639 501
4468	19 96 30 24	89 194 791 232	843100 7480	1·376441 23654	470409 1229	2238138 501
4469	19 97 19 61	89 254 693 709	850580 7479	1·400095 23650	471638 1228	2237637 501
4470	19 98 09 00	89 314 623 000	858059 7478	1·423745 23648	472866 1229	2237136 500
4471	19 98 98 41	89 374 579 111	865537 7477	1·447393 23645	474095 1228	2236636 500
4472	19 99 87 84	89 434 562 048	873014 7476	1·471038 23643	475323 1228	2236136 500
4473	20 00 77 29	89 494 571 817	880490 7476	1·494681 23640	476551 1227	2235636 500
4474	20 01 66 76	89 554 608 424	887966 7475	1·518321 23637	477778 1228	2235136 499
4475	20 02 56 25	89 614 671 875	895441 7474	1·541958 23635	479006 1227	2234637 499
4476	20 03 45 76	89 674 762 176	902915 7473	1·565593 23632	480233 1228	2234138 499
4477	20 04 35 29	89 734 879 333	910388 7472	1·589225 23629	481461 1227	2233639 499
4478	20 05 24 84	89 795 023 352	917860 7472	1·612854 23627	482688 1227	2233140 499
4479	20 06 14 41	89 855 194 239	925332 7470	1·636481 23624	483915 1226	2232641 498
4480	20 07 04 00	89 915 392 000	932802 7470	1·660105 23621	485141 1227	2232143 498
4481	20 07 93 61	89 975 616 641	940272 7469	1·683726 23619	486368 1226	2231645 498
4482	20 08 83 24	90 035 868 168	947741 7468	1·707345 23616	487594 1226	2231147 498
4483	20 09 72 89	90 096 146 587	955209 7467	1·730961 23614	488820 1226	2230649 497
4484	20 10 62 56	90 156 451 904	962676 7467	1·754575 23611	490046 1226	2230152 498
4485	20 11 52 25	90 216 784 125	970143 7465	1·778186 23608	491272 1225	2229654 497
4486	20 12 41 96	90 277 143 256	977608 7465	1·801794 23606	492497 1226	2229157 497
4487	20 13 31 69	90 337 529 303	985073 7464	1·825400 23603	493723 1225	2228661 496
4488	20 14 21 44	90 397 942 272	992537 7463	1·849003 23600	494948 1225	2228164 497
4489	20 15 11 21	90 458 382 169	*000000 7462	1·872603 23598	496173 1225	2227668 496
4490	20 16 01 00	90 518 849 000	007462 7462	1·896201 23595	497398 1224	2227171 497
4491	20 16 90 81	90 579 342 771	014924 7460	1·919796 23593	498622 1225	2226676 495
4492	20 17 80 64	90 639 863 488	022384 7460	1·943389 23590	499847 1224	2226180 496
4493	20 18 70 49	90 700 411 157	029844 7459	1·966979 23587	501071 1224	2225684 496
4494	20 19 60 36	90 760 985 784	037303 7458	1·990566 23584	502295 1224	2225189 495
4495	20 20 50 25	90 821 587 375	044761 7457	2·014150 23582	503519 1224	2224694 495
4496	20 21 40 16	90 882 215 936	052218 7457	2·037732 23580	504743 1224	2224199 495
4497	20 22 30 09	90 942 871 473	059675 7456	2·061312 23577	505967 1223	2223705 495
4498	20 23 20 04	91 003 553 992	067131 7454	2·084889 23574	507190 1223	2223210 494
4499	20 24 10 01	91 064 263 499	074585 7454	2·108463 23571	508413 1223	2222716 494
4500	20 25 00 00	91 125 000 000	082039 67·	2·132034 210 +	509636 16·	2222222 0·000

No. n	Square n²	Cube n³	Square root √n	Sq. rt. of 10n √10n	Cube root ∛n	Reciprocal 1/n
			67·	210 +	16·	0·000
4500	20 25 00 00	91 125 000 000	082039 7453	2·132034 23569	509636 1223	2222222
4501	20 25 90 01	91 185 763 501	089492 7453	2·155603 23567	510859 1223	2221729 493
4502	20 26 80 04	91 246 554 008	096945 7451	2·179170 23563	512082 1222	2221235 494
4503	20 27 70 09	91 307 371 527	104396 7451	2·202733 23561	513304 1223	2220742 493
4504	20 28 60 16	91 368 216 064	111847 7450	2·226294 23559	514527 1222	2220249 493
4505	20 29 50 25	91 429 087 625	119297 7449	2·249853 23556	515749 1222	2219756 493
4506	20 30 40 36	91 489 986 216	126746 7448	2·273409 23553	516971 1221	2219263 493
4507	20 31 30 49	91 550 911 843	134194 7447	2·296962 23550	518192 1222	2218771 492
4508	20 32 20 64	91 611 864 512	141641 7447	2·320512 23548	519414 1221	2218279 492
4509	20 33 10 81	91 672 844 229	149088 7446	2·344060 23546	520635 1222	2217787 492
4510	20 34 01 00	91 733 851 000	156534 7444	2·367606 23543	521857 1221	2217295 492
4511	20 34 91 21	91 794 884 831	163978 7444	2·391149 23540	523078 1221	2216803 492
4512	20 35 81 44	91 855 945 728	171422 7444	2·414689 23537	524298 1220	2216312 491
4513	20 36 71 69	91 917 033 697	178866 7442	2·438226 23535	525519 1221	2215821 491
4514	20 37 61 96	91 978 148 744	186308 7442	2·461761 23533	526740 1220	2215330 491
4515	20 38 52 25	92 039 290 875	193750 7440	2·485294 23529	527960 1220	2214839 490
4516	20 39 42 56	92 100 460 096	201190 7440	2·508823 23527	529180 1220	2214349 490
4517	20 40 32 89	92 161 656 413	208630 7440	2·532350 23525	530400 1220	2213859 490
4518	20 41 23 24	92 222 879 832	216070 7438	2·555875 23522	531620 1219	2213369 490
4519	20 42 13 61	92 284 130 359	223508 7437	2·579397 23519	532839 1220	2212879 490
4520	20 43 04 00	92 345 408 000	230945 7437	2·602916 23517	534059 1219	2212389 489
4521	20 43 94 41	92 406 712 761	238382 7436	2·626433 23514	535278 1219	2211900 489
4522	20 44 84 84	92 468 044 648	245818 7435	2·649947 23512	536497 1219	2211411 489
4523	20 45 75 29	92 529 403 667	253253 7434	2·673459 23509	537716 1219	2210922 489
4524	20 46 65 76	92 590 789 824	260687 7433	2·696968 23506	538935 1218	2210433 488
4525	20 47 56 25	92 652 203 125	268120 7433	2·720474 23504	540153 1219	2209945 489
4526	20 48 46 76	92 713 643 576	275553 7431	2·743978 23501	541372 1218	2209456 488
4527	20 49 37 29	92 775 111 183	282984 7431	2·767479 23498	542590 1218	2208968 488
4528	20 50 27 84	92 836 605 952	290415 7430	2·790977 23496	543808 1218	2208481 487
4529	20 51 18 41	92 898 127 889	297845 7430	2·814473 23494	545025 1217	2207993 488
4530	20 52 09 00	92 959 677 000	305275 7428	2·837967 23490	546243 1218	2207506 488
4531	20 52 99 61	93 021 253 291	312703 7428	2·861457 23490	547461 1217	2207018 487
4532	20 53 90 24	93 082 856 768	320131 7427	2·884945 23488	548678 1217	2206531 486
4533	20 54 80 89	93 144 487 437	327558 7425	2·908431 23486	549895 1217	2206045 486
4534	20 55 71 56	93 206 145 304	334983 7426	2·931914 23483	551112 1217	2205558 486
4535	20 56 62 25	93 267 830 375	342409 7424	2·955394 23478	552329 1216	2205072 486
4536	20 57 52 96	93 329 542 656	349833 7423	2·978872 23475	553545 1216	2204586 486
4537	20 58 43 69	93 391 282 153	357256 7423	3·002347 23473	554761 1217	2204100 486
4538	20 59 34 44	93 453 048 872	364679 7422	3·025820 23470	555978 1216	2203614 486
4539	20 60 25 21	93 514 842 819	372101 7421	3·049290 23468	557194 1215	2203128 485
4540	20 61 16 00	93 576 664 000	379522 7420	3·072758 23464	558409 1216	2202643 485
4541	20 62 06 81	93 638 512 421	386942 7420	3·096222 23463	559625 1216	2202158 485
4542	20 62 97 64	93 700 388 088	394362 7418	3·119685 23459	560841 1215	2201673 485
4543	20 63 88 49	93 762 291 007	401780 7418	3·143144 23458	562056 1215	2201189 484
4544	20 64 79 36	93 824 221 184	409198 7417	3·166602 23454	563271 1215	2200704 485
4545	20 65 70 25	93 886 178 625	416615 7416	3·190056 23452	564486 1215	2200220 484
4546	20 66 61 16	93 948 163 336	424031 7416	3·213508 23449	565701 1214	2199736 484
4547	20 67 52 09	94 010 175 323	431447 7414	3·236957 23447	566915 1215	2199252 484
4548	20 68 43 04	94 072 214 592	438861 7414	3·260404 23444	568130 1214	2198769 483
4549	20 69 34 01	94 134 281 149	446275 7413	3·283848 23442	569344 1214	2198285 484
4550	20 70 25 00	94 196 375 000	453688	3·307290	570558	2197802
			67·	210 +	16·	0·000

No. n	Square n^2	Cube n^3	Square root $\sqrt{n}$	Sq. rt. of $10n$ $\sqrt{10n}$	Cube root $\sqrt[3]{n}$	Reciprocal $\dfrac{1}{n}$
			67·	210 +	16·	0·000
4550	20 70 25 00	94 196 375 000	453688 7412	3·307290 23439	570558 1214	2197802 483
4551	20 71 16 01	94 258 496 151	461100 7411	3·330729 23437	571772 1214	2197319 482
4552	20 72 07 04	94 320 644 608	468511 7411	3·354166 23434	572986 1213	2196837 483
4553	20 72 98 09	94 382 820 377	475922 7409	3·377600 23431	574199 1213	2196354 483
4554	20 73 89 16	94 445 023 464	483331 7409	3·401031 23429	575412 1214	2195872 482
4555	20 74 80 25	94 507 253 875	490740 7408	3·424460 23426	576626 1213	2195390 482
4556	20 75 71 36	94 569 511 616	498148 7407	3·447886 23424	577839 1212	2194908 482
4557	20 76 62 49	94 631 796 693	505555 7407	3·471310 23421	579051 1213	2194426 481
4558	20 77 53 64	94 694 109 112	512962 7405	3·494731 23418	580264 1212	2193945 482
4559	20 78 44 81	94 756 448 879	520367 7405	3·518149 23416	581476 1213	2193463 481
4560	20 79 36 00	94 818 816 000	527772 7404	3·541565 23413	582689 1212	2192982 480
4561	20 80 27 21	94 881 210 481	535176 7403	3·564978 23411	583901 1212	2192502 480
4562	20 81 18 44	94 943 632 328	542579 7402	3·588389 23408	585113 1211	2192021 481
4563	20 82 09 69	95 006 081 547	549981 7402	3·611797 23406	586324 1212	2191541 480
4564	20 83 00 96	95 068 558 144	557383 7401	3·635203 23403	587536 1211	2191060 481
4565	20 83 92 25	95 131 062 125	564784 7400	3·658606 23401	588747 1212	2190581 480
4566	20 84 83 56	95 193 593 496	572184 7399	3·682007 23398	589959 1211	2190101 480
4567	20 85 74 89	95 256 152 263	579583 7398	3·705405 23395	591170 1210	2189621 480
4568	20 86 66 24	95 318 738 432	586981 7397	3·728800 23393	592380 1211	2189142 479
4569	20 87 57 61	95 381 352 000	594378 7397	3·752193 23390	593591 1211	2188663 479
4570	20 88 49 00	95 443 993 000	601775 7396	3·775583 23388	594802 1210	2188184 479
4571	20 89 40 41	95 506 661 411	609171 7395	3·798971 23385	596012 1210	2187705 479
4572	20 90 31 84	95 569 357 248	616566 7395	3·822356 23383	597222 1210	2187227 478
4573	20 91 23 29	95 632 080 517	623960 7394	3·845739 23380	598432 1210	2186748 479
4574	20 92 14 76	95 694 831 224	631354 7392	3·869119 23377	599642 1209	2186270 478
4575	20 93 06 25	95 757 609 375	638746 7392	3·892496 23375	600851 1210	2185792 477
4576	20 93 97 76	95 820 414 976	646138 7391	3·915871 23373	602061 1209	2185315 478
4577	20 94 89 29	95 883 248 033	653529 7390	3·939244 23370	603270 1209	2184837 477
4578	20 95 80 84	95 946 108 552	660919 7390	3·962614 23367	604479 1209	2184360 477
4579	20 96 72 41	96 008 996 539	668309 7388	3·985981 23365	605688 1209	2183883 477
4580	20 97 64 00	96 071 912 000	675697 7388	4·009346 23362	606897 1209	2183406 477
4581	20 98 55 61	96 134 854 941	683085 7387	4·032708 23359	608106 1209	2182929 477
4582	20 99 47 24	96 197 825 368	690472 7387	4·056067 23358	609314 1208	2182453 476
4583	21 00 38 89	96 260 823 287	697858 7386	4·079425 23354	610522 1208	2181977 476
4584	21 01 30 56	96 323 848 704	705244 7384	4·102779 23352	611730 1208	2181501 476
4585	21 02 22 25	96 386 901 625	712628 7384	4·126131 23350	612938 1208	2181025 476
4586	21 03 13 96	96 449 982 056	720012 7383	4·149481 23346	614146 1207	2180549 475
4587	21 04 05 69	96 513 090 003	727395 7382	4·172827 23345	615353 1208	2180074 475
4588	21 04 97 44	96 576 225 472	734777 7381	4·196172 23342	616561 1207	2179599 475
4589	21 05 89 21	96 639 388 469	742158 7381	4·219514 23339	617768 1207	2179124 475
4590	21 06 81 00	96 702 579 000	749539 7379	4·242853 23337	618975 1207	2178649 474
4591	21 07 72 81	96 765 797 071	756918 7379	4·266190 23334	620182 1206	2178175 475
4592	21 08 64 64	96 829 042 688	764297 7378	4·289524 23331	621388 1207	2177700 474
4593	21 09 56 49	96 892 315 857	771675 7378	4·312855 23330	622595 1206	2177226 474
4594	21 10 48 36	96 955 616 584	779053 7376	4·336185 23326	623801 1206	2176752 473
4595	21 11 40 25	97 018 944 875	786429 7376	4·359511 23324	625007 1206	2176279 474
4596	21 12 32 16	97 082 300 736	793805 7375	4·382835 23322	626213 1206	2175805 473
4597	21 13 24 09	97 145 684 173	801180 7374	4·406157 23319	627419 1205	2175332 473
4598	21 14 16 04	97 209 095 192	808554 7373	4·429476 23316	628624 1206	2174859 473
4599	21 15 08 01	97 272 533 799	815927 7373	4·452792 23314	629830 1205	2174386 473
4600	21 16 00 00	97 336 000 000	823300	4·476106	631035	2173913
			67·	210 +	16·	0·000

No. n	Square n^2	Cube n^3	Square root $\sqrt{n}$	Sq. rt. of 10n $\sqrt{10n}$	Cube root $\sqrt[3]{n}$	Reciprocal $\dfrac{1}{n}$
			67·	210 +	16·	0·000
4600	21 16 00 00	97 336 000 000	823300 7372	4·476106 23311	631035 1205	2173913 472
4601	21 16 92 01	97 399 493 801	830672 7370	4·499417 23309	632240 1205	2173441 473
4602	21 17 84 04	97 463 015 208	838042 7371	4·522726 23306	633445 1205	2172968 473
4603	21 18 76 09	97 526 564 227	845413 7369	4·546032 23304	634650 1204	2172496 472
4604	21 19 68 16	97 590 140 864	852782 7368	4·569336 23301	635854 1205	2172024 471
4605	21 20 60 25	97 653 745 125	860150 7368	4·592637 23299	637059 1204	2171553 472
4606	21 21 52 36	97 717 377 016	867518 7367	4·615936 23296	638263 1204	2171081 471
4607	21 22 44 49	97 781 036 543	874885 7366	4·639232 23294	639467 1204	2170610 471
4608	21 23 36 64	97 844 723 712	882251 7365	4·662526 23291	640671 1203	2170139 471
4609	21 24 28 81	97 908 438 529	889616 7365	4·685817 23289	641874 1204	2169668 471
4610	21 25 21 00	97 972 181 000	896981 7363	4·709106 23286	643078 1203	2169197 470
4611	21 26 13 21	98 035 951 131	904344 7363	4·732392 23283	644281 1203	2168727 470
4612	21 27 05 44	98 099 748 928	911707 7362	4·755675 23281	645484 1203	2168257 470
4613	21 27 97 69	98 163 574 397	919069 7362	4·778956 23279	646687 1203	2167787 470
4614	21 28 89 96	98 227 427 544	926431 7360	4·802235 23276	647890 1203	2167317 470
4615	21 29 82 25	98 291 308 375	933791 7360	4·825511 23273	649093 1202	2166847 469
4616	21 30 74 56	98 355 216 896	941151 7359	4·848784 23271	650295 1202	2166378 469
4617	21 31 66 89	98 419 153 113	948510 7358	4·872055 23268	651497 1202	2165909 469
4618	21 32 59 24	98 483 117 032	955868 7357	4·895323 23266	652699 1202	2165440 469
4619	21 33 51 61	98 547 108 659	963225 7357	4·918589 23264	653901 1202	2164971 469
4620	21 34 44 00	98 611 128 000	970582 7356	4·941853 23260	655103 1202	2164502 468
4621	21 35 36 41	98 675 175 061	977938 7355	4·965113 23259	656305 1201	2164034 468
4622	21 36 28 84	98 739 249 848	985293 7354	4·988372 23256	657506 1201	2163566 468
4623	21 37 21 29	98 803 352 367	992647 7353	5·011628 23253	658707 1201	2163098 468
4624	21 38 13 76	98 867 482 624	*000000 7353	5·034881 23251	659908 1201	2162630 468
4625	21 39 06 25	98 931 640 625	007353 7351	5·058132 23248	661109 1201	2162162 467
4626	21 39 98 76	98 995 826 376	014704 7351	5·081380 23246	662310 1201	2161695 467
4627	21 40 91 29	99 060 039 883	022055 7350	5·104626 23243	663511 1200	2161228 467
4628	21 41 83 84	99 124 281 152	029405 7350	5·127869 23241	664711 1200	2160761 467
4629	21 42 76 41	99 188 550 189	036755 7348	5·151110 23238	665911 1200	2160294 467
4630	21 43 69 00	99 252 847 000	044103 7348	5·174348 23236	667111 1200	2159827 466
4631	21 44 61 61	99 317 171 591	051451 7347	5·197584 23233	668311 1200	2159361 466
4632	21 45 54 24	99 381 523 968	058798 7347	5·220817 23231	669511 1199	2158895 466
4633	21 46 46 89	99 445 904 137	066144 7346	5·244048 23228	670710 1199	2158429 466
4634	21 47 39 56	99 510 312 104	073490 7346	5·267276 23225	671909 1200	2157963 466
4635	21 48 32 25	99 574 747 875	080834 7344	5·290501 23224	673109 1199	2157497 465
4636	21 49 24 96	99 639 211 456	088178 7343	5·313725 23220	674308 1198	2157032 465
4637	21 50 17 69	99 703 702 853	095521 7342	5·336945 23218	675506 1199	2156567 465
4638	21 51 10 44	99 768 222 072	102863 7342	5·360163 23216	676705 1199	2156102 465
4639	21 52 03 21	99 832 769 119	110205 7340	5·383379 23213	677904 1198	2155637 465
4640	21 52 96 00	99 897 344 000	117545 7340	5·406592 23211	679102 1198	2155172 464
4641	21 53 88 81	99 961 946 721	124885 7339	5·429803 23208	680300 1198	2154708 464
4642	21 54 81 64	100 026 577 288	132224 7339	5·453011 23206	681498 1198	2154244 464
4643	21 55 74 49	100 091 235 707	139563 7337	5·476217 23203	682696 1197	2153780 464
4644	21 56 67 36	100 155 921 984	146900 7337	5·499420 23201	683893 1198	2153316 463
4645	21 57 60 25	100 220 636 125	154237 7336	5·522621 23198	685091 1197	2152853 464
4646	21 58 53 16	100 285 378 136	161573 7335	5·545819 23195	686288 1197	2152389 463
4647	21 59 46 09	100 350 148 023	168908 7335	5·569014 23194	687485 1197	2151926 463
4648	21 60 39 04	100 414 945 792	176242 7334	5·592208 23190	688682 1197	2151463 463
4649	21 61 32 01	100 479 771 449	183576 7334	5·615398 23189	689879 1196	2151000 462
4650	21 62 25 00	100 544 625 000	190908 68·	5·638587 210 +	691075 16·	2150538 0·000

No. n	Square n^2	Cube n^3	Square root $\sqrt{n}$	Sq. rt. of 10n $\sqrt{10n}$	Cube root $\sqrt[3]{n}$	Reciprocal $\dfrac{1}{n}$
			68·	210 +	16·	0·000
4650	21 62 25 00	100 544 625 000	190908 _7332_	5·638587 _23185_	691075 _1197_	2150538 _463_
4651	21 63 18 01	100 609 506 451	198240 _7332_	5·661772 _23183_	692272 _1196_	2150075 _462_
4652	21 64 11 04	100 674 415 808	205572 _7330_	5·684955 _23181_	693468 _1196_	2149613 _462_
4653	21 65 04 09	100 739 353 077	212902 _7330_	5·708136 _23178_	694664 _1196_	2149151 _462_
4654	21 65 97 16	100 804 318 264	220232 _7328_	5·731314 _23176_	695860 _1196_	2148689 _461_
4655	21 66 90 25	100 869 311 375	227560 _7328_	5·754490 _23173_	697056 _1195_	2148228 _462_
4656	21 67 83 36	100 934 332 416	234888 _7328_	5·777663 _23171_	698251 _1196_	2147766 _461_
4657	21 68 76 49	100 999 381 393	242216 _7326_	5·800834 _23168_	699447 _1195_	2147305 _461_
4658	21 69 69 64	101 064 458 312	249542 _7326_	5·824002 _23166_	700642 _1195_	2146844 _461_
4659	21 70 62 81	101 129 563 179	256868 _7325_	5·847168 _23163_	701837 _1195_	2146383 _460_
4660	21 71 56 00	101 194 696 000	264193 _7324_	5·870331 _23161_	703032 _1194_	2145923 _461_
4661	21 72 49 21	101 259 856 781	271517 _7323_	5·893492 _23159_	704226 _1195_	2145462 _460_
4662	21 73 42 44	101 325 045 528	278840 _7323_	5·916651 _23155_	705421 _1194_	2145002 _460_
4663	21 74 35 69	101 390 262 247	286163 _7321_	5·939806 _23154_	706615 _1194_	2144542 _460_
4664	21 75 28 96	101 455 506 944	293484 _7321_	5·962960 _23151_	707809 _1194_	2144082 _459_
4665	21 76 22 25	101 520 779 625	300805 _7320_	5·986111 _23148_	709003 _1194_	2143623 _460_
4666	21 77 15 56	101 586 080 296	308125 _7320_	6·009259 _23146_	710197 _1194_	2143163 _460_
4667	21 78 08 89	101 651 408 963	315445 _7318_	6·032405 _23143_	711391 _1193_	2142704 _459_
4668	21 79 02 24	101 716 765 632	322763 _7318_	6·055548 _23141_	712584 _1194_	2142245 _459_
4669	21 79 95 61	101 782 150 309	330081 _7317_	6·078689 _23139_	713778 _1193_	2141786 _458_
4670	21 80 89 00	101 847 563 000	337398 _7316_	6·101828 _23136_	714971 _1193_	2141328 _459_
4671	21 81 82 41	101 913 003 711	344714 _7316_	6·124964 _23133_	716164 _1193_	2140869 _458_
4672	21 82 75 84	101 978 472 448	352030 _7315_	6·148097 _23131_	717357 _1192_	2140411 _458_
4673	21 83 69 29	102 043 969 217	359345 _7314_	6·171228 _23129_	718549 _1193_	2139953 _458_
4674	21 84 62 76	102 109 494 024	366659 _7313_	6·194357 _23126_	719742 _1192_	2139495 _458_
4675	21 85 56 25	102 175 046 875	373972 _7312_	6·217483 _23124_	720934 _1192_	2139037 _457_
4676	21 86 49 76	102 240 627 776	381284 _7312_	6·240607 _23121_	722126 _1192_	2138580 _457_
4677	21 87 43 29	102 306 236 733	388596 _7310_	6·263728 _23119_	723318 _1192_	2138123 _457_
4678	21 88 36 84	102 371 873 752	395906 _7310_	6·286847 _23116_	724510 _1192_	2137666 _457_
4679	21 89 30 41	102 437 538 839	403216 _7310_	6·309963 _23114_	725702 _1191_	2137209 _457_
4680	21 90 24 00	102 503 232 000	410526 _7308_	6·333077 _23111_	726893 _1192_	2136752 _456_
4681	21 91 17 61	102 568 953 241	417834 _7308_	6·356188 _23109_	728085 _1191_	2136296 _457_
4682	21 92 11 24	102 634 702 568	425142 _7306_	6·379297 _23106_	729276 _1191_	2135839 _456_
4683	21 93 04 89	102 700 479 987	432448 _7307_	6·402403 _23104_	730467 _1190_	2135383 _456_
4684	21 93 98 56	102 766 285 504	439755 _7305_	6·425507 _23101_	731657 _1191_	2134927 _455_
4685	21 94 92 25	102 832 119 125	447060 _7304_	6·448608 _23099_	732848 _1190_	2134472 _456_
4686	21 95 85 96	102 897 980 856	454364 _7304_	6·471707 _23097_	734038 _1191_	2134016 _455_
4687	21 96 79 69	102 963 870 703	461668 _7303_	6·494804 _23094_	735229 _1190_	2133561 _455_
4688	21 97 73 44	103 029 788 672	468971 _7302_	6·517898 _23091_	736419 _1190_	2133106 _455_
4689	21 98 67 21	103 095 734 769	476273 _7302_	6·540989 _23089_	737609 _1189_	2132651 _455_
4690	21 99 61 00	103 161 709 000	483575 _7300_	6·564078 _23087_	738798 _1190_	2132196 _454_
4691	22 00 54 81	103 227 711 371	490875 _7300_	6·587165 _23084_	739988 _1190_	2131742 _455_
4692	22 01 48 64	103 293 741 888	498175 _7299_	6·610249 _23082_	741178 _1189_	2131287 _454_
4693	22 02 42 49	103 359 800 557	505474 _7299_	6·633331 _23079_	742367 _1189_	2130833 _454_
4694	22 03 36 36	103 425 887 384	512773 _7297_	6·656410 _23077_	743556 _1189_	2130379 _454_
4695	22 04 30 25	103 492 002 375	520070 _7297_	6·679487 _23074_	744745 _1189_	2129925 _453_
4696	22 05 24 16	103 558 145 536	527367 _7296_	6·702561 _23072_	745934 _1188_	2129472 _453_
4697	22 06 18 09	103 624 316 873	534663 _7295_	6·725633 _23069_	747122 _1189_	2129019 _453_
4698	22 07 12 04	103 690 516 392	541958 _7294_	6·748702 _23067_	748311 _1188_	2128565 _454_
4699	22 08 06 01	103 756 744 099	549252 _7294_	6·771769 _23065_	749499 _1188_	2128112 _453_
4700	22 09 00 00	103 823 000 000	556546 68·	6·794834 210 +	750687 16·	2127660 0·000 _452_

No. n	Square n^2	Cube n^3	Square root $\sqrt{n}$	Sq. rt. of 10n $\sqrt{10n}$	Cube root $\sqrt[3]{n}$	Reciprocal $\dfrac{1}{n}$
			68·	210 +	16·	0·000
4700	22 09 00 00	103 823 000 000	556546 7293	6·794834 23062	750687 1188	2127660
4701	22 09 94 01	103 889 284 101	563839 7292	6·817896 23060	751875 1187	2127207 453
4702	22 10 88 04	103 955 596 408	571131 7291	6·840956 23057	753062 1188	2126755 452
4703	22 11 82 09	104 021 936 927	578422 7291	6·864013 23054	754250 1187	2126302 453
4704	22 12 76 16	104 088 305 664	585713 7290	6·887067 23053	755437 1188	2125850 452 451
4705	22 13 70 25	104 154 702 625	593003 7289	6·910120 23049	756625 1187	2125399 452
4706	22 14 64 36	104 221 127 816	600292 7288	6·933169 23048	757812 1187	2124947 452
4707	22 15 58 49	104 287 581 243	607580 7287	6·956217 23045	758999 1186	2124495 452
4708	22 16 52 64	104 354 062 912	614867 7287	6·979262 23042	760185 1187	2124044 451
4709	22 17 46 81	104 420 572 829	622154 7286	7·002304 23040	761372 1186	2123593 451 451
4710	22 18 41 00	104 487 111 000	629440 7285	7·025344 23038	762558 1187	2123142
4711	22 19 35 21	104 553 677 431	636725 7284	7·048382 23035	763745 1186	2122692 450
4712	22 20 29 44	104 620 272 128	644009 7284	7·071417 23032	764931 1186	2122241 451
4713	22 21 23 69	104 686 895 097	651293 7283	7·094449 23031	766117 1185	2121791 450
4714	22 22 17 96	104 753 546 344	658576 7282	7·117480 23028	767302 1186	2121341 450 450
4715	22 23 12 25	104 820 225 875	665858 7281	7·140508 23025	768488 1185	2120891
4716	22 24 06 56	104 886 933 696	673139 7280	7·163533 23023	769673 1185	2120441 450
4717	22 25 00 89	104 953 669 813	680419 7280	7·186556 23020	770858 1185	2119992 449
4718	22 25 95 24	105 020 434 232	687699 7279	7·209576 23018	772043 1185	2119542 450
4719	22 26 89 61	105 087 226 959	694978 7278	7·232594 23016	773228 1185	2119093 449 449
4720	22 27 84 00	105 154 048 000	702256 7278	7·255610 23013	774413 1185	2118644
4721	22 28 78 41	105 220 897 361	709534 7276	7·278623 23011	775598 1184	2118195 449
4722	22 29 72 84	105 287 775 048	716810 7276	7·301634 23008	776782 1184	2117747 448
4723	22 30 67 29	105 354 681 067	724086 7275	7·324642 23006	777966 1184	2117298 449
4724	22 31 61 76	105 421 615 424	731361 7274	7·347648 23003	779150 1184	2116850 448 448
4725	22 32 56 25	105 488 578 125	738635 7274	7·370651 23001	780334 1184	2116402
4726	22 33 50 76	105 555 569 176	745909 7273	7·393652 22999	781518 1183	2115954 448
4727	22 34 45 29	105 622 588 583	753182 7272	7·416651 22996	782701 1184	2115507 447
4728	22 35 39 84	105 689 636 352	760454 7271	7·439647 22993	783885 1183	2115059 448
4729	22 36 34 41	105 756 712 489	767725 7270	7·462640 22992	785068 1183	2114612 447 447
4730	22 37 29 00	105 823 817 000	774995 7270	7·485632 22989	786251 1183	2114165
4731	22 38 23 61	105 890 949 891	782265 7269	7·508621 22986	787434 1183	2113718 447
4732	22 39 18 24	105 958 111 168	789534 7268	7·531607 22984	788617 1182	2113271 447
4733	22 40 12 89	106 025 300 837	796802 7268	7·554591 22981	789799 1183	2112825 446
4734	22 41 07 56	106 092 518 904	804070 7266	7·577572 22979	790982 1182	2112379 446 447
4735	22 42 02 25	106 159 765 375	811336 7266	7·600551 22977	792164 1182	2111932
4736	22 42 96 96	106 227 040 256	818602 7265	7·623528 22974	793346 1182	2111486 446
4737	22 43 91 69	106 294 343 553	825867 7265	7·646502 22972	794528 1181	2111041 445
4738	22 44 86 44	106 361 675 272	833132 7263	7·669474 22970	795709 1182	2110595 446
4739	22 45 81 21	106 429 035 419	840395 7263	7·692444 22967	796891 1181	2110150 445 445
4740	22 46 76 00	106 496 424 000	847658 7262	7·715411 22964	798072 1182	2109705
4741	22 47 70 81	106 563 841 021	854920 7262	7·738375 22962	799254 1181	2109260 445
4742	22 48 65 64	106 631 286 488	862181 7261	7·761337 22960	800435 1180	2108815 445
4743	22 49 60 49	106 698 760 407	869442 7261	7·784297 22957	801615 1181	2108370 445
4744	22 50 55 36	106 766 262 784	876701 7259	7·807254 22955	802796 1181	2107926 444 444
4745	22 51 50 25	106 833 793 625	883960 7259	7·830209 22953	803977 1180	2107482
4746	22 52 45 16	106 901 352 936	891219 7258	7·853162 22950	805157 1180	2107038 444
4747	22 53 40 09	106 968 940 723	898476 7257	7·876112 22947	806337 1180	2106594 444
4748	22 54 35 04	107 036 556 992	905733 7257	7·899059 22945	807517 1180	2106150 444
4749	22 55 30 01	107 104 201 749	912989 7256	7·922004 22943	808697 1180	2105706 444 443
4750	22 56 25 00	107 171 875 000	920244 7255	7·944947	809877	2105263
			68·	210 +	16·	0·000

96

No. n	Square n²	Cube n³	Square root √n	Sq. rt. of 10n √10n	Cube root ∛n	Reciprocal 1/n
			68·	210 +	16·	· 0·000
4750	22 56 25 00	107 171 875 000	920244 7254	7·944947 22941	809877 1180	2105263
4751	22 57 20 01	107 239 576 751	927498 7254	7·967888 22937	811057 1179	2104820 443
4752	22 58 15 04	107 307 307 008	934752 7253	7·990825 22936	812236 1179	2104377 443
4753	22 59 10 09	107 375 065 777	942005 7252	8·013761 22933	813415 1179	2103934 443
4754	22 60 05 16	107 442 853 064	949257 7251	8·036694 22931	814594 1179	2103492 442 443
4755	22 61 00 25	107 510 668 875	956508 7251	8·059625 22928	815773 1179	2103049
4756	22 61 95 36	107 578 513 216	963759 7249	8·082553 22926	816952 1178	2102607 442
4757	22 62 90 49	107 646 386 093	971008 7249	8·105479 22924	818130 1179	2102165 442
4758	22 63 85 64	107 714 287 512	978257 7249	8·128403 22921	819309 1178	2101723 442
4759	22 64 80 81	107 782 217 479	985506 7247	8·151324 22918	820487 1178	2101282 441 442
4760	22 65 76 00	107 850 176 000	992753 7247	8·174242 22917	821665 1178	2100840
4761	22 66 71 21	107 918 163 081	*000000 7246	8·197159 22913	822843 1178	2100399 441
4762	22 67 66 44	107 986 178 728	007246 7246	8·220072 22913	824021 1177	2099958 441
4763	22 68 61 69	108 054 222 947	014491 7245	8·242984 22912	825198 1178	2099517 441
4764	22 69 56 96	108 122 295 744	021736 7245	8·265893 22909	826376 1177	2099076 441 440
4765	22 70 52 25	108 190 397 125	028979 7243	8·288800 22907	827553 1177	2098636
4766	22 71 47 56	108 258 527 096	036222 7243	8·311704 22904	828730 1177	2098196 440
4767	22 72 42 89	108 326 685 663	043465 7243	8·334606 22902	829907 1177	2097755 441
4768	22 73 38 24	108 394 872 832	050706 7241	8·357505 22899	831084 1177	2097315 440
4769	22 74 33 61	108 463 088 609	057947 7241	8·380402 22897	832260 1176	2096876 439 440
4770	22 75 29 00	108 531 333 000	065187 7239	8·403297 22895	833437 1177	2096436
4771	22 76 24 41	108 599 606 011	072426 7238	8·426189 22892	834613 1176	2095997 439
4772	22 77 19 84	108 667 907 648	079664 7238	8·449079 22890	835789 1176	2095557 440
4773	22 78 15 29	108 736 237 917	086902 7237	8·471966 22887	836965 1176	2095118 439
4774	22 79 10 76	108 804 596 824	094139 7236	8·494851 22885	838141 1175	2094680 438 439
4775	22 80 06 25	108 872 984 375	101375 7235	8·517734 22883	839316 1176	2094241
4776	22 81 01 76	108 941 400 576	108610 7235	8·540614 22880	840492 1175	2093802 439
4777	22 81 97 29	109 009 845 433	115845 7234	8·563492 22878	841667 1175	2093364 438
4778	22 82 92 84	109 078 318 952	123079 7233	8·586367 22875	842842 1175	2092926 438
4779	22 83 88 41	109 146 821 139	130312 7232	8·609240 22873	844017 1175	2092488 438 438
4780	22 84 84 00	109 215 352 000	137544 7232	8·632111 22871	845192 1175	2092050
4781	22 85 79 61	109 283 911 541	144776 7230	8·654979 22868	846367 1174	2091613 437
4782	22 86 75 24	109 352 499 768	152006 7231	8·677845 22866	847541 1174	2091175 438
4783	22 87 70 89	109 421 116 687	159237 7229	8·700709 22864	848715 1174	2090738 437
4784	22 88 66 56	109 489 762 304	166466 7228	8·723570 22861	849889 1174	2090301 437 437
4785	22 89 62 25	109 558 436 625	173694 7228	8·746429 22859	851063 1174	2089864
4786	22 90 57 96	109 627 139 656	180922 7227	8·769285 22856	852237 1174	2089427 437
4787	22 91 53 69	109 695 871 403	188149 7227	8·792139 22854	853411 1173	2088991 436
4788	22 92 49 44	109 764 631 872	195376 7225	8·814990 22851	854584 1173	2088555 436
4789	22 93 45 21	109 833 421 069	202601 7225	8·837840 22850	855758 1173	2088119 436 436
4790	22 94 41 00	109 902 239 000	209826 7224	8·860686 22846	856931 1173	2087683
4791	22 95 36 81	109 971 085 671	217050 7224	8·883531 22845	858104 1173	2087247 436
4792	22 96 32 64	110 039 961 088	224273 7223	8·906373 22842	859277 1172	2086811 436
4793	22 97 28 49	110 108 865 257	231496 7223	8·929212 22839	860449 1173	2086376 435
4794	22 98 24 36	110 177 798 184	238717 7221	8·952050 22838	861622 1172	2085941 435 435
4795	22 99 20 25	110 246 759 875	245939 7220	8·974884 22834	862794 1172	2085506
4796	23 00 16 16	110 315 750 336	253159 7220	8·997717 22833	863966 1172	2085071 435
4797	23 01 12 09	110 384 769 573	260378 7219	9·020547 22830	865138 1172	2084636 435
4798	23 02 08 04	110 453 817 592	267597 7219	9·043375 22828	866310 1172	2084202 434
4799	23 03 04 01	110 522 894 399	274815 7218	9·066200 22825	867482 1171	2083767 435 434
4800	23 04 00 00	110 592 000 000	282032	9·089023	868653	2083333
			69·	210 +	16·	0·000

No. n	Square n^2	Cube n^3	Square root $\sqrt{n}$	Sq. rt. of 10n $\sqrt{10n}$	Cube root $\sqrt[3]{n}$	Reciprocal $\frac{1}{n}$
			69·	210 +	16·	0·000
4800	23 04 00 00	110 592 000 000	282032 7217	9·089023 22821	868653 1172	2083333 434
4801	23 04 96 01	110 661 134 401	289249 7216	9·111844 22818	869825 1171	2082899 433
4802	23 05 92 04	110 730 297 608	296465 7215	9·134662 22816	870996 1171	2082466 434
4803	23 06 88 09	110 799 489 627	303680 7214	9·157478 22813	872167 1171	2082032 433
4804	23 07 84 16	110 868 710 464	310894 7213	9·180291 22811	873338 1170	2081599 434
4805	23 08 80 25	110 937 960 125	318107 7213	9·203102 22809	874508 1171	2081165 433
4806	23 09 76 36	111 007 238 616	325320 7212	9·225911 22806	875679 1170	2080732 433
4807	23 10 72 49	111 076 545 943	332532 7211	9·248717 22804	876849 1171	2080300 432
4808	23 11 68 64	111 145 882 112	339743 7211	9·271521 22802	878020 1170	2079867 433
4809	23 12 64 81	111 215 247 129	346954 7210	9·294323 22799	879190 1170	2079434 432
4810	23 13 61 00	111 284 641 000	354164 7209	9·317122 22797	880360 1169	2079002 432
4811	23 14 57 21	111 354 063 731	361373 7208	9·339919 22794	881529 1170	2078570 432
4812	23 15 53 44	111 423 515 328	368581 7207	9·362713 22792	882699 1169	2078138 432
4813	23 16 49 69	111 492 995 797	375788 7207	9·385505 22790	883868 1169	2077706 432
4814	23 17 45 96	111 562 505 144	382995 7206	9·408295 22788	885037 1169	2077275 431
4815	23 18 42 25	111 632 043 375	390201 7205	9·431083 22785	886207 1168	2076843 431
4816	23 19 38 56	111 701 610 496	397406 7205	9·453868 22782	887375 1169	2076412 431
4817	23 20 34 89	111 771 206 513	404611 7204	9·476650 22781	888544 1169	2075981 431
4818	23 21 31 24	111 840 831 432	411815 7203	9·499431 22777	889713 1168	2075550 431
4819	23 22 27 61	111 910 485 259	419018 7202	9·522208 22776	890881 1169	2075119 430
4820	23 23 24 00	111 980 168 000	426220 7201	9·544984 22773	892050 1168	2074689 431
4821	23 24 20 41	112 049 879 661	433421 7201	9·567757 22771	893218 1168	2074258 431
4822	23 25 16 84	112 119 620 248	440622 7200	9·590528 22769	894386 1167	2073828 430
4823	23 26 13 29	112 189 389 767	447822 7199	9·613297 22766	895553 1168	2073398 430
4824	23 27 09 76	112 259 188 224	455021 7199	9·636063 22763	896721 1167	2072968 430
4825	23 28 06 25	112 329 015 625	462220 7198	9·658826 22762	897888 1168	2072539 430
4826	23 29 02 76	112 398 871 976	469418 7197	9·681588 22759	899056 1167	2072109 430
4827	23 29 99 29	112 468 757 283	476615 7196	9·704347 22756	900223 1167	2071680 429
4828	23 30 95 84	112 538 671 552	483811 7196	9·727103 22755	901390 1167	2071251 429
4829	23 31 92 41	112 608 614.789	491007 7194	9·749858 22752	902557 1166	2070822 429
4830	23 32 89 00	112 678 587 000	498201 7194	9·772610 22749	903723 1167	2070393 428
4831	23 33 85 61	112 748 588 191	505395 7194	9·795359 22748	904890 1166	2069965 429
4832	23 34 82 24	112 818 618 368	512589 7192	9·818107 22745	906056 1166	2069536 428
4833	23 35 78 89	112 888 677 537	519781 7192	9·840852 22742	907222 1166	2069108 428
4834	23 36 75 56	112 958 765 704	526973 7191	9·863594 22740	908388 1166	2068680 428
4835	23 37 72 25	113 028 882 875	534164 7191	9·886334 22738	909554 1166	2068252 427
4836	23 38 68 96	113 099 029 056	541355 7189	9·909072 22736	910720 1165	2067825 428
4837	23 39 65 69	113 169 204 253	548544 7189	9·931808 22733	911885 1166	2067397 427
4838	23 40 62 44	113 239 408 472	555733 7188	9·954541 22731	913051 1165	2066970 427
4839	23 41 59 21	113 309 641 719	562921 7188	9·977272 22728	914216 1165	2066543 427
4840	23 42 56 00	113 379 904 000	570109 7186	*0·000000 22726	915381 1165	2066116 427
4841	23 43 52 81	113 450 195 321	577295 7186	0·022726 22724	916546 1165	2065689 427
4842	23 44 49 64	113 520 515 688	584481 7185	0·045450 22721	917711 1164	2065262 427
4843	23 45 46 49	113 590 865 107	591666 7185	0·068171 22719	918875 1165	2064836 426
4844	23 46 43 36	113 661 243 584	598851 7183	0·090890 22717	920040 1164	2064410 426
4845	23 47 40 25	113 731 651 125	606034 7183	0·113607 22714	921204 1164	2063983 425
4846	23 48 37 16	113 802 087 736	613217 7182	0·136321 22712	922368 1164	2063558 426
4847	23 49 34 09	113 872 553 423	620399 7182	0·159033 22710	923532 1164	2063132 426
4848	23 50 31 04	113 943 048 192	627581 7180	0·181743 22707	924696 1163	2062706 426
4849	23 51 28 01	114 013 572 049	634761 7180	0·204450 22705	925859 1164	2062281 425
4850	23 52 25 00	114 084 125 000	641941	0·227155	927023	2061856
			69·	220 +	16·	0·000

No. n	Square n^2	Cube n^3	Square root $\sqrt{n}$	Sq. rt. of $10n$ $\sqrt{10n}$	Cube root $\sqrt[3]{n}$	Reciprocal $\dfrac{1}{n}$
			69·	220 +	16·	0·000
4850	23 52 25 00	114 084 125 000	641941 7180	0·227155 22703	927023 1163	2061856
4851	23 53 22 01	114 154 707 051	649121 7178	0·249858 22703	928186 1163	2061431 425
4852	23 54 19 04	114 225 318 208	656299 7178	0·272558 22700	929349 1163	2061006 425
4853	23 55 16 09	114 295 958 477	663477 7177	0·295256 22698	930512 1163	2060581 425
4854	23 56 13 16	114 366 627 864	670654 7176	0·317952 22696	931675 1163	2060157 424
4855	23 57 10 25	114 437 326 375	677830 7176	0·340645 22691	932838 1162	2059732 424
4856	23 58 07 36	114 508 054 016	685006 7174	0·363336 22689	934000 1162	2059308 424
4857	23 59 04 49	114 578 810 793	692180 7174	0·386025 22686	935162 1163	2058884 424
4858	23 60 01 64	114 649 596 712	699354 7174	0·408711 22684	936325 1162	2058460 424
4859	23 60 98 81	114 720 411 779	706528 7172	0·431395 22682	937487 1162	2058037 423
4860	23 61 96 00	114 791 256 000	713700 7172	0·454077 22679	938649 1161	2057613 424
4861	23 62 93 21	114 862 129 381	720872 7172 7171	0·476756 22677	939810 1162	2057190 423
4862	23 63 90 44	114 933 031 928	728043 7170	0·499433 22675	940972 1161	2056767 423
4863	23 64 87 69	115 003 963 647	735213 7170	0·522108 22672	942133 1161	2056344 423
4864	23 65 84 96	115 074 924 544	742383 7169	0·544780 22670	943294 1161	2055921 423
4865	23 66 82 25	115 145 914 625	749552 7168	0·567450 22668	944455 1161	2055498 422
4866	23 67 79 56	115 216 933 896	756720 7168	0·590118 22665	945620 1161	2055076 422
4867	23 68 76 89	115 287 982 363	763888 7166	0·612783 22663	946777 1161	2054654 422
4868	23 69 74 24	115 359 060 032	771054 7166	0·635446 22661	947938 1160	2054232 422
4869	23 70 71 61	115 430 166 909	778220 7165	0·658107 22658	949098 1160	2053810 422
4870	23 71 69 00	115 501 303 000	785385 7165	0·680765 22656	950258 1160	2053388 421
4871	23 72 66 41	115 572 468 311	792550 7163	0·703421 22654	951418 1160	2052967 421
4872	23 73 63 84	115 643 662 848	799713 7163	0·726075 22651	952578 1160	2052545 421
4873	23 74 61 29	115 714 886 617	806876 7163	0·748726 22649	953738 1160	2052124 421
4874	23 75 58 76	115 786 139 624	814039 7161	0·771375 22647	954898 1159	2051703 421
4875	23 76 56 25	115 857 421 875	821200 7161	0·794022 22644	956057 1160	2051282 421
4876	23 77 53 76	115 928 733 376	828361 7160	0·816666 22642	957217 1159	2050861 420
4877	23 78 51 29	116 000 074 133	835521 7159	0·839308 22640	958376 1159	2050441 420
4878	23 79 48 84	116 071 444 152	842680 7159	0·861948 22637	959535 1159	2050021 420
4879	23 80 46 41	116 142 843 439	849839 7158	0·884585 22635	960694 1158	2049600 421
4880	23 81 44 00	116 214 272 000	856997 7157	0·907220 22633	961852 1159	2049180 420
4881	23 82 41 61	116 285 729 841	864154 7156	0·929853 22631	963011 1158	2048760 420
4882	23 83 39 24	116 357 216 968	871310 7156	0·952484 22628	964169 1158	2048341 419
4883	23 84 36 89	116 428 733 387	878466 7155	0·975112 22626	965327 1158	2047921 419
4884	23 85 34 56	116 500 279 104	885621 7154	0·997738 22623	966485 1158	2047502 419
4885	23 86 32 25	116 571 854 125	892775 7153	1·020361 22621	967643 1158	2047083 419
4886	23 87 29 96	116 643 458 456	899928 7153	1·042982 22619	968801 1157	2046664 419
4887	23 88 27 69	116 715 092 103	907081 7152	1·065601 22617	969958 1158	2046245 419
4888	23 89 25 44	116 786 755 072	914233 7151	1·088218 22614	971116 1157	2045827 418
4889	23 90 23 21	116 858 447 369	921384 7151	1·110832 22612	972273 1157	2045408 419
4890	23 91 21 00	116 930 169 000	928535 7150	1·133444 22610	973430 1157	2044990 418
4891	23 92 18 81	117 001 919 971	935685 7149	1·156054 22607	974587 1157	2044572 418
4892	23 93 16 64	117 073 700 288	942834 7148	1·178661 22605	975744 1157	2044154 418
4893	23 94 14 49	117 145 509 957	949982 7148	1·201266 22603	976901 1156	2043736 418
4894	23 95 12 36	117 217 348 984	957130 7147	1·223869 22600	978057 1156	2043318 417
4895	23 96 10 25	117 289 217 375	964277 7146	1·246469 22598	979213 1156	2042901 417
4896	23 97 08 16	117 361 115 136	971423 7145	1·269067 22596	980369 1156	2042484 417
4897	23 98 06 09	117 433 042 273	978568 7145	1·291663 22593	981525 1156	2042067 417
4898	23 99 04 04	117 504 998 792	985713 7144	1·314256 22593	982681 1156	2041650 417
4899	24 00 02 01	117 576 984 699	992857 7143	1·336847 22591	983837 1156	2041233 417
4900	24 01 00 00	117 649 000 000	*000000 70·	1·359436 220 +	984993 16·	2040816 0·000

No. n	Square n²	Cube n³	Square root √n	Sq. rt. of 10n √10n	Cube root ∛n	Reciprocal 1/n
			70·	220 +	16·	0·000
4900	24 01 00 00	117 649 000 000	000000 7142	1·359436 22587	984993 1155	2040816 416
4901	24 01 98 01	117 721 044 701	007142 7142	1·382023 22584	986148 1155	2040400 416
4902	24 02 96 04	117 793 118 808	014284 7141	1·404607 22582	987303 1155	2039984 416
4903	24 03 94 09	117 865 222 327	021425 7141	1·427189 22580	988458 1155	2039568 416
4904	24 04 92 16	117 937 355 264	028566 7139	1·449769 22577	989613 1155	2039152 416
4905	24 05 90 25	118 009 517 625	035705 7139	1·472346 22575	990768 1154	2038736 416
4906	24 06 88 36	118 081 709 416	042844 7138	1·494921 22573	991922 1155	2038320 415
4907	24 07 86 49	118 153 930 643	049982 7138	1·517494 22570	993077 1154	2037905 415
4908	24 08 84 64	118 226 181 312	057120 7136	1·540064 22568	994231 1154	2037490 415
4909	24 09 82 81	118 298 461 429	064256 7136	1·562632 22566	995385 1154	2037075 415
4910	24 10 81 00	118 370 771 000	071392 7135	1·585198 22564	996539 1154	2036660 415
4911	24 11 79 21	118 443 110 031	078527 7135	1·607762 22561	997693 1154	2036245 414
4912	24 12 77 44	118 515 478 528	085662 7134	1·630323 22559	998847 1153	2035831 415
4913	24 13 75 69	118 587 876 497	092796 7134	1·652882 22559	*000000 1153	2035416 414
4914	24 14 73 96	118 660 303 944	099929 7133	1·675438 22556	001153 1153	2035002 414
4915	24 15 72 25	118 732 760 875	107061 7132	1·697993 22555	002306 1154	2034588 414
4916	24 16 70 56	118 805 247 296	114193 7132	1·720545 22552	003460 1152	2034174 414
4917	24 17 68 89	118 877 763 213	121323 7130	1·743095 22550	004612 1153	2033760 414
4918	24 18 67 24	118 950 308 632	128454 7131	1·765642 22547	005765 1153	2033347 413
4919	24 19 65 61	119 022 883 559	135583 7129	1·788187 22545	006918 1152	2032934 413
4920	24 20 64 00	119 095 488 000	142712 7128	1·810730 22543	008070 1152	2032520 414
4921	24 21 62 41	119 168 121 961	149840 7127	1·833271 22541	009222 1152	2032107 413
4922	24 22 60 84	119 240 785 448	156967 7126	1·855809 22538	010374 1152	2031694 413
4923	24 23 59 29	119 313 478 467	164093 7126	1·878345 22536	011526 1152	2031282 412
4924	24 24 57 76	119 386 201 024	171219 7125	1·900879 22534	012678 1152	2030869 413
4925	24 25 56 25	119 458 953 125	178344 7125	1·923410 22531	013830 1151	2030457 412
4926	24 26 54 76	119 531 734 776	185469 7123	1·945939 22529	014981 1151	2030045 412
4927	24 27 53 29	119 604 545 983	192592 7123	1·968466 22527	016132 1151	2029633 412
4928	24 28 51 84	119 677 386 752	199715 7122	1·990991 22525	017283 1151	2029221 412
4929	24 29 50 41	119 750 257 089	206837 7122	2·013513 22522	018434 1151	2028809 411
4930	24 30 49 00	119 823 157 000	213959 7120	2·036033 22520	019585 1151	2028398 412
4931	24 31 47 61	119 896 086 491	221079 7120	2·058551 22518	020736 1150	2027986 412
4932	24 32 46 24	119 969 045 568	228199 7120	2·081066 22515	021886 1151	2027575 411
4933	24 33 44 89	120 042 034 237	235319 7118	2·103579 22513	023037 1150	2027164 411
4934	24 34 43 56	120 115 052 504	242437 7118	2·126090 22511	024187 1150	2026753 411
4935	24 35 42 25	120 188 100 375	249555 7117	2·148599 22509	025337 1150	2026342 411
4936	24 36 40 96	120 261 177 856	256672 7117	2·171105 22506	026487 1150	2025932 410
4937	24 37 39 69	120 334 284 953	263789 7117	2·193609 22504	027637 1150	2025522 410
4938	24 38 38 44	120 407 421 672	270904 7115	2·216111 22502	028786 1149	2025111 411
4939	24 39 37 21	120 480 588 019	278019 7115	2·238611 22500	029936 1150	2024701 410
4940	24 40 36 00	120 553 784 000	285134 7113	2·261108 22497	031085 1149	2024291 410
4941	24 41 34 81	120 627 009 621	292247 7113	2·283603 22495	032234 1149	2023882 409
4942	24 42 33 64	120 700 264 888	299360 7112	2·306095 22492	033383 1149	2023472 409
4943	24 43 32 49	120 773 549 807	306472 7111	2·328586 22491	034532 1149	2023063 409
4944	24 44 31 36	120 846 864 384	313583 7111	2·351074 22488	035681 1148	2022654 409
4945	24 45 30 25	120 920 208 625	320694 7110	2·373560 22486	036829 1148	2022245 409
4946	24 46 29 16	120 993 582 536	327804 7109	2·396043 22483	037977 1149	2021836 409
4947	24 47 28 09	121 066 986 123	334913 7109	2·418524 22481	039126 1148	2021427 409
4948	24 48 27 04	121 140 419 392	342022 7107	2·441003 22479	040274 1147	2021019 408
4949	24 49 26 01	121 213 882 349	349129 7107	2·463480 22477	041421 1148	2020610 409
4950	24 50 25 00	121 287 375 000	356236 70·	2·485955 220 +	042569 17·	2020202 0·000

No. n	Square n²	Cube n³	Square root √n	Sq. rt. of 10n √10n	Cube root ∛n	Reciprocal 1/n
			70·	220 +	17·	0·000
4950	24 50 25 00	121 287 375 000	356236 7107	2·485955 22472	042569 1148	2020202 408
4951	24 51 24 01	121 360 897 351	363343 7107	2·508427 22470	043717 1147	2019794 408
4952	24 52 23 04	121 434 449 408	370448 7105	2·530897 22467	044864 1147	2019386 408
4953	24 53 22 09	121 508 031 177	377553 7105	2·553364 22466	046011 1148	2018978 407
4954	24 54 21 16	121 581 642 664	384657 7104	2·575830 22463	047159 1147	2018571 408
4955	24 55 20 25	121 655 283 875	391761 7104	2·598293 22461	048306 1146	2018163 407
4956	24 56 19 36	121 728 954 816	398864 7103	2·620754 22458	049452 1147	2017756 407
4957	24 57 18 49	121 802 655 493	405966 7102	2·643212 22457	050599 1146	2017349 407
4958	24 58 17 64	121 876 385 912	413067 7101	2·665669 22454	051745 1146	2016942 406
4959	24 59 16 81	121 950 146 079	420168 7101	2·688123 22452	052892 1146	2016536 406
4960	24 60 16 00	122 023 936 000	427267 7099	2·710575 22449	054038 1146	2016129 407
4961	24 61 15 21	122 097 755 681	434367 7100	2·733024 22447	055184 1146	2015723 406
4962	24 62 14 44	122 171 605 128	441465 7098	2·755471 22445	056330 1146	2015316 407
4963	24 63 13 69	122 245 484 347	448563 7098	2·777916 22443	057476 1145	2014910 406
4964	24 64 12 96	122 319 393 344	455660 7097	2·800359 22441	058621 1146	2014504 406
4965	24 65 12 25	122 393 332 125	462756 7096	2·822800 22438	059767 1145	2014099 405
4966	24 66 11 56	122 467 300 696	469852 7096	2·845238 22436	060912 1145	2013693 406
4967	24 67 10 89	122 541 299 063	476947 7095	2·867674 22433	062057 1145	2013288 405
4968	24 68 10 24	122 615 327 232	484041 7094	2·890107 22432	063202 1145	2012882 406
4969	24 69 09 61	122 689 385 209	491134 7093	2·912539 22429	064347 1144	2012477 405
4970	24 70 09 00	122 763 473 000	498227 7093	2·934968 22427	065491 1145	2012072 405
4971	24 71 08 41	122 837 590 611	505319 7092	2·957395 22425	066636 1145	2011668 404
4972	24 72 07 84	122 911 738 048	512410 7091	2·979820 22422	067780 1144	2011263 405
4973	24 73 07 29	122 985 915 317	519501 7091	3·002242 22420	068924 1144	2010859 404
4974	24 74 06 76	123 060 122 424	526591 7090	3·024662 22418	070068 1144	2010454 405
4975	24 75 06 25	123 134 359 375	533680 7089	3·047080 22416	071212 1144	2010050 404
4976	24 76 05 76	123 208 626 176	540768 7088	3·069496 22413	072356 1144	2009646 404
4977	24 77 05 29	123 282 922 833	547856 7088	3·091909 22411	073500 1143	2009243 403
4978	24 78 04 84	123 357 249 352	554943 7087	3·114320 22409	074643 1143	2008839 404
4979	24 79 04 41	123 431 605 739	562029 7086	3·136729 22407	075786 1143	2008435 404
4980	24 80 04 00	123 505 992 000	569115 7086	3·159136 22404	076929 1143	2008032 403
4981	24 81 03 61	123 580 408 141	576200 7085	3·181540 22403	078072 1143	2007629 403
4982	24 82 03 24	123 654 854 168	583284 7084	3·203943 22400	079215 1143	2007226 403
4983	24 83 02 89	123 729 330 087	590368 7084	3·226343 22397	080358 1142	2006823 402
4984	24 84 02 56	123 803 835 904	597450 7082	3·248740 22396	081500 1143	2006421 403
4985	24 85 02 25	123 878 371 625	604532 7082	3·271136 22393	082643 1142	2006018 402
4986	24 86 01 96	123 952 937 256	611614 7082	3·293529 22391	083785 1142	2005616 402
4987	24 87 01 69	124 027 532 803	618694 7080	3·315920 22388	084927 1142	2005214 402
4988	24 88 01 44	124 102 158 272	625774 7080	3·338308 22387	086069 1141	2004812 402
4989	24 89 01 21	124 176 813 669	632854 7080	3·360695 22384	087210 1142	2004410 402
4990	24 90 01 00	124 251 499 000	639932 7078	3·383079 22382	088352 1141	2004008 402
4991	24 91 00 81	124 326 214 271	647010 7078	3·405461 22380	089493 1141	2003606 401
4992	24 92 00 64	124 400 959 488	654087 7077	3·427841 22377	090635 1141	2003205 401
4993	24 93 00 49	124 475 734 657	661163 7076	3·450218 22375	091776 1141	2002804 401
4994	24 94 00 36	124 550 539 784	668239 7076	3·472593 22373	092917 1141	2002403 401
4995	24 95 00 25	124 625 374 875	675314 7075	3·494966 22371	094058 1140	2002002 401
4996	24 96 00 16	124 700 239 936	682388 7074	3·517337 22369	095198 1141	2001601 400
4997	24 97 00 09	124 775 134 973	689462 7074	3·539706 22366	096339 1140	2001201 400
4998	24 98 00 04	124 850 059 992	696535 7073	3·562072 22364	097479 1140	2000800 401
4999	24 99 00 01	124 925 014 999	703607 7072	3·584436 22362	098619 1140	2000400 400
5000	25 00 00 00	125 000 000 000	710678 70·	3·606798 220+	099759 17·	2000000 0·000

No. n	Square n²	Cube n³	Square root √n	Sq. rt. of 10n √10n	Cube root ∛n	Reciprocal 1/n
			70·	220 +	17·	0·000
5000	25 00 00 00	125 000 000 000	710678 _7071_	3·606798 _22359_	099759 _1140_	2000000 _400_
5001	25 01 00 01	125 075 015 001	717749 _7071_	3·629157 _22358_	100899 _1140_	1999600 _400_
5002	25 02 00 04	125 150 060 008	724819 _7070_	3·651515 _22355_	102039 _1140_	1999200 _400_
5003	25 03 00 09	125 225 135 027	731888 _7069_	3·673870 _22353_	103179 _1139_	1998801 _400_
5004	25 04 00 16	125 300 240 064	738957 _7069/7068_	3·696223 _22350_	104318 _1139_	1998401 _399_
5005	25 05 00 25	125 375 375 125	746025 _7067_	3·718573 _22349_	105457 _1140_	1998002 _399_
5006	25 06 00 36	125 450 540 216	753092 _7066_	3·740922 _22346_	106597 _1139_	1997603 _399_
5007	25 07 00 49	125 525 735 343	760158 _7066_	3·763268 _22344_	107736 _1138_	1997204 _399_
5008	25 08 00 64	125 600 960 512	767224 _7065_	3·785612 _22341_	108874 _1139_	1996805 _399_
5009	25 09 00 81	125 676 215 729	774289 _7064_	3·807953 _22340_	110013 _1139_	1996406 _398_
5010	25 10 01 00	125 751 501 000	781353 _7064_	3·830293 _22337_	111152 _1138_	1996008 _398_
5011	25 11 01 21	125 826 816 331	788417 _7063_	3·852630 _22335_	112290 _1138_	1995610 _399_
5012	25 12 01 44	125 902 161 728	795480 _7062_	3·874965 _22333_	113428 _1138_	1995211 _398_
5013	25 13 01 69	125 977 537 197	802542 _7062_	3·897298 _22330_	114566 _1138_	1994813 _397_
5014	25 14 01 96	126 052 942 744	809604 _7061_	3·919628 _22329_	115704 _1138_	1994416 _398_
5015	25 15 02 25	126 128 378 375	816665 _7060_	3·941957 _22326_	116842 _1138_	1994018 _398_
5016	25 16 02 56	126 203 844 096	823725 _7059_	3·964283 _22324_	117980 _1137_	1993620 _397_
5017	25 17 02 89	126 279 339 913	830784 _7059_	3·986607 _22321_	119117 _1138_	1993223 _397_
5018	25 18 03 24	126 354 865 832	837843 _7058_	4·008928 _22320_	120255 _1137_	1992826 _397_
5019	25 19 03 61	126 430 421 859	844901 _7057_	4·031248 _22317_	121392 _1137_	1992429 _397_
5020	25 20 04 00	126 506 008 000	851958 _7057_	4·053565 _22315_	122529 _1137_	1992032 _397_
5021	25 21 04 41	126 581 624 261	859015 _7056_	4·075880 _22313_	123666 _1137_	1991635 _397_
5022	25 22 04 84	126 657 270 648	866071 _7055_	4·098193 _22310_	124802 _1136_	1991239 _396_
5023	25 23 05 29	126 732 947 167	873126 _7055_	4·120503 _22309_	125939 _1137_	1990842 _397_
5024	25 24 05 76	126 808 653 824	880181 _7053_	4·142812 _22306_	127075 _1137_	1990446 _396_
5025	25 25 06 25	126 884 390 625	887234 _7053_	4·165118 _22304_	128212 _1136_	1990050 _396_
5026	25 26 06 76	126 960 157 576	894287 _7053_	4·187422 _22301_	129348 _1136_	1989654 _396_
5027	25 27 07 29	127 035 954 683	901340 _7052_	4·209723 _22300_	130484 _1136_	1989258 _396_
5028	25 28 07 84	127 111 781 952	908392 _7051_	4·232023 _22297_	131620 _1136_	1988862 _395_
5029	25 29 08 41	127 187 639 389	915443 _7050_	4·254320 _22295_	132755 _1135_	1988467 _395_
5030	25 30 09 00	127 263 527 000	922493 _7050_	4·276615 _22293_	133891 _1135_	1988072 _396_
5031	25 31 09 61	127 339 444 791	929543 _7048_	4·298908 _22290_	135026 _1135_	1987676 _395_
5032	25 32 10 24	127 415 392 768	936591 _7049_	4·321198 _22289_	136161 _1135_	1987281 _394_
5033	25 33 10 89	127 491 370 937	943640 _7047_	4·343487 _22286_	137296 _1135_	1986887 _395_
5034	25 34 11 56	127 567 379 304	950687 _7047_	4·365773 _22284_	138431 _1135_	1986492 _394_
5035	25 35 12 25	127 643 417 875	957734 _7046_	4·388057 _22281_	139566 _1135_	1986097 _394_
5036	25 36 12 96	127 719 486 656	964780 _7045_	4·410338 _22280_	140701 _1134_	1985703 _394_
5037	25 37 13 69	127 795 585 653	971825 _7045_	4·432618 _22277_	141835 _1135_	1985309 _394_
5038	25 38 14 44	127 871 714 872	978870 _7044_	4·454895 _22275_	142970 _1134_	1984915 _394_
5039	25 39 15 21	127 947 874 319	985914 _7043_	4·477170 _22273_	144104 _1134_	1984521 _394_
5040	25 40 16 00	128 024 064 000	992957 _7043_	4·499443 _22271_	145238 _1134_	1984127 _394_
5041	25 41 16 81	128 100 283 921	*000000 _7042_	4·521714 _22268_	146372 _1134_	1983733 _394_
5042	25 42 17 64	128 176 534 088	007042 _7041_	4·543982 _22267_	147505 _1133_	1983340 _393_
5043	25 43 18 49	128 252 814 507	014083 _7041_	4·566249 _22264_	148639 _1134_	1982947 _393_
5044	25 44 19 36	128 329 125 184	021124 _7039_	4·588513 _22261_	149772 _1134_	1982554 _393_
5045	25 45 20 25	128 405 466 125	028163 _7040_	4·610774 _22260_	150906 _1133_	1982161 _393_
5046	25 46 21 16	128 481 837 336	035203 _7038_	4·633034 _22258_	152039 _1133_	1981768 _393_
5047	25 47 22 09	128 558 238 823	042241 _7038_	4·655292 _22255_	153172 _1133_	1981375 _392_
5048	25 48 23 04	128 634 670 592	049279 _7037_	4·677547 _22253_	154305 _1132_	1980983 _393_
5049	25 49 24 01	128 711 132 649	056316 _7036_	4·699800 _22251_	155437 _1133_	1980590 _392_
5050	25 50 25 00	128 787 625 000	063352	4·722051	156570	1980198
			71·	220 +	17·	0·000

No. n	Square n^2	Cube n^3	Square root $\sqrt{n}$	Sq. rt. of 10n $\sqrt{10n}$	Cube root $\sqrt[3]{n}$	Reciprocal $\frac{1}{n}$
			71·	**220 +**	**17·**	**0·000**
5050	25 50 25 00	128 787 625 000	063352 7036	4·722051 22248	156570 1132	1980198 392
5051	25 51 26 01	128 864 147 651	070388 7035	4·744299 22247	157702 1132	1979806 392
5052	25 52 27 04	128 940 700 608	077423 7034	4·766546 22244	158834 1132	1979414 392
5053	25 53 28 09	129 017 283 877	084457 7033	4·788790 22242	159966 1132	1979022 391
5054	25 54 29 16	129 093 897 464	091490 7033	4·811032 22240	161098 1132	1978631 392
5055	25 55 30 25	129 170 541 375	098523 7032	4·833272 22237	162230 1132	1978239 391
5056	25 56 31 36	129 247 215 616	105555 7032	4·855509 22236	163362 1131	1977848 391
5057	25 57 32 49	129 323 920 193	112587 7031	4·877745 22233	164493 1132	1977457 391
5058	25 58 33 64	129 400 655 112	119618 7030	4·899978 22231	165625 1131	1977066 391
5059	25 59 34 81	129 477 420 379	126648 7029	4·922209 22229	166756 1131	1976675 391
5060	25 60 36 00	129 554 216 000	133677 7029	4·944438 22226	167887 1131	1976285
5061	25 61 37 21	129 631 041 981	140706 7028	4·966664 22225	169018 1131	1975894 391
5062	25 62 38 44	129 707 898 328	147734 7027	4·988889 22222	170148 1130	1975504 390
5063	25 63 39 69	129 784 785 047	154761 7026	5·011111 22220	171279 1131	1975114 390
5064	25 64 40 96	129 861 702 144	161787 7026	5·033331 22218	172409 1131	1974724 390
5065	25 65 42 25	129 938 649 625	168813 7026	5·055549 22215	173540 1130	1974334 390
5066	25 66 43 56	130 015 627 496	175839 7024	5·077764 22214	174670 1130	1973944 390
5067	25 67 44 89	130 092 635 763	182863 7024	5·099978 22211	175800 1130	1973554 389
5068	25 68 46 24	130 169 674 432	189887 7023	5·122189 22209	176930 1129	1973165 389
5069	25 69 47 61	130 246 743 509	196910 7022	5·144398 22207	178059 1130	1972776 389
5070	25 70 49 00	130 323 843 000	203932 7022	5·166605 22205	179189 1129	1972387 389
5071	25 71 50 41	130 400 972 911	210954 7021	5·188810 22202	180318 1129	1971998 389
5072	25 72 51 84	130 478 133 248	217975 7021	5·211012 22200	181447 1130	1971609 389
5073	25 73 53 29	130 555 324 017	224996 7019	5·233212 22199	182577 1128	1971220 388
5074	25 74 54 76	130 632 545 224	232015 7019	5·255411 22196	183705 1129	1970832 389
5075	25 75 56 25	130 709 796 875	239034 7019	5·277607 22193	184834 1129	1970443 388
5076	25 76 57 76	130 787 078 976	246053 7017	5·299800 22192	185963 1128	1970055 388
5077	25 77 59 29	130 864 391 533	253070 7017	5·321992 22189	187091 1129	1969667 388
5078	25 78 60 84	130 941 734 552	260087 7016	5·344181 22187	188220 1128	1969279 387
5079	25 79 62 41	131 019 108 039	267103 7016	5·366368 22185	189348 1128	1968892 388
5080	25 80 64 00	131 096 512 000	274119 7015	5·388553 22183	190476 1128	1968504 387
5081	25 81 65 61	131 173 946 441	281134 7014	5·410736 22181	191604 1128	1968117 388
5082	25 82 67 24	131 251 411 368	288148 7013	5·432917 22178	192732 1127	1967729 387
5083	25 83 68 89	131 328 906 787	295161 7013	5·455095 22177	193859 1128	1967342 387
5084	25 84 70 56	131 406 432 704	302174 7012	5·477272 22174	194987 1127	1966955 387
5085	25 85 72 25	131 483 989 125	309186 7011	5·499446 22172	196114 1127	1966568 386
5086	25 86 73 96	131 561 576 056	316197 7011	5·521618 22169	197241 1127	1966182 387
5087	25 87 75 69	131 639 193 503	323208 7010	5·543787 22168	198368 1127	1965795 386
5088	25 88 77 44	131 716 841 472	330218 7009	5·565955 22165	199495 1127	1965409 386
5089	25 89 79 21	131 794 519 969	337227 7009	5·588120 22163	200622 1127	1965023 386
5090	25 90 81 00	131 872 229 000	344236 7008	5·610283 22161	201749 1126	1964637 386
5091	25 91 82 81	131 949 968 571	351244 7007	5·632444 22159	202875 1126	1964251 386
5092	25 92 84 64	132 027 738 688	358251 7007	5·654603 22157	204001 1126	1963865 386
5093	25 93 86 49	132 105 539 357	365258 7006	5·676760 22154	205127 1126	1963479 385
5094	25 94 88 36	132 183 370 584	372264 7005	5·698914 22153	206253 1126	1963094 385
5095	25 95 90 25	132 261 232 375	379269 7004	5·721067 22150	207379 1126	1962709 386
5096	25 96 92 16	132 339 124 736	386273 7004	5·743217 22148	208505 1125	1962323 385
5097	25 97 94 09	132 417 047 673	393277 7003	5·765365 22146	209630 1126	1961938 385
5098	25 98 96 04	132 495 001 192	400280 7003	5·787511 22143	210756 1125	1961554 384
5099	25 99 98 01	132 572 985 299	407283 7001	5·809654 22142	211881 1125	1961169 385
5100	26 01 00 00	132 651 000 000	414284	5·831796	213006	1960784
			71·	**220 +**	**17·**	**0·000**

No. n	Square n^2	Cube n^3	Square root $\sqrt{n}$	Sq. rt. of 10n $\sqrt{10n}$	Cube root $\sqrt[3]{n}$	Reciprocal $\frac{1}{n}$
			71·	220 +	17·	0·000
5100	26 01 00 00	132 651 000 000	414284	5·831796	213006	1960784
5101	26 02 02 01	132 729 045 301	421285 7001	5·853935 22139	214131 1125	1960400 384
5102	26 03 04 04	132 807 121 208	428286 7001	5·876072 22137	215256 1125	1960016 384
5103	26 04 06 09	132 885 227 727	435285 6999	5·898207 22135	216381 1125	1959632 384
5104	26 05 08 16	132 963 364 864	442284 6999	5·920340 22133	217505 1124	1959248 384
				22131	1125	
5105	26 06 10 25	133 041 532 625	449283 6997	5·942471 22128	218630 1124	1958864 384
5106	26 07 12 36	133 119 731 016	456280 6997	5·964599 22126	219754 1124	1958480 384
5107	26 08 14 49	133 197 960 043	463277 6997	5·986725 22124	220878 1124	1958097 383
5108	26 09 16 64	133 276 219 712	470274 6995	6·008849 22122	222002 1124	1957713 384
5109	26 10 18 81	133 354 510 029	477269 6995	6·030971 22120	223126 1123	1957330 383
						383
5110	26 11 21 00	133 432 831 000	484264	6·053091 22118	224249	1956947 383
5111	26 12 23 21	133 511 182 631	491258 6994	6·075209 22115	225373 1124	1956564 383
5112	26 13 25 44	133 589 564 928	498252 6994	6·097324 22113	226496 1123	1956182 382
5113	26 14 27 69	133 667 977 897	505245 6993	6·119437 22112	227619 1123	1955799 383
5114	26 15 29 96	133 746 421 544	512237 6992	6·141549 22109	228742 1123	1955417 382
			6991		1123	383
5115	26 16 32 25	133 824 895 875	519228 6991	6·163658 22106	229865 1123	1955034 382
5116	26 17 34 56	133 903 400 896	526219 6990	6·185764 22105	230988 1123	1954652 382
5117	26 18 36 89	133 981 936 613	533209 6989	6·207869 22102	232111 1122	1954270 382
5118	26 19 39 24	134 060 503 032	540198 6989	6·229971 22101	233233 1122	1953888 381
5119	26 20 41 61	134 139 100 159	547187 6988	6·252072 22098	234355 1123	1953507 382
			6988			381
5120	26 21 44 00	134 217 728 000	554175	6·274170 22096	235478 1122	1953125 381
5121	26 22 46 41	134 296 386 561	561163 6988	6·296266 22094	236600 1121	1952744 381
5122	26 23 48 84	134 375 075 848	568149 6986	6·318360 22092	237721 1122	1952362 382
5123	26 24 51 29	134 453 795 867	575135 6986	6·340452 22089	238843 1122	1951981 381
5124	26 25 53 76	134 532 546 624	582121 6984	6·362541 22087	239965 1121	1951600 381
			6984			380
5125	26 26 56 25	134 611 328 125	589105 6084	6·384628 22086	241086 1122	1951220 381
5126	26 27 58 76	134 690 140 376	596089 6084	6·406714 22083	242208 1121	1950839 381
5127	26 28 61 29	134 768 983 383	603073 6982	6·428797 22081	243329 1121	1950458 380
5128	26 29 63 84	134 847 857 152	610055 6982	6·450878 22078	244450 1121	1950078 380
5129	26 30 66 41	134 926 761 689	617037 6981	6·472956 22077	245571 1120	1949698 380
			6981			380
5130	26 31 69 00	135 005 697 000	624018 6981	6·495033 22075	246691 1121	1949318 380
5131	26 32 71 61	135 084 663 091	630999 6980	6·517108 22072	247812 1120	1948938 380
5132	26 33 74 24	135 163 659 968	637979 6979	6·539180 22070	248932 1121	1948558 380
5133	26 34 76 89	135 242 687 637	644958 6978	6·561250 22068	250053 1120	1948178 380
5134	26 35 79 56	135 321 746 104	651936 6978	6·583318 22066	251173 1120	1947799 379
						379
5135	26 36 82 25	135 400 835 375	658914 6977	6·605384 22064	252293 1119	1947420 380
5136	26 37 84 96	135 479 955 456	665891 6977	6·627448 22061	253412 1120	1947040 379
5137	26 38 87 69	135 559 106 353	672868 6976	6·649509 22060	254532 1120	1946661 379
5138	26 39 90 44	135 638 288 072	679844 6975	6·671569 22057	255652 1120	1946283 378
5139	26 40 93 21	135 717 500 619	686819 6974	6·693626 22055	256771 1119	1945904 379
						379
5140	26 41 96 00	135 796 744 000	693793 6974	6·715681 22053	257890 1120	1945525 378
5141	26 42 98 81	135 876 018 221	700767 6973	6·737734 22051	259010 1118	1945147 378
5142	26 44 01 64	135 955 323 288	707740 6973	6·759785 22048	260128 1119	1944769 379
5143	26 45 04 49	136 034 659 207	714713 6971	6·781833 22047	261247 1119	1944390 378
5144	26 46 07 36	136 114 025 984	721684 6971	6·803880 22044	262366 1119	1944012 377
						377
5145	26 47 10 25	136 193 423 625	728655 6971	6·825924 22043	263485 1118	1943635 378
5146	26 48 13 16	136 272 852 136	735626 6969	6·847967 22040	264603 1118	1943257 378
5147	26 49 16 09	136 352 311 523	742595 6969	6·870007 22038	265721 1118	1942879 378
5148	26 50 19 04	136 431 801 792	749564 6969	6·892045 22036	266839 1118	1942502 377
5149	26 51 22 01	136 511 322 949	756533 6967	6·914081 22033	267957 1118	1942125 377
						377
5150	26 52 25 00	136 590 875 000	763500	6·936114	269075	1941748
			71·	220 +	17·	0·000

No. n	Square n^2	Cube n^3	Square root $\sqrt{n}$	Sq. rt. of 10n $\sqrt{10n}$	Cube root $\sqrt[3]{n}$	Reciprocal $\frac{1}{n}$
			71·	220 +	17·	0·000
5150	26 52 25 00	136 590 875 000	763500 6967	6·936114 22032	269075 1118	1941748 377
5151	26 53 28 01	136 670 457 951	770467 6967	6·958144 22029	270193 1117	1941371 377
5152	26 54 31 04	136 750 071 808	777434 6965	6·980175 22028	271310 1118	1940994 377
5153	26 55 34 09	136 829 716 577	784399 6965	7·002203 22025	272428 1117	1940617 376
5154	26 56 37 16	136 909 392 264	791364 6965	7·024228 22023	273545 1117	1940241 377
5155	26 57 40 25	136 989 098 875	798329 6963	7·046251 22021	274662 1117	1939864 376
5156	26 58 43 36	137 068 836 416	805292 6963	7·068272 22018	275779 1117	1939488 376
5157	26 59 46 49	137 148 604 893	812255 6962	7·090290 22017	276896 1116	1939112 376
5158	26 60 49 64	137 228 404 312	819217 6962	7·112307 22014	278012 1117	1938736 376
5159	26 61 52 81	137 308 234 679	826179 6961	7·134321 22013	279129 1116	1938360 376
5160	26 62 56 00	137 388 096 000	833140 6960	7·156334 22010	280245 1116	1937984 375
5161	26 63 59 21	137 467 988 281	840100 6960	7·178344 22008	281361 1116	1937609 375
5162	26 64 62 44	137 547 911 528	847060 6959	7·200352 22006	282477 1116	1937234 376
5163	26 65 65 69	137 627 865 747	854019 6958	7·222358 22004	283593 1116	1936858 375
5164	26 66 68 96	137 707 850 944	860977 6957	7·244362 22002	284709 1116	1936483 375
5165	26 67 72 25	137 787 867 125	867934 6957	7·266364 21999	285825 1115	1936108 374
5166	26 68 75 56	137 867 914 296	874891 6956	7·288363 21998	286940 1115	1935734 375
5167	26 69 78 89	137 947 992 463	881847 6956	7·310361 21995	288056 1115	1935359 374
5168	26 70 82 24	138 028 101 632	888803 6955	7·332356 21993	289171 1115	1934985 375
5169	26 71 85 61	138 108 241 809	895758 6954	7·354349 21991	290286 1115	1934610 374
5170	26 72 89 00	138 188 413 000	902712 6954	7·376340 21989	291401 1115	1934236 374
5171	26 73 92 41	138 268 615 211	909666 6952	7·398329 21987	292516 1114	1933862 374
5172	26 74 95 84	138 348 848 448	916618 6953	7·420316 21984	293630 1115	1933488 374
5173	26 75 99 29	138 429 112 717	923571 6951	7·442300 21983	294745 1114	1933114 373
5174	26 77 02 76	138 509 408 024	930522 6951	7·464283 21980	295859 1114	1932741 374
5175	26 78 06 25	138 589 734 375	937473 6950	7·486263 21979	296973 1114	1932367 373
5176	26 79 09 76	138 670 091 776	944423 6949	7·508242 21976	298087 1114	1931994 373
5177	26 80 13 29	138 750 480 233	951372 6949	7·530218 21974	299201 1114	1931621 373
5178	26 81 16 84	138 830 899 752	958321 6948	7·552192 21972	300315 1114	1931248 373
5179	26 82 20 41	138 911 350 339	965269 6948	7·574164 21970	301429 1113	1930875 373
5180	26 83 24 00	138 991 832 000	972217 6947	7·596134 21967	302542 1114	1930502 373
5181	26 84 27 61	139 072 344 741	979164 6946	7·618101 21966	303656 1113	1930129 372
5182	26 85 31 24	139 152 888 568	986110 6945	7·640067 21963	304769 1113	1929757 372
5183	26 86 34 89	139 233 463 487	993055 6945	7·662030 21962	305882 1113	1929385 373
5184	26 87 38 56	139 314 069 504	*000000 6944	7·683992 21959	306995 1113	1929012 372
5185	26 88 42 25	139 394 706 625	006944 6944	7·705951 21957	308108 1112	1928640 372
5186	26 89 45 96	139 475 374 856	013888 6942	7·727908 21955	309220 1113	1928268 371
5187	26 90 49 69	139 556 074 203	020830 6942	7·749863 21953	310333 1112	1927897 372
5188	26 91 53 44	139 636 804 672	027772 6942	7·771816 21950	311445 1112	1927525 371
5189	26 92 57 21	139 717 566 269	034714 6941	7·793766 21949	312557 1112	1927154 372
5190	26 93 61 00	139 798 359 000	041655 6940	7·815715 21947	313669 1112	1926782 371
5191	26 94 64 81	139 879 182 871	048595 6939	7·837662 21944	314781 1112	1926411 371
5192	26 95 68 64	139 960 037 888	055534 6939	7·859606 21942	315893 1112	1926040 371
5193	26 96 72 49	140 040 924 057	062473 6938	7·881548 21940	317005 1111	1925669 371
5194	26 97 76 36	140 121 841 384	069411 6937	7·903488 21938	318116 1112	1925298 370
5195	26 98 80 25	140 202 789 875	076348 6937	7·925426 21936	319228 1111	1924928 371
5196	26 99 84 16	140 283 769 536	083285 6936	7·947362 21934	320339 1111	1924557 370
5197	27 00 88 09	140 364 780 373	090221 6936	7·969296 21932	321450 1111	1924187 370
5198	27 01 92 04	140 445 822 392	097157 6934	7·991228 21930	322561 1110	1923817 370
5199	27 02 96 01	140 526 895 599	104091 6935	8·013158 21927	323671 1111	1923447 370
5200	27 04 00 00	140 608 000 000	111026 72·	8·035085 220 +	324782 17·	1923077 0·000

No. n	Square n^2	Cube n^3	Square root $\sqrt{n}$	Sq. rt. of $10n$ $\sqrt{10n}$	Cube root $\sqrt[3]{n}$	Reciprocal $\frac{1}{n}$
			72·	220 +	17·	0·000
5200	27 04 00 00	140 608 000 000	111026 6933	8·035085 21925	324782 1111	1923077 370
5201	27 05 04 01	140 689 135 601	117959 6933	8·057010 21924	325893 1110	1922707 369
5202	27 06 08 04	140 770 302 408	124892 6932	8·078934 21921	327003 1110	1922338 370
5203	27 07 12 09	140 851 500 427	131824 6931	8·100855 21919	328113 1110	1921968 369
5204	27 08 16 16	140 932 729 664	138755 6931	8·122774 21917	329223 1110	1921599 369
5205	27 09 20 25	141 013 990 125	145686 6930	8·144691 21915	330333 1110	1921230 369
5206	27 10 24 36	141 095 281 816	152616 6930	8·166606 21913	331443 1110	1920861 369
5207	27 11 28 49	141 176 604 743	159545 6929	8·188519 21910	332553 1109	1920492 369
5208	27 12 32 64	141 257 958 912	166474 6928	8·210429 21900	333662 1109	1920123 369
5209	27 13 36 81	141 339 344 329	173402 6928	8·232338 21906	334771 1110	1919754 368
5210	27 14 41 00	141 420 761 000	180330 6926	8·254244 21905	335881 1109	1919386 369
5211	27 15 45 21	141 502 208 931	187256 6927	8·276149 21902	336990 1109	1919017 368
5212	27 16 49 44	141 583 688 128	194183 6925	8·298051 21900	338099 1108	1918649 368
5213	27 17 53 69	141 665 198 597	201108 6925	8·319951 21898	339207 1109	1918281 368
5214	27 18 57 96	141 746 740 344	208033 6924	8·341849 21896	340316 1109	1917913 367
5215	27 19 62 25	141 828 313 375	214957 6923	8·363745 21894	341425 1108	1917546 368
5216	27 20 66 56	141 909 917 696	221880 6923	8·385639 21892	342533 1108	1917178 368
5217	27 21 70 89	141 991 553 313	228803 6922	8·407531 21889	343641 1108	1916810 367
5218	27 22 75 24	142 073 220 232	235725 6922	8·429420 21888	344749 1108	1916443 367
5219	27 23 79 61	142 154 918 459	242647 6920	8·451308 21885	345857 1108	1916076 367
5220	27 24 84 00	142 236 648 000	249567 6921	8·473193 21884	346965 1108	1915709 367
5221	27 25 88 41	142 318 408 861	256488 6919	8·495077 21881	348073 1107	1915342 367
5222	27 26 92 84	142 400 201 048	263407 6919	8·516958 21879	349180 1107	1914975 367
5223	27 27 97 29	142 482 024 567	270326 6918	8·538837 21877	350287 1108	1914608 366
5224	27 29 01 76	142 563 879 424	277244 6917	8·560714 21875	351395 1107	1914242 366
5225	27 30 06 25	142 645 765 625	284161 6917	8·582589 21873	352502 1107	1913876 367
5226	27 31 10 76	142 727 683 176	291078 6916	8·604462 21871	353609 1107	1913509 366
5227	27 32 15 29	142 809 632 083	297994 6916	8·626333 21868	354716 1106	1913143 366
5228	27 33 19 84	142 891 612 352	304910 6915	8·648201 21867	355822 1107	1912777 366
5229	27 34 24 41	142 973 623 989	311825 6914	8·670068 21865	356929 1106	1912412 366
5230	27 35 29 00	143 055 667 000	318739 6913	8·691933 21862	358035 1106	1912046 366
5231	27 36 33 61	143 137 741 391	325652 6913	8·713795 21860	359141 1106	1911680 365
5232	27 37 38 24	143 219 847 168	332565 6912	8·735655 21859	360247 1106	1911315 365
5233	27 38 42 89	143 301 984 337	339477 6912	8·757514 21856	361353 1106	1910950 365
5234	27 39 47 56	143 384 152 904	346389 6911	8·779370 21854	362459 1106	1910585 365
5235	27 40 52 25	143 466 352 875	353300 6910	8·801224 21852	363565 1105	1910220 365
5236	27 41 56 96	143 548 584 256	360210 6910	8·823076 21850	364670 1105	1909855 365
5237	27 42 61 69	143 630 847 053	367120 6908	8·844926 21847	365776 1105	1909490 365
5238	27 43 66 44	143 713 141 272	374028 6909	8·866773 21846	366881 1105	1909126 364
5239	27 44 71 21	143 795 466 919	380937 6907	8·888619 21844	367986 1105	1908761 364
5240	27 45 76 00	143 877 824 000	387844 6907	8·910463 21841	369091 1105	1908397 364
5241	27 46 80 81	143 960 212 521	394751 6906	8·932304 21840	370196 1105	1908033 364
5242	27 47 85 64	144 042 632 488	401657 6906	8·954144 21837	371301 1104	1907669 364
5243	27 48 90 49	144 125 083 907	408563 6905	8·975981 21836	372405 1105	1907305 364
5244	27 49 95 36	144 207 566 784	415468 6904	8·997817 21833	373510 1104	1906941 363
5245	27 51 00 25	144 290 081 125	422372 6904	9·019650 21831	374614 1104	1906578 364
5246	27 52 05 16	144 372 626 936	429276 6903	9·041481 21829	375718 1104	1906214 363
5247	27 53 10 09	144 455 204 223	436179 6902	9·063310 21827	376822 1104	1905851 363
5248	27 54 15 04	144 537 812 992	443081 6902	9·085137 21825	377926 1104	1905488 363
5249	27 55 20 01	144 620 453 249	449983 6901	9·106962 21823	379030 1103	1905125 363
5250	27 56 25 00	144 703 125 000	456884 72·	9·128785 220 +	380133 17·	1904762 0·000

106

No. n	Square n^2	Cube n^3	Square root $\sqrt{n}$	Sq. rt. of 10n $\sqrt{10n}$	Cube root $\sqrt[3]{n}$	Reciprocal $\dfrac{1}{n}$
			72·	220 +	17·	0·000
5250	27 56 25 00	144 703 125 000	456884 6900	9·128785 21820	380133 1104	1904762 363
5251	27 57 30 01	144 785 828 251	463784 6900	9·150605 21819	381237 1103	1904399 362
5252	27 58 35 04	144 868 563 008	470684 6899	9·172424 21817	382340 1103	1904037 363
5253	27 59 40 09	144 951 329 277	477583 6898	9·194241 21814	383443 1103	1903674 362
5254	27 60 45 16	145 034 127 064	484481 6898	9·216055 21813	384546 1103	1903312 362
5255	27 61 50 25	145 116 956 375	491379 6897	9·237868 21810	385649 1103	1902950 362
5256	27 62 55 36	145 199 817 216	498276 6896	9·259678 21808	386752 1103	1902588 362
5257	27 63 60 49	145 282 709 593	505172 6896	9·281486 21807	387854 1102	1902226 362
5258	27 64 65 64	145 365 633 512	512068 6895	9·303293 21804	388957 1102	1901864 362
5259	27 65 70 81	145 448 588 979	518963 6894	9·325097 21802	390059 1102	1901502 361
5260	27 66 76 00	145 531 576 000	525857 6894	9·346899 21800	391161 1102	1901141 362
5261	27 67 81 21	145 614 594 581	532751 6893	9·368699 21798	392263 1102	1900779 361
5262	27 68 86 44	145 697 644 728	539644 6893	9·390497 21796	393365 1102	1900418 361
5263	27 69 91 69	145 780 726 447	546537 6892	9·412293 21793	394467 1102	1900057 361
5264	27 70 96 96	145 863 839 744	553429 6891	9·434086 21792	395569 1101	1899696 361
5265	27 72 02 25	145 946 984 625	560320 6890	9·455878 21790	396670 1101	1899335 360
5266	27 73 07 56	146 030 161 096	567210 6890	9·477668 21787	397771 1102	1898975 361
5267	27 74 12 89	146 113 369 163	574100 6889	9·499455 21786	398873 1101	1898614 360
5268	27 75 18 24	146 196 608 832	580989 6889	9·521241 21783	399974 1101	1898254 361
5269	27 76 23 61	146 279 880 109	587878 6888	9·543024 21782	401074 1101	1897893 360
5270	27 77 29 00	146 363 183 000	594766 6887	9·564806 21779	402175 1101	1897533 360
5271	27 78 34 41	146 446 517 511	601653 6886	9·586585 21777	403276 1100	1897173 360
5272	27 79 39 84	146 529 883 648	608539 6886	9·608362 21775	404376 1101	1896813 359
5273	27 80 45 29	146 613 281 417	615425 6886	9·630137 21774	405477 1100	1896454 360
5274	27 81 50 76	146 696 710 824	622311 6884	9·651911 21771	406577 1100	1896094 359
5275	27 82 56 25	146 780 171 875	629195 6884	9·673682 21769	407677 1100	1895735 360
5276	27 83 61 76	146 863 664 576	636079 6883	9·695451 21766	408777 1100	1895375 359
5277	27 84 67 29	146 947 188 933	642962 6883	9·717217 21765	409877 1099	1895016 359
5278	27 85 72 84	147 030 744 952	649845 6882	9·738982 21763	410976 1100	1894657 359
5279	27 86 78 41	147 114 332 639	656727 6881	9·760745 21761	412076 1099	1894298 359
5280	27 87 84 00	147 197 952 000	663608 6881	9·782506 21759	413175 1100	1893939 358
5281	27 88 89 61	147 281 603 041	670489 6880	9·804265 21756	414275 1099	1893581 359
5282	27 89 95 24	147 365 285 768	677369 6880	9·826021 21755	415374 1099	1893222 358
5283	27 91 00 89	147 449 000 187	684249 6878	9·847776 21752	416473 1099	1892864 358
5284	27 92 06 56	147 532 746 304	691127 6878	9·869528 21751	417572 1098	1892506 358
5285	27 93 12 25	147 616 524 125	698005 6878	9·891279 21748	418670 1099	1892148 358
5286	27 94 17 96	147 700 333 656	704883 6877	9·913027 21746	419769 1098	1891790 358
5287	27 95 23 69	147 784 174 903	711760 6876	9·934773 21745	420867 1098	1891432 358
5288	27 96 29 44	147 868 047 872	718636 6875	9·956518 21742	421965 1099	1891074 357
5289	27 97 35 21	147 951 952 569	725511 6875	9·978260 21740	423064 1098	1890717 358
5290	27 98 41 00	148 035 889 000	732386 6874	*0·000000 21738	424162 1097	1890359 357
5291	27 99 46 81	148 119 857 171	739260 6874	0·021738 21736	425259 1098	1890002 357
5292	28 00 52 64	148 203 857 088	746134 6873	0·043474 21734	426357 1098	1889645 357
5293	28 01 58 49	148 287 888 757	753007 6872	0·065208 21732	427455 1097	1889288 357
5294	28 02 64 36	148 371 952 184	759879 6872	0·086940 21730	428552 1098	1888931 357
5295	28 03 70 25	148 456 047 375	766751 6871	0·108670 21728	429650 1097	1888574 356
5296	28 04 76 16	148 540 174 336	773622 6870	0·130398 21726	430747 1097	1888218 357
5297	28 05 82 09	148 624 333 073	780492 6870	0·152124 21723	431844 1097	1887861 357
5298	28 06 88 04	148 708 523 592	787362 6869	0·173847 21722	432941 1096	1887505 356
5299	28 07 94 01	148 792 745 899	794231 6868	0·195569 21720	434037 1097	1887149 357
5300	28 09 00 00	148 877 000 000	801099	0·217289	435134	1886792
			72·	230 +	17·	0·000

No. n	Square n²	Cube n³	Square root √n	Sq. rt. of 10n √10n	Cube root ∛n	Reciprocal 1/n
			72·	230 +	17·	0·000
5300	28 09 00 00	148 877 000 000	801099 6868	0·217289 21717	435134 1096	1886792 355
5301	28 10 06 01	148 961 285 901	807967 6867	0·239006 21716	436230 1097	1886437 355
5302	28 11 12 04	149 045 603 608	814834 6866	0·260722 21713	437327 1096	1886081 356
5303	28 12 18 09	149 129 953 127	821700 6866	0·282435 21712	438423 1096	1885725 356
5304	28 13 24 16	149 214 334 464	828566 6865	0·304147 21709	439519 1096	1885370 355 356
5305	28 14 30 25	149 298 747 625	835431 6864	0·325856 21707	440615 1096	1885014 355
5306	28 15 36 36	149 383 192 616	842295 6864	0·347563 21706	441711 1095	1884659 355
5307	28 16 42 49	149 467 669 443	849159 6863	0·369269 21703	442806 1096	1884304 355
5308	28 17 48 64	149 552 178 112	856022 6863	0·390972 21701	443902 1095	1883949 355
5309	28 18 54 81	149 636 718 629	862885 6862	0·412673 21699	444997 1096	1883594 355
5310	28 19 61 00	149 721 291 000	869747 6861	0·434372 21698	446093 1095	1883239 354
5311	28 20 67 21	149 805 895 231	876608 6861	0·456070 21695	447188 1095	1882885 355
5312	28 21 73 44	149 890 531 328	883469 6860	0·477765 21693	448283 1095	1882530 354
5313	28 22 79 69	149 975 199 297	890329 6859	0·499458 21691	449378 1094	1882176 354
5314	28 23 85 96	150 059 899 144	897188 6859	0·521149 21689	450472 1095	1881822 354 354
5315	28 24 92 25	150 144 630 875	904047 6858	0·542838 21687	451567 1094	1881468 354
5316	28 25 98 56	150 229 394 496	910905 6857	0·564525 21684	452661 1094	1881114 354
5317	28 27 04 89	150 314 190 013	917762 6857	0·586209 21683	453755 1095	1880760 354
5318	28 28 11 24	150 399 017 432	924619 6856	0·607892 21681	454850 1094	1880406 354
5319	28 29 17 61	150 483 876 759	931475 6855	0·629573 21679	455944 1093	1880053 353 354
5320	28 30 24 00	150 568 768 000	938330 6855	0·651252 21677	457037 1094	1879699 353
5321	28 31 30 41	150 653 691 161	945185 6854	0·672929 21674	458131 1094	1879346 353
5322	28 32 36 84	150 738 646 248	952039 6854	0·694603 21673	459225 1093	1878993 353
5323	28 33 43 29	150 823 633 267	958893 6852	0·716276 21671	460318 1094	1878640 353
5324	28 34 49 76	150 908 652 224	965745 6853	0·737947 21668	461412 1093	1878287 353 353
5325	28 35 56 25	150 993 703 125	972598 6851	0·759615 21667	462505 1093	1877934 352
5326	28 36 62 76	151 078 785 976	979449 6851	0·781282 21664	463598 1093	1877582 353
5327	28 37 69 29	151 163 900 783	986300 6850	0·802946 21663	464691 1092	1877229 352
5328	28 38 75 84	151 249 047 552	993150 6850	0·824609 21660	465783 1093	1876877 352
5329	28 39 82 41	151 334 226 289	*000000 6849	0·846269 21659	466876 1093	1876525 352 352
5330	28 40 89 00	151 419 437 000	006849 6848	0·867928 21656	467969 1092	1876173
5331	28 41 95 61	151 504 679 691	013697 6848	0·889584 21654	469061 1092	1875821 352
5332	28 43 02 24	151 589 954 368	020545 6847	0·911238 21653	470153 1092	1875469 352
5333	28 44 08 89	151 675 261 037	027392 6847	0·932891 21650	471245 1092	1875117 352
5334	28 45 15 56	151 760 599 704	034239 6845	0·954541 21648	472337 1092	1874766 351 352
5335	28 46 22 25	151 845 970 375	041084 6845	0·976189 21646	473429 1092	1874414 351
5336	28 47 28 96	151 931 373 056	047929 6845	0·997835 21645	474521 1091	1874063 351
5337	28 48 35 69	152 016 807 753	054774 6844	1·019480 21642	475612 1092	1873712 351
5338	28 49 42 44	152 102 274 472	061618 6843	1·041122 21640	476704 1091	1873361 351
5339	28 50 49 21	152 187 773 219	068461 6843	1·062762 21638	477795 1091	1873010 351 351
5340	28 51 56 00	152 273 304 000	075304 6842	1·084400 21636	478886 1091	1872659
5341	28 52 62 81	152 358 866 821	082146 6842	1·106036 21634	479977 1091	1872309 350
5342	28 53 69 64	152 444 461 688	088987 6841	1·127670 21632	481068 1091	1871958 351
5343	28 54 76 49	152 530 088 607	095828 6840	1·149302 21630	482159 1090	1871608 350
5344	28 55 83 36	152 615 747 584	102668 6839	1·170932 21628	483249 1091	1871257 351 351
5345	28 56 90 25	152 701 438 625	109507 6839	1·192560 21626	484340 1090	1870907
5346	28 57 97 16	152 787 161 736	116346 6838	1·214186 21624	485430 1090	1870557 350
5347	28 59 04 09	152 872 916 923	123184 6837	1·235810 21622	486520 1090	1870208 349
5348	28 60 11 04	152 958 704 192	130021 6837	1·257432 21620	487610 1090	1869858 350
5349	28 61 18 01	153 044 523 549	136858 6836	1·279052 21618	488700 1090	1869508 350 349
5350	28 62 25 00	153 130 375 000	143694 73·	1·300670 230 +	489790 17·	1869159 0·000

No. n	Square n²	Cube n³	Square root √n	Sq. rt. of 10n √10n	Cube root ∛n	Reciprocal 1/n
			73·	230 +	17·	0·000
5350	28 62 25 00	153 130 375 000	143694 6836	1·300670 21616	489790 1090	1869159 349
5351	28 63 32 01	153 216 258 551	150530 6835	1·322286 21614	490880 1089	1868810 349
5352	28 64 39 04	153 302 174 208	157365 6834	1·343900 21612	491969 1089	1868460 350
5353	28 65 46 09	153 388 121 977	164199 6834	1·365512 21610	493058 1090	1868111 349
5354	28 66 53 16	153 474 101 864	171033 6833	1·387122 21607	494148 1089	1867762 348
5355	28 67 60 25	153 560 113 875	177866 6832	1·408729 21606	495237 1089	1867414 349
5356	28 68 67 36	153 646 158 016	184698 6832	1·430335 21604	496326 1089	1867065 349
5357	28 69 74 49	153 732 234 293	191530 6831	1·451939 21602	497415 1088	1866716 349
5358	28 70 81 64	153 818 342 712	198361 6830	1·473541 21599	498503 1089	1866368 348
5359	28 71 88 81	153 904 483 279	205191 6830	1·495140 21598	499592 1088	1866020 348
5360	28 72 96 00	153 990 656 000	212021 6829	1·516738 21596	500680 1089	1865672 348
5361	28 74 03 21	154 076 860 881	218850 6829	1·538334 21593	501769 1088	1865324 348
5362	28 75 10 44	154 163 097 928	225679 6827	1·559927 21592	502857 1088	1864976 348
5363	28 76 17 69	154 249 367 147	232506 6828	1·581519 21590	503945 1088	1864628 348
5364	28 77 24 96	154 335 668 544	239334 6826	1·603109 21587	505033 1087	1864280 347
5365	28 78 32 25	154 422 002 125	246160 6826	1·624696 21586	506120 1088	1863933 347
5366	28 79 39 56	154 508 367 896	252986 6826	1·646282 21584	507208 1087	1863586 348
5367	28 80 46 89	154 594 765 863	259812 6824	1·667866 21581	508295 1088	1863238 347
5368	28 81 54 24	154 681 196 032	266636 6824	1·689447 21580	509383 1087	1862891 347
5369	28 82 61 61	154 767 658 409	273460 6824	1·711027 21578	510470 1087	1862544 347
5370	28 83 69 00	154 854 153 000	280284 6823	1·732605 21575	511557 1087	1862197 346
5371	28 84 76 41	154 940 679 811	287107 6822	1·754180 21574	512644 1087	1861851 347
5372	28 85 83 84	155 027 238 848	293929 6821	1·775754 21571	513731 1086	1861504 347
5373	28 86 91 29	155 113 830 117	300750 6821	1·797325 21570	514817 1087	1861158 347
5374	28 87 98 76	155 200 453 624	307571 6820	1·818895 21567	515904 1086	1860811 346
5375	28 89 06 25	155 287 109 375	314391 6820	1·840462 21566	516990 1087	1860465 346
5376	28 90 13 76	155 373 797 376	321211 6819	1·862028 21563	518077 1086	1860119 346
5377	28 91 21 29	155 460 517 633	328030 6818	1·883591 21562	519163 1086	1859773 346
5378	28 92 28 84	155 547 270 152	334848 6818	1·905153 21560	520249 1086	1859427 345
5379	28 93 36 41	155 634 054 939	341666 6817	1·926713 21557	521335 1085	1859082 346
5380	28 94 44 00	155 720 872 000	348483 6817	1·948270 21556	522420 1086	1858736 345
5381	28 95 51 61	155 807 721 341	355300 6816	1·969826 21553	523506 1085	1858391 345
5382	28 96 59 24	155 894 602 968	362116 6815	1·991379 21552	524591 1086	1858045 346
5383	28 97 66 89	155 981 516 887	368931 6814	2·012931 21549	525677 1085	1857700 345
5384	28 98 74 56	156 068 463 104	375745 6814	2·034480 21548	526762 1085	1857355 345
5385	28 99 82 25	156 155 441 625	382559 6814	2·056028 21545	527847 1085	1857010 345
5386	29 00 89 96	156 242 452 456	389373 6812	2·077573 21544	528932 1085	1856665 344
5387	29 01 97 69	156 329 495 603	396185 6812	2·099117 21541	530017 1084	1856321 345
5388	29 03 05 44	156 416 571 072	402997 6812	2·120658 21540	531101 1085	1855976 344
5389	29 04 13 21	156 503 678 869	409809 6810	2·142198 21537	532186 1084	1855632 344
5390	29 05 21 00	156 590 819 000	416619 6811	2·163735 21536	533270 1084	1855288 345
5391	29 06 28 81	156 677 991 471	423430 6809	2·185271 21533	534354 1084	1854943 345
5392	29 07 36 64	156 765 196 288	430239 6809	2·206804 21532	535438 1084	1854599 344
5393	29 08 44 49	156 852 433 457	437048 6808	2·228336 21529	536522 1084	1854256 343
5394	29 09 52 36	156 939 702 984	443856 6808	2·249865 21528	537606 1084	1853912 344
5395	29 10 60 25	157 027 004 875	450664 6807	2·271393 21526	538690 1083	1853568 343
5396	29 11 68 16	157 114 339 136	457471 6806	2·292919 21523	539773 1084	1853225 344
5397	29 12 76 09	157 201 705 773	464277 6806	2·314442 21522	540857 1083	1852881 343
5398	29 13 84 04	157 289 104 792	471083 6805	2·335964 21519	541940 1083	1852538 343
5399	29 14 92 01	157 376 536 199	477888 6804	2·357483 21518	543023 1083	1852195 343
5400	29 16 00 00	157 464 000 000	484692	2·379001	544106	1851852
			73·	230 +	17·	0·000

No. n	Square n^2	Cube n^3	Square root $\sqrt{n}$	Sq. rt. of $10n$ $\sqrt{10n}$	Cube root $\sqrt[3]{n}$	Reciprocal $\dfrac{1}{n}$
			73·	230 +	17·	0·000
5400	29 16 00 00	157 464 000 000	484692 6804	2·379001 21515	544106 1083	1851852
5401	29 17 08 01	157 551 496 201	491496 6803	2·400516 21514	545189 1083	1851509 343
5402	29 18 16 04	157 639 024 808	498299 6803	2·422030 21512	546272 1083	1851166 343
5403	29 19 24 09	157 726 585 827	505102 6802	2·443542 21509	547355 1082	1850824 342
5404	29 20 32 16	157 814 179 264	511904 6801	2·465051 21508	548437 1083	1850481 343 342
5405	29 21 40 25	157 901 805 125	518705 6801	2·486559 21505	549520 1082	1850139
5406	29 22 48 36	157 989 463 416	525506 6800	2·508064 21504	550602 1082	1849797 342
5407	29 23 56 49	158 077 154 143	532306 6799	2·529568 21502	551684 1082	1849454 343
5408	29 24 64 64	158 164 877 312	539105 6799	2·551070 21499	552766 1082	1849112 342
5409	29 25 72 81	158 252 632 929	545904 6798	2·572569 21498	553848 1081	1848771 341 342
5410	29 26 81 00	158 340 421 000	552702 6798	2·594067 21496	554929 1082	1848429
5411	29 27 89 21	158 428 241 531	559500 6797	2·615563 21493	556011 1081	1848087 342
5412	29 28 97 44	158 516 094 528	566297 6796	2·637056 21492	557092 1082	1847746 341
5413	29 30 05 69	158 603 979 997	573093 6796	2·658548 21490	558174 1081	1847404 342
5414	29 31 13 96	158 691 897 944	579889 6795	2·680038 21488	559255 1081	1847063 341 341
5415	29 32 22 25	158 779 848 375	586684 6794	2·701526 21485	560336 1081	1846722
5416	29 33 30 56	158 867 831 296	593478 6794	2·723011 21484	561417 1081	1846381 341
5417	29 34 38 89	158 955 846 713	600272 6793	2·744495 21482	562498 1080	1846040 341
5418	29 35 47 24	159 043 894 632	607065 6792	2·765977 21480	563578 1081	1845700 340
5419	29 36 55 61	159 131 975 059	613857 6792	2·787457 21478	564659 1080	1845359 341 341
5420	29 37 64 00	159 220 088 000	620649 6792	2·808935 21475	565739 1080	1845018
5421	29 38 72 41	159 308 233 461	627441 6790	2·830410 21474	566819 1080	1844678 340
5422	29 39 80 84	159 396 411 448	634231 6790	2·851884 21472	567899 1080	1844338 340
5423	29 40 89 29	159 484 621 967	641021 6790	2·873356 21470	568979 1080	1843998 340
5424	29 41 97 76	159 572 865 024	647811 6788	2·894826 21468	570059 1080	1843658 340 340
5425	29 43 06 25	159 661 140 625	654599 6788	2·916294 21466	571139 1080	1843318
5426	29 44 14 76	159 749 448 776	661387 6788	2·937760 21464	572219 1079	1842978 340
5427	29 45 23 29	159 837 789 483	668175 6787	2·959224 21462	573298 1079	1842639 339
5428	29 46 31 84	159 926 162 752	674962 6786	2·980686 21460	574377 1079	1842299 340
5429	29 47 40 41	160 014 568 589	681748 6786	3·002146 21458	575456 1080	1841960 339 339
5430	29 48 49 00	160 103 007 000	688534 6785	3·023604 21456	576536 1078	1841621
5431	29 49 57 61	160 191 477 991	695319 6784	3·045060 21454	577614 1079	1841282 339
5432	29 50 66 24	160 279 981 568	702103 6784	3·066514 21452	578693 1079	1840943 339
5433	29 51 74 89	160 368 517 737	708887 6783	3·087966 21450	579772 1079	1840604 339
5434	29 52 83 56	160 457 086 504	715670 6782	3·109416 21449	580850 1079	1840265 339 339
5435	29 53 92 25	160 545 687 875	722452 6782	3·130865 21446	581929 1078	1839926
5436	29 55 00 96	160 634 321 856	729234 6782	3·152311 21444	583007 1078	1839588 338
5437	29 56 09 69	160 722 988 453	736016 6780	3·173755 21442	584085 1078	1839250 338
5438	29 57 18 44	160 811 687 672	742796 6780	3·195197 21440	585163 1078	1838911 339
5439	29 58 27 21	160 900 419 519	749576 6780	3·216637 21439	586241 1078	1838573 338 338
5440	29 59 36 00	160 989 184 000	756356 6778	3·238076 21436	587319 1077	1838235
5441	29 60 44 81	161 077 981 121	763134 6779	3·259512 21435	588396 1078	1837897 338
5442	29 61 53 64	161 166 810 888	769913 6777	3·280947 21432	589474 1077	1837560 337
5443	29 62 62 49	161 255 673 307	776690 6777	3·302379 21430	590551 1077	1837222 338
5444	29 63 71 36	161 344 568 384	783467 6776	3·323809 21429	591628 1077	1836885 338
5445	29 64 80 25	161 433 496 125	790243 6776	3·345238 21426	592705 1077	1836547
5446	29 65 89 16	161 522 456 536	797019 6775	3·366664 21425	593782 1077	1836210 337
5447	29 66 98 09	161 611 449 623	803794 6774	3·388089 21422	594859 1077	1835873 337
5448	29 68 07 04	161 700 475 392	810568 6774	3·409511 21421	595936 1076	1835536 337
5449	29 69 16 01	161 789 533 849	817342 6773	3·430932 21419	597012 1077	1835199 337 337
5450	29 70 25 00	161 878 625 000	824115 73·	3·452351 230 +	598089 17·	1834862 0·000

No. n	Square n²	Cube n³	Square root √n	Sq. rt. of 10n √10n	Cube root ∛n	Reciprocal 1/n
			73·	230 +	17·	0·000
5450	29 70 25 00	161 878 625 000	824115 6773	3·452351 21416	598089 1076	1834862 336
5451	29 71 34 01	161 967 748 851	830888 6772	3·473767 21415	599165 1076	1834526 337
5452	29 72 43 04	162 056 905 408	837660 6771	3·495182 21413	600241 1076	1834189 336
5453	29 73 52 09	162 146 094 677	844431 6771	3·516595 21410	601317 1076	1833853 336
5454	29 74 61 16	162 235 316 664	851202 6770	3·538005 21409	602393 1076	1833517 336
5455	29 75 70 25	162 324 571 375	857972 6769	3·559414 21407	603469 1075	1833181 336
5456	29 76 79 36	162 413 858 816	864741 6769	3·580821 21405	604544 1076	1832845 336
5457	29 77 88 49	162 503 178 993	871510 6768	3·602226 21403	605620 1075	1832509 336
5458	29 78 97 64	162 592 531 912	878278 6768	3·623629 21401	606695 1075	1832173 336
5459	29 80 06 81	162 681 917 579	885046 6767	3·645030 21399	607770 1075	1831837 335
5460	29 81 16 00	162 771 336 000	891813 6766	3·666429 21397	608845 1075	1831502 336
5461	29 82 25 21	162 860 787 181	898579 6766	3·687826 21395	609920 1075	1831166 336
5462	29 83 34 44	162 950 271 128	905345 6765	3·709221 21393	610995 1075	1830831 335
5463	29 84 43 69	163 039 787 847	912110 6764	3·730614 21391	612070 1074	1830496 335
5464	29 85 52 96	163 129 337 344	918874 6764	3·752005 21390	613144 1075	1830161 335
5465	29 86 62 25	163 218 919 625	925638 6764	3·773395 21387	614219 1074	1829826 335
5466	29 87 71 56	163 308 534 696	932402 6762	3·794782 21385	615293 1074	1829491 335
5467	29 88 80 89	163 398 182 563	939164 6762	3·816167 21383	616367 1074	1829157 334
5468	29 89 90 24	163 487 863 232	945926 6762	3·837550 21382	617441 1074	1828822 335
5469	29 90 99 61	163 577 576 709	952688 6760	3·858932 21379	618515 1074	1828488 334
5470	29 92 09 00	163 667 323 000	959448 6761	3·880311 21378	619589 1074	1828154 335
5471	29 93 18 41	163 757 102 111	966209 6759	3·901689 21375	620663 1074	1827819 335
5472	29 94 27 84	163 846 914 048	972968 6759	3·923064 21374	621736 1073	1827485 334
5473	29 95 37 29	163 936 758 817	979727 6758	3·944438 21371	622810 1073	1827151 334
5474	29 96 46 76	164 026 636 424	986485 6758	3·965809 21370	623883 1073	1826818 333
5475	29 97 56 25	164 116 546 875	*993243 6757	3·987179 21368	624956 1073	1826484 334
5476	29 98 65 76	164 206 490 176	*000000 6756	4·008547 21366	626029 1073	1826150 334
5477	29 99 75 29	164 296 466 333	006756 6756	4·029913 21363	627102 1073	1825817 333
5478	30 00 84 84	164 386 475 352	013512 6755	4·051276 21362	628175 1072	1825484 333
5479	30 01 94 41	164 476 517 239	020267 6755	4·072638 21360	629247 1072	1825151 333
5480	30 03 04 00	164 566 592 000	027022 6754	4·093998 21358	630320 1072	1824818 333
5481	30 04 13 61	164 656 699 641	033776 6753	4·115356 21356	631392 1072	1824485 333
5482	30 05 23 24	164 746 840 168	040529 6753	4·136712 21354	632464 1072	1824152 333
5483	30 06 32 89	164 837 013 587	047282 6752	4·158066 21352	633536 1072	1823819 332
5484	30 07 42 56	164 927 219 904	054034 6752	4·179418 21351	634608 1072	1823487 333
5485	30 08 52 25	165 017 459 125	060786 6751	4·200769 21348	635680 1072	1823154 332
5486	30 09 61 96	165 107 731 256	067537 6750	4·222117 21346	636752 1071	1822822 332
5487	30 10 71 69	165 198 036 303	074287 6750	4·243463 21344	637823 1072	1822490 332
5488	30 11 81 44	165 288 374 272	081037 6749	4·264807 21343	638895 1071	1822157 333
5489	30 12 91 21	165 378 745 169	087786 6748	4·286150 21340	639966 1071	1821825 331
5490	30 14 01 00	165 469 149 000	094534 6748	4·307490 21339	641037 1071	1821494 332
5491	30 15 10 81	165 559 585 771	101282 6747	4·328829 21336	642108 1071	1821162 332
5492	30 16 20 64	165 650 055 488	108029 6747	4·350165 21335	643179 1071	1820830 331
5493	30 17 30 49	165 740 558 157	114776 6746	4·371500 21333	644250 1071	1820499 332
5494	30 18 40 36	165 831 093 784	121522 6745	4·392833 21330	645321 1070	1820167 331
5495	30 19 50 25	165 921 662 375	128267 6745	4·414163 21329	646391 1070	1819836 331
5496	30 20 60 16	166 012 263 936	135012 6744	4·435492 21327	647461 1071	1819505 331
5497	30 21 70 09	166 102 898 473	141756 6744	4·456819 21325	648532 1070	1819174 331
5498	30 22 80 04	166 193 565 992	148500 6743	4·478144 21323	649602 1070	1818843 331
5499	30 23 90 01	166 284 266 499	155243 6742	4·499467 21321	650672 1070	1818512 330
5500	30 25 00 00	166 375 000 000	161985	4·520788	651742	1818182
			74·	230 +	17·	0·000

No. n	Square n²	Cube n³	Square root √n	Sq. rt. of 10n √10n	Cube root ∛n	Reciprocal 1/n
			74·	230 +	17·	0·000
5500	30 25 00 00	166 375 000 000	161985 6742	4·520788 21319	651742 1069	1818182
5501	30 26 10 01	166 465 766 501	168727 6741	4·542107 21317	652811 1070	1817851 331
5502	30 27 20 04	166 556 566 008	175468 6740	4·563424 21315	653881 1070	1817521 330
5503	30 28 30 09	166 647 398 527	182208 6740	4·584739 21314	654951 1069	1817191 330
5504	30 29 40 16	166 738 264 064	188948 6739	4·606053 21311	656020 1069	1816860 331 330
5505	30 30 50 25	166 829 162 625	195687 6739	4·627364 21310	657089 1069	1816530
5506	30 31 60 36	166 920 094 216	202426 6738	4·648674 21307	658158 1069	1816201 329
5507	30 32 70 49	167 011 058 843	209164 6737	4·669981 21306	659227 1069	1815871 330
5508	30 33 80 64	167 102 056 512	215901 6737	4·691287 21303	660296 1069	1815541 330
5509	30 34 90 81	167 193 087 229	222638 6736	4·712590 21302	661365 1068	1815211 330 329
5510	30 36 01 00	167 284 151 000	229374 6736	4·733892 21300	662433 1069	1814882
5511	30 37 11 21	167 375 247 831	236110 6735	4·755192 21297	663502 1068	1814553 329
5512	30 38 21 44	167 466 377 728	242845 6734	4·776489 21296	664570 1068	1814224 329
5513	30 39 31 69	167 557 540 697	249579 6734	4·797785 21294	665638 1068	1813894 330
5514	30 40 41 96	167 648 736 744	256313 6733	4·819079 21292	666706 1068	1813565 329 328
5515	30 41 52 25	167 739 965 875	263046 6733	4·840371 21290	667774 1068	1813237
5516	30 42 62 56	167 831 228 096	269779 6731	4·861661 21289	668842 1068	1812908 329
5517	30 43 72 89	167 922 523 413	276510 6732	4·882950 21286	669910 1067	1812579 329
5518	30 44 83 24	168 013 851 832	283242 6730	4·904236 21284	670977 1068	1812251 328
5519	30 45 93 61	168 105 213 359	289972 6730	4·925520 21282	672045 1067	1811922 329 328
5520	30 47 04 00	168 196 608 000	296702 6730	4·946802 21281	673112 1067	1811594
5521	30 48 14 41	168 288 035 761	303432 6729	4·968083 21278	674179 1067	1811266 328
5522	30 49 24 84	168 379 496 648	310161 6728	4·989361 21277	675246 1067	1810938 328
5523	30 50 35 29	168 470 990 667	316889 6728	5·010638 21275	676313 1067	1810610 328
5524	30 51 45 76	168 562 517 824	323617 6727	5·031913 21272	677380 1066	1810282 328 327
5525	30 52 56 25	168 654 078 125	330344 6726	5·053185 21271	678446 1067	1809955
5526	30 53 66 76	168 745 671 576	337070 6726	5·074456 21269	679513 1066	1809627 328
5527	30 54 77 29	168 837 298 183	343796 6725	5·095725 21267	680579 1066	1809300 327
5528	30 55 87 84	168 928 957 952	350521 6725	5·116992 21267	681645 1066	1808973 327
5529	30 56 98 41	169 020 650 889	357246 6724	5·138257 21263	682712 1066	1808645 328 327
5530	30 58 09 00	169 112 377 000	363970 6723	5·159520 21262	683778 1065	1808318
5531	30 59 19 61	169 204 136 291	370693 6723	5·180782 21259	684843 1066	1807991 327
5532	30 60 30 24	169 295 928 768	377416 6722	5·202041 21257	685909 1065	1807664 327
5533	30 61 40 89	169 387 754 437	384138 6722	5·223298 21256	686975 1065	1807338 326
5534	30 62 51 56	169 479 613 304	390860 6721	5·244554 21253	688040 1066	1807011 327 326
5535	30 63 62 25	169 571 505 375	397581 6720	5·265807 21252	689106 1065	1806685
5536	30 64 72 96	169 663 430 656	404301 6720	5·287059 21249	690171 1065	1806358 327
5537	30 65 83 69	169 755 389 153	411021 6719	5·308308 21248	691236 1065	1806032 326
5538	30 66 94 44	169 847 380 872	417740 6718	5·329556 21246	692301 1065	1805706 326
5539	30 68 05 21	169 939 405 819	424458 6718	5·350802 21244	693366 1064	1805380 326 326
5540	30 69 16 00	170 031 464 000	431176 6718	5·372046 21242	694430 1065	1805054
5541	30 70 26 81	170 123 555 421	437894 6716	5·393288 21240	695495 1064	1804728 326
5542	30 71 37 64	170 215 680 088	444610 6716	5·414528 21238	696559 1064	1804403 325
5543	30 72 48 49	170 307 838 007	451326 6716	5·435766 21236	697624 1064	1804077 325
5544	30 73 59 36	170 400 029 184	458042 6715	5·457002 21235	698688 1064	1803752 325 325
5545	30 74 70 25	170 492 253 625	464757 6714	5·478237 21232	699752 1064	1803427
5546	30 75 81 16	170 584 511 336	471471 6714	5·499469 21231	700816 1064	1803101 326
5547	30 76 92 09	170 676 802 323	478185 6713	5·520700 21228	701880 1064	1802776 325
5548	30 78 03 04	170 769 126 592	484898 6712	5·541928 21227	702944 1063	1802451 325
5549	30 79 14 01	170 861 484 149	491610 6712	5·563155 21225	704007 1064	1802127 324 325
5550	30 80 25 00	170 953 875 000	498322	5·584380	705071	1801802
			74·	230 +	17·	0·000

No. n	Square n²	Cube n³	Square root √n	Sq. rt. of 10n √10n	Cube root ∛n	Reciprocal 1/n
			74·	230 +	17·	0·000
5550	30 80 25 00	170 953 875·000	498322 6711	5·584380 21223	705071 1063	1801802 325
5551	30 81 36 01	171 046 299 151	505033 6711	5·605603 21221	706134 1063	1801477 324
5552	30 82 47 04	171 138 756 608	511744 6710	5·626824 21219	707197 1063	1801153 325
5553	30 83 58 09	171 231 247 377	518454 6710	5·648043 21217	708260 1063	1800828 324
5554	30 84 69 16	171 323 771 464	525164 6708	5·669260 21215	709323 1063	1800504 324
5555	30 85 80 25	171 416 328 875	531872 6709	5·690475 21213	710386 1062	1800180 324
5556	30 86 91 36	171 508 919 616	538581 6707	5·711688 21212	711448 1063	1799856 324
5557	30 88 02 49	171 601 543 693	545288 6707	5·732900 21209	712511 1062	1799532 324
5558	30 89 13 64	171 694 201 112	551995 6707	5·754109 21208	713573 1063	1799208 323
5559	30 90 24 81	171 786 891·879	558702 6706	5·775317 21205	714636 1062	1798885 324
5560	30 91 36 00	171 879 616 000	565408 6705	5·796522 21204	715698 1062	1798561 323
5561	30 92 47 21	171 972 373 481	572113 6704	5·817726 21202	716760 1062	1798238 324
5562	30 93 58 44	172 065 164 328	578817 6704	5·838928 21200	717822 1062	1797914 323
5563	30 94 69 69	172 157 988 547	585521 6704	5·860128 21198	718884 1061	1797591 323
5564	30 95 80 96	172 250 846 144	592225 6703	5·881326 21196	719945 1062	1797268 323
5565	30 96 92 25	172 343 737 125	598928 6702	5·902522 21194	721007 1061	1796945 323
5566	30 98 03 56	172 436 661 496	605630 6701	5·923716 21193	722068 1061	1796622 323
5567	30 99 14 89	172 529 619 263	612331 6701	5·944909 21190	723129 1061	1796300 322
5568	31 00 26 24	172 622 610 432	619032 6701	5·966099 21189	724190 1061	1795977 323
5569	31 01 37 61	172 715 635 009	625733 6700	5·987288 21186	725251 1061	1795655 322
5570	31 02 49 00	172 808 693 000	632433 6699	6·008474 21185	726312 1061	1795332 323
5571	31 03 60 41	172 901 784 411	639132 6698	6·029659 21183	727373 1061	1795010 322
5572	31 04 71 84	172 994 909 248	645830 6698	6·050842 21181	728434 1060	1794688 322
5573	31 05 83 29	173 088 067 517	652528 6698	6·072023 21179	729494 1061	1794366 322
5574	31 06 94 76	173 181 259 224	659226 6697	6·093202 21177	730555 1060	1794044 322
5575	31 08 06 25	173 274 484 375	665923 6696	6·114379 21175	731615 1060	1793722 322
5576	31 09 17 76	173 367 742 976	672619 6695	6·135554 21174	732675 1060	1793400 322
5577	31 10 29 29	173 461 035 033	679314 6695	6·156728 21171	733735 1060	1793079 321
5578	31 11 40 84	173 554 360 552	686009 6695	6·177899 21170	734795 1060	1792757 322
5579	31 12 52 41	173 647 719 539	692704 6694	6·199069 21167	735855 1059	1792436 321
5580	31 13 64 00	173 741 112 000	699398 6693	6·220236 21166	736914 1060	1792115 321
5581	31 14 75 61	173 834 537 941	706091 6692	6·241402 21164	737974 1059	1791794 321
5582	31 15 87 24	173 927 997 368	712783 6692	6·262566 21162	739033 1059	1791473 321
5583	31 16 98 89	174 021 490 287	719475 6692	6·283728 21160	740092 1059	1791152 321
5584	31 18 10 56	174 115 016 704	726167 6691	6·304888 21158	741151 1059	1790831 321
5585	31 19 22 25	174 208 576 625	732858 6690	6·326046 21156	742210 1059	1790510 320
5586	31 20 33 96	174 302 170 056	739548 6689	6·347202 21155	743269 1059	1790190 321
5587	31 21 45 69	174 395 797 003	746237 6689	6·368357 21152	744328 1059	1789869 320
5588	31 22 57 44	174 489 457 472	752926 6689	6·389509 21151	745387 1058	1789549 320
5589	31 23 69 21	174 583 151 469	759615 6688	6·410660 21148	746445 1058	1789229 320
5590	31 24 81 00	174 676 879 000	766303 6687	6·431808 21147	747503 1059	1788909 320
5591	31 25 92 81	174 770 640 071	772990 6686	6·452955 21145	748562 1058	1788589 320
5592	31 27 04 64	174 864 434 688	779676 6686	6·474100 21143	749620 1058	1788269 320
5593	31 28 16 49	174 958 262 857	786362 6686	6·495243 21141	750678 1058	1787949 320
5594	31 29 28 36	175 052 124 584	793048 6685	6·516384 21139	751736 1057	1787630 319
5595	31 30 40 25	175 146 019 875	799733 6684	6·537523 21138	752793 1058	1787310 320
5596	31 31 52 16	175 239 948 736	806417 6683	6·558661 21135	753851 1057	1786991 319
5597	31 32 64 09	175 333 911 173	813100 6683	6·579796 21134	754908 1058	1786671 320
5598	31 33 76 04	175 427 907 192	819783 6683	6·600930 21132	755966 1057	1786352 319
5599	31 34 88 01	175 521 936 799	826466 6682	6·622062 21129	757023 1057	1786033 319
5600	31 36 00 00	175 616 000 000	833148	6·643191	758080	1785714
			74·	230 +	17·	0·000

No. n	Square n^2	Cube n^3	Square root $\sqrt{n}$	Sq. rt. of $10n$ $\sqrt{10n}$	Cube root $\sqrt[3]{n}$	Reciprocal $\dfrac{1}{n}$
			74·	230 +	17·	0·000
5600	31 36 00 00	175 616 000 000	833148 6681	6·643191 21128	758080 1057	1785714 319
5601	31 37 12 01	175 710 096 801	839829 6681	6·664319 21126	759137 1057	1785395 318
5602	31 38 24 04	175 804 227 208	846510 6680	6·685445 21124	760194 1057	1785077 319
5603	31 39 36 09	175 898 391 227	853190 6679	6·706569 21123	761251 1056	1784758 318
5604	31 40 48 16	175 992 588 864	859869 6679	6·727692 21120	762307 1057	1784440 319
5605	31 41 60 25	176 086 820 125	866548 6678	6·748812 21119	763364 1056	1784121 318
5606	31 42 72 36	176 181 085 016	873226 6678	6·769931 21116	764420 1056	1783803 318
5607	31 43 84 49	176 275 383 543	879904 6677	6·791047 21115	765476 1056	1783485 318
5608	31 44 96 64	176 369 715 712	886581 6676	6·812162 21113	766532 1056	1783167 318
5609	31 46 08 81	176 464 081 529	893257 6676	6·833275 21111	767588 1056	1782849 318
5610	31 47 21 00	176 558 481 000	899933 6676	6·854386 21109	768644 1056	1782531 317
5611	31 48 33 21	176 652 914 131	906609 6674	6·875495 21107	769700 1055	1782214 318
5612	31 49 45 44	176 747 380 928	913283 6674	6·896602 21105	770755 1056	1781896 318
5613	31 50 57 69	176 841 881 397	919957 6674	6·917707 21104	771811 1055	1781578 317
5614	31 51 69 96	176 936 415 544	926631 6673	6·938811 21101	772866 1055	1781261 317
5615	31 52 82 25	177 030 983 375	933304 6672	6·959912 21100	773921 1055	1780944 317
5616	31 53 94 56	177 125 584 896	939976 6672	6·981012 21098	774976 1055	1780627 317
5617	31 55 06 89	177 220 220 113	946648 6671	7·002110 21096	776031 1055	1780310 317
5618	31 56 19 24	177 314 889 032	953319 6670	7·023206 21094	777086 1055	1779993 317
5619	31 57 31 61	177 409 591 659	959989 6670	7·044300 21092	778141 1054	1779676 317
5620	31 58 44 00	177 504 328 000	966659 6670	7·065392 21090	779195 1055	1779359 316
5621	31 59 56 41	177 599 098 061	973329 6668	7·086482 21089	780250 1054	1779043 316
5622	31 60 68 84	177 693 901 848	979997 6668	7·107571 21086	781304 1054	1778726 316
5623	31 61 81 29	177 788 739 367	986665 6668	7·128657 21085	782358 1055	1778410 316
5624	31 62 93 76	177 883 610 624	993333 6667	7·149742 21083	783413 1054	1778094 316
5625	31 64 06 25	177 978 515 625	*000000 6666	7·170825 21080	784467 1053	1777778 316
5626	31 65 18 76	178 073 454 376	006666 6666	7·191905 21079	785520 1054	1777462 316
5627	31 66 31 29	178 168 426 883	013332 6665	7·212984 21078	786574 1054	1777146 316
5628	31 67 43 84	178 263 433 152	019997 6665	7·234062 21075	787628 1053	1776830 316
5629	31 68 56 41	178 358 473 189	026662 6664	7·255137 21073	788681 1053	1776514 315
5630	31 69 69 00	178 453 547 000	033326 6663	7·276210 21072	789734 1054	1776199 315
5631	31 70 81 61	178 548 654 591	039989 6663	7·297282 21070	790788 1053	1775884 316
5632	31 71 94 24	178 643 795 968	046652 6662	7·318352 21067	791841 1053	1775568 315
5633	31 73 06 89	178 738 971 137	053314 6662	7·339419 21066	792894 1053	1775253 315
5634	31 74 19 56	178 834 180 104	059976 6661	7·360485 21064	793947 1052	1774938 315
5635	31 75 32 25	178 929 422 875	066637 6661	7·381549 21063	794999 1053	1774623 315
5636	31 76 44 96	179 024 699 456	073298 6659	7·402612 21060	796052 1052	1774308 315
5637	31 77 57 69	179 120 009 853	079957 6659	7·423672 21058	797104 1053	1773993 314
5638	31 78 70 44	179 215 354 072	086617 6658	7·444730 21057	798157 1052	1773679 314
5639	31 79 83 21	179 310 732 119	093275 6658	7·465787 21055	799209 1052	1773364 314
5640	31 80 96 00	179 406 144 000	099933 6658	7·486842 21053	800261 1052	1773050 315
5641	31 82 08 81	179 501 589 721	106591 6657	7·507895 21051	801313 1052	1772735 314
5642	31 83 21 64	179 597 069 288	113248 6656	7·528946 21049	802365 1051	1772421 314
5643	31 84 34 49	179 692 582 707	119904 6656	7·549995 21047	803416 1052	1772107 314
5644	31 85 47 36	179 788 129 984	126560 6655	7·571042 21045	804468 1051	1771793 314
5645	31 86 60 25	179 883 711 125	133215 6655	7·592087 21044	805519 1052	1771479 314
5646	31 87 73 16	179 979 326 136	139870 6654	7·613131 21042	806571 1051	1771165 313
5647	31 88 86 09	180 074 975 023	146524 6653	7·634173 21039	807622 1051	1770852 314
5648	31 89 99 04	180 170 657 792	153177 6653	7·655212 21038	808673 1051	1770538 313
5649	31 91 12 01	180 266 374 449	159830 6652	7·676250 21036	809724 1051	1770225 313
5650	31 92 25 00	180 362 125 000	166482	7·697286	810775	1769912
			75·	230 +	17·	0·000

No. n	Square n^2	Cube n^3	Square root $\sqrt{n}$	Sq. rt. of 10n $\sqrt{10n}$	Cube root $\sqrt[3]{n}$	Reciprocal $\frac{1}{n}$
			75·	230 +	17·	0·000
5650	31 92 25 00	180 362 125 000	166482 6651	7·697286 21035	810775 1051	1769912 314
5651	31 93 38 01	180 457 909 451	173133 6652	7·718321 21032	811826 1050	1769598 313
5652	31 94 51 04	180 553 727 808	179785 6650	7·739353 21031	812876 1051	1769285 313
5653	31 95 64 09	180 649 580 077	186435 6650	7·760384 21028	813927 1050	1768972 313
5654	31 96 77 16	180 745 466 264	193085 6649	7·781412 21027	814977 1050	1768659 312
5655	31 97 90 25	180 841 386 375	199734 6649	7·802439 21025	816027 1050	1768347 313
5656	31 99 03 36	180 937 340 416	206383 6648	7·823464 21023	817077 1050	1768034 313
5657	32 00 16 49	181 033 328 393	213031 6647	7·844487 21021	818127 1050	1767721 312
5658	32 01 29 64	181 129 350 312	219678 6647	7·865508 21020	819177 1050	1767409 312
5659	32 02 42 81	181 225 406 179	226325 6646	7·886528 21017	820227 1050	1767097 313
5660	32 03 56 00	181 321 496 000	232971 6646	7·907545 21016	821277 1049	1766784 312
5661	32 04 69 21	181 417 619 781	239617 6645	7·928561 21013	822326 1049	1766472 312
5662	32 05 82 44	181 513 777 528	246262 6645	7·949574 21012	823375 1050	1766160 312
5663	32 06 95 69	181 609 969 247	252907 6644	7·970586 21010	824425 1049	1765848 311
5664	32 08 08 96	181 706 194 944	259551 6643	7·991596 21009	825474 1049	1765537 312
5665	32 09 22 25	181 802 454 625	266194 6643	8·012605 21006	826523 1049	1765225 311
5666	32 10 35 56	181 898 748 296	272837 6642	8·033611 21005	827572 1048	1764914 312
5667	32 11 48 89	181 995 075 963	279479 6642	8·054616 21002	828620 1049	1764602 311
5668	32 12 62 24	182 091 437 632	286121 6641	8·075618 21001	829669 1048	1764291 311
5669	32 13 75 61	182 187 833 309	292762 6640	8·096619 20999	830717 1049	1763980 312
5670	32 14 89 00	182 284 263 000	299402 6640	8·117618 20997	831766 1048	1763668 311
5671	32 16 02 41	182 380 726 711	306042 6640	8·138615 20995	832814 1048	1763357 310
5672	32 17 15 84	182 477 224 448	312682 6638	8·159610 20994	833862 1048	1763047 311
5673	32 18 29 29	182 573 756 217	319320 6638	8·180604 20991	834910 1048	1762736 311
5674	32 19 42 76	182 670 322 024	325958 6638	8·201595 20990	835958 1048	1762425 310
5675	32 20 56 25	182 766 921 875	332596 6637	8·222585 20988	837006 1048	1762115 311
5676	32 21 69 76	182 863 555 776	339233 6636	8·243573 20986	838054 1047	1761804 310
5677	32 22 83 29	182 960 223 733	345869 6636	8·264559 20984	839101 1047	1761494 310
5678	32 23 96 84	183 056 925 752	352505 6635	8·285543 20982	840148 1048	1761184 310
5679	32 25 10 41	183 153 661 839	359140 6635	8·306525 20981	841196 1047	1760873 311
5680	32 26 24 00	183 250 432 000	365775 6634	8·327506 20978	842243 1047	1760563 310
5681	32 27 37 61	183 347 236 241	372409 6633	8·348484 20977	843290 1047	1760253 310
5682	32 28 51 24	183 444 074 568	379042 6633	8·369461 20975	844337 1046	1759944 309
5683	32 29 64 89	183 540 946 987	385675 6632	8·390436 20973	845383 1047	1759634 310
5684	32 30 78 56	183 637 853 504	392307 6632	8·411409 20971	846430 1047	1759324 310
5685	32 31 92 25	183 734 794 125	398939 6631	8·432380 20970	847477 1046	1759015 309
5686	32 33 05 96	183 831 768 856	405570 6631	8·453350 20967	848523 1046	1758706 309
5687	32 34 19 69	183 928 777 703	412201 6630	8·474317 20966	849569 1047	1758396 310
5688	32 35 33 44	184 025 820 672	418831 6629	8·495283 20964	850616 1046	1758087 309
5689	32 36 47 21	184 122 897 769	425460 6629	8·516247 20962	851662 1045	1757778 309
5690	32 37 61 00	184 220 009 000	432089 6628	8·537209 20960	852707 1046	1757469 309
5691	32 38 74 81	184 317 154 371	438717 6627	8·558169 20958	853753 1046	1757160 309
5692	32 39 88 64	184 414 333 888	445344 6627	8·579127 20957	854799 1045	1756852 308
5693	32 41 02 49	184 511 547 557	451971 6627	8·600084 20954	855844 1046	1756543 309
5694	32 42 16 36	184 608 795 384	458598 6626	8·621038 20953	856890 1045	1756235 309
5695	32 43 30 25	184 706 077 375	465224 6625	8·641991 20951	857935 1045	1755926 308
5696	32 44 44 16	184 803 393 536	471849 6625	8·662942 20949	858980 1045	1755618 308
5697	32 45 58 09	184 900 743 873	478474 6624	8·683891 20948	860025 1045	1755310 308
5698	32 46 72 04	184 998 128 392	485098 6623	8·704839 20945	861070 1045	1755002 308
5699	32 47 86 01	185 095 547 099	491721 6623	8·725784 20944	862115 1045	1754694 308
5700	32 49 00 00	185 193 000 000	498344	8·746728	863160	1754386
			75·	230 +	17·	0·000

No. n	Square n^2	Cube n^3	Square root $\sqrt{n}$	Sq. rt. of 10n $\sqrt{10n}$	Cube root $\sqrt[3]{n}$	Reciprocal $\dfrac{1}{n}$
			75·	230 +	17·	0·000
5700	32 49 00 00	185 193 000 000	498344 6623	8·746728	863160 1044	1754386 308
5701	32 50 14 01	185 290 487 101	504967 6622	8·767670 20042	864204 1045	1754078 308
5702	32 51 28 04	185 388 008 408	511589 6621	8·788609 20939	865249 1044	1753771 307
5703	32 52 42 09	185 485 563 927	518210 6620	8·809548 20939	866293 1044	1753463 308
5704	32 53 56 16	185 583 153 664	524830 6620	8·830484 20936	867337 1044	1753156 307
				20934		308
5705	32 54 70 25	185 680 777 625	531450 6620	8·851418 20933	868381 1044	1752848 307
5706	32 55 84 36	185 778 435 816	538070 6619	8·872351 20931	869425 1044	1752541 307
5707	32 56 98 49	185 876 128 243	544689 6618	8·893282 20929	870469 1044	1752234 307
5708	32 58 12 64	185 973 854 912	551307 6618	8·914211 20927	871513 1044	1751927 307
5709	32 59 26 81	186 071 615 829	557925 6617	8·935138 20925	872557 1043	1751620 307
						307
5710	32 60 41 00	186 169 411 000	564542 6617	8·956063 20923	873600 1043	1751313 306
5711	32 61 55 21	186 267 240 431	571159 6616	8·976986 20922	874643 1044	1751007 307
5712	32 62 69 44	186 365 104 128	577775 6615	8·997908 20920	875687 1043	1750700 306
5713	32 63 83 69	186 463 002 097	584390 6615	9·018828 20918	876730 1043	1750394 306
5714	32 64 97 96	186 560 934 344	591005 6614	9·039746 20916	877773 1043	1750088 306
						307
5715	32 66 12 25	186 658 900 875	597619 6614	9·060662 20914	878816 1042	1749781 306
5716	32 67 26 56	186 756 901 696	604233 6613	9·081576 20912	879858 1043	1749475 306
5717	32 68 40 89	186 854 936 813	610846 6612	9·102488 20911	880901 1042	1749169 306
5718	32 69 55 24	186 953 006 232	617458 6612	9·123399 20909	881943 1043	1748863 306
5719	32 70 69 61	187 051 109 959	624070 6612	9·144308 20907	882986 1042	1748557 306
						305
5720	32 71 84 00	187 149 248 000	630682 6610	9·165215 20905	884028 1042	1748252 306
5721	32 72 98 41	187 247 420 361	637292 6611	9·186120 20903	885070 1042	1747946 305
5722	32 74 12 84	187 345 627 048	643903 6609	9·207023 20902	886112 1042	1747641 305
5723	32 75 27 29	187 443 868 067	650512 6609	9·227925 20899	887154 1042	1747335 306
5724	32 76 41 76	187 542 143 424	657121 6609	9·248824 20898	888196 1042	1747030 305
						305
5725	32 77 56 25	187 640 453 125	663730 6608	9·269722 20896	889238 1041	1746725 305
5726	32 78 70 76	187 738 797 176	670338 6607	9·290618 20894	890279 1041	1746420 305
5727	32 79 85 29	187 837 175 583	676945 6607	9·311512 20893	891320 1042	1746115 305
5728	32 80 99 84	187 935 588 352	683552 6606	9·332405 20890	892362 1041	1745810 305
5729	32 82 14 41	188 034 035 489	690158 6605	9·353295 20889	893403 1041	1745505 305
						304
5730	32 83 29 00	188 132 517 000	696763 6605	9·374184 20887	894444 1041	1745201 305
5731	32 84 43 61	188 231 032 891	703368 6605	9·395071 20885	895485 1041	1744896 304
5732	32 85 58 24	188 329 583 168	709973 6604	9·415956 20883	896526 1040	1744592 304
5733	32 86 72 89	188 428 167 837	716577 6603	9·436839 20882	897566 1041	1744287 305
5734	32 87 87 56	188 526 786 904	723180 6603	9·457721 20879	898607 1040	1743983 304
						304
5735	32 89 02 25	188 625 440 375	729783 6602	9·478600 20878	899647 1041	1743679 304
5736	32 90 16 96	188 724 128 256	736385 6601	9·499478 20876	900688 1040	1743375 304
5737	32 91 31 69	188 822 850 553	742986 6601	9·520354 20874	901728 1040	1743071 304
5738	32 92 46 44	188 921 607 272	749587 6601	9·541228 20873	902768 1040	1742768 303
5739	32 93 61 21	189 020 398 419	756188 6600	9·562101 20870	903808 1040	1742464 304
						304
5740	32 94 76 00	189 119 224 000	762788 6599	9·582971 20869	904848 1039	1742160 303
5741	32 95 90 81	189 218 084 021	769387 6599	9·603840 20867	905887 1040	1741857 303
5742	32 97 05 64	189 316 978 488	775986 6598	9·624707 20865	906927 1039	1741553 304
5743	32 98 20 49	189 415 907 407	782584 6597	9·645572 20863	907966 1040	1741250 303
5744	32 99 35 36	189 514 870 784	789181 6597	9·666435 20861	909006 1039	1740947 303
						303
5745	33 00 50 25	189 613 868 625	795778 6597	9·687296 20860	910045 1039	1740644 303
5746	33 01 65 16	189 712 900 936	802375 6595	9·708156 20858	911084 1039	1740341 303
5747	33 02 80 09	189 811 967 723	808970 6596	9·729014 20856	912123 1039	1740038 303
5748	33 03 95 04	189 911 068 992	815566 6594	9·749870 20854	913162 1039	1739736 302
5749	33 05 10 01	190 010 204 749	822160 6594	9·770724 20852	914201 1038	1739433 303
						303
5750	33 06 25 00	190 109 375 000	828754 75·	9·791576 230 +	915239 17·	1739130 0·000

No. n	Square n^2	Cube n^3	Square root $\sqrt{n}$	Sq. rt. of 10n $\sqrt{10n}$	Cube root $\sqrt[3]{n}$	Reciprocal $\dfrac{1}{n}$
			75·	230 +	17·	0·000
5750	33 06 25 00	190 109 375 000	828754 $_{6594}$	9·791576 $_{20851}$	915239 $_{1039}$	1739130 $_{302}$
5751	33 07 40 01	190 208 579 751	835348 $_{6593}$	9·812427 $_{20848}$	916278 $_{1038}$	1738828 $_{302}$
5752	33 08 55 04	190 307 819 008	841941 $_{6592}$	9·833275 $_{20847}$	917316 $_{1039}$	1738526 $_{302}$
5753	33 09 70 09	190 407 092 777	848533 $_{6592}$	9·854122 $_{20845}$	918355 $_{1038}$	1738224 $_{303}$
5754	33 10 85 16	190 506 401 064	855125 $_{6591}$	9·874967 $_{20844}$	919393 $_{1038}$	1737921 $_{302}$
5755	33 12 00 25	190 605 743 875	861716 $_{6591}$	9·895811 $_{20841}$	920431 $_{1038}$	1737619 $_{301}$
5756	33 13 15 36	190 705 121 216	868307 $_{6590}$	9·916652 $_{20840}$	921469 $_{1037}$	1737318 $_{302}$
5757	33 14 30 49	190 804 533 093	874897 $_{6590}$	9·937492 $_{20838}$	922506 $_{1038}$	1737016 $_{302}$
5758	33 15 45 64	190 903 979 512	881487 $_{6588}$	9·958330 $_{20836}$	923544 $_{1038}$	1736714 $_{302}$
5759	33 16 60 81	191 003 460 479	888075 $_{6589}$	9·979166 $_{20834}$	924582 $_{1037}$	1736413 $_{302}$
5760	33 17 76 00	191 102 976 000	894664 $_{6588}$	*0·000000 $_{20832}$	925619 $_{1037}$	1736111 $_{301}$
5761	33 18 91 21	191 202 526 081	901252 $_{6587}$	0·020832 $_{20831}$	926656 $_{1037}$	1735810 $_{301}$
5762	33 20 06 44	191 302 110 728	907839 $_{6587}$	0·041663 $_{20829}$	927693 $_{1038}$	1735509 $_{302}$
5763	33 21 21 69	191 401 729 947	914426 $_{6586}$	0·062492 $_{20827}$	928731 $_{1036}$	1735207 $_{301}$
5764	33 22 36 96	191 501 383 744	921012 $_{6585}$	0·083319 $_{20825}$	929767 $_{1037}$	1734906 $_{301}$
5765	33 23 52 25	191 601 072 125	927597 $_{6585}$	0·104144 $_{20823}$	930804 $_{1037}$	1734605 $_{300}$
5766	33 24 67 56	191 700 795 096	934182 $_{6584}$	0·124967 $_{20822}$	931841 $_{1037}$	1734305 $_{301}$
5767	33 25 82 89	191 800 552 663	940766 $_{6584}$	0·145789 $_{20820}$	932878 $_{1036}$	1734004 $_{301}$
5768	33 26 98 24	191 900 344 832	947350 $_{6583}$	0·166609 $_{20818}$	933914 $_{1036}$	1733703 $_{301}$
5769	33 28 13 61	192 000 171 609	953933 $_{6583}$	0·187427 $_{20816}$	934950 $_{1037}$	1733403 $_{301}$
5770	33 29 29 00	192 100 033 000	960516 $_{6582}$	0·208243 $_{20814}$	935987 $_{1036}$	1733102 $_{300}$
5771	33 30 44 41	192 199 929 011	967098 $_{6582}$	0·229057 $_{20813}$	937023 $_{1036}$	1732802 $_{300}$
5772	33 31 59 84	192 299 859 648	973680 $_{6581}$	0·249870 $_{20811}$	938059 $_{1036}$	1732502 $_{300}$
5773	33 32 75 29	192 399 824 917	980261 $_{6580}$	0·270681 $_{20809}$	939095 $_{1035}$	1732202 $_{300}$
5774	33 33 90 76	192 499 824 824	986841 $_{6580}$	0·291490 $_{20807}$	940130 $_{1036}$	1731902 $_{300}$
5775	33 35 06 25	192 599 859 375	*993421 $_{6579}$	0·312297 $_{20805}$	941166 $_{1035}$	1731602 $_{300}$
5776	33 36 21 76	192 699 928 576	*000000 $_{6579}$	0·333102 $_{20804}$	942201 $_{1036}$	1731302 $_{300}$
5777	33 37 37 29	192 800 032 433	006579 $_{6578}$	0·353906 $_{20801}$	943237 $_{1035}$	1731002 $_{299}$
5778	33 38 52 84	192 900 170 952	013157 $_{6577}$	0·374707 $_{20800}$	944272 $_{1035}$	1730703 $_{300}$
5779	33 39 68 41	193 000 344 139	019734 $_{6577}$	0·395507 $_{20799}$	945307 $_{1035}$	1730403 $_{299}$
5780	33 40 84 00	193 100 552 000	026311 $_{6577}$	0·416306 $_{20796}$	946342 $_{1035}$	1730104 $_{299}$
5781	33 41 99 61	193 200 794 541	032888 $_{6575}$	0·437102 $_{20795}$	947377 $_{1035}$	1729805 $_{299}$
5782	33 43 15 24	193 301 071 768	039463 $_{6576}$	0·457897 $_{20792}$	948412 $_{1035}$	1729505 $_{300}$
5783	33 44 30 89	193 401 383 687	046039 $_{6574}$	0·478689 $_{20791}$	949447 $_{1034}$	1729206 $_{299}$
5784	33 45 46 56	193 501 730 304	052613 $_{6574}$	0·499480 $_{20789}$	950481 $_{1035}$	1728907 $_{299}$
5785	33 46 62 25	193 602 111 625	059187 $_{6574}$	0·520269 $_{20788}$	951516 $_{1034}$	1728608 $_{298}$
5786	33 47 77 96	193 702 527 656	065761 $_{6573}$	0·541057 $_{20785}$	952550 $_{1034}$	1728310 $_{299}$
5787	33 48 93 69	193 802 978 403	072334 $_{6572}$	0·561842 $_{20784}$	953584 $_{1034}$	1728011 $_{298}$
5788	33 50 09 44	193 903 463 872	078906 $_{6572}$	0·582626 $_{20782}$	954618 $_{1034}$	1727713 $_{299}$
5789	33 51 25 21	194 003 984 069	085478 $_{6572}$	0·603408 $_{20780}$	955652 $_{1034}$	1727414 $_{298}$
5790	33 52 41 00	194 104 539 000	092050 $_{6570}$	0·624188 $_{20779}$	956686 $_{1034}$	1727116 $_{299}$
5791	33 53 56 81	194 205 128 671	098620 $_{6570}$	0·644967 $_{20776}$	957720 $_{1034}$	1726817 $_{298}$
5792	33 54 72 64	194 305 753 088	105190 $_{6570}$	0·665743 $_{20775}$	958753 $_{1033}$	1726519 $_{298}$
5793	33 55 88 49	194 406 412 257	111760 $_{6569}$	0·686518 $_{20773}$	959787 $_{1034}$	1726221 $_{298}$
5794	33 57 04 36	194 507 106 184	118329 $_{6568}$	0·707291 $_{20771}$	960820 $_{1033}$	1725923 $_{297}$
5795	33 58 20 25	194 607 834 875	124897 $_{6568}$	0·728062 $_{20770}$	961853 $_{1033}$	1725626 $_{298}$
5796	33 59 36 16	194 708 598 336	131465 $_{6568}$	0·748832 $_{20767}$	962886 $_{1033}$	1725328 $_{298}$
5797	33 60 52 09	194 809 396 573	138033 $_{6566}$	0·769599 $_{20766}$	963919 $_{1033}$	1725030 $_{297}$
5798	33 61 68 04	194 910 229 592	144599 $_{6566}$	0·790365 $_{20764}$	964952 $_{1033}$	1724733 $_{298}$
5799	33 62 84 01	195 011 097 399	151165 $_{6566}$	0·811129 $_{20763}$	965985 $_{1033}$	1724435 $_{297}$
5800	33 64 00 00	195 112 000 000	157731	0·831892	967018	1724138
			76·	240 +	17·	0·000

No. n	Square n^2	Cube n^3	Square root $\sqrt{n}$	Sq. rt. of $10n$ $\sqrt{10n}$	Cube root $\sqrt[3]{n}$	Reciprocal $\dfrac{1}{n}$
			76·	240 +	17·	0·000
5800	33 64 00 00	195 112 000 000	157731 6565	0·831892 20760	967018 1032	1724138 297
5801	33 65 16 01	195 212 937 401	164296 6565	0·852652 20759	968050 1033	1723841 297
5802	33 66 32 04	195 313 909 608	170861 6563	0·873411 20757	969083 1032	1723544 297
5803	33 67 48 09	195 414 916 627	177424 6564	0·894168 20755	970115 1032	1723247 297
5804	33 68 64 16	195 515 958 464	183988 6563	0·914923 20753	971147 1032	1722950 297
5805	33 69 80 25	195 617 035 125	190551 6562	0·935676 20752	972179 1032	1722653 297
5806	33 70 96 36	195 718 146 616	197113 6561	0·956428 20749	973211 1032	1722356 297
5807	33 72 12 49	195 819 292 943	203674 6562	0·977177 20748	974243 1032	1722060 296
5808	33 73 28 64	195 920 474 112	210236 6560	0·997925 20746	975275 1031	1721763 296
5809	33 74 44 81	196 021 690 129	216796 6560	1·018671 20745	976306 1032	1721467 297
5810	33 75 61 00	196 122 941 000	223356 6559	1·039416 20742	977338 1031	1721170 296
5811	33 76 77 21	196 224 226 731	229915 6559	1·060158 20741	978369 1031	1720874 296
5812	33 77 93 44	196 325 547 328	236474 6558	1·080899 20739	979400 1031	1720578 296
5813	33 79 09 69	196 426 902 797	243032 6558	1·101638 20738	980431 1031	1720282 296
5814	33 80 25 96	196 528 293 144	249590 6557	1·122376 20735	981462 1031	1719986 296
5815	33 81 42 25	196 629 718 375	256147 6557	1·143111 20734	982493 1031	1719690 295
5816	33 82 58 56	196 731 178 496	262704 6556	1·163845 20732	983524 1031	1719395 296
5817	33 83 74 89	196 832 673 513	269260 6555	1·184577 20730	984555 1031	1719099 295
5818	33 84 91 24	196 934 203 432	275815 6555	1·205307 20728	985585 1030	1718804 296
5819	33 86 07 61	197 035 768 259	282370 6554	1·226035 20727	986616 1030	1718508 295
5820	33 87 24 00	197 137 368 000	288924 6554	1·246762 20724	987646 1030	1718213 295
5821	33 88 40 41	197 239 002 661	295478 6553	1·267486 20723	988676 1030	1717918 295
5822	33 89 56 84	197 340 672 248	302031 6553	1·288209 20722	989706 1030	1717623 295
5823	33 90 73 29	197 442 376 767	308584 6552	1·308931 20719	990736 1030	1717328 295
5824	33 91 89 76	197 544 116 224	315136 6552	1·329650 20718	991766 1029	1717033 295
5825	33 93 06 25	197 645 890 625	321688 6551	1·350368 20716	992795 1030	1716738 294
5826	33 94 22 76	197 747 699 976	328239 6550	1·371084 20714	993825 1029	1716444 295
5827	33 95 39 29	197 849 544 283	334789 6550	1·391798 20712	994854 1030	1716149 295
5828	33 96 55 84	197 951 423 552	341339 6549	1·412510 20711	995884 1029	1715854 294
5829	33 97 72 41	198 053 337 789	347888 6549	1·433221 20708	996913 1029	1715560 294
5830	33 98 89 00	198 155 287 000	354437 6548	1·453929 20707	997942 1029	1715266 294
5831	34 00 05 61	198 257 271 191	360985 6547	1·474636 20706	998971 1029	1714972 294
5832	34 01 22 24	198 359 290 368	367532 6547	1·495342 20703	*000000 1029	1714678 294
5833	34 02 38 89	198 461 344 537	374079 6547	1·516045 20702	001029 1028	1714384 294
5834	34 03 55 56	198 563 433 704	380626 6546	1·536747 20700	002057 1029	1714090 294
5835	34 04 72 25	198 665 557 875	387172 6545	1·557447 20698	003086 1028	1713796 294
5836	34 05 88 96	198 767 717 056	393717 6545	1·578145 20696	004114 1029	1713502 293
5837	34 07 05 69	198 869 911 253	400262 6544	1·598841 20695	005143 1028	1713209 294
5838	34 08 22 44	198 972 140 472	406806 6544	1·619536 20692	006171 1028	1712915 293
5839	34 09 39 21	199 074 404 719	413350 6543	1·640228 20691	007199 1028	1712622 293
5840	34 10 56 00	199 176 704 000	419893 6542	1·660919 20690	008227 1028	1712329 293
5841	34 11 72 81	199 279 038 321	426435 6542	1·681609 20687	009255 1027	1712036 293
5842	34 12 89 64	199 381 407 688	432977 6542	1·702296 20686	010282 1027	1711743 293
5843	34 14 06 49	199 483 812 107	439519 6540	1·722982 20684	011310 1027	1711450 293
5844	34 15 23 36	199 586 251 584	446059 6541	1·743666 20682	012337 1028	1711157 293
5845	34 16 40 25	199 688 726 125	452600 6539	1·764348 20680	013365 1027	1710864 293
5846	34 17 57 16	199 791 235 736	459139 6540	1·785028 20679	014392 1027	1710571 292
5847	34 18 74 09	199 893 780 423	465679 6538	1·805707 20677	015419 1027	1710279 293
5848	34 19 91 04	199 996 360 192	472217 6538	1·826384 20675	016446 1027	1709986 292
5849	34 21 08 01	200 098 975 049	478755 6538	1·847059 20673	017473 1026	1709694 292
5850	34 22 25 00	200 201 625 000	485203 76·	1·867732 240 +	018499 18·	1709402 0·000

No. n	Square n²	Cube n³	Square root √n	Sq. rt. of 10n √10n	Cube root ∛n	Reciprocal 1/n
			76·	240 +	18·	0·000
5850	34 22 25 00	200 201 625 000	485293 6537	1·867732 20672	018499 1027	1709402 292
5851	34 23 42 01	200 304 310 051	491830 6536	1·888404 20670	019526 1027	1709110 293
5852	34 24 59 04	200 407 030 208	498366 6536	1·909074 20668	020553 1026	1708817 291
5853	34 25 76 09	200 509 785 477	504902 6535	1·929742 20666	021579 1026	1708526 292
5854	34 26 93 16	200 612 575 864	511437 6535	1·950408 20665	022605 1027	1708234 292
5855	34 28 10 25	200 715 401 375	517972 6534	1·971073 20662	023632 1026	1707942 292
5856	34 29 27 36	200 818 262 016	524506 6533	1·991735 20661	024658 1026	1707650 291
5857	34 30 44 49	200 921 157 793	531039 6533	2·012396 20660	025684 1025	1707359 292
5858	34 31 61 64	201 024 088 712	537572 6533	2·033056 20657	026709 1026	1707067 291
5859	34 32 78 81	201 127 054 779	544105 6532	2·053713 20656	027735 1026	1706776 291
5860	34 33 96 00	201 230 056 000	550637 6531	2·074369 20654	028761 1025	1706485 292
5861	34 35 13 21	201 333 092 381	557168 6531	2·095023 20652	029786 1025	1706193 291
5862	34 36 30 44	201 436 163 928	563699 6530	2·115675 20650	030811 1026	1705902 291
5863	34 37 47 69	201 539 270 647	570229 6530	2·136325 20649	031837 1025	1705611 290
5864	34 38 64 96	201 642 412 544	576759 6529	2·156974 20647	032862 1025	1705321 291
5865	34 39 82 25	201 745 589 625	583288 6529	2·177621 20645	033887 1025	1705030 291
5866	34 40 99 56	201 848 801 896	589817 6528	2·198266 20643	034912 1024	1704739 290
5867	34 42 16 89	201 952 049 363	596345 6527	2·218909 20642	035936 1025	1704449 291
5868	34 43 34 24	202 055 332 032	602872 6527	2·239551 20640	036961 1025	1704158 290
5869	34 44 51 61	202 158 649 909	609399 6526	2·260191 20638	037986 1024	1703868 290
5870	34 45 69 00	202 262 003 000	615925 6526	2·280829 20636	039010 1024	1703578 291
5871	34 46 86 41	202 365 391 311	622451 6525	2·301465 20635	040034 1024	1703287 290
5872	34 48 03 84	202 468 814 848	628976 6525	2·322100 20633	041059 1024	1702997 290
5873	34 49 21 29	202 572 273 617	635501 6524	2·342733 20631	042083 1024	1702707 290
5874	34 50 38 76	202 675 767 624	642025 6524	2·363364 20629	043107 1023	1702417 289
5875	34 51 56 25	202 779 296 875	648549 6523	2·383993 20627	044130 1024	1702128 290
5876	34 52 73 76	202 882 861 376	655072 6522	2·404620 20626	045154 1024	1701838 290
5877	34 53 91 29	202 986 461 133	661594 6522	2·425246 20624	046178 1023	1701548 289
5878	34 55 08 84	203 090 096 152	668116 6521	2·445870 20623	047201 1024	1701259 289
5879	34 56 26 41	203 193 766 439	674637 6521	2·466493 20620	048225 1023	1700970 290
5880	34 57 44 00	203 297 472 000	681158 6520	2·487113 20619	049248 1023	1700680 289
5881	34 58 61 61	203 401 212 841	687678 6520	2·507732 20617	050271 1023	1700391 289
5882	34 59 79 24	203 504 988 968	694198 6519	2·528349 20615	051294 1023	1700102 289
5883	34 60 96 89	203 608 800 387	700717 6519	2·548964 20614	052317 1023	1699813 289
5884	34 62 14 56	203 712 647 104	707236 6518	2·569578 20611	053340 1022	1699524 289
5885	34 63 32 25	203 816 529 125	713754 6517	2·590189 20610	054362 1023	1699235 288
5886	34 64 49 96	203 920 446 456	720271 6517	2·610799 20609	055385 1022	1698947 287
5887	34 65 67 69	204 024 399 103	726788 6516	2·631408 20606	056407 1023	1698658 288
5888	34 66 85 44	204 128 387 072	733304 6516	2·652014 20605	057430 1022	1698370 289
5889	34 68 03 21	204 232 410 369	739820 6515	2·672619 20603	058452 1022	1698081 288
5890	34 69 21 00	204 336 469 000	746335 6515	2·693222 20601	059474 1022	1697793 288
5891	34 70 38 81	204 440 562 971	752850 6515	2·713823 20600	060496 1022	1697505 288
5892	34 71 56 64	204 544 692 288	759364 6514	2·734423 20598	061518 1022	1697217 288
5893	34 72 74 49	204 648 856 957	765878 6513	2·755021 20596	062540 1021	1696929 288
5894	34 73 92 36	204 753 056 984	772391 6512	2·775617 20594	063561 1022	1696641 288
5895	34 75 10 25	204 857 292 375	778903 6512	2·796211 20592	064583 1021	1696353 288
5896	34 76 28 16	204 961 563 136	785415 6512	2·816803 20591	065604 1022	1696065 287
5897	34 77 46 09	205 065 869 273	791927 6510	2·837394 20589	066626 1021	1695778 288
5898	34 78 64 04	205 170 210 792	798437 6511	2·857983 20589	067647 1021	1695490 287
5899	34 79 82 01	205 274 587 699	804948 6509	2·878570 20587	068668 1021	1695203 288
5900	34 81 00 00	205 379 000 000	811457	2·899156	069689	1694915
			76·	240 +	18·	0·000

No. n	Square n²	Cube n³	Square root √n	Sq. rt. of 10n √10n	Cube root ∛n	Reciprocal 1/n
			76·	240 +	18·	0·000
5900	34 81 00 00	205 379 000 000	811457 (6510)	2·899156 (20584)	069689 (1021)	1694915 (287)
5901	34 82 18 01	205 483 447 701	817967 (6508)	2·919740 (20582)	070710 (1020)	1694628 (287)
5902	34 83 36 04	205 587 930 808	824475 (6508)	2·940322 (20580)	071730 (1021)	1694341 (287)
5903	34 84 54 09	205 692 449 327	830983 (6508)	2·960902 (20579)	072751 (1020)	1694054 (287)
5904	34 85 72 16	205 797 003 264	837491 (6507)	2·981481 (20577)	073771 (1021)	1693767 (287)
5905	34 86 90 25	205 901 592 625	843998 (6506)	3·002058 (20575)	074792 (1020)	1693480 (287)
5906	34 88 08 36	206 006 217 416	850504 (6506)	3·022633 (20573)	075812 (1020)	1693193 (286)
5907	34 89 26 49	206 110 877 643	857010 (6505)	3·043206 (20572)	076832 (1020)	1692907 (287)
5908	34 90 44 64	206 215 573 312	863515 (6505)	3·063778 (20570)	077852 (1020)	1692620 (286)
5909	34 91 62 81	206 320 304 429	870020 (6504)	3·084348 (20568)	078872 (1020)	1692334 (287)
5910	34 92 81 00	206 425 071 000	876524 (6504)	3·104916 (20566)	079892 (1019)	1692047 (286)
5911	34 93 99 21	206 529 873 031	883028 (6503)	3·125482 (20565)	080911 (1020)	1691761 (286)
5912	34 95 17 44	206 634 710 528	889531 (6503)	3·146047 (20563)	081931 (1019)	1691475 (286)
5913	34 96 35 69	206 739 583 497	896034 (6502)	3·166610 (20561)	082950 (1020)	1691189 (286)
5914	34 97 53 96	206 844 491 944	902536 (6501)	3·187171 (20559)	083970 (1019)	1690903 (286)
5915	34 98 72 25	206 949 435 875	909037 (6501)	3·207730 (20558)	084989 (1019)	1690617 (286)
5916	34 99 90 56	207 054 415 296	915538 (6500)	3·228288 (20556)	086008 (1019)	1690331 (285)
5917	35 01 08 89	207 159 430 213	922038 (6500)	3·248844 (20554)	087027 (1019)	1690046 (286)
5918	35 02 27 24	207 264 480 632	928538 (6500)	3·269398 (20552)	088046 (1019)	1689760 (285)
5919	35 03 45 61	207 369 566 559	935038 (6498)	3·289950 (20551)	089065 (1018)	1689475 (286)
5920	35 04 64 00	207 474 688 000	941536 (6498)	3·310501 (20549)	090083 (1019)	1689189 (285)
5921	35 05 82 41	207 579 844 961	948034 (6498)	3·331050 (20547)	091102 (1018)	1688904 (285)
5922	35 07 00 84	207 685 037 448	954532 (6497)	3·351597 (20546)	092120 (1019)	1688619 (285)
5923	35 08 19 29	207 790 265 467	961029 (6497)	3·372143 (20544)	093139 (1018)	1688334 (285)
5924	35 09 37 76	207 895 529 024	967526 (6496)	3·392687 (20542)	094157 (1018)	1688049 (285)
5925	35 10 56 25	208 000 828 125	974022 (6495)	3·413229 (20540)	095175 (1018)	1687764 (285)
5926	35 11 74 76	208 106 162 776	980517 (6495)	3·433769 (20539)	096193 (1018)	1687479 (285)
5927	35 12 93 29	208 211 532 983	987012 (6494)	3·454308 (20537)	097211 (1018)	1687194 (284)
5928	35 14 11 84	208 316 938 752	993506 (6494)	3·474845 (20535)	098228 (1017)	1686910 (285)
5929	35 15 30 41	208 422 380 089	*000000 (6493)	3·495380 (20533)	099246 (1018)	1686625 (284)
5930	35 16 49 00	208 527 857 000	006493 (6493)	3·515913 (20532)	100264 (1017)	1686341 (285)
5931	35 17 67 61	208 633 369 491	012986 (6492)	3·536445 (20530)	101281 (1017)	1686056 (284)
5932	35 18 86 24	208 738 917 568	019478 (6492)	3·556975 (20528)	102298 (1017)	1685772 (284)
5933	35 20 04 89	208 844 501 237	025970 (6491)	3·577503 (20527)	103315 (1017)	1685488 (284)
5934	35 21 23 56	208 950 120 504	032461 (6490)	3·598030 (20524)	104332 (1017)	1685204 (284)
5935	35 22 42 25	209 055 775 375	038951 (6490)	3·618554 (20523)	105349 (1017)	1684920 (284)
5936	35 23 60 96	209 161 465 856	045441 (6490)	3·639077 (20522)	106366 (1017)	1684636 (284)
5937	35 24 79 69	209 267 191 953	051931 (6488)	3·659599 (20519)	107383 (1016)	1684352 (283)
5938	35 25 98 44	209 372 953 672	058419 (6489)	3·680118 (20518)	108399 (1017)	1684069 (284)
5939	35 27 17 21	209 478 751 019	064908 (6487)	3·700636 (20516)	109416 (1016)	1683785 (283)
5940	35 28 36 00	209 584 584 000	071395 (6488)	3·721152 (20515)	110432 (1016)	1683502 (284)
5941	35 29 54 81	209 690 452 621	077883 (6486)	3·741667 (20512)	111448 (1017)	1683218 (283)
5942	35 30 73 64	209 796 356 888	084369 (6486)	3·762179 (20511)	112465 (1016)	1682935 (283)
5943	35 31 92 49	209 902 296 807	090855 (6486)	3·782690 (20509)	113481 (1015)	1682652 (283)
5944	35 33 11 36	210 008 272 384	097341 (6485)	3·803199 (20508)	114496 (1016)	1682369 (283)
5945	35 34 30 25	210 114 283 625	103826 (6485)	3·823707 (20506)	115512 (1016)	1682086 (283)
5946	35 35 49 16	210 220 330 536	110311 (6484)	3·844213 (20504)	116528 (1016)	1681803 (283)
5947	35 36 68 09	210 326 413 123	116795 (6483)	3·864717 (20502)	117544 (1015)	1681520 (283)
5948	35 37 87 04	210 432 531 392	123278 (6483)	3·885219 (20500)	118559 (1015)	1681237 (282)
5949	35 39 06 01	210 538 685 349	129761 (6482)	3·905719 (20499)	119574 (1015)	1680955 (283)
5950	35 40 25 00	210 644 875 000	136243	3·926218	120589	1680672
			77·	240 +	18·	0·000

No. n	Square n^2	Cube n^3	Square root $\sqrt{n}$	Sq. rt. of 10n $\sqrt{10n}$	Cube root $\sqrt[3]{n}$	Reciprocal $\dfrac{1}{n}$
			77·	240 +	18·	0·000
5950	35 40 25 00	210 644 875 000	136243 6482	3·926218 20497	120589 1016	1680672 282
5951	35 41 44 01	210 751 100 351	142725 6481	3·946715 20496	121605 1015	1680390 282
5952	35 42 63 04	210 857 361 408	149206 6481	3·967211 20494	122620 1014	1680108 282
5953	35 43 82 09	210 963 658 177	155687 6480	3·987705 20492	123634 1015	1679825 283
5954	35 45 01 16	211 069 990 664	162167 6479	4·008197 20490	124649 1015	1679543 282
5955	35 46 20 25	211 176 358 875	168646 6480	4·028687 20488	125664 1014	1679261 282
5956	35 47 39 36	211 282 762 816	175126 6478	4·049175 20487	126678 1015	1678979 282
5957	35 48 58 49	211 389 202 493	181604 6478	4·069662 20485	127693 1014	1678697 281
5958	35 49.77 64	211 495 677 912	188082 6477	4·090147 20484	128707 1014	1678416 282
5959	35 50 96 81	211 602 189 079	194559 6477	4·110631 20481	129721 1014	1678134 282
5960	35 52 16 00	211 708 736 000	201036 6477	4·131112 20480	130735 1014	1677852 281
5961	35 53 35 21	211 815 318 681	207513 6475	4·151592 20478	131749 1014	1677571 281
5962	35 54 54 44	211 921 937 128	213988 6476	4·172070 20477	132763 1014	1677290 282
5963	35 55 73 69	212 028 591 347	220464 6474	4·192547 20475	133777 1014	1677008 281
5964	35 56 92 96	212 135 281 344	226938 6474	4·213022 20473	134791 1013	1676727 281
5965	35 58 12 25	212 242 007 125	233412 6474	4·233495 20471	135804 1014	1676446 281
5966	35 59 31 56	212 348 768 696	239886 6473	4·253966 20470	136818 1013	1676165 281
5967	35 60 50 89	212 455 566 063	246359 6473	4·274436 20468	137831 1013	1675884 281
5968	35 61 70 24	212 562 399 232	252832 6472	4·294904 20466	138844 1013	1675603 281
5969	35 62 89 61	212 669 268 209	259304 6471	4·315370 20464	139857 1013	1675322 280
5970	35 64 09 00	212 776 173 000	265775 6471	4·335834 20463	140870 1013	1675042 281
5971	35 65 28 41	212 883 113 611	272246 6470	4·356297 20461	141883 1013	1674761 281
5972	35 66 47 84	212 990 090 048	278716 6470	4·376758 20460	142896 1012	1674481 280
5973	35 67 67 29	213 097 102 317	285186 6469	4·397218 20457	143908 1013	1674201 281
5974	35 68 86 76	213 204 150 424	291655 6469	4·417675 20456	144921 1012	1673920 280
5975	35 70.06 25	213 311 234 375	298124 6468	4·438131 20454	145933 1012	1673640 280
5976	35 71 25 76	213 418 354 176	304592 6468	4·458585 20453	146945 1012	1673360 280
5977	35 72 45 29	213 525 509 833	311060 6467	4·479038 20451	147957 1012	1673080 280
5978	35 73 64 84	213 632 701 352	317527 6467	4·499489 20449	148969 1012	1672800 280
5979	35 74 84 41	213 739 928 739	323994 6466	4·519938 20447	149981 1012	1672520 279
5980	35 76 04 00	213 847 192 000	330460 6465	4·540385 20446	150993 1012	1672241 280
5981	35 77 23 61	213 954 491 141	336925 6465	4·560831 20444	152005 1012	1671961 279
5982	35 78 43 24	214 061 826 168	343390 6465	4·581275 20442	153017 1011	1671682 279
5983	35 79 62 89	214 169 197 087	349855 6463	4·601717 20441	154028 1011	1671402 279
5984	35 80 82 56	214 276 603 904	356318 6464	4·622158 20438	155039 1012	1671123 279
5985	35 82 02 25	214 384 046 625	362782 6463	4·642596 20438	156051 1011	1670844 279
5986	35 83 21 96	214 491 525 256	369245 6462	4·663034 20435	157062 1011	1670565 279
5987	35 84 41 69	214 599 039 803	375707 6461	4·683469 20434	158073 1011	1670286 279
5988	35 85 61 44	214 706 590 272	382168 6462	4·703903 20432	159084 1011	1670007 279
5989	35 86 81 21	214 814 176 669	388630 6460	4·724335 20430	160095 1010	1669728 279
5990	35 88 01 00	214 921 799 000	395090 6460	4·744765 20429	161105 1011	1669449 279
5991	35 89 20 81	215 029 457 271	401550 6460	4·765194 20426	162116 1010	1669170 279
5992	35 90 40 64	215 137 151 488	408010 6459	4·785620 20426	163126 1011	1668892 278
5993	35 91 60 49	215 244 881 657	414469 6458	4·806046 20423	164137 1010	1668613 278
5994	35 92 80 36	215 352 647 784	420927 6458	4·826469 20422	165147 1010	1668335 278
5995	35 94 00 25	215 460 449 875	427385 6458	4·846891 20420	166157 1010	1668057 278
5996	35 95 20 16	215 568 287 936	433843 6457	4·867311 20418	167167 1010	1667779 279
5997	35 96 40 09	215 676 161 973	440300 6456	4·887729 20417	168177 1010	1667500 278
5998	35 97 60 04	215 784 071 992	446756 6456	4·908146 20415	169187 1009	1667222 278
5999	35 98 80 01	215 892 017 999	453212 6455	4·928561 20413	170196 1009	1666944 277
6000	36 00 00 00	216 000 000 000	459667	4·948974	171206	1666667
			77·	240 +	18·	0·000

No. n	Square n²	Cube n³	Square root √n	Sq. rt. of 10n √10n	Cube root ∛n	Reciprocal 1/n
			77·	240 +	18·	0·000
6000	36 00 00 00	216 000 000 000	459667 6455	4·948974 20412	171206 1009	1666667 278
6001	36 01 20 01	216 108 018 001	466122 6454	4·969386 20410	172215 1010	1666389 278
6002	36 02 40 04	216 216 072 008	472576 6453	4·989796 20408	173225 1009	1666111 277
6003	36 03 60 09	216 324 162 027	479029 6454	5·010204 20406	174234 1009	1665834 278
6004	36 04 80 16	216 432 288 064	485483 6452	5·030610 20405	175243 1009	1665556 277
6005	36 06 00 25	216 540 450 125	491935 6452	5·051015 20403	176252 1009	1665279 277
6006	36 07 20 36	216 648 648 216	498387 6452	5·071418 20402	177261 1009	1665002 278
6007	36 08 40 49	216 756 882 343	504839 6451	5·091820 20399	178270 1008	1664724 277
6008	36 09 60 64	216 865 152 512	511290 6450	5·112219 20398	179278 1008	1664447 277
6009	36 10 80 81	216 973 458 729	517740 6450	5·132617 20396	180287 1008	1664170 276
6010	36 12 01 00	217 081 801 000	524190 6449	5·153013 20395	181295 1009	1663894 277
6011	36 13 21 21	217 190 179 331	530639 6449	5·173408 20393	182304 1008	1663617 277
6012	36 14 41 44	217 298 593 728	537088 6448	5·193801 20391	183312 1008	1663340 277
6013	36 15 61 69	217 407 044 197	543536 6448	5·214192 20390	184320 1008	1663063 277
6014	36 16 81 96	217 515 530 744	549984 6447	5·234582 20387	185328 1008	1662787 277
6015	36 18 02 25	217 624 053 375	556431 6447	5·254969 20386	186336 1008	1662510 276
6016	36 19 22 56	217 732 612 096	562878 6446	5·275355 20385	187344 1007	1662234 276
6017	36 20 42 89	217 841 206 913	569324 6445	5·295740 20383	188351 1007	1661958 276
6018	36 21 63 24	217 949 837 832	575769 6445	5·316123 20381	189359 1007	1661682 276
6019	36 22 83 61	218 058 504 859	582214 6445	5·336504 20379	190366 1008	1661406 276
6020	36 24 04 00	218 167 208 000	588659 6444	5·356883 20378	191374 1007	1661130 276
6021	36 25 24 41	218 275 947 261	595103 6443	5·377261 20376	192381 1007	1660854 276
6022	36 26 44 84	218 384 722 648	601546 6443	5·397637 20374	193388 1007	1660578 276
6023	36 27 65 29	218 493 534 167	607989 6443	5·418011 20372	194395 1007	1660302 275
6024	36 28 85 76	218 602 381 824	614432 6441	5·438383 20371	195402 1007	1660027 276
6025	36 30 06 25	218 711 265 625	620873 6442	5·458754 20369	196409 1006	1659751 275
6026	36 31 26 76	218 820 185 576	627315 6441	5·479123 20368	197415 1007	1659476 275
6027	36 32 47 29	218 929 141 683	633756 6440	5·499491 20366	198422 1007	1659200 275
6028	36 33 67 84	219 038 133 952	640196 6439	5·519857 20364	199428 1007	1658925 275
6029	36 34 88 41	219 147 162 389	646635 6440	5·540221 20362	200435 1006	1658650 275
6030	36 36 09 00	219 256 227 000	653075 6438	5·560583 20361	201441 1006	1658375 275
6031	36 37 29 61	219 365 327 791	659513 6438	5·580944 20359	202447 1006	1658100 275
6032	36 38 50 24	219 474 464 768	665951 6438	5·601303 20357	203453 1006	1657825 275
6033	36 39 70 89	219 583 637 937	672389 6437	5·621660 20356	204459 1006	1657550 275
6034	36 40 91 56	219 692 847 304	678826 6436	5·642016 20354	205465 1005	1657275 274
6035	36 42 12 25	219 802 092 875	685262 6436	5·662370 20352	206470 1006	1657001 275
6036	36 43 32 96	219 911 374 656	691698 6436	5·682722 20351	207476 1005	1656726 274
6037	36 44 53 69	220 020 692 653	698134 6435	5·703073 20349	208481 1006	1656452 274
6038	36 45 74 44	220 130 046 872	704569 6434	5·723422 20347	209487 1005	1656178 275
6039	36 46 95 21	220 239 437 319	711003 6434	5·743769 20346	210492 1005	1655903 274
6040	36 48 16 00	220 348 864 000	717437 6433	5·764115 20343	211497 1005	1655629 274
6041	36 49 36 81	220 458 326 921	723870 6433	5·784458 20343	212502 1005	1655355 274
6042	36 50 57 64	220 567 826 088	730303 6432	5·804801 20340	213507 1005	1655081 274
6043	36 51 78 49	220 677 361 507	736735 6432	5·825141 20339	214512 1004	1654807 274
6044	36 52 99 36	220 786 933 184	743167 6431	5·845480 20337	215516 1005	1654533 273
6045	36 54 20 25	220 896 541 125	749598 6431	5·865817 20336	216521 1004	1654260 274
6046	36 55 41 16	221 006 185 336	756029 6430	5·886152 20333	217525 1005	1653986 273
6047	36 56 62 09	221 115 865 823	762459 6430	5·906486 20333	218530 1004	1653713 273
6048	36 57 83 04	221 225 582 592	768888 6429	5·926818 20332	219534 1004	1653439 273
6049	36 59 04 01	221 335 335 649	775317 6429	5·947149 20331	220538 1004	1653166 273
6050	36 60 25 00	221 445 125 000	781746	5·967478	221542	1652893
			77·	240 +	18·	0·000

No. n	Square n^2	Cube n^3	Square root $\sqrt{n}$	Sq. rt. of 10n $\sqrt{10n}$	Cube root $\sqrt[3]{n}$	Reciprocal $\dfrac{1}{n}$
			77·	240 +	18·	0·000
6050	36 60 25 00	221 445 125 000	781746 6428	5·967478 20327	221542 1004	1652893 274
6051	36 61 46 01	221 554 950 651	788174 6427	5·987805 20325	222546 1004	1652619 273
6052	36 62 67 04	221 664 812 608	794601 6427	6·008130 20324	223550 1003	1652346 273
6053	36 63 88 09	221 774 710 877	801028 6427	6·028454 20322	224553 1004	1652073 273
6054	36 65 09 16	221 884 645 464	807455 6426	6·048776 20320	225557 1003	1651800 272
6055	36 66 30 25	221 994 616 375	813881 6425	6·069096 20319	226560 1004	1651528 273
6056	36 67 51 36	222 104 623 616	820306 6425	6·089415 20317	227564 1003	1651255 273
6057	36 68 72 49	222 214 667 193	826731 6424	6·109732 20315	228567 1003	1650982 272
6058	36 69 93 64	222 324 747 112	833155 6424	6·130047 20314	229570 1003	1650710 273
6059	36 71 14 81	222 434 863 379	839579 6423	6·150361 20312	230573 1003	1650437 272
6060	36 72 36 00	222 545 016 000	846002 6422	6·170673 20310	231576 1003	1650165 272
6061	36 73 57 21	222 655 204 981	852424 6423	6·190983 20308	232579 1002	1649893 272
6062	36 74 78 44	222 765 430 328	858847 6421	6·211291 20307	233581 1003	1649621 272
6063	36 75 99 69	222 875 692 047	865268 6421	6·231598 20306	234584 1002	1649349 272
6064	36 77 20 96	222 985 990 144	871689 6421	6·251904 20303	235586 1003	1649077 272
6065	36 78 42 25	223 096 324 625	878110 6420	6·272207 20302	236589 1002	1648805 272
6066	36 79 63 56	223 206 695 496	884530 6419	6·292509 20300	237591 1002	1648533 272
6067	36 80 84 89	223 317 102 763	890949 6419	6·312809 20299	238593 1002	1648261 272
6068	36 82 06 24	223 427 546 432	897368 6419	6·333108 20297	239595 1002	1647989 271
6069	36 83 27 61	223 538 026 509	903787 6418	6·353405 20295	240597 1002	1647718 272
6070	36 84 49 00	223 648 543 000	910205 6417	6·373700 20293	241599 1001	1647446 271
6071	36 85 70 41	223 759 095 911	916622 6417	6·393993 20292	242600 1002	1647175 271
6072	36 86 91 84	223 869 685 248	923039 6416	6·414285 20290	243602 1001	1646904 271
6073	36 88 13 29	223 980 311 017	929455 6416	6·434575 20289	244603 1001	1646633 271
6074	36 89 34 76	224 090 973 224	935871 6415	6·454864 20287	245605 1001	1646362 271
6075	36 90 56 25	224 201 671 875	942286 6415	6·475151 20285	246606 1001	1646091 271
6076	36 91 77 76	224 312 406 976	948701 6414	6·495436 20284	247607 1001	1645820 271
6077	36 92 99 29	224 423 178 533	955115 6414	6·515720 20281	248608 1001	1645549 271
6078	36 94 20 84	224 533 986 552	961529 6413	6·536001 20281	249609 1001	1645278 271
6079	36 95 42 41	224 644 831 039	967942 6413	6·556282 20278	250610 1001	1645007 270
6080	36 96 64 00	224 755 712 000	974355 6412	6·576560 20277	251611 1000	1644737 271
6081	36 97 85 61	224 866 629 441	980767 6411	6·596837 20275	252611 1001	1644466 270
6082	36 99 07 24	224 977 583 368	987178 6411	6·617112 20274	253612 1000	1644196 270
6083	37 00 28 89	225 088 573 787	993589 6411	6·637386 20271	254612 1000	1643926 271
6084	37 01 50 56	225 199 600 704	*000000 6410	6·657657 20271	255612 1000	1643655 270
6085	37 02 72 25	225 310 664 125	006410 6409	6·677928 20268	256612 1000	1643385 270
6086	37 03 93 96	225 421 764 056	012819 6409	6·698196 20267	257612 1000	1643115 270
6087	37 05 15 69	225 532 900 503	019228 6409	6·718463 20265	258612 1000	1642845 269
6088	37 06 37 44	225 644 073 472	025637 6408	6·738728 20264	259612 1000	1642576 270
6089	37 07 59 21	225 755 282 969	032045 6407	6·758992 20262	260612 999	1642306 270
6090	37 08 81 00	225 866 529 000	038452 6407	6·779254 20260	261611 1000	1642036 269
6091	37 10 02 81	225 977 811 571	044859 6406	6·799514 20258	262611 999	1641767 270
6092	37 11 24 64	226 089 130 688	051265 6406	6·819772 20257	263610 1000	1641497 269
6093	37 12 46 49	226 200 486 357	057671 6405	6·840029 20255	264610 999	1641228 270
6094	37 13 68 36	226 311 878 584	064076 6405	6·860284 20254	265609 999	1640958 269
6095	37 14 90 25	226 423 307 375	070481 6404	6·880538 20252	266608 999	1640689 269
6096	37 16 12 16	226 534 772 736	076885 6404	6·900790 20250	267607 999	1640420 269
6097	37 17 34 09	226 646 274 673	083289 6403	6·921040 20249	268606 998	1640151 269
6098	37 18 56 04	226 757 813 192	089692 6403	6·941289 20246	269604 999	1639882 269
6099	37 19 78 01	226 869 388 299	096095 6402	6·961535 20246	270603 998	1639613 269
6100	37 21 00 00	226 981 000 000	102497	6·981781	271601	1639344
			78·	240 +	18·	0·000

No. n	Square n^2	Cube n^3	Square root $\sqrt{n}$	Sq. rt. of $10n$ $\sqrt{10n}$	Cube root $\sqrt[3]{n}$	Reciprocal $\dfrac{1}{n}$
			78·	240 +	18·	0·000
6100	37 21 00 00	226 981 000 000	102497 6401	6·981781 20243	271601 999	1639344 268
6101	37 22 22 01	227 092 648 301	108898 6401	7·002024 20242	272600 999	1639076 269
6102	37 23 44 04	227 204 333 208	115299 6401	7·022266 20240	273598 998	1638807 269
6103	37 24 66 09	227 316 054 727	121700 6400	7·042506 20239	274596 998	1638538 268
6104	37 25 88 16	227 427 812 864	128100 6399	7·062745 20237	275594 998	1638270 268
6105	37 27 10 25	227 539 607 625	134499 6399	7·082982 20235	276592 998	1638002 269
6106	37 28 32 36	227 651 439 016	140898 6399	7·103217 20234	277590 998	1637733 268
6107	37 29 54 49	227 763 307 043	147297 6398	7·123451 20232	278588 998	1637465 268
6108	37 30 76 64	227 875 211 712	153695 6397	7·143683 20230	279585 998	1637197 268
6109	37 31 98 81	227 987 153 029	160092 6397	7·163913 20229	280583 997	1636929 268
6110	37 33 21 00	228 099 131 000	166489 6396	7·184142 20227	281580 998	1636661 268
6111	37 34 43 21	228 211 145 631	172885 6396	7·204369 20225	282578 997	1636393 267
6112	37 35 65 44	228 323 196 928	179281 6395	7·224594 20224	283575 997	1636126 267
6113	37 36 87 69	228 435 284 897	185676 6395	7·244818 20222	284572 997	1635858 268
6114	37 38 09 96	228 547 409 544	192071 6394	7·265040 20220	285569 997	1635590 268
6115	37 39 32 25	228 659 570 875	198465 6394	7·285260 20219	286566 997	1635323 267
6116	37 40 54 56	228 771 768 896	204859 6394	7·305479 20217	287563 997	1635056 268
6117	37 41 76 89	228 884 003 613	211252 6393	7·325696 20216	288559 996	1634788 267
6118	37 42 99 24	228 996 275 032	217645 6392	7·345912 20213	289556 997	1634521 267
6119	37 44 21 61	229 108 583 159	224037 6392	7·366125 20213	290552 997	1634254 267
6120	37 45 44 00	229 220 928 000	230429 6391	7·386338 20210	291549 996	1633987 267
6121	37 46 66 41	229 333 309 561	236820 6391	7·406548 20209	292545 996	1633720 267
6122	37 47 88 84	229 445 727 848	243211 6390	7·426757 20207	293541 996	1633453 267
6123	37 49 11 29	229 558 182 867	249601 6389	7·446964 20206	294537 996	1633186 266
6124	37 50 33 76	229 670 674 624	255990 6389	7·467170 20203	295533 996	1632920 267
6125	37 51 56 25	229 783 203 125	262379 6389	7·487373 20203	296529 995	1632653 266
6126	37 52 78 76	229 895 768 376	268768 6388	7·507576 20200	297524 996	1632387 267
6127	37 54 01 29	230 008 370 383	275156 6387	7·527776 20199	298520 995	1632120 266
6128	37 55 23 84	230 121 009 152	281543 6387	7·547975 20197	299515 996	1631854 266
6129	37 56 46 41	230 233 684 689	287930 6387	7·568172 20196	300511 995	1631588 267
6130	37 57 69 00	230 346 397 000	294317 6385	7·588368 20194	301506 995	1631321 266
6131	37 58 91 61	230 459 146 091	300702 6386	7·608562 20192	302501 995	1631055 266
6132	37 60 14 24	230 571 931 968	307088 6385	7·628754 20191	303496 995	1630789 266
6133	37 61 36 89	230 684 754 637	313473 6384	7·648945 20189	304491 995	1630523 265
6134	37 62 59 56	230 797 614 104	319857 6384	7·669134 20188	305486 994	1630258 266
6135	37 63 82 25	230 910 510 375	326241 6383	7·689322 20185	306480 995	1629992 266
6136	37 65 04 96	231 023 443 456	332624 6383	7·709507 20184	307475 995	1629726 265
6137	37 66 27 69	231 136 413 353	339007 6382	7·729691 20183	308470 994	1629461 266
6138	37 67 50 44	231 249 420 072	345389 6382	7·749874 20181	309464 994	1629195 265
6139	37 68 73 21	231 362 463 619	351771 6381	7·770055 20179	310458 994	1628930 266
6140	37 69 96 00	231 475 544 000	358152 6381	7·790234 20177	311452 994	1628664 265
6141	37 71 18 81	231 588 661 221	364533 6380	7·810411 20176	312446 994	1628399 265
6142	37 72 41 64	231 701 815 288	370913 6380	7·830587 20175	313440 994	1628134 265
6143	37 73 64 49	231 815 006 207	377293 6379	7·850762 20172	314434 994	1627869 265
6144	37 74 87 36	231 928 233 984	383672 6378	7·870934 20171	315428 994	1627604 265
6145	37 76 10 25	232 041 498 625	390050 6378	7·891105 20169	316422 993	1627339 264
6146	37 77 33 16	232 154 800 136	396428 6378	7·911274 20168	317415 993	1627075 265
6147	37 78 56 09	232 268 138 523	402806 6377	7·931442 20166	318408 994	1626810 265
6148	37 79 79 04	232 381 513 792	409183 6377	7·951608 20165	319402 993	1626545 264
6149	37 81 02 01	232 494 925 949	415560 6376	7·971773 20162	320395 993	1626281 265
6150	37 82 25 00	232 608 375 000	421936 78·	7·991935 240 +	321388 18·	1626016 0·000

No. n	Square n²	Cube n³	Square root √n	Sq. rt. of 10n √10n	Cube root ∛n	Reciprocal 1/n
			78·	240 +	18·	0·000
6150	37 82 25 00	232 608 375 000	421936 6375	7·991935 20161	321388 993	1626016 264
6151	37 83 48 01	232 721 860 951	428311 6375	8·012096 20160	322381 993	1625752 264
6152	37 84 71 04	232 835 383 808	434686 6375	8·032256 20158	323374 993	1625488 265
6153	37 85 94 09	232 948 943 577	441061 6374	8·052414 20156	324367 993	1625223 264
6154	37 87 17 16	233 062 540 264	447435 6373	8·072570 20155	325359 993	1624959 264
6155	37 88 40 25	233 176 173 875	453808 6373	8·092725 20153	326352 992	1624695 264
6156	37 89 63 36	233 289 844 416	460181 6372	8·112878 20151	327344 993	1624431 263
6157	37 90 86 49	233 403 551 893	466553 6372	8·133029 20150	328337 992	1624168 264
6158	37 92 09 64	233 517 296 312	472925 6372	8·153179 20148	329329 992	1623904 264
6159	37 93 32 81	233 631 077 679	479297 6370	8·173327 20146	330321 992	1623640 263
6160	37 94 56 00	233 744 896 000	485667 6371	8·193473 20145	331313 992	1623377 264
6161	37 95 79 21	233 858 751 281	492038 6370	8·213618 20143	332305 992	1623113 263
6162	37 97 02 44	233 972 643 528	498408 6369	8·233761 20141	333297 992	1622850 264
6163	37 98 25 69	234 086 572 747	504777 6369	8·253902 20140	334288 991	1622586 263
6164	37 99 48 96	234 200 538 944	511146 6368	8·274042 20138	335280 991	1622323 263
6165	38 00 72 25	234 314 542 125	517514 6368	8·294180 20137	336271 992	1622060 263
6166	38 01 95 56	234 428 582 296	523882 6367	8·314317 20135	337263 991	1621797 263
6167	38 03 18 89	234 542 659 463	530249 6367	8·334452 20133	338254 991	1621534 263
6168	38 04 42 24	234 656 773 632	536616 6366	8·354585 20132	339245 991	1621271 263
6169	38 05 65 61	234 770 924 809	542982 6366	8·374717 20130	340236 991	1621008 262
6170	38 06 89 00	234 885 113 000	549348 6365	8·394847 20128	341227 991	1620746 263
6171	38 08 12 41	234 999 338 211	555713 6364	8·414975 20127	342218 991	1620483 263
6172	38 09 35 84	235 113 600 448	562077 6365	8·435102 20125	343209 991	1620220 263
6173	38 10 59 29	235 227 899 717	568442 6363	8·455227 20124	344199 990	1619958 263
6174	38 11 82 76	235 342 236 024	574805 6363	8·475351 20122	345190 990	1619695 262
6175	38 13 06 25	235 456 609 375	581168 6363	8·495473 20120	346180 990	1619433 262
6176	38 14 29 76	235 571 019 776	587531 6362	8·515593 20119	347170 991	1619171 262
6177	38 15 53 29	235 685 467 233	593893 6361	8·535712 20117	348161 990	1618909 262
6178	38 16 76 84	235 799 951 752	600254 6361	8·555829 20115	349151 990	1618647 262
6179	38 18 00 41	235 914 473 339	606615 6361	8·575944 20114	350141 990	1618385 262
6180	38 19 24 00	236 029 032 000	612976 6360	8·596058 20112	351131 989	1618123 262
6181	38 20 47 61	236 143 627 741	619336 6360	8·616170 20111	352120 990	1617861 262
6182	38 21 71 24	236 258 260 568	625696 6359	8·636281 20108	353110 990	1617599 261
6183	38 22 94 89	236 372 930 487	632055 6358	8·656389 20108	354100 989	1617338 262
6184	38 24 18 56	236 487 637 504	638413 6358	8·676497 20105	355089 989	1617076 261
6185	38 25 42 25	236 602 381 625	644771 6357	8·696602 20104	356078 990	1616815 261
6186	38 26 65 96	236 717 162 856	651128 6357	8·716706 20103	357068 989	1616554 262
6187	38 27 89 69	236 831 981 203	657485 6357	8·736809 20100	358057 989	1616292 261
6188	38 29 13 44	236 946 836 672	663842 6356	8·756909 20100	359046 989	1616031 261
6189	38 30 37 21	237 061 729 269	670198 6355	8·777009 20097	360035 988	1615770 261
6190	38 31 61 00	237 176 659 000	676553 6355	8·797106 20096	361023 989	1615509 261
6191	38 32 84 81	237 291 625 871	682908 6355	8·817202 20094	362012 989	1615248 261
6192	38 34 08 64	237 406 629 888	689262 6354	8·837296 20093	363001 989	1614987 261
6193	38 35 32 49	237 521 671 057	695616 6353	8·857389 20091	363989 988	1614726 260
6194	38 36 56 36	237 636 749 384	701969 6353	8·877480 20089	364977 989	1614466 261
6195	38 37 80 25	237 751 864 875	708322 6353	8·897569 20088	365966 988	1614205 261
6196	38 39 04 16	237 867 017 536	714675 6351	8·917657 20086	366954 988	1613944 260
6197	38 40 28 09	237 982 207 373	721026 6352	8·937743 20085	367942 988	1613684 260
6198	38 41 52 04	238 097 434 392	727378 6350	8·957828 20083	368930 988	1613424 261
6199	38 42 76 01	238 212 698 599	733728 6351	8·977911 20081	369918 988	1613163 260
6200	38 44 00 00	238 328 000 000	740079	8·997992	370906	1612903
			78·	240 +	18·	0·000

No. n	Square n²	Cube n³	Square root √n	Sq. rt. of 10n √10n	Cube root ∛n	Reciprocal 1/n
			78·	240 +	18·	0·000
6200	38 44 00 00	238 328 000 000	740079 6349	8·997992 20080	370906 987	1612903 260
6201	38 45 24 01	238 443 338 601	746428 6350	9·018072 20078	371893 988	1612643 260
6202	38 46 48 04	238 558 714 408	752778 6348	9·038150 20078 20076	372881 987	1612383 260
6203	38 47 72 09	238 674 127 427	759126 6349	9·058226 20075	373868 987	1612123 260
6204	38 48 96 16	238 789 577 664	765475 6347	9·078301 20073	374855 988	1611863 259
6205	38 50 20 25	238 905 065 125	771822 6348	9·098374 20072	375843 987	1611604 260
6206	38 51 44 36	239 020 589 816	778170 6346	9·118446 20070	376830 987	1611344 260
6207	38 52 68 49	239 136 151 743	784516 6346	9·138516 20068	377817 987	1611084 259
6208	38 53 92 64	239 251 750 912	790862 6346	9·158584 20067	378804 986	1610825 260
6209	38 55 16 81	239 367 387 329	797208 6345	9·178651 20065	379790 987	1610565 259
6210	38 56 41 00	239 483 061 000	803553 6345	9·198716 20063	380777 987	1610306 259
6211	38 57 65 21	239 598 771 931	809898 6345	9·218779 20062	381764 986	1610047 259
6212	38 58 89 44	239 714 520 128	816242 6344	9·238841 20061	382750 986	1609788 260
6213	38 60 13 69	239 830 305 597	822586 6344 6343	9·258902 20058	383736 987	1609528 259
6214	38 61 37 96	239 946 128 344	828929 6342	9·278960 20057	384723 986	1609269 259
6215	38 62 62 25	240 061 988 375	835271 6342	9·299017 20056	385709 986	1609010 258
6216	38 63 86 56	240 177 885 696	841613 6342	9·319073 20053	386695 986	1608752 259
6217	38 65 10 89	240 293 820 313	847955 6341	9·339126 20053	387681 986	1608493 259
6218	38 66 35 24	240 409 792 232	854296 6341	9·359179 20050	388667 986	1608234 258
6219	38 67 59 61	240 525 801 459	860637 6340	9·379229 20049	389652 985 986	1607976 259
6220	38 68 84 00	240 641 848 000	866977 6339	9·399278 20048	390638 985	1607717 258
6221	38 70 08 41	240 757 931 861	873316 6339	9·419326 20045	391623 986	1607459 258
6222	38 71 32 84	240 874 053 048	879655 6339	9·439371 20045	392609 985	1607200 259
6223	38 72 57 29	240 990 211 567	885994 6338	9·459416 20042	393594 985	1606942 258
6224	38 73 81 76	241 106 407 424	892332 6337	9·479458 20041	394579 985	1606684 258
6225	38 75 06 25	241 222 640 625	898669 6337	9·499499 20039	395564 985	1606426 258
6226	38 76 30 76	241 338 911 176	905006 6337	9·519538 20038	396549 985	1606168 258
6227	38 77 55 29	241 455 219 083	911343 6336	9·539576 20036	397534 985	1605910 258
6228	38 78 79 84	241 571 564 352	917679 6335	9·559612 20035	398519 985	1605652 258
6229	38 80 04 41	241 687 946 989	924014 6335	9·579647 20032	399504 984	1605394 258
6230	38 81 29 00	241 804 367 000	930349 6334	9·599679 20032	400488 985	1605136 257
6231	38 82 53 61	241 920 824 391	936683 6334	9·619711 20029	401473 984	1604879 258
6232	38 83 78 24	242 037 319 168	943017 6334	9·639740 20028	402457 984	1604621 257
6233	38 85 02 89	242 153 851 337	949351 6333	9·659768 20027	403441 985	1604364 257
6234	38 86 27 56	242 270 420 904	955684 6332	9·679795 20025	404426 984	1604107 258
6235	38 87 52 25	242 387 027 875	962016 6332	9·699820 20023	405410 983	1603849 257
6236	38 88 76 96	242 503 672 256	968348 6331	9·719843 20022	406393 984	1603592 257
6237	38 90 01 69	242 620 354 053	974679 6331	9·739865 20020	407377 984	1603335 257
6238	38 91 26 44	242 737 073 272	981010 6331	9·759885 20018	408361 984	1603078 257
6239	38 92 51 21	242 853 829 919	987341 6330	9·779903 20017	409345 983	1602821 257
6240	38 93 76 00	242 970 624 000	·993671 6329	9·799920 20015	410328 984	1602564 257
6241	38 95 00 81	243 087 455 521	*000000 6329	9·819935 20014	411312 984	1602307 257
6242	38 96 25 64	243 204 324 488	006329 6328	9·839949 20012	412295 983	1602051 256
6243	38 97 50 49	243 321 230 907	012657 6328	9·859961 20010	413278 983	1601794 257
6244	38 98 75 36	243 438 174 784	018985 6327	9·879971 20009	414261 983	1601537 256
6245	39 00 00 25	243 555 156 125	025312 6327	9·899980 20007	415244 983	1601281 256
6246	39 01 25 16	243 672 174 936	031639 6327	9·919987 20006	416227 983	1601025 256
6247	39 02 50 09	243 789 231 223	037966 6325	9·939993 20004	417210 982	1600768 257
6248	39 03 75 04	243 906 324 992	044291 6326	9·959997 20002	418192 983	1600512 256
6249	39 05 00 01	244 023 456 249	050617 6325	9·979999 20001	419175 982	1600256 256
6250	39 06 25 00	244 140 625 000	056942	10·000000	420157	1600000
			79·	240 +	18·	0·000

No. n	Square n^2	Cube n^3	Square root $\sqrt{n}$	Sq. rt. of 10n $\sqrt{10n}$	Cube root $\sqrt[3]{n}$	Reciprocal $\dfrac{1}{n}$
			79·	250·	18·	0·000
6250	39 06 25 00	244 140 625 000	$056942_{\,6324}$	$000000_{\,19999}$	$420157_{\,983}$	$1600000_{\,256}$
6251	39 07 50 01	244 257 831 251	$063266_{\,6324}$	$019999_{\,19998}$	$421140_{\,982}$	$1599744_{\,256}$
6252	39 08 75 04	244 375 075 008	$069590_{\,6323}$	$039997_{\,19996}$	$422122_{\,982}$	$1599488_{\,256}$
6253	39 10 00 09	244 492 356 277	$075913_{\,6323}$	$059993_{\,19994}$	$423104_{\,982}$	$1599232_{\,255}$
6254	39 11 25 16	244 609 675 064	$082236_{\,6322}$	$079987_{\,19993}$	$424086_{\,982}$	$1598977_{\,256}$
6255	39 12 50 25	244 727 031 375	$088558_{\,6322}$	$099980_{\,19991}$	$425068_{\,982}$	$1598721_{\,256}$
6256	39 13 75 36	244 844 425 216	$094880_{\,6321}$	$119971_{\,19990}$	$426050_{\,982}$	$1598465_{\,255}$
6257	39 15 00 49	244 961 856 593	$101201_{\,6321}$	$139961_{\,19988}$	$427032_{\,981}$	$1598210_{\,255}$
6258	39 16 25 64	245 079 325 512	$107522_{\,6320}$	$159949_{\,19986}$	$428013_{\,982}$	$1597955_{\,256}$
6259	39 17 50 81	245 196 831 979	$113842_{\,6320}$	$179935_{\,19985}$	$428995_{\,981}$	$1597699_{\,255}$
6260	39 18 76 00	245 314 376 000	$120162_{\,6319}$	$199920_{\,19983}$	$429976_{\,982}$	$1597444_{\,255}$
6261	39 20 01 21	245 431 957 581	$126481_{\,6319}$	$219903_{\,19982}$	$430958_{\,981}$	$1597189_{\,255}$
6262	39 21 26 44	245 549 576 728	$132800_{\,6318}$	$239885_{\,19980}$	$431939_{\,981}$	$1596934_{\,255}$
6263	39 22 51 69	245 667 233 447	$139118_{\,6318}$	$259865_{\,19978}$	$432920_{\,981}$	$1596679_{\,255}$
6264	39 23 76 96	245 784 927 744	$145436_{\,6317}$	$279843_{\,19977}$	$433901_{\,981}$	$1596424_{\,255}$
6265	39 25 02 25	245 902 659 625	$151753_{\,6317}$	$299820_{\,19975}$	$434882_{\,981}$	$1596169_{\,255}$
6266	39 26 27 56	246 020 429 096	$158070_{\,6316}$	$319795_{\,19974}$	$435863_{\,980}$	$1595914_{\,254}$
6267	39 27 52 89	246 138 236 163	$164386_{\,6316}$	$339769_{\,19972}$	$436843_{\,981}$	$1595660_{\,254}$
6268	39 28 78 24	246 256 080 832	$170702_{\,6315}$	$359741_{\,19971}$	$437824_{\,980}$	$1595405_{\,254}$
6269	39 30 03 61	246 373 963 109	$177017_{\,6315}$	$379712_{\,19969}$	$438804_{\,981}$	$1595151_{\,255}$
6270	39 31 29 00	246 491 883 000	$183332_{\,6314}$	$399681_{\,19967}$	$439785_{\,980}$	$1594896_{\,254}$
6271	39 32 54 41	246 609 840 511	$189646_{\,6313}$	$419648_{\,19965}$	$440765_{\,980}$	$1594642_{\,254}$
6272	39 33 79 84	246 727 835 648	$195959_{\,6314}$	$439613_{\,19965}$	$441745_{\,980}$	$1594388_{\,254}$
6273	39 35 05 29	246 845 868 417	$202273_{\,6312}$	$459578_{\,19962}$	$442725_{\,980}$	$1594134_{\,254}$
6274	39 36 30 76	246 963 938 824	$208585_{\,6313}$	$479540_{\,19961}$	$443705_{\,980}$	$1593880_{\,255}$
6275	39 37 56 25	247 082 046 875	$214898_{\,6311}$	$499501_{\,19959}$	$444685_{\,980}$	$1593625_{\,253}$
6276	39 38 81 76	247 200 192 576	$221209_{\,6311}$	$519460_{\,19958}$	$445665_{\,979}$	$1593372_{\,254}$
6277	39 40 07 29	247 318 375 933	$227520_{\,6311}$	$539418_{\,19956}$	$446644_{\,980}$	$1593118_{\,254}$
6278	39 41 32 84	247 436 596 952	$233831_{\,6310}$	$559374_{\,19955}$	$447624_{\,979}$	$1592864_{\,254}$
6279	39 42 58 41	247 554 855 639	$240141_{\,6310}$	$579329_{\,19953}$	$448603_{\,980}$	$1592610_{\,253}$
6280	39 43 84 00	247 673 152 000	$246451_{\,6309}$	$599282_{\,19951}$	$449583_{\,979}$	$1592357_{\,254}$
6281	39 45 09 61	247 791 486 041	$252760_{\,6309}$	$619233_{\,19950}$	$450562_{\,979}$	$1592103_{\,253}$
6282	39 46 35 24	247 909 857 768	$259069_{\,6308}$	$639183_{\,19948}$	$451541_{\,979}$	$1591850_{\,254}$
6283	39 47 60 89	248 028 267 187	$265377_{\,6308}$	$659131_{\,19947}$	$452520_{\,979}$	$1591596_{\,253}$
6284	39 48 86 56	248 146 714 304	$271685_{\,6307}$	$679078_{\,19945}$	$453499_{\,979}$	$1591343_{\,253}$
6285	39 50 12 25	248 265 199 125	$277992_{\,6307}$	$699023_{\,19943}$	$454478_{\,979}$	$1591090_{\,253}$
6286	39 51 37 96	248 383 721 656	$284299_{\,6306}$	$718966_{\,19942}$	$455457_{\,978}$	$1590837_{\,253}$
6287	39 52 63 69	248 502 281 903	$290605_{\,6305}$	$738908_{\,19940}$	$456435_{\,979}$	$1590584_{\,253}$
6288	39 53 89 44	248 620 879 872	$296910_{\,6306}$	$758848_{\,19939}$	$457414_{\,978}$	$1590331_{\,253}$
6289	39 55 15 21	248 739 515 569	$303216_{\,6304}$	$778787_{\,19937}$	$458392_{\,978}$	$1590078_{\,253}$
6290	39 56 41 00	248 858 189 000	$309520_{\,6304}$	$798724_{\,19936}$	$459370_{\,978}$	$1589825_{\,253}$
6291	39 57 66 81	248 976 900 171	$315824_{\,6304}$	$818660_{\,19934}$	$460348_{\,979}$	$1589572_{\,252}$
6292	39 58 92 64	249 095 649 088	$322128_{\,6303}$	$838594_{\,19932}$	$461327_{\,978}$	$1589320_{\,253}$
6293	39 60 18 49	249 214 435 757	$328431_{\,6303}$	$858526_{\,19931}$	$462305_{\,977}$	$1589067_{\,252}$
6294	39 61 44 36	249 333 260 184	$334734_{\,6302}$	$878457_{\,19929}$	$463282_{\,978}$	$1588815_{\,253}$
6295	39 62 70 25	249 452 122 375	$341036_{\,6302}$	$898386_{\,19927}$	$464260_{\,978}$	$1588562_{\,252}$
6296	39 63 96 16	249 571 022 336	$347338_{\,6301}$	$918313_{\,19926}$	$465238_{\,977}$	$1588310_{\,252}$
6297	39 65 22 09	249 689 960 073	$353639_{\,6301}$	$938239_{\,19924}$	$466215_{\,978}$	$1588058_{\,252}$
6298	39 66 48 04	249 808 935 592	$359940_{\,6300}$	$958164_{\,19923}$	$467193_{\,977}$	$1587806_{\,252}$
6299	39 67 74 01	249 927 948 899	$366240_{\,6299}$	$978087_{\,19921}$	$468170_{\,978}$	$1587554_{\,252}$
6300	39 69 00 00	250 047 000 000	372539	998008	469148	1587302
			79·	250·	18·	0·000

No. n	Square n^2	Cube n^3	Square root $\sqrt{n}$	Sq. rt. of 10n $\sqrt{10n}$	Cube root $\sqrt[3]{n}$	Reciprocal $\frac{1}{n}$
			79·	250·	18·	0·000
6300	39 69 00 00	250 047 000 000	372539 6299	998008	469148 977	1587302
6301	39 70 26 01	250 166 088 901	378838 6299	*017928 19920	470125 977	1587050 252
6302	39 71 52 04	250 285 215 608	385137 6298	037846 19918	471102 977	1586798 252
6303	39 72 78 09	250 404 380 127	391435 6298	057762 19916	472079 977	1586546 252
6304	39 74 04 16	250 523 582 464	397733 6297	077677 19915	473055 976	1586294 252
				19914	977	251
6305	39 75 30 25	250 642 822 625	404030 6297	097591 19911	474032 977	1586043 252
6306	39 76 56 36	250 762 100 616	410327 6296	117502 19911	475009 977	1585791 252
6307	39 77 82 49	250 881 416 443	416623 6296	137413 19908	475985 976	1585540 251
6308	39 79 08 64	251 000 770 112	422919 6295	157321 19907	476962 976	1585289 251
6309	39 80 34 81	251 120 161 629	429214 6294	177228 19906	477938 976	1585037 252
						251
6310	39 81 61 00	251 239 591 000	435508 6295	197134 19904	478914 976	1584786 251
6311	39 82 87 21	251 359 058 231	441803 6293	217038 19902	479890 977	1584535 251
6312	39 84 13 44	251 478 563 328	448096 6293	236940 19901	480867 975	1584284 251
6313	39 85 39 69	251 598 106 297	454389 6293	256841 19899	481842 976	1584033 251
6314	39 86 65 96	251 717 687 144	460682 6292	276740 19897	482818 976	1583782 251
						251
6315	39 87 92 25	251 837 305 875	466974 6292	296637 19896	483794 976	1583531 250
6316	39 89 18 56	251 956 962 496	473266 6291	316533 19895	484770 975	1583281 251
6317	39 90 44 89	252 076 657 013	479557 6291	336428 19893	485745 975	1583030 251
6318	39 91 71 24	252 196 389 432	485848 6290	356321 19891	486720 976	1582779 250
6319	39 92 97 61	252 316 159 759	492138 6290	376212 19890	487696 975	1582529 251
6320	39 94 24 00	252 435 968 000	498428 6289	396102 19888	488671 975	1582278 250
6321	39 95 50 41	252 555 814 161	504717 6289	415990 19887	489646 975	1582028 250
6322	39 96 76 84	252 675 698 248	511006 6288	435877 19885	490621 975	1581778 250
6323	39 98 03 29	252 795 620 267	517294 6287	455762 19883	491596 975	1581528 250
6324	39 99 29 76	252 915 580 224	523581 6288	475645 19882	492571 974	1581278 250
6325	40 00 56 25	253 035 578 125	529869 6286	495527 19880	493545 975	1581028 250
6326	40 01 82 76	253 155 613 976	536155 6287	515407 19879	494520 974	1580778 250
6327	40 03 09 29	253 275 687 783	542442 6285	535286 19877	495494 974	1580528 250
6328	40 04 35 84	253 395 799 552	548727 6285	555163 19876	496469 974	1580278 250
6329	40 05 62 41	253 515 949 289	555012 6285	575039 19874	497443 974	1580028 249
6330	40 06 89 00	253 636 137 000	561297 6284	594913 19872	498417 974	1579779 250
6331	40 08 15 61	253 756 362 691	567581 6284	614785 19871	499391 974	1579529 250
6332	40 09 42 24	253 876 626 368	573865 6283	634656 19869	500365 974	1579280 249
6333	40 10 68 89	253 996 928 037	580148 6283	654525 19868	501339 974	1579030 250
6334	40 11 95 56	254 117 267 704	586431 6282	674393 19866	502313 973	1578781 249
						249
6335	40 13 22 25	254 237 645 375	592713 6282	694259 19865	503286 974	1578532 249
6336	40 14 48 96	254 358 061 056	598995 6281	714124 19863	504260 973	1578283 249
6337	40 15 75 69	254 478 514 753	605276 6281	733987 19861	505233 973	1578034 249
6338	40 17 02 44	254 599 006 472	611557 6280	753848 19860	506207 973	1577785 249
6339	40 18 29 21	254 719 536 219	617837 6280	773708 19858	507180 973	1577536 249
6340	40 19 56 00	254 840 104 000	624117 6279	793566 19857	508153 973	1577287 249
6341	40 20 82 81	254 960 709 821	630396 6279	813423 19855	509126 973	1577038 248
6342	40 22 09 64	255 081 353 688	636675 6278	833278 19854	510099 973	1576790 249
6343	40 23 36 49	255 202 035 607	642953 6278	853132 19852	511072 973	1576541 248
6344	40 24 63 36	255 322 755 584	649231 6277	872984 19850	512045 972	1576293 249
6345	40 25 90 25	255 443 513 625	655508 6277	892834 19849	513017 973	1576044 248
6346	40 27 17 16	255 564 309 736	661785 6276	912683 19848	513990 972	1575796 248
6347	40 28 44 09	255 685 143 923	668061 6276	932531 19845	514962 973	1575548 249
6348	40 29 71 04	255 806 016 192	674337 6275	952376 19845	515935 972	1575299 248
6349	40 30 98 01	255 926 926 549	680612 6275	972221 19842	516907 972	1575051 248
6350	40 32 25 00	256 047 875 000	686887	992063	517879	1574803
			79·	251·	18·	0·000

No. n	Square n^2	Cube n^3	Square root $\sqrt{n}$	Sq. rt. of $10n$ $\sqrt{10n}$	Cube root $\sqrt[3]{n}$	Reciprocal $\dfrac{1}{n}$
			79·	251·	18·	0·000
6350	40 32 25 00	256 047 875 000	686887 _6275_	992063 _19841_	517879	1574803 _248_
6351	40 33 52 01	256 168 861 551	693162 _6273_	*011904 _19840_	518851 _972_	1574555 _248_
6352	40 34 79 04	256 289 886 208	699435 _6274_	031744 _19838_	519823 _972_	1574307 _248_
6353	40 36 06 09	256 410 948 977	705709 _6273_	051582 _19836_	520795 _972_	1574059 _247_
6354	40 37 33 16	256 532 049 864	711982 _6272_	071418 _19835_	521766 _971 972_	1573812 _248_
6355	40 38 60 25	256 653 188 875	718254 _6272_	091253 _19834_	522738 _972_	1573564 _247_
6356	40 39 87 36	256 774 366 016	724526 _6271_	111087 _19831_	523710 _972_	1573317 _248_
6357	40 41 14 49	256 895 581 293	730797 _6271_	130918 _19831_	524681 _971_	1573069 _247_
6358	40 42 41 64	257 016 834 712	737068 _6270_	150749 _19828_	525652 _971_	1572822 _248_
6359	40 43 68 81	257 138 126 279	743338 _6270_	170577 _19827_	526623 _971 972_	1572574 _247_
6360	40 44 96 00	257 259 456 000	749608 _6270_	190404 _19826_	527595	1572327 _247_
6361	40 46 23 21	257 380 823 881	755878 _6268_	210230 _19824_	528566 _971_	1572080 _247_
6362	40 47 50 44	257 502 229 928	762146 _6269_	230054 _19822_	529536 _970_	1571833 _247_
6363	40 48 77 69	257 623 674 147	768415 _6268_	249876 _19821_	530507 _971_	1571586 _247_
6364	40 50 04 96	257 745 156 544	774683 _6267_	269697 _19819_	531478 _971_	1571339 _247_
6365	40 51 32 25	257 866 677 125	780950 _6267_	289516 _19818_	532449 _970_	1571092 _247_
6366	40 52 59 56	257 988 235 896	787217 _6266_	309334 _19816_	533419 _970_	1570845 _247_
6367	40 53 86 89	258 109 832 863	793483 _6266_	329150 _19815_	534389 _971_	1570598 _247_
6368	40 55 14 24	258 231 468 032	799749 _6266_	348965 _19813_	535360 _970_	1570352 _247_
6369	40 56 41 61	258 353 141 409	806015 _6265_	368778 _19811_	536330 _970_	1570105 _246_
6370	40 57 69 00	258 474 853 000	812280 _6264_	388589 _19810_	537300 _970_	1569859 _247_
6371	40 58 96 41	258 596 602 811	818544 _6264_	408399 _19809_	538270 _970_	1569612 _246_
6372	40 60 23 84	258 718 390 848	824808 _6264_	428208 _19806_	539240 _970_	1569366 _246_
6373	40 61 51 29	258 840 217 117	831072 _6263_	448014 _19806_	540210 _969_	1569120 _246_
6374	40 62 78 76	258 962 081 624	837335 _6262_	467820 _19803_	541179 _970_	1568874 _247_
6375	40 64 06 25	259 083 984 375	843597 _6262_	487623 _19803_	542149 _969_	1568627 _246_
6376	40 65 33 76	259 205 925 376	849859 _6262_	507426 _19800_	543118 _970_	1568381 _246_
6377	40 66 61 29	259 327 904 633	856121 _6261_	527226 _19799_	544088 _969_	1568135 _245_
6378	40 67 88 84	259 449 922 152	862382 _6260_	547025 _19798_	545057 _969_	1567890 _246_
6379	40 69 16 41	259 571 977 939	868642 _6260_	566823 _19796_	546026 _969_	1567644 _246_
6380	40 70 44 00	259 694 072 000	874902 _6260_	586619 _19794_	546995 _969_	1567398 _246_
6381	40 71 71 61	259 816 204 341	881162 _6259_	606413 _19793_	547964 _969_	1567152 _245_
6382	40 72 99 24	259 938 374 968	887421 _6258_	626206 _19791_	548933 _969_	1566907 _246_
6383	40 74 26 89	260 060 583 887	893679 _6258_	645997 _19790_	549902 _968_	1566661 _245_
6384	40 75 54 56	260 182 831 104	899937 _6258_	665787 _19788_	550870 _969_	1566416 _245_
6385	40 76 82 25	260 305 116 625	906195 _6257_	685575 _19787_	551839 _968_	1566171 _246_
6386	40 78 09 96	260 427 440 456	912452 _6257_	705362 _19785_	552807 _969_	1565925 _245_
6387	40 79 37 69	260 549 802 603	918709 _6256_	725147 _19784_	553776 _968_	1565680 _245_
6388	40 80 65 44	260 672 203 072	924965 _6255_	744931 _19782_	554744 _968_	1565435 _245_
6389	40 81 93 21	260 794 641 869	931220 _6256_	764713 _19780_	555712 _968_	1565190 _245_
6390	40 83 21 00	260 917 119 000	937476 _6254_	784493 _19779_	556680 _968_	1564945 _245_
6391	40 84 48 81	261 039 634 471	943730 _6254_	804272 _19777_	557648 _968_	1564700 _244_
6392	40 85 76 64	261 162 188 288	949984 _6254_	824049 _19776_	558616 _968_	1564456 _245_
6393	40 87 04 49	261 284 780 457	956238 _6253_	843825 _19775_	559584 _968_	1564211 _245_
6394	40 88 32 36	261 407 410 984	962491 _6253_	863600 _19772_	560552 _967_	1563966 _244_
6395	40 89 60 25	261 530 079 875	968744 _6252_	883372 _19772_	561519 _968_	1563722 _245_
6396	40 90 88 16	261 652 787 136	974996 _6252_	903144 _19769_	562487 _967_	1563477 _244_
6397	40 92 16 09	261 775 532 773	981248 _6251_	922913 _19768_	563454 _967_	1563233 _244_
6398	40 93 44 04	261 898 316 792	987499 _6251_	942681 _19767_	564421 _967_	1562988 _245_
6399	40 94 72 01	262 021 139 199	993750 _6250_	962448 _19765_	565388 _967_	1562744 _244_
6400	40 96 00 00	262 144 000 000	*000000 / 80·	982213 / 252·	566355 / 18·	1562500 / 0·000

No. n	Square n^2	Cube n^3	Square root $\sqrt{n}$	Sq. rt. of 10n $\sqrt{10n}$	Cube root $\sqrt[3]{n}$	Reciprocal $\frac{1}{n}$
			80·	252·	18·	0·000
6400	40 96 00 00	262 144 000 000	000000 6250	982213 19763	566355 967	1562500 244
6401	40 97 28 01	262 266 899 201	006250 6249	*001976 19762	567322 967	1562256 244
6402	40 98 56 04	262 389 836 808	012499 6249	021738 19761	568289 967	1562012 244
6403	40 99 84 09	262 512 812 827	018748 6248	041499 19758	569256 967	1561768 244
6404	41 01 12 16	262 635 827 264	024996 6248	061257 19758	570223 966	1561524 244
6405	41 02 40 25	262 758 880 125	031244 6247	081015 19755	571189 967	1561280 243
6406	41 03 68 36	262 881 971 416	037491 6247	100770 19755	572156 966	1561037 244
6407	41 04 96 49	263 005 101 143	043738 6246	120525 19752	573122 966	1560793 244
6408	41 06 24 64	263 128 269 312	049984 6246	140277 19751	574088 966	1560549 243
6409	41 07 52 81	263 251 475 929	056230 6246	160028 19750	575054 966	1560306 244
6410	41 08 81 00	263 374 721 000	062476 6244	179778 19748	576020 966	1560062 243
6411	41 10 09 21	263 498 004 531	068720 6245	199526 19747	576986 966	1559819 243
6412	41 11 37 44	263 621 326 528	074965 6244	219273 19745	577952 966	1559576 243
6413	41 12 65 69	263 744 686 997	081209 6243	239018 19743	578918 965	1559333 244
6414	41 13 93 96	263 868 085 944	087452 6243	258761 19742	579883 966	1559089 243
6415	41 15 22 25	263 991 523 375	093695 6243	278503 19740	580849 965	1558846 243
6416	41 16 50 56	264 114 999 296	099938 6242	298243 19739	581814 966	1558603 243
6417	41 17 78 89	264 238 513 713	106180 6241	317982 19737	582780 965	1558361 242
6418	41 19 07 24	264 362 066 632	112421 6241	337719 19736	583745 965	1558118 243
6419	41 20 35 61	264 485 658 059	118662 6240	357455 19734	584710 965	1557875 243
6420	41 21 64 00	264 609 288 000	124902 6241	377189 19733	585675 965	1557632 242
6421	41 22 92 41	264 732 956 461	131143 6239	396922 19731	586640 965	1557390 243
6422	41 24 20 84	264 856 663 448	137382 6239	416653 19730	587605 965	1557147 242
6423	41 25 49 29	264 980 408 967	143621 6239	436383 19728	588570 964	1556905 242
6424	41 26 77 76	265 104 193 024	149860 6238	456111 19726	589534 965	1556663 243
6425	41 28 06 25	265 228 015 625	156098 6237	475837 19725	590499 964	1556420 242
6426	41 29 34 76	265 351 876 776	162335 6237	495562 19724	591463 965	1556178 242
6427	41 30 63 29	265 475 776 483	168572 6237	515286 19721	592428 964	1555936 242
6428	41 31 91 84	265 599 714 752	174809 6236	535007 19721	593392 964	1555694 242
6429	41 33 20 41	265 723 691 589	181045 6236	554728 19719	594356 964	1555452 242
6430	41 34 49 00	265 847 707 000	187281 6235	574447 19717	595320 964	1555210 242
6431	41 35 77 61	265 971 760 991	193516 6235	594164 19716	596284 964	1554968 242
6432	41 37 06 24	266 095 853 568	199751 6234	613880 19714	597248 964	1554726 241
6433	41 38 34 89	266 219 984 737	205985 6234	633594 19713	598212 963	1554485 242
6434	41 39 63 56	266 344 154 504	212219 6233	653307 19711	599175 964	1554243 241
6435	41 40 92 25	266 468 362 875	218452 6232	673018 19710	600139 963	1554002 242
6436	41 42 20 96	266 592 609 856	224684 6233	692728 19708	601102 964	1553760 241
6437	41 43 49 69	266 716 895 453	230917 6232	712436 19706	602066 963	1553519 242
6438	41 44 78 44	266 841 219 672	237149 6231	732142 19705	603029 963	1553277 241
6439	41 46 07 21	266 965 582 519	243380 6231	751847 19704	603992 963	1553036 241
6440	41 47 36 00	267 089 984 000	249611 6230	771551 19702	604955 963	1552795 241
6441	41 48 64 81	267 214 424 121	255841 6230	791253 19700	605918 963	1552554 241
6442	41 49 93 64	267 338 902 888	262071 6229	810953 19699	606881 962	1552313 241
6443	41 51 22 49	267 463 420 307	268300 6229	830652 19698	607843 963	1552072 241
6444	41 52 51 36	267 587 976 384	274529 6228	850350 19695	608806 963	1551831 241
6445	41 53 80 25	267 712 571 125	280757 6228	870045 19695	609769 962	1551590 240
6446	41 55 09 16	267 837 204 536	286985 6228	889740 19693	610731 962	1551350 241
6447	41 56 38 09	267 961 876 623	293213 6227	909433 19691	611693 963	1551109 241
6448	41 57 67 04	268 086 587 ~92	299440 6226	929124 19690	612656 962	1550868 240
6449	41 58 96 01	268 211 336 849	305666 6226	948814 19688	613618 962	1550628 240
6450	41 60 25 00	268 336 125 000	311892	968502	614580	1550388
			80·	253·	18·	0·000

130

No. n	Square n^2	Cube n^3	Square root $\sqrt{n}$	Sq. rt. of 10n $\sqrt{10n}$	Cube root $\sqrt[3]{n}$	Reciprocal $\frac{1}{n}$
			80·	253·	18·	0·000
6450	41 60 25 00	268 336 125 000	311892 6226	968502 19687	614580 962	1550388 241
6451	41 61 54 01	268 460 951 851	318118 6225	988189 19685	615542 962	1550147 240
6452	41 62 83 04	268 585 817 408	324343 6224	*007874 19684	616504 961	1549907 240
6453	41 64 12 09	268 710 721 677	330567 6224	027558 19682	617465 962	1549667 240
6454	41 65 41 16	268 835 664 664	336791 6224	047240 19680	618427 962	1549427 240
6455	41 66 70 25	268 960 646 375	343015 6223	066920 19679	619389 961	1549187 240
6456	41 67 99 36	269 085 666 816	349238 6222	086599 19678	620350 961	1548947 240
6457	41 69 28 49	269 210 725 993	355460 6222	106277 19676	621311 962	1548707 240
6458	41 70 57 64	269 335 823 912	361682 6222	125953 19675	622273 961	1548467 240
6459	41 71 86 81	269 460 960 579	367904 6221	145628 19673	623234 961	1548227 239
6460	41 73 16 00	269 586 136 000	374125 6221	165301 19671	624195 961	1547988 240
6461	41 74 45 21	269 711 350 181	380346 6220	184972 19670	625156 961	1547748 239
6462	41 75 74 44	269 836 603 128	386566 6220	204642 19668	626117 960	1547509 240
6463	41 77 03 69	269 961 894 847	392786 6219	224310 19667	627077 961	1547269 239
6464	41 78 32 96	270 087 225 344	399005 6219	243977 19666	628038 961	1547030 240
6465	41 79 62 25	270 212 594 625	405224 6218	263643 19664	628999 960	1546790 239
6466	41 80 91 56	270 338 002 696	411442 6218	283307 19662	629959 960	1546551 239
6467	41 82 20 89	270 463 449 563	417660 6217	302969 19661	630919 961	1546312 239
6468	41 83 50 24	270 588 935 232	423877 6217	322630 19659	631880 960	1546073 239
6469	41 84 79 61	270 714 459 709	430094 6216	342289 19658	632840 960	1545834 239
6470	41 86 09 00	270 840 023 000	436310 6216	361947 19656	633800 960	1545595 239
6471	41 87 38 41	270 965 625 111	442526 6215	381603 19655	634760 960	1545356 239
6472	41 88 67 84	271 091 266 048	448741 6215	401258 19653	635720 959	1545117 238
6473	41 89 97 29	271 216 945 817	454956 6215	420911 19652	636679 960	1544879 239
6474	41 91 26 76	271 342 664 424	461171 6214	440563 19650	637639 960	1544640 238
6475	41 92 56 25	271 468 421 875	467385 6213	460213 19649	638599 959	1544402 239
6476	41 93 85 76	271 594 218 176	473598 6213	479862 19647	639558 960	1544163 238
6477	41 95 15 29	271 720 053 333	479811 6213	499509 19645	640518 959	1543925 239
6478	41 96 44 84	271 845 927 352	486024 6212	519154 19645	641477 959	1543686 238
6479	41 97 74 41	271 971 840 239	492236 6211	538799 19642	642436 959	1543448 238
6480	41 99 04 00	272 097 792 000	498447 6211	558441 19641	643395 959	1543210 238
6481	42 00 33 61	272 223 782 641	504658 6211	578082 19640	644354 959	1542972 238
6482	42 01 63 24	272 349 812 168	510869 6210	597722 19638	645313 959	1542734 238
6483	42 02 92 89	272 475 880 587	517079 6210	617360 19637	646272 958	1542496 238
6484	42 04 22 56	272 601 987 904	523289 6209	636997 19635	647230 959	1542258 238
6485	42 05 52 25	272 728 134 125	529498 6208	656632 19633	648189 958	1542020 238
6486	42 06 81 96	272 854 319 256	535706 6209	676265 19632	649147 959	1541782 237
6487	42 08 11 69	272 980 543 303	541915 6207	695897 19631	650106 958	1541545 238
6488	42 09 41 44	273 106 806 272	548122 6207	715528 19629	651064 958	1541307 237
6489	42 10 71 21	273 233 108 169	554329 6207	735157 19627	652022 958	1541070 238
6490	42 12 01 00	273 359 449 000	560536 6207	754784 19626	652980 958	1540832 237
6491	42 13 30 81	273 485 828 771	566743 6205	774410 19624	653938 958	1540595 238
6492	42 14 60 64	273 612 247 488	572948 6206	794034 19623	654896 958	1540357 237
6493	42 15 90 49	273 738 705 157	579154 6204	813657 19622	655854 958	1540120 237
6494	42 17 20 36	273 865 201 784	585358 6205	833279 19620	656812 957	1539883 237
6495	42 18 50 25	273 991 737 375	591563 6204	852899 19618	657769 958	1539646 237
6496	42 19 80 16	274 118 311 936	597767 6203	872517 19617	658727 957	1539409 237
6497	42 21 10 09	274 244 925 473	603970 6203	892134 19615	659684 957	1539172 237
6498	42 22 40 04	274 371 577 992	610173 6203	911749 19614	660641 957	1538935 237
6499	42 23 70 01	274 498 269 499	616376 6201	931363 19613	661599 958	1538698 236
6500	42 25 00 00	274 625 000 000	622577	950976	662556	1538462
			80·	254·	18·	0·000

No. n	Square n^2	Cube n^3	Square root $\sqrt{n}$	Sq. rt. of $10n$ $\sqrt{10n}$	Cube root $\sqrt[3]{n}$	Reciprocal $\dfrac{1}{n}$
			80·	254·	18·	0·000
6500	42 25 00 00	274 625 000 000	622577 6202	950976 19611	662556 957	1538462 237
6501	42 26 30 01	274 751 769 501	628779 6201	970587 19609	663513 957	1538225 237
6502	42 27 60 04	274 878 578 008	634980 6201	990196 19608	664470 957	1537988 237
6503	42 28 90 09	275 005 425 527	641181 6200	*009804 19606	665427 956	1537752 237
6504	42 30 20 16	275 132 312 064	647381 6199	029410 19605	666383 957	1537515 236
6505	42 31 50 25	275 259 237 625	653580 6199	049015 19603	667340 956	1537279 236
6506	42 32 80 36	275 386 202 216	659779 6199	068618 19602	668296 957	1537043 236
6507	42 34 10 49	275 513 205 843	665978 6198	088220 19600	669253 957	1536807 237
6508	42 35 40 64	275 640 248 512	672176 6198	107820 19599	670209 956	1536570 236
6509	42 36 70 81	275 767 330 229	678374 6197	127419 19597	671165 956	1536334 236
6510	42 38 01 00	275 894 451 000	684571 6197	147016 19596	672121 956	1536098 236
6511	42 39 31 21	276 021 610 831	690768 6197	166612 19595	673077 956	1535862 236
6512	42 40 61 44	276 148 809 728	696964 6196	186207 19592	674033 956	1535627 235
6513	42 41 91 69	276 276 047 697	703160 6195	205799 19592	674989 956	1535391 236
6514	42 43 21 96	276 403 324 744	709355 6195	225391 19589	675945 956	1535155 236
6515	42 44 52 25	276 530 640 875	715550 6194	244980 19589	676901 955	1534919 235
6516	42 45 82 56	276 657 996 096	721744 6194	264569 19586	677856 956	1534684 236
6517	42 47 12 89	276 785 390 413	727938 6194	284155 19586	678812 955	1534448 235
6518	42 48 43 24	276 912 823 832	734132 6192	303741 19583	679767 955	1534213 235
6519	42 49 73 61	277 040 296 359	740324 6193	323324 19583	680722 955	1533978 236
6520	42 51 04 00	277 167 808 000	746517 6192	342907 19580	681677 955	1533742 235
6521	42 52 34 41	277 295 358 761	752709 6191	362487 19580	682632 955	1533507 235
6522	42 53 64 84	277 422 948 648	758900 6191	382067 19577	683587 955	1533272 235
6523	42 54 95 29	277 550 577 667	765091 6191	401644 19577	684542 955	1533037 235
6524	42 56 25 76	277 678 245 824	771282 6190	421221 19574	685497 955	1532802 235
6525	42 57 56 25	277 805 953 125	777472 6190	440795 19574	686452 954	1532567 235
6526	42 58 86 76	277 933 699 576	783662 6189	460369 19572	687406 955	1532332 235
6527	42 60 17 29	278 061 485 183	789851 6189	479941 19570	688361 954	1532097 235
6528	42 61 47 84	278 189 309 952	796040 6188	499511 19569	689315 954	1531863 234
6529	42 62 78 41	278 317 173 889	802228 6187	519080 19567	690269 954	1531628 235
6530	42 64 09 00	278 445 077 000	808415 6188	538647 19566	691223 954	1531394 235
6531	42 65 39 61	278 573 019 291	814603 6186	558213 19564	692177 954	1531159 234
6532	42 66 70 24	278 701 000 768	820789 6187	577777 19563	693131 954	1530925 235
6533	42 68 00 89	278 829 021 437	826976 6186	597340 19561	694085 954	1530690 234
6534	42 69 31 56	278 957 081 304	833162 6185	616901 19560	695039 954	1530456 234
6535	42 70 62 25	279 085 180 375	839347 6185	636461 19558	695993 953	1530222 234
6536	42 71 92 96	279 213 318 656	845532 6184	656019 19557	696946 953	1529988 234
6537	42 73 23 69	279 341 496 153	851716 6184	675576 19555	697900 953	1529754 234
6538	42 74 54 44	279 469 712 872	857900 6183	695131 19554	698853 953	1529520 234
6539	42 75 85 21	279 597 968 819	864083 6183	714685 19552	699806 954	1529286 234
6540	42 77 16 00	279 726 264 000	870266 6183	734237 19551	700760 953	1529052 234
6541	42 78 46 81	279 854 598 421	876449 6182	753788 19549	701713 953	1528818 234
6542	42 79 77 64	279 982 972 088	882631 6182	773337 19548	702666 953	1528585 233
6543	42 81 08 49	280 111 385 007	888813 6181	792885 19546	703619 953	1528351 234
6544	42 82 39 36	280 239 837 184	894994 6180	812431 19545	704572 952	1528117 233
6545	42 83 70 25	280 368 328 625	.901174 6180	831976 19543	705524 953	1527884 234
6546	42 85 01 16	280 496 859 336	907354 6180	851519 19542	706477 952	1527650 233
6547	42 86 32 09	280 625 429 323	913534 6179	871061 19541	707429 953	1527417 233
6548	42 87 63 04	280 754 038 592	919713 6179	890602 19541	708382 952	1527184 233
6549	42 88 94 01	280 882 687 149	925892 6178	910140 19538	709334 952	1526951 233
6550	42 90 25 00	281 011 375 000	932070 80·	929678 255·	710286 18·	1526718 0·000

No. n	Square n²	Cube n³	Square root √n	Sq. rt. of 10n √10n	Cube root ∛n	Reciprocal 1/n
			80·	255·	18·	0·000
6550	42 90 25 00	281 011 375 000	932070 6178	929678 19536	710286	1526718 233
6551	42 91 56 01	281 140 102 151	938248 6177	949214 19534	711238 952	1526485 233
6552	42 92 87 04	281 268 868 608	944425 6177	968748 19533	712190 952	1526252 233
6553	42 94 18 09	281 397 674 377	950602 6177	988281 19531	713142 952	1526019 233
6554	42 95 49 16	281 526 519 464	956779 6175	*007812 19530	714094 952	1525786 233
6555	42 96 80 25	281 655 403 875	962954 6176	027342 19529	715046 952	1525553 233
6556	42 98 11 36	281 784 327 616	969130 6175	046871 19527	715998 952	1525320 233
6557	42 99 42 49	281 913 290 693	975305 6174	066398 19525	716949 951	1525088 232
6558	43 00 73 64	282 042 293 112	981479 6174	085923 19524	717901 952	1524855 233
6559	43 02 04 81	282 171 334 879	987653 6174	105447 19522	718852 951	1524623 232
6560	43 03 36 00	282 300 416 000	993827 6173	124969 19521	719803 951	1524390 232
6561	43 04 67 21	282 429 536 481	*000000 6173	144490 19520	720754 951	1524158 232
6562	43 05 98 44	282 558 696 328	006173 6172	164010 19518	721705 951	1523926 232
6563	43 07 29 69	282 687 895 547	012345 6171	183528 19516	722656 951	1523693 233
6564	43 08 60 96	282 817 134 144	018516 6172	203044 19516	723607 951	1523461 232
6565	43 09 92 25	282 946 412 125	024688 6170	222560 19513	724558 951	1523229 232
6566	43 11 23 56	283 075 729 496	030858 6171	242073 19512	725509 950	1522997 232
6567	43 12 54 89	283 205 086 263	037029 6169	261585 19511	726459 950	1522765 232
6568	43 13 86 24	283 334 482 432	043198 6170	281096 19509	727410 950	1522533 232
6569	43 15 17 61	283 463 918 009	049368 6169	300605 19507	728360 951	1522302 231
6570	43 16 49 00	283 593 393 000	055537 6168	320112 19506	729311 950	1522070 232
6571	43 17 80 41	283 722 907 411	061705 6168	339618 19505	730261 950	1521838 232
6572	43 19 11 84	283 852 461 248	067873 6167	359123 19503	731211 950	1521607 231
6573	43 20 43 29	283 982 054 517	074040 6167	378626 19502	732161 950	1521375 232
6574	43 21 74 76	284 111 687 224	080207 6167	398128 19500	733111 950	1521144 231
6575	43 23 06 25	284 241 359 375	086374 6166	417628 19499	734061 949	1520913 232
6576	43 24 37 76	284 371 070 976	092540 6165	437127 19497	735010 950	1520681 231
6577	43 25 69 29	284 500 822 033	098705 6165	456624 19496	735960 950	1520450 231
6578	43 27 00 84	284 630 612 552	104870 6165	476120 19494	736909 950	1520219 231
6579	43 28 32 41	284 760 442 539	111035 6164	495614 19493	737859 949	1519988 231
6580	43 29 64 00	284 890 312 000	117199 6164	515107 19491	738808 949	1519757 231
6581	43 30 95 61	285 020 220 941	123363 6163	534598 19490	739757 950	1519526 231
6582	43 32 27 24	285 150 169 368	129526 6163	554088 19488	740707 949	1519295 231
6583	43 33 58 89	285 280 157 287	135689 6162	573576 19487	741656 948	1519064 230
6584	43 34 90 56	285 410 184 704	141851 6162	593063 19485	742604 949	1518834 231
6585	43 36 22 25	285 540 251 625	148013 6161	612548 19484	743553 949	1518603 231
6586	43 37 53 96	285 670 358 056	154174 6161	632032 19483	744502 949	1518372 230
6587	43 38 85 69	285 800 504 003	160335 6161	651515 19481	745451 948	1518142 231
6588	43 40 17 44	285 930 689 472	166496 6159	670996 19479	746399 949	1517911 230
6589	43 41 49 21	286 060 914 469	172655 6160	690475 19478	747348 948	1517681 230
6590	43 42 81 00	286 191 179 000	178815 6159	709953 19477	748296 948	1517451 231
6591	43 44 12 81	286 321 483 071	184974 6159	729430 19475	749244 949	1517220 230
6592	43 45 44 64	286 451 826 688	191133 6158	748905 19473	750193 948	1516990 230
6593	43 46 76 49	286 582 209 857	197291 6157	768378 19472	751141 948	1516760 230
6594	43 48 08 36	286 712 632 584	203448 6157	787850 19471	752089 948	1516530 230
6595	43 49 40 25	286 843 094 875	209605 6157	807321 19469	753037 947	1516300 230
6596	43 50 72 16	286 973 596 736	215762 6156	826790 19468	753984 948	1516070 229
6597	43 52 04 09	287 104 138 173	221918 6156	846258 19466	754932 948	1515841 230
6598	43 53 36 04	287 234 719 192	228074 6155	865724 19464	755880 947	1515611 230
6599	43 54 68 01	287 365 339 799	234229 6155	885188 19464	756827 948	1515381 229
6600	43 56 00 00	287 496 000 000	240384	904652	757775	1515152
			81·	256·	18·	0·000

No. n	Square n^2	Cube n^3	Square root $\sqrt{n}$	Sq. rt. of $10n$ $\sqrt{10n}$	Cube root $\sqrt[3]{n}$	Reciprocal $\dfrac{1}{n}$
			81·	256·	18·	0·000
6600	43 56 00 00	287 496 000 000	240384 6154	904652 19461	757775 947	1515152 230
6601	43 57 32 01	287 626 699 801	246538 6154	924113 19461	758722 947	1514922 230
6602	43 58 64 04	287 757 439 208	252692 6154	943574 19458	759669 947	1514693 230
6603	43 59 96 09	287 888 218 227	258846 6153	963032 19458	760616 947	1514463 229
6604	43 61 28 16	288 019 036 864	264999 6152	982490 19456	761563 947	1514234 229
6605	43 62 60 25	288 149 895 125	271151 6152	*001946 19454	762510 947	1514005 230
6606	43 63 92 36	288 280 793 016	277303 6152	021400 19453	763457 947	1513775 229
6607	43 65 24 49	288 411 730 543	283455 6151	040853 19451	764404 946	1513546 229
6608	43 66 56 64	288 542 707 712	289606 6150	060304 19450	765350 947	1513317 229
6609	43 67 88 81	288 673 724 529	295756 6150	079754 19449	766297 946	1513088 229
6610	43 69 21 00	288 804 781 000	301906 6150	099203 19447	767243 947	1512859 229
6611	43 70 53 21	288 935 877 131	308056 6149	118650 19445	768190 946	1512630 228
6612	43 71 85 44	289 067 012 928	314205 6149	138095 19444	769136 946	1512402 229
6613	43 73 17 69	289 198 188 397	320354 6148	157539 19443	770082 946	1512173 229
6614	43 74 49 96	289 329 403 544	326502 6148	176982 19441	771028 946	1511944 228
6615	43 75 82 25	289 460 658 375	332650 6148	196423 19440	771974 946	1511716 229
6616	43 77 14 56	289 591 952 896	338798 6147	215863 19438	772920 946	1511487 228
6617	43 78 46 89	289 723 287 113	344945 6146	235301 19437	773866 946	1511259 228
6618	43 79 79 24	289 854 661 032	351091 6146	254738 19435	774812 945	1511031 229
6619	43 81 11 61	289 986 074 659	·357237 6145	274173 19434	775757 946	1510802 228
6620	43 82 44 00	290 117 528 000	363382 6145	293607 19432	776703 945	1510574 228
6621	43 83 76 41	290 249 021 061	369527 6145	313039 19431	777648 945	1510346 228
6622	43 85 08 84	290 380 553 848	375672 6144	332470 19429	778593 946	1510118 228
6623	43 86 41 29	290 512 126 367	381816 6144	351899 19428	779539 945	1509890 228
6624	43 87 73 76	290 643 738 624	387960 6143	371327 19427	780484 945	1509662 228
6625	43 89 06 25	290 775 390 625	394103 6143	390754 19425	781429 945	1509434 228
6626	43 90 38 76	290 907 082 376	400246 6142	410179 19423	782374 945	1509206 228
6627	43 91 71 29	291 038 813 883	406388 6142	429602 19422	783319 944	1508978 227
6628	43 93 03 84	291 170 585 152	412530 6141	449024 19421	784263 945	1508751 228
6629	43 94 36 41	291 302 396 189	418671 6141	468445 19419	785208 944	1508523 227
6630	43 95 69 00	291 434 247 000	424812 6140	487864 19417	786152 945	1508296 228
6631	43 97 01 61	291 566 137 591	430952 6140	507281 19417	787097 944	1508068 227
6632	43 98 34 24	291 698 067 968	437092 6140	526698 19414	788041 945	1507841 228
6633	43 99 66 89	291 830 038 137	443232 6139	546112 19414	788986 944	1507613 227
6634	44 00 99 56	291 962 048 104	449371 6138	565526 19411	789930 944	1507386 227
6635	44 02 32 25	292 094 097 875	455509 6138	584937 19411	790874 944	1507159 227
6636	44 03 64 96	292 226 187 456	461647 6138	604348 19409	791818 944	1506932 227
6637	44 04 97 69	292 358 316 853	467785 6137	623757 19407	792762 943	1506705 227
6638	44 06 30 44	292 490 486 072	473922 6137	643164 19406	793705 944	1506478 227
6639	44 07 63 21	292 622 695 119	480059 6136	662570 19405	794649 944	1506251 227
6640	44 08 96 00	292 754 944 000	486195 6136	681975 19403	795593 943	1506024 227
6641	44 10 28 81	292 887 232 721	492331 6135	701378 19401	796536 943	1505797 226
6642	44 11 61 64	293 019 561 288	498466 6135	720779 19400	797480 943	1505571 227
6643	44 12 94 49	293 151 929 707	504601 6134	740179 19399	798423 943	1505344 227
6644	44 14 27 36	293 284 337 984	510735 6134	759578 19397	799366 943	1505117 226
6645	44 15 60 25	293 416 786 125	516869 6134	778975 19396	800309 943	1504891 227
6646	44 16 93 16	293 549 274 136	523003 6133	798371 19394	801252 943	1504664 226
6647	44 18 26 09	293 681 802 023	529136 6132	817765 19393	802195 943	1504438 226
6648	44 19 59 04	293 814 369 792	535268 6133	837158 19391	803138 943	1504212 226
6649	44 20 92 01	293 946 977 449	541401 6131	856549 19390	804081 943	1503986 227
6650	44 22 25 00	294 079 625 000	547532 81·	875939 257·	805024 18·	1503759 0·000

No. n	Square n^2	Cube n^3	Square root $\sqrt{n}$	Sq. rt. of $10n$ $\sqrt{10n}$	Cube root $\sqrt[3]{n}$	Reciprocal $\frac{1}{n}$
			$81\cdot$	$257\cdot$	$18\cdot$	$0\cdot000$
6650	44 22 25 00	294 079 625 000	547532 $_{6131}$	875939 $_{19389}$	805024 $_{942}$	1503759 $_{226}$
6651	44 23 58 01	294 212 312 451	553663 $_{6131}$	895328 $_{19387}$	805966 $_{942}$	1503533 $_{226}$
6652	44 24 91 04	294 345 039 808	559794 $_{6130}$	914715 $_{19385}$	806909 $_{943}$	1503307 $_{226}$
6653	44 26 24 09	294 477 807 077	565924 $_{6130}$	934100 $_{19384}$	807851 $_{942}$	1503081 $_{226}$
6654	44 27 57 16	294 610 614 264	572054 $_{6129}$	953484 $_{19383}$	808793 $_{942}$	1502855 $_{225}$
6655	44 28 90 25	294 743 461 375	578183 $_{6129}$	972867 $_{19381}$	809735 $_{943}$	1502630 $_{226}$
6656	44 30 23 36	294 876 348 416	584312 $_{6129}$	992248 $_{19380}$	810678 $_{941}$	1502404 $_{226}$
6657	44 31 56 49	295 009 275 393	590441 $_{6128}$	*011628 $_{19378}$	811619 $_{941}$	1502178 $_{225}$
6658	44 32 89 64	295 142 242 312	596569 $_{6127}$	031006 $_{19377}$	812561 $_{942}$	1501953 $_{226}$
6659	44 34 22 81	295 275 249 179	602696 $_{6127}$	050383 $_{19375}$	813503 $_{942}$	1501727 $_{225}$
6660	44 35 56 00	295 408 296 000	608823 $_{6127}$	069758 $_{19374}$	814445 $_{942}$	1501502 $_{226}$
6661	44 36 89 21	295 541 382 781	614950 $_{6126}$	089132 $_{19372}$	815387 $_{942}$	1501276 $_{226}$
6662	44 38 22 44	295 674 509 528	621076 $_{6125}$	108504 $_{19371}$	816328 $_{941}$	1501051 $_{226}$
6663	44 39 55 69	295 807 676 247	627201 $_{6126}$	127875 $_{19370}$	817269 $_{942}$	1500825 $_{225}$
6664	44 40 88 96	295 940 882 944	633327 $_{6124}$	147245 $_{19368}$	818211 $_{941}$	1500600 $_{225}$
6665	44 42 22 25	296 074 129 625	639451 $_{6125}$	166613 $_{19366}$	819152 $_{941}$	1500375 $_{225}$
6666	44 43 55 56	296 207 416 296	645576 $_{6123}$	185979 $_{19366}$	820093 $_{941}$	1500150 $_{225}$
6667	44 44 88 89	296 340 742 963	651699 $_{6124}$	205345 $_{19363}$	821034 $_{941}$	1499925 $_{225}$
6668	44 46 22 24	296 474 109 632	657823 $_{6123}$	224708 $_{19363}$	821975 $_{941}$	1499700 $_{225}$
6669	44 47 55 61	296 607 516 309	663946 $_{6122}$	244071 $_{19360}$	822916 $_{941}$	1499475 $_{225}$
6670	44 48 89 00	296 740 963 000	670068 $_{6122}$	263431 $_{19360}$	823857 $_{941}$	1499250 $_{224}$
6671	44 50 22 41	296 874 449 711	676190 $_{6121}$	282791 $_{19358}$	824798 $_{941}$	1499026 $_{225}$
6672	44 51 55 84	297 007 976 448	682311 $_{6121}$	302149 $_{19356}$	825738 $_{940}$	1498801 $_{225}$
6673	44 52 89 29	297 141 543 217	688432 $_{6121}$	321505 $_{19355}$	826679 $_{940}$	1498576 $_{224}$
6674	44 54 22 76	297 275 150 024	694553 $_{6120}$	340860 $_{19354}$	827619 $_{940}$	1498352 $_{225}$
6675	44 55 56 25	297 408 796 875	700673 $_{6120}$	360214 $_{19352}$	828559 $_{940}$	1498127 $_{224}$
6676	44 56 89 76	297 542 483 776	706793 $_{6119}$	379566 $_{19350}$	829499 $_{941}$	1497903 $_{224}$
6677	44 58 23 29	297 676 210 733	712912 $_{6119}$	398916 $_{19350}$	830440 $_{940}$	1497679 $_{225}$
6678	44 59 56 84	297 809 977 752	719031 $_{6118}$	418266 $_{19347}$	831380 $_{940}$	1497454 $_{224}$
6679	44 60 90 41	297 943 784 839	725149 $_{6118}$	437613 $_{19347}$	832320 $_{939}$	1497230 $_{224}$
6680	44 62 24 00	298 077 632 000	731267 $_{6117}$	456960 $_{19345}$	833259 $_{940}$	1497006 $_{224}$
6681	44 63 57 61	298 211 519 241	737384 $_{6117}$	476305 $_{19343}$	834199 $_{940}$	1496782 $_{224}$
6682	44 64 91 24	298 345 446 568	743501 $_{6117}$	495648 $_{19342}$	835139 $_{939}$	1496558 $_{224}$
6683	44 66 24 89	298 479 413 987	749618 $_{6116}$	514990 $_{19340}$	836078 $_{940}$	1496334 $_{224}$
6684	44 67 58 56	298 613 421 504	755734 $_{6115}$	534330 $_{19339}$	837018 $_{940}$	1496110 $_{224}$
6685	44 68 92 25	298 747 469 125	761849 $_{6115}$	553669 $_{19338}$	837957 $_{939}$	1495886 $_{223}$
6686	44 70 25 96	298 881 556 856	767964 $_{6115}$	573007 $_{19336}$	838896 $_{940}$	1495663 $_{224}$
6687	44 71 59 69	299 015 684 703	774079 $_{6114}$	592343 $_{19335}$	839836 $_{939}$	1495439 $_{224}$
6688	44 72 93 44	299 149 852 672	780193 $_{6114}$	611678 $_{19333}$	840775 $_{939}$	1495215 $_{223}$
6689	44 74 27 21	299 284 060 769	786307 $_{6113}$	631011 $_{19332}$	841714 $_{939}$	1494992 $_{224}$
6690	44 75 61 00	299 418 309 000	792420 $_{6113}$	650343 $_{19331}$	842653 $_{938}$	1494768 $_{223}$
6691	44 76 94 81	299 552 597 371	798533 $_{6112}$	669674 $_{19328}$	843591 $_{939}$	1494545 $_{223}$
6692	44 78 28 64	299 686 925 888	804645 $_{6112}$	689002 $_{19328}$	844530 $_{939}$	1494322 $_{224}$
6693	44 79 62 49	299 821 294 557	810757 $_{6112}$	708330 $_{19326}$	845469 $_{938}$	1494098 $_{223}$
6694	44 80 96 36	299 955 703 384	816869 $_{6111}$	727656 $_{19325}$	846407 $_{939}$	1493875 $_{223}$
6695	44 82 30 25	300 090 152 375	822980 $_{6110}$	746981 $_{19323}$	847346 $_{938}$	1493652 $_{223}$
6696	44 83 64 16	300 224 641 536	829090 $_{6110}$	766304 $_{19322}$	848284 $_{938}$	1493429 $_{223}$
6697	44 84 98 09	300 359 170 873	835200 $_{6110}$	785626 $_{19320}$	849222 $_{938}$	1493206 $_{223}$
6698	44 86 32 04	300 493 740 392	841310 $_{6109}$	804946 $_{19319}$	850160 $_{938}$	1492983 $_{223}$
6699	44 87 66 01	300 628 350 099	847419 $_{6109}$	824265 $_{19317}$	851098 $_{938}$	1492760 $_{223}$
6700	44 89 00 00	300 763 000 000	853528 $81\cdot$	843582 $258\cdot$	852036 $18\cdot$	1492537 $0\cdot000$

No. n	Square n^2	Cube n^3	Square root $\sqrt{n}$	Sq. rt. of $10n$ $\sqrt{10n}$	Cube root $\sqrt[3]{n}$	Reciprocal $\frac{1}{n}$
			81·	258·	18·	0·000
6700	44 89 00 00	300 763 000 000	853528 6108	843582 19316	852036 938	1492537 222
6701	44 90 34 01	300 897 690 101	859636 6108	862898 19315	852974 938	1492315 223
6702	44 91 68 04	301 032 420 408	865744 6107	882213 19313	853912 938	1492092 223
6703	44 93 02 09	301 167 190 927	871851 6107	901526 19313	854850 937	1491869 222
6704	44 94 36 16	301 302 001 664	877958 6106	920837 19311	855787 938	1491647 223
6705	44 95 70 25	301 436 852 625	884064 6106	940148 19308	856725 937	1491424 222
6706	44 97 04 36	301 571 743 816	890170 6106	959456 19308	857662 937	1491202 222
6707	44 98 38 49	301 706 675 243	896276 6105	978764 19305	858599 938	1490980 222
6708	44 99 72 64	301 841 646 912	902381 6105	998069 19305	859537 937	1490757 223
6709	45 01 06 81	301 976 658 829	908486 6104	*017374 19303	860474 937	1490535 222
6710	45 02 41 00	302 111 711 000	914590 6103	036677 19302	861411 937	1490313 222
6711	45 03 75 21	302 246 803 431	920693 6104	055979 19300	862348 937	1490091 222
6712	45 05 09 44	302 381 936 128	926797 6102	075279 19298	863285 936	1489869 222
6713	45 06 43 69	302 517 109 097	932899 6103	094577 19298	864221 937	1489647 222
6714	45 07 77 96	302 652 322 344	939002 6102	113875 19295	865158 937	1489425 222
6715	45 09 12 25	302 787 575 875	945104 6101	133170 19295	866095 936	1489203 221
6716	45 10 46 56	302 922 869 696	951205 6101	152465 19293	867031 936	1488982 222
6717	45 11 80 89	303 058 203 813	957306 6100	171758 19291	867967 937	1488760 222
6718	45 13 15 24	303 193 578 232	963406 6101	191049 19290	868904 936	1488538 221
6719	45 14 49 61	303 328 992 959	969507 6099	210339 19289	869840 936	1488317 222
6720	45 15 84 00	303 464 448 000	975606 6099	229628 19287	870776 936	1488095 221
6721	45 17 18 41	303 599 943 361	981705 6099	248915 19286	871712 936	1487874 222
6722	45 18 52 84	303 735 479 048	987804 6098	268201 19284	872648 936	1487652 221
6723	45 19 87 29	303 871 055 067	993902 6098	287485 19283	873584 935	1487431 221
6724	45 21 21 76	304 006 671 424	*000000 6097	306768 19282	874519 936	1487210 221
6725	45 22 56 25	304 142 328 125	006097 6097	326050 19280	875455 936	1486989 221
6726	45 23 90 76	304 278 025 176	012194 6097	345330 19278	876391 935	1486768 221
6727	45 25 25 29	304 413 762 583	018291 6096	364608 19277	877326 935	1486547 221
6728	45 26 59 84	304 549 540 352	024387 6095	383885 19276	878261 936	1486326 221
6729	45 27 94 41	304 685 358 489	030482 6095	403161 19274	879197 935	1486105 221
6730	45 29 29 00	304 821 217 000	036577 6095	422435 19273	880132 935	1485884 221
6731	45 30 63 61	304 957 115 891	042672 6094	441708 19272	881067 935	1485663 221
6732	45 31 98 24	305 093 055 168	048766 6094	460980 19270	882002 935	1485443 221
6733	45 33 32 89	305 229 034 837	054860 6093	480250 19268	882937 935	1485222 221
6734	45 34 67 56	305 365 054 904	060953 6093	499518 19267	883872 934	1485001 220
6735	45 36 02 25	305 501 115 375	067046 6092	518785 19266	884806 935	1484781 220
6736	45 37 36 96	305 637 216 256	073138 6092	538051 19264	885741 934	1484561 221
6737	45 38 71 69	305 773 357 553	079230 6091	557315 19263	886675 935	1484340 220
6738	45 40 06 44	305 909 539 272	085321 6091	576578 19262	887610 934	1484120 220
6739	45 41 41 21	306 045 761 419	091412 6091	595840 19260	888544 934	1483900 220
6740	45 42 76 00	306 182 024 000	097503 6090	615100 19258	889478 935	1483680 221
6741	45 44 10 81	306 318 327 021	103593 6090	634358 19257	890413 934	1483459 220
6742	45 45 45 64	306 454 670 488	109683 6089	653615 19256	891347 934	1483239 220
6743	45 46 80 49	306 591 054 407	115772 6089	672871 19254	892281 933	1483019 219
6744	45 48 15 36	306 727 478 784	121861 6088	692125 19253	893214 934	1482800 220
6745	45 49 50 25	306 863 943 625	127949 6088	711378 19252	894148 934	1482580 220
6746	45 50 85 16	307 000 448 936	134037 6087	730630 19250	895082 934	1482360 220
6747	45 52 20 09	307 136 994 723	140124 6087	749880 19248	896016 933	1482140 219
6748	45 53 55 04	307 273 580 992	146211 6087	769128 19247	896949 933	1481921 220
6749	45 54 90 01	307 410 207 749	152298 6086	788375 19246	897882 933	1481701 220
6750	45 56 25 00	307 546 875 000	158384 82·	807621 259·	898816 18·	1481481 0·000

No. n	Square n^2	Cube n^3	Square root $\sqrt{n}$	Sq. rt. of 10n $\sqrt{10n}$	Cube root $\sqrt[3]{n}$	Reciprocal $\dfrac{1}{n}$
			82·	259·	18·	0·000
6750	45 56 25 00	307 546 875 000	158384 6085	807621 19244	898816 933	1481481
6751	45 57 60 01	307 683 582 751	164469 6085	826865 19243	899749 933	1481262 219
6752	45 58 95 04	307 820 331 008	170554 6085	846108 19242	900682 933	1481043 219
6753	45 60 30 09	307 957 119 777	176639 6084	865350 19240	901615 933	1480823 220
6754	45 61 65 16	308 093 949 064	182723 6084	884590 19238	902548 933	1480604 219
						216
6755	45 63 00 25	308 230 818 875	188807 6083	903828 19238	903481 933	1480385 219
6756	45 64 35 36	308 367 729 216	194890 6083	923066 19235	904414 932	1480166 219
6757	45 65 70 49	308 504 680 093	200973 6083	942301 19235	905346 933	1479947 219
6758	45 67 05 64	308 641 671 512	207056 6082	961536 19233	906279 932	1479728 219
6759	45 68 40 81	308 778 703 479	213138 6081	980769 19231	907211 933	1479509 219
6760	45 69 76 00	308 915 776 000	219219 6081	*000000 19230	908144 932	1479290 219
6761	45 71 11 21	309 052 889 081	225300 6081	019230 19229	909076 932	1479071 219
6762	45 72 46 44	309 190 042 728	231381 6080	038459 19227	910008 033	1478852 218
6763	45 73 81 69	309 327 236 947	237461 6080	057686 19226	910941 933	1478634 219
6764	45 75 16 96	309 464 471 744	243541 6079	076912 19224	911873 932	1478415 218
6765	45 76 52 25	309 601 747 125	249620 6079	096136 19223	912805 931	1478197 219
6766	45 77 87 56	309 739 063 096	255699 6078	115359 19222	913736 932	1477978 218
6767	45 79 22 89	309 876 419 663	261777 6078	134581 19220	914668 932	1477760 219
6768	45 80 58 24	310 013 816 832	267855 6078	153801 19218	915600 931	1477541 218
6769	45 81 93 61	310 151 254 609	273933 6077	173019 19218	916531 932	1477323 218
6770	45 83 29 00	310 288 733 000	280010 6076	192237 19215	917463 931	1477105 218
6771	45 84 64 41	310 426 252 011	286086 6076	211452 19215	918394 932	1476887 218
6772	45 85 99 84	310 563 811 648	292162 6076	230667 19213	919326 931	1476669 218
6773	45 87 35 29	310 701 411 917	298238 6075	249880 19212	920257 931	1476451 218
6774	45 88 70 76	310 839 052 824	304313 6075	269092 19210	921188 931	1476233 218
6775	45 90 06 25	310 976 734 375	310388 6075	288302 19208	922119 931	1476015 218
6776	45 91 41 76	311 114 456 576	316463 6073	307510 19208	923050 931	1475797 218
6777	45 92 77 29	311 252 219 433	322536 6074	326718 19206	923981 930	1475579 218
6778	45 94 12 84	311 390 022 952	328610 6073	345924 19204	924911 931	1475361 217
6779	45 95 48 41	311 527 867 139	334683 6072	365128 19203	925842 931	1475144 218
6780	45 96 84 00	311 665 752 000	340755 6073	384331 19202	926773 930	1474926 217
6781	45 98 19 61	311 803 677 541	346828 6071	403533 19200	927703 930	1474709 218
6782	45 99 55 24	311 941 643 768	352899 6071	422733 19199	928633 931	1474491 217
6783	46 00 90 89	312 079 650 687	358970 6071	441932 19198	929564 930	1474274 217
6784	46 02 26 56	312 217 698 304	365041 6070	461130 19196	930494 930	1474057 218
6785	46 03 62 25	312 355 786 625	371111 6070	480326 19194	931424 930	1473839 217
6786	46 04 97 96	312 493 915 656	377181 6070	499520 19193	932354 930	1473622 217
6787	46 06 33 69	312 632 085 403	383251 6069	518713 19192	933284 930	1473405 217
6788	46 07 69 44	312 770 295 872	389320 6068	537905 19190	934214 930	1473188 217
6789	46 09 05 21	312 908 547 069	395388 6068	557095 19189	935144 929	1472971 217
6790	46 10 41 00	313 046 839 000	401456 6068	576284 19188	936073 930	1472754 217
6791	46 11 76 81	313 185 171 671	407524 6067	595472 19186	937003 929	1472537 217
6792	46 13 12 64	313 323 545 088	413591 6067	614658 19185	937932 930	1472320 216
6793	46 14 48 49	313 461 959 257	419658 6066	633843 19183	938862 929	1472104 217
6794	46 15 84 36	313 600 414 184	425724 6066	653026 19182	939791 929	1471887 217
6795	46 17 20 25	313 738 909 875	431790 6065	672208 19180	940720 929	1471670 216
6796	46 18 56 16	313 877 446 336	437855 6065	691388 19179	941649 929	1471454 217
6797	46 19 92 09	314 016 023 573	443920 6065	710567 19178	942578 929	1471237 216
6798	46 21 28 04	314 154 641 592	449985 6064	729745 19176	943507 929	1471021 216
6799	46 22 64 01	314 293 300 399	456049 6064	748921 19175	944436 929	1470805 217
6800	46 24 00 00	314 432 000 000	462113 82·	768096 260·	945365 18·	1470588 0·000

No. n	Square n^2	Cube n^3	Square root $\sqrt{n}$	Sq. rt. of $10n$ $\sqrt{10n}$	Cube root $\sqrt[3]{n}$	Reciprocal $\dfrac{1}{n}$
			82·	260·	18·	0·000
6800	46 24 00 00	314 432 000 000	462113 6063	768096 19174	945365 928	1470588 216
6801	46 25 36 01	314 570 740 401	468176 6062	787270 19172	946293 929	1470372 216
6802	46 26 72 04	314 709 521 608	474238 6063	806442 19170	947222 928	1470156 216
6803	46 28 08 09	314 848 343 627	480301 6062	825612 19169	948150 929	1469940 216
6804	46 29 44 16	314 987 206 464	486363 6061	844781 19168	949079 928	1469724 216
6805	46 30 80 25	315 126 110 125	492424 6061	863949 19167	950007 928	1469508 216
6806	46 32 16 36	315 265 054 616	498485 6060	883116 19165	950935 928	1469292 216
6807	46 33 52 49	315 404 039 943	504545 6060	902281 19163	951863 928	1469076 216
6808	46 34 88 64	315 543 066 112	510605 6060	921444 19162	952791 928	1468860 216
6809	46 36 24 81	315 682 133 129	516665 6059	940606 19161	953719 928	1468644 215
6810	46 37 61 00	315 821 241 000	522724 6059	959767 19159	954647 928	1468429 216
6811	46 38 97 21	315 960 389 731	528783 6058	978926 19158	955575 928	1468213 215
6812	46 40 33 44	316 099 579 328	534841 6058	998084 19157	956503 927	1467998 215
6813	46 41 69 69	316 238 809 797	540899 6057	*017241 19155	957430 928	1467782 216
6814	46 43 05 96	316 378 081 144	546956 6057	036396 19154	958358 927	1467567 216
6815	46 44 42 25	316 517 393 375	553013 6057	055550 19152	959285 927	1467351 215
6816	46 45 78 56	316 656 746 496	559070 6056	074702 19151	960212 927	1467136 215
6817	46 47 14 89	316 796 140 513	565126 6055	093853 19149	961139 928	1466921 215
6818	46 48 51 24	316 935 575 432	571181 6056	113002 19148	962067 927	1466706 215
6819	46 49 87 61	317 075 051 259	577237 6054	132150 19147	962994 926	1466491 215
6820	46 51 24 00	317 214 568 000	583291 6055	151297 19145	963920 927	1466276 215
6821	46 52 60 41	317 354 125 661	589346 6053	170442 19144	964847 927	1466061 215
6822	46 53 96 84	317 493 724 248	595399 6054	189586 19143	965774 927	1465846 215
6823	46 55 33 29	317 633 363 767	601453 6053	208729 19141	966701 926	1465631 215
6824	46 56 69 76	317 773 044 224	607506 6052	227870 19140	967627 927	1465416 215
6825	46 58 06 25	317 912 765 625	613558 6052	247010 19138	968554 926	1465201 214
6826	46 59 42 76	318 052 527 976	619610 6052	266148 19137	969480 926	1464987 214
6827	46 60 79 29	318 192 331 283	625662 6051	285285 19135	970406 927	1464772 215
6828	46 62 15 84	318 332 175 552	631713 6051	304420 19134	971333 926	1464558 215
6829	46 63 52 41	318 472 060 789	637764 6050	323554 19133	972259 926	1464343 214
6830	46 64 89 00	318 611 987 000	643814 6050	342687 19131	973185 926	1464129 214
6831	46 66 25 61	318 751 954 191	649864 6049	361818 19130	974111 926	1463915 215
6832	46 67 62 24	318 891 962 368	655913 6049	380948 19129	975036 926	1463700 214
6833	46 68 98 89	319 032 011 537	661962 6049	400077 19127	975962 926	1463486 214
6834	46 70 35 56	319 172 101 704	668011 6048	419204 19125	976888 925	1463272 214
6835	46 71 72 25	319 312 232 875	674059 6047	438329 19125	977813 926	1463058 214
6836	46 73 08 96	319 452 405 056	680106 6048	457454 19122	978739 925	1462844 214
6837	46 74 45 69	319 592 618 253	686154 6046	476576 19122	979664 926	1462630 214
6838	46 75 82 44	319 732 872 472	692200 6047	495698 19120	980590 925	1462416 214
6839	46 77 19 21	319 873 167 719	698247 6046	514818 19119	981515 925	1462202 214
6840	46 78 56 00	320 013 504 000	704293 6045	533937 19117	982440 925	1461988 213
6841	46 79 92 81	320 153 881 321	710338 6045	553054 19116	983365 925	1461775 214
6842	46 81 29 64	320 294 299 688	716383 6044	572170 19114	984290 925	1461561 214
6843	46 82 66 49	320 434 759 107	722427 6045	591284 19113	985215 924	1461347 214
6844	46 84 03 36	320 575 259 584	728472 6043	610397 19112	986139 924	1461134 214
6845	46 85 40 25	320 715 801 125	734515 6043	629509 19110	987064 925	1460920 213
6846	46 86 77 16	320 856 383 736	740558 6043	648619 19109	987989 925	1460707 213
6847	46 88 14 09	320 997 007 423	746601 6042	667728 19108	988913 924	1460494 213
6848	46 89 51 04	321 137 672 192	752643 6042	686836 19106	989838 925	1460280 213
6849	46 90 88 01	321 278 378 049	758685 6042	705942 19105	990762 924	1460067 213
6850	46 92 25 00	321 419 125 000	764727 82·	725047 261·	991686 18·	1459854 0·000

No. n	Square n^2	Cube n^3	Square root $\sqrt{n}$	Sq. rt. of $10n$ $\sqrt{10n}$	Cube root $\sqrt[3]{n}$	Reciprocal $\frac{1}{n}$
			82·	261·	18·	0·000
6850	46 92 25 00	321 419 125 000	764727 _6041_	725047 _19103_	991686 _924_	145985₄ _213_
6851	46 93 62 01	321 559 913 051	770768 _6040_	744150 _19102_	992610 _924_	1459641 _213_
6852	46 94 99 04	321 700 742 208	776808 _6040_	763252 _19100_	993534 _924_	1459428 _213_
6853	46 96 36 09	321 841 612 477	782848 _6040_	782352 _19099_	994458 _924_	1459215 _213_
6854	46 97 73 16	321 982 523 864	788888 _6039_	801451 _19098_	995382 _924_	1459002 _213_
6855	46 99 10 25	322 123 476 375	794927 _6039_	820549 _19097_	996306 _924_	1458789 _213_
6856	47 00 47 36	322 264 470 016	800966 _6039_	839646 _19095_	997230 _924_	1458576 _212_
6857	47 01 84 49	322 405 504 793	807005 _6037_	858741 _19093_	998153 _924_	1458364 _213_
6858	47 03 21 64	322 546 580 712	813042 _6038_	877834 _19092_	999077 _924_	1458151 _213_
6859	47 04 58 81	322 687 697 779	819080 _6037_	896926 _19091_	*000000 _923_	1457938 _213_
6860	47 05 96 00	322 828 856 000	825117 _6037_	916017 _19089_	000923 _924_	1457726 _213_
6861	47 07 33 21	322 970 055 381	831154 _6036_	935106 _19088_	001847 _923_	1457513 _212_
6862	47 08 70 44	323 111 295 928	837190 _6035_	954194 _19087_	002770 _923_	1457301 _212_
6863	47 10 07 69	323 252 577 647	843225 _6036_	973281 _19085_	003693 _923_	1457089 _213_
6864	47 11 44 96	323 393 900 544	849261 _6035_	992366 _19084_	004616 _923_	1456876 _212_
6865	47 12 82 25	323 535 264 625	855296 _6034_	*011450 _19083_	005539 _922_	1456664 _212_
6866	47 14 19 56	323 676 669 896	861330 _6034_	030533 _19081_	006461 _923_	1456452 _212_
6867	47 15 56 89	323 818 116 363	867364 _6033_	049614 _19079_	007384 _923_	1456240 _212_
6868	47 16 94 24	323 959 604 032	873397 _6033_	068693 _19079_	008307 _922_	1456028 _212_
6869	47 18 31 61	324 101 132 909	879430 _6033_	087772 _19076_	009229 _923_	1455816 _212_
6870	47 19 69 00	324 242 703 000	885463 _6032_	106848 _19076_	010152 _922_	1455604 _212_
6871	47 21 06 41	324 384 314 311	891495 _6032_	125924 _19074_	011074 _922_	1455392 _212_
6872	47 22 43 84	324 525 966 848	897527 _6031_	144998 _19073_	011996 _922_	1455180 _212_
6873	47 23 81 29	324 667 660 617	903558 _6031_	164071 _19071_	012918 _922_	1454969 _211_
6874	47 25 18 76	324 809 395 624	909589 _6031_	183142 _19070_	013840 _922_	1454757 _212_
6875	47 26 56 25	324 951 171 875	915620 _6030_	202212 _19069_	014762 _922_	1454545 _211_
6876	47 27 93 76	325 092 989 376	921650 _6029_	221281 _19067_	015684 _922_	1454334 _212_
6877	47 29 31 29	325 234 848 133	927679 _6029_	240348 _19066_	016606 _922_	1454122 _211_
6878	47 30 68 84	325 376 748 152	933708 _6029_	259414 _19064_	017528 _921_	1453911 _211_
6879	47 32 06 41	325 518 689 439	939737 _6028_	278478 _19063_	018449 _922_	1453700 _212_
6880	47 33 44 00	325 660 672 000	945765 _6028_	297541 _19062_	019371 _921_	1453488 _211_
6881	47 34 81 61	325 802 695 841	951793 _6028_	316603 _19060_	020292 _922_	1453277 _211_
6882	47 36 19 24	325 944 760 968	957821 _6027_	335663 _19059_	021214 _921_	1453066 _211_
6883	47 37 56 89	326 086 867 387	963848 _6026_	354722 _19057_	022135 _921_	1452855 _211_
6884	47 38 94 56	326 229 015 104	969874 _6026_	373779 _19056_	023056 _921_	1452644 _211_
6885	47 40 32 25	326 371 204 125	975900 _6026_	392835 _19055_	023977 _921_	1452433 _211_
6886	47 41 69 96	326 513 434 456	981926 _6025_	411890 _19053_	024898 _921_	1452222 _211_
6887	47 43 07 69	326 655 706 103	987951 _6025_	430943 _19052_	025819 _921_	1452011 _211_
6888	47 44 45 44	326 798 019 072	993976 _6024_	449995 _19051_	026740 _921_	1451800 _211_
6889	47 45 83 21	326 940 373 369	*000000 _6024_	469046 _19049_	027661 _920_	1451589 _210_
6890	47 47 21 00	327 082 769 000	006024 _6023_	488095 _19048_	028581 _921_	1451379 _211_
6891	47 48 58 81	327 225 205 971	012047 _6023_	507143 _19046_	029502 _920_	1451168 _211_
6892	47 49 96 64	327 367 684 288	018070 _6023_	526189 _19045_	030422 _921_	1450958 _210_
6893	47 51 34 49	327 510 203 957	024093 _6022_	545234 _19044_	031343 _920_	1450747 _210_
6894	47 52 72 36	327 652 764 984	030115 _6022_	564278 _19042_	032263 _920_	1450537 _211_
6895	47 54 10 25	327 795 367 375	036137 _6021_	583320 _19041_	033183 _920_	1450326 _210_
6896	47 55 48 16	327 938 011 136	042158 _6021_	602361 _19039_	034103 _920_	1450116 _210_
6897	47 56 86 09	328 080 696 273	048179 _6020_	621400 _19039_	035023 _920_	1449906 _210_
6898	47 58 24 04	328 223 422 792	054199 _6020_	640439 _19036_	035943 _920_	1449696 _211_
6899	47 59 62 01	328 366 190 699	060219 _6020_	659475 _19036_	036863 _920_	1449485 _210_
6900	47 61 00 00	328 509 000 000	066239 83·	678511 262·	037783 19·	1449275 0·000

No. n	Square n²	Cube n³	Square root √n	Sq. rt. of 10n √10n	Cube root ∛n	Reciprocal 1/n
			83·	262·	19·	0·000
6900	47 61 00 00	328 509 000 000	066239 6019	678511 19034	037783 919	1449275 210
6901	47 62 38 01	328 651 850 701	072258 6018	697545 19032	038702 920	1449065 210
6902	47 63 76 04	328 794 742 808	078276 6019	716577 19032	039622 920	1448855 209
6903	47 65 14 09	328 937 676 327	084295 6017	735609 19029	040541 920	1448646 210
6904	47 66 52 16	329 080 651 264	090312 6018	754638 19029	041461 919	1448436 210
6905	47 67 90 25	329 223 667 625	096330 6017	773667 19027	042380 919	1448226 210
6906	47 69 28 36	329 366 725 416	102347 6016	792694 19026	043299 919	1448016 210
6907	47 70 66 49	329 509 824 643	108363 6016	811720 19024	044218 919	1447807 209
6908	47 72 04 64	329 652 965 312	114379 6016	830744 19023	045137 919	1447597 210
6909	47 73 42 81	329 796 147 429	120395 6015	849767 19022	046056 919	1447387 209
6910	47 74 81 00	329 939 371 000	126410 6014	868789 19020	046975 919	1447178 209
6911	47 76 19 21	330 082 636 031	132424 6015	887809 19019	047894 919	1446969 210
6912	47 77 57 44	330 225 942 528	138439 6014	906828 19017	048813 918	1446759 209
6913	47 78 95 69	330 369 290 497	144453 6013	925845 19016	049731 919	1446550 209
6914	47 80 33 96	330 512 679 944	150466 6013	944861 19015	050650 918	1446341 209
6915	47 81 72 25	330 656 110 875	156479 6013	963876 19013	051568 918	1446132 210
6916	47 83 10 56	330 799 583 296	162492 6012	982889 19012	052486 919	1445922 209
6917	47 84 48 89	330 943 097 213	168504 6011	*001901 19011	053405 918	1445713 209
6918	47 85 87 24	331 086 652 632	174515 6012	020912 19011	054323 918	1445504 208
6919	47 87 25 61	331 230 249 559	180527 6010	039921 19008	055241 918	1445296 208
6920	47 88 64 00	331 373 888 000	186537 6011	058929 19006	056159 918	1445087 209
6921	47 90 02 41	331 517 567 961	192548 6010	077935 19005	057077 918	1444878 209
6922	47 91 40 84	331 661 289 448	198558 6009	096940 19004	057995 917	1444669 209
6923	47 92 79 29	331 805 052 467	204567 6009	115944 19002	058912 918	1444460 208
6924	47 94 17 76	331 948 857 024	210576 6009	134946 19001	059830 917	1444252 209
6925	47 95 56 25	332 092 703 125	216585 6008	153947 19000	060747 918	1444043 208
6926	47 96 94 76	332 236 590 776	222593 6008	172947 18998	061665 917	1443835 209
6927	47 98 33 29	332 380 519 983	228601 6007	191945 18997	062582 917	1443626 208
6928	47 99 71 84	332 524 490 752	234608 6007	210942 18996	063499 918	1443418 208
6929	48 01 10 41	332 668 503 089	240615 6007	229938 18994	064417 917	1443210 209
6930	48 02 49 00	332 812 557 000	246622 6006	248932 18992	065334 917	1443001 208
6931	48 03 87 61	332 956 652 491	252628 6005	267924 18992	066251 917	1442793 208
6932	48 05 26 24	333 100 789 568	258633 6005	286916 18990	067168 916	1442585 208
6933	48 06 64 89	333 244 968 237	264638 6005	305906 18988	068084 917	1442377 208
6934	48 08 03 56	333 389 188 504	270643 6004	324894 18988	069001 917	1442169 208
6935	48 09 42 25	333 533 450 375	276647 6004	343882 18986	069918 916	1441961 208
6936	48 10 80 96	333 677 753 856	282651 6004	362868 18984	070834 917	1441753 208
6937	48 12 19 69	333 822 098 953	288655 6003	381852 18983	071751 916	1441545 207
6938	48 13 58 44	333 966 485 672	294658 6002	400835 18982	072667 917	1441338 208
6939	48 14 97 21	334 110 914 019	300660 6002	419817 18980	073584 916	1441130 208
6940	48 16 36 00	334 255 384 000	306662 6002	438797 18980	074500 916	1440922 207
6941	48 17 74 81	334 399 895 621	312664 6002	457777 18977	075416 916	1440715 208
6942	48 19 13 64	334 544 448 888	318665 6001	476754 18977	076332 916	1440507 207
6943	48 20 52 49	334 689 043 807	324666 6001	495731 18974	077248 916	1440300 208
6944	48 21 91 36	334 833 680 384	330667 6000	514705 18974	078164 915	1440092 207
6945	48 23 30 25	334 978 358 625	336667 5999	533679 18972	079079 916	1439885 207
6946	48 24 69 16	335 123 078 536	342666 5999	552651 18971	079995 916	1439678 208
6947	48 26 08 09	335 267 840 123	348665 5999	571622 18970	080911 915	1439470 207
6948	48 27 47 04	335 412 643 392	354664 5998	590592 18968	081826 916	1439263 207
6949	48 28 86 01	335 557 488 349	360662 5998	609560 18967	082742 915	1439056 207
6950	48 30 25 00	335 702 375 000	366660	628527	083657	1438849
			83·	263·	19·	0·000

No. n	Square n²	Cube n³	Square root √n		Sq. rt. of 10n √10n		Cube root ∛n		Reciprocal 1/n
			83·		263·		19·		0·000
6950	48 30 25 00	335 702 375 000	366660		628527	18965	083657		1438849
6951	48 31 64 01	335 847 303 351	372657	5997	647492	18964	084572	915	1438642	207
6952	48 33 03 04	335 992 273 408	378654	5997	666456	18963	085487	915	1438435	207
6953	48 34 42 09	336 137 285 177	384651	5997	685419	18961	086402	915	1438228	207
6954	48 35 81 16	336 282 338 664	390647	5996	704380	18960	087317	915	1438021	207
				5996				915		206
6955	48 37 20 25	336 427 433 875	396643		723340	18958	088232		1437815	
6956	48 38 59 36	336 572 570 816	402638	5995	742298	18958	089147	915	1437608	207
6957	48 39 98 49	336 717 749 493	408633	5995	761256	18956	090062	915	1437401	207
6958	48 41 37 64	336 862 969 912	414627	5994	780212	18954	090976	914	1437195	206
6959	48 42 76 81	337 008 232 079	420621	5994	799166	18953	091891	915	1436988	207
				5993				914		206
6960	48 44 16 00	337 153 536 000	426614		818119	18952	092805		1436782	
6961	48 45 55 21	337 298 881 681	432608	5994	837071	18950	093720	915	1436575	207
6962	48 46 94 44	337 444 269 128	438600	5992	856021	18949	094634	914	1436369	206
6963	48 48 33 69	337 589 698 347	444592	5992	874970	18948	095548	914	1436163	207
6964	48 49 72 96	337 735 169 344	450584	5992	893918	18946	096462	914	1435956	206
				5992				914		
6965	48 51 12 25	337 880 682 125	456576		912864	18945	097376		1435750	
6966	48 52 51 56	338 026 236 696	462566	5990	931809	18944	098290	914	1435544	206
6967	48 53 90 89	338 171 833 063	468557	5991	950753	18942	099204	914	1435338	206
6968	48 55 30 24	338 317 471 232	474547	5990	969695	18941	100118	914	1435132	206
6969	48 56 69 61	338 463 151 209	480537	5990	988636	18940	101032	913	1434926	206
				5989						206
6970	48 58 09 00	338 608 873 000	486526		*007576	18938	101945	914	1434720	
6971	48 59 48 41	338 754 636 611	492515	5989	026514	18937	102859	914	1434514	206
6972	48 60 87 84	338 900 442 048	498503	5988	045451	18935	103772	913	1434309	205
6973	48 62 27 29	339 046 289 317	504491	5988	064386	18934	104685	913	1434103	206
6974	48 63 66 76	339 192 178 424	510478	5987	083320	18933	105599	914	1433897	206
				5987				913		205
6975	48 65 06 25	339 338 109 375	516465		102253	18931	106512		1433692	
6976	48 66 45 76	339 484 082 176	522452	5987	121184	18930	107425	913	1433486	206
6977	48 67 85 29	339 630 096 833	528438	5986	140114	18929	108338	913	1433281	205
6978	48 69 24 84	339 776 153 352	534424	5986	159043	18927	109251	913	1433075	206
6979	48 70 64 41	339 922 251 739	540409	5985	177970	18926	110163	912	1432870	205
				5985				913		205
6980	48 72 04 00	340 068 392 000	546394		196896	18925	111076		1432665	
6981	48 73 43 61	340 214 574 141	552379	5985	215821	18923	111989	913	1432460	205
6982	48 74 83 24	340 360 798 168	558363	5984	234744	18922	112901	912	1432254	206
6983	48 76 22 89	340 507 064 087	564346	5983	253666	18921	113814	913	1432049	205
6984	48 77 62 56	340 653 371 904	570330	5984	272587	18919	114726	912	1431844	205
				5982				912		205
6985	48 79 02 25	340 799 721 625	576312		291506	18918	115638		1431639	
6986	48 80 41 96	340 946 113 256	*582295	5983	310424	18916	116550	912	1431434	205
6987	48 81 81 69	341 092 546 803	588277	5982	329340	18915	117463	913	1431229	205
6988	48 83 21 44	341 239 022 272	594258	5981	348255	18914	118375	912	1431024	204
6989	48 84 61 21	341 385 539 669	600239	5981	367169	18912	119286	911	1430820	205
				5981				912		205
6990	48 86 01 00	341 532 099 000	606220		386081	18911	120198		1430615	
6991	48 87 40 81	341 678 700 271	612200	5980	404992	18910	121110	912	1430411	204
6992	48 88 80 64	341 825 343 488	618180	5980	423902	18908	122022	912	1430206	205
6993	48 90 20 49	341 972 028 657	624159	5979	442810	18907	122933	911	1430001	205
6994	48 91 60 36	342 118 755 784	630138	5979	461717	18906	123845	912	1429797	204
				5979				911		204
6995	48 93 00 25	342 265 524 875	636117		480623	18904	124756		1429593	
6996	48 94 40 16	342 412 335 936	642095	5978	499527	18903	125667	911	1429388	205
6997	48 95 80 09	342 559 188 973	648072	5977	518430	18902	126579	912	1429184	204
6998	48 97 20 04	342 706 083 992	654050	5978	537332	18900	127490	911	1428980	204
6999	48 98 60 01	342 853 020 999	660026	5976	556232	18899	128401	911	1428776	204
				5977						205
7000	49 00 00 00	343 000 000 000	666003		575131		129312		1428571	
			83·		264·		19·		0·000	

No. n	Square n²	Cube n³	Square root √n	Sq. rt. of 10n √10n	Cube root ∛n	Reciprocal 1/n
			83·	264·	19·	0·000
7000	49 00 00 00	343 000 000 000	666003 ₅₉₇₆	575131 ₁₈₈₉₈	129312 ₉₁₁	1428571 ₂₀₄
7001	49 01 40 01	343 147 021 001	671979 ₅₉₇₅	594029 ₁₈₈₉₆	130223 ₉₁₀	1428367 ₂₀₄
7002	49 02 80 04	343 294 084 008	677954 ₅₉₇₅	612925 ₁₈₈₉₅	131133 ₉₁₁	1428163 ₂₀₄
7003	49 04 20 09	343 441 189 027	683929 ₅₉₇₅	631820 ₁₈₈₉₃	132044 ₉₁₁	1427959 ₂₀₃
7004	49 05 60 16	343 588 336 064	689904 ₅₉₇₄	650713 ₁₈₈₉₂	132955 ₉₁₀	1427756 ₂₀₄
7005	49 07 00 25	343 735 525 125	695878 ₅₉₇₄	669605 ₁₈₈₉₁	133865 ₉₁₁	1427552 ₂₀₄
7006	49 08 40 36	343 882 756 216	701852 ₅₉₇₃	688496 ₁₈₈₉₀	134776 ₉₁₀	1427348 ₂₀₄
7007	49 09 80 49	344 030 029 343	707825 ₅₉₇₃	707386 ₁₈₈₈₈	135686 ₉₁₀	1427144 ₂₀₃
7008	49 11 20 64	344 177 344 512	713798 ₅₉₇₃	726274 ₁₈₈₈₆	136596 ₉₁₁	1426941 ₂₀₄
7009	49 12 60 81	344 324 701 729	719771 ₅₉₇₂	745160 ₁₈₈₈₆	137507 ₉₁₀	1426737 ₂₀₃
7010	49 14 01 00	344 472 101 000	725743 ₅₉₇₁	764046 ₁₈₈₈₄	138417 ₉₁₀	1426534 ₂₀₄
7011	49 15 41 21	344 619 542 331	731714 ₅₉₇₂	782930 ₁₈₈₈₃	139327 ₉₁₀	1426330 ₂₀₃
7012	49 16 81 44	344 767 025 728	737686 ₅₉₇₀	801813 ₁₈₈₈₁	140237 ₉₀₉	1426127 ₂₀₄
7013	49 18 21 69	344 914 551 197	743656 ₅₉₇₁	820694 ₁₈₈₈₀	141146 ₉₁₀	1425923 ₂₀₃
7014	49 19 61 96	345 062 118 744	749627 ₅₉₇₀	839574 ₁₈₈₇₉	142056 ₉₁₀	1425720 ₂₀₃
7015	49 21 02 25	345 209 728 375	755597 ₅₉₆₉	858453 ₁₈₈₇₇	142966 ₉₀₉	1425517 ₂₀₃
7016	49 22 42 56	345 357 380 096	761566 ₅₉₆₉	877330 ₁₈₈₇₆	143875 ₉₁₀	1425314 ₂₀₄
7017	49 23 82 89	345 505 073 913	767535 ₅₉₆₉	896206 ₁₈₈₇₅	144785 ₉₀₉	1425110 ₂₀₃
7018	49 25 23 24	345 652 809 832	773504 ₅₉₆₈	915081 ₁₈₈₇₃	145694 ₉₁₀	1424907 ₂₀₃
7019	49 26 63 61	345 800 587 859	779472 ₅₉₆₈	933954 ₁₈₈₇₂	146604 ₉₀₉	1424704 ₂₀₃
7020	49 28 04 00	345 948 408 000	785440 ₅₉₆₈	952826 ₁₈₈₇₁	147513 ₉₀₉	1424501 ₂₀₂
7021	49 29 44 41	346 096 270 261	791408 ₅₉₆₇	971697 ₁₈₈₆₉	148422 ₉₀₉	1424299 ₂₀₃
7022	49 30 84 84	346 244 174 648	797375 ₅₉₆₆	990566 ₁₈₈₆₈	149331 ₉₀₉	1424096 ₂₀₃
7023	49 32 25 29	346 392 121 167	803341 ₅₉₆₆	*009434 ₁₈₈₆₆	150240 ₉₀₉	1423893 ₂₀₃
7024	49 33 65 76	346 540 109 824	809307 ₅₉₆₆	028300 ₁₈₈₆₆	151149 ₉₀₉	1423690 ₂₀₂
7025	49 35 06 25	346 688 140 625	815273 ₅₉₆₅	047166 ₁₈₈₆₄	152058 ₉₀₈	1423488 ₂₀₃
7026	49 36 46 76	346 836 213 576	821238 ₅₉₆₅	066030 ₁₈₈₆₂	152966 ₉₀₉	1423285 ₂₀₃
7027	49 37 87 29	346 984 328 683	827203 ₅₉₆₅	084892 ₁₈₈₆₁	153875 ₉₀₉	1423082 ₂₀₂
7028	49 39 27 84	347 132 485 952	833168 ₅₉₆₄	103753 ₁₈₈₆₀	154784 ₉₀₈	1422880 ₂₀₃
7029	49 40 68 41	347 280 685 389	839132 ₅₉₆₃	122613 ₁₈₈₅₉	155692 ₉₀₈	1422677 ₂₀₂
7030	49 42 09 00	347 428 927 000	845095 ₅₉₆₃	141472 ₁₈₈₅₇	156600 ₉₀₉	1422475 ₂₀₂
7031	49 43 49 61	347 577 210 791	851058 ₅₉₆₃	160329 ₁₈₈₅₆	157509 ₉₀₈	1422273 ₂₀₂
7032	49 44 90 24	347 725 536 768	857021 ₅₉₆₂	179185 ₁₈₈₅₄	158417 ₉₀₈	1422071 ₂₀₃
7033	49 46 30 89	347 873 904 937	862983 ₅₉₆₂	198039 ₁₈₈₅₃	159325 ₉₀₈	1421868 ₂₀₂
7034	49 47 71 56	348 022 315 304	868945 ₅₉₆₂	216892 ₁₈₈₅₂	160233 ₉₀₈	1421666 ₂₀₂
7035	49 49 12 25	348 170 767 875	874907 ₅₉₆₁	235744 ₁₈₈₅₁	161141 ₉₀₈	1421464 ₂₀₂
7036	49 50 52 96	348 319 262 656	880868 ₅₉₆₁	254595 ₁₈₈₄₉	162049 ₉₀₈	1421262 ₂₀₂
7037	49 51 93 69	348 467 799 653	886829 ₅₉₆₀	273444 ₁₈₈₄₈	162957 ₉₀₇	1421060 ₂₀₂
7038	49 53 34 44	348 616 378 872	892789 ₅₉₆₀	292292 ₁₈₈₄₆	163864 ₉₀₈	1420858 ₂₀₂
7039	49 54 75 21	348 765 000 319	898749 ₅₉₅₉	311138 ₁₈₈₄₅	164772 ₉₀₇	1420656 ₂₀₁
7040	49 56 16 00	348 913 664 000	904708 ₅₉₅₉	329983 ₁₈₈₄₄	165679 ₉₀₈	1420455 ₂₀₂
7041	49 57 56 81	349 062 369 921	910667 ₅₉₅₈	348827 ₁₈₈₄₂	166587 ₉₀₇	1420253 ₂₀₂
7042	49 58 97 64	349 211 118 088	916625 ₅₉₅₈	367669 ₁₈₈₄₂	167494 ₉₀₇	1420051 ₂₀₂
7043	49 60 38 49	349 359 908 507	922583 ₅₉₅₈	386511 ₁₈₈₃₉	168401 ₉₀₈	1419849 ₂₀₁
7044	49 61 79 36	349 508 741 184	928541 ₅₉₅₇	405350 ₁₈₈₃₉	169309 ₉₀₇	1419648 ₂₀₂
7045	49 63 20 25	349 657 616 125	934498 ₅₉₅₇	424189 ₁₈₈₃₇	170216 ₉₀₇	1419446 ₂₀₁
7046	49 64 61 16	349 806 533 336	940455 ₅₉₅₆	443026 ₁₈₈₃₆	171123 ₉₀₇	1419245 ₂₀₁
7047	49 66 02 09	349 955 492 823	946411 ₅₉₅₆	461862 ₁₈₈₃₄	172030 ₉₀₆	1419044 ₂₀₂
7048	49 67 43 04	350 104 494 592	952367 ₅₉₅₆	480696 ₁₈₈₃₃	172936 ₉₀₇	1418842 ₂₀₁
7049	49 68 84 01	350 253 538 649	958323 ₅₉₅₅	499529 ₁₈₈₃₂	173843 ₉₀₇	1418641 ₂₀₁
7050	49 70 25 00	350 402 625 000	964278 83·	518361 265·	174750 19·	1418440 0·000

No. n	Square n^2	Cube n^3	Square root $\sqrt{n}$	Sq. rt. of 10n $\sqrt{10n}$	Cube root $\sqrt[3]{n}$	Reciprocal $\frac{1}{n}$
			83·	265·	19·	0·000
7050	49 70 25 00	350 402 625 000	964278 5955	518361 18830	174750 906	1418440 201
7051	49 71 66 01	350 551 753 651	970233 5954	537191 18829	175656 907	1418239 202
7052	49 73 07 04	350 700 924 608	976187 5954	556020 18828	176563 906	1418037 202
7053	49 74 48 09	350 850 137 877	982141 5953	574848 18827	177469 907	1417836 201
7054	49 75 89 16	350 999 393 464	988094 5953	593675 18825	178376 906	1417635 201
7055	49 77 30 25	351 148 691 375	*994047 5953	612500 18823	179282 906	1417434 200
7056	49 78 71 36	351 298 031 616	*000000 5952	631323 18823	180188 906	1417234 201
7057	49 80 12 49	351 447 414 193	005952 5952	650146 18821	181094 906	1417033 201
7058	49 81 53 64	351 596 839 112	011904 5951	668967 18820	182000 906	1416832 201
7059	49 82 94 81	351 746 306 379	017855 5951	687787 18818	182906 906	1416631 201
7060	49 84 36 00	351 895 816 000	023806 5951	706605 18817	183812 905	1416431 201
7061	49 85 77 21	352 045 367 981	029757 5950	725422 18816	184717 906	1416230 201
7062	49 87 18 44	352 194 962 328	035707 5949	744238 18814	185623 905	1416029 201
7063	49 88 59 69	352 344 599 047	041656 5950	763052 18813	186528 906	1415829 200
7064	49 90 00 96	352 494 278 144	047606 5948	781865 18812	187434 905	1415629 201
7065	49 91 42 25	352 643 999 625	053554 5949	800677 18811	188339 906	1415428 200
7066	49 92 83 56	352 793 763 496	059503 5948	819488 18809	189245 905	1415228 200
7067	49 94 24 89	352 943 569 763	065451 5947	838297 18807	190150 905	1415028 200
7068	49 95 66 24	353 093 418 432	071398 5947	857104 18807	191055 905	1414827 201
7069	49 97 07 61	353 243 309 509	077345 5947	875911 18805	191960 905	1414627 200
7070	49 98 49 00	353 393 243 000	083292 5946	894716 18804	192865 905	1414427 200
7071	49 99 90 41	353 543 218 911	089238 5946	913520 18802	193770 904	1414227 200
7072	50 01 31 84	353 693 237 248	095184 5946	932322 18801	194674 905	1414027 200
7073	50 02 73 29	353 843 298 017	101130 5945	951123 18800	195579 905	1413827 200
7074	50 04 14 76	353 993 401 224	107075 5944	969923 18799	196484 904	1413627 199
7075	50 05 56 25	354 143 546 875	113019 5944	*988722 18797	197388 905	1413428 200
7076	50 06 97 76	354 293 734 976	118963 5944	*007519 18795	198293 904	1413228 200
7077	50 08 39 29	354 443 965 533	124907 5943	026314 18795	199197 904	1413028 200
7078	50 09 80 84	354 594 238 552	130850 5943	045109 18793	200101 904	1412828 200
7079	50 11 22 41	354 744 554 039	136793 5943	063902 18792	201005 905	1412629 199
7080	50 12 64 00	354 894 912 000	142736 5942	082694 18790	201910 904	1412429 200
7081	50 14 05 61	355 045 312 441	148678 5942	101484 18790	202814 904	1412230 199
7082	50 15 47 24	355 195 755 368	154620 5941	120274 18787	203717 903	1412030 200
7083	50 16 88 89	355 346 240 787	160561 5941	139061 18787	204621 904	1411831 199
7084	50 18 30 56	355 496 768 704	166502 5940	157848 18785	205525 904	1411632 199
7085	50 19 72 25	355 647 339 125	172442 5940	176633 18784	206429 903	1411433 200
7086	50 21 13 96	355 797 952 056	178382 5940	195417 18782	207332 904	1411233 199
7087	50 22 55 69	355 948 607 503	184322 5939	214199 18782	208236 903	1411034 199
7088	50 23 97 44	356 099 305 472	190261 5938	232981 18780	209139 903	1410835 199
7089	50 25 39 21	356 250 045 969	196199 5938	251761 18778	210042 903	1410636 199
7090	50 26 81 00	356 400 829 000	202138 5938	270539 18777	210946 903	1410437 199
7091	50 28 22 81	356 551 654 571	208076 5937	289316 18776	211849 903	1410238 199
7092	50 29 64 64	356 702 522 688	214013 5937	308092 18775	212752 903	1410039 198
7093	50 31 06 49	356 853 433 357	219950 5937	326867 18773	213655 903	1409841 199
7094	50 32 48 36	357 004 386 584	225887 5936	345640 18772	214558 903	1409642 199
7095	50 33 90 25	357 155 382 375	231823 5936	364412 18771	215461 902	1409443 198
7096	50 35 32 16	357 306 420 736	237759 5935	383183 18769	216363 903	1409245 199
7097	50 36 74 09	357 457 501 673	243694 5935	401952 18768	217266 903	1409046 198
7098	50 38 16 04	357 608 625 192	249629 5935	420720 18767	218169 902	1408848 199
7099	50 39 58 01	357 759 791 299	255564 5934	439487 18765	219071 902	1408649 198
7100	50 41 00 00	357 911 000 000	261498	458252	219973	1408451
			84·	266·	19·	0·000

No. n	Square n^2	Cube n^3	Square root $\sqrt{n}$	Sq. rt. of 10n $\sqrt{10n}$	Cube root $\sqrt[3]{n}$	Reciprocal $\frac{1}{n}$
			84·	266·	19·	0·000
7100	50 41 00 00	357 911 000 000	261498 5933	458252 18764	219973 903	1408451
7101	50 42 42 01	358 062 251 301	267431 5934	477016 18763	220876 903	1408252 199
7102	50 43 84 04	358 213 545 208	273365 5933	495779 18761	221778 902	1408054 198
7103	50 45 26 09	358 364 881 727	279298 5932	514540 18760	222680 902	1407856 198
7104	50 46 68 16	358 516 260 864	285230 5932	533300 18759	223582 902	1407658 198
7105	50 48 10 25	358 667 682 625	291162 5932	552059 18757	224484 902	1407460 199
7106	50 49 52 36	358 819 147 016	297094 5931	570816 18756	225386 902	1407261 198
7107	50 50 94 49	358 970 654 043	303025 5931	589572 18755	226288 901	1407063 197
7108	50 52 36 64	359 122 203 712	308956 5930	608327 18753	227189 902	1406866 198
7109	50 53 78 81	359 273 796 029	314886 5930	627080 18753	228091 902	1406668 198
7110	50 55 21 00	359 425 431 000	320816 5929	645833 18750	228993 901	1406470 198
7111	50 56 63 21	359 577 108 631	326745 5930	664583 18750	229894 901	1406272 198
7112	50 58 05 44	359 728 828 928	332675 5928	683333 18748	230795 902	1406074 197
7113	50 59 47 69	359 880 591 897	338603 5929	702081 18747	231697 901	1405877 198
7114	50 60 89 96	360 032 397 544	344532 5927	720828 18745	232598 901	1405679 198
7115	50 62 32 25	360 184 245 875	350459 5928	739573 18745	233499 901	1405481 197
7116	50 63 74 56	360 336 136 896	356387 5927	758318 18742	234400 901	1405284 198
7117	50 65 16 89	360 488 070 613	362314 5926	777060 18742	235301 901	1405086 197
7118	50 66 59 24	360 640 047 032	368240 5927	795802 18740	236202 901	1404889 197
7119	50 68 01 61	360 792 066 159	374167 5925	814542 18739	237103 900	1404692 198
7120	50 69 44 00	360 944 128 000	380092 5926	833281 18738	238003 901	1404494 197
7121	50 70 86 41	361 096 232 561	386018 5925	852019 18736	238904 901	1404297 197
7122	50 72 28 84	361 248 379 848	391943 5924	870755 18735	239805 900	1404100 197
7123	50 73 71 29	361 400 569 867	397867 5924	889490 18734	240705 900	1403903 197
7124	50 75 13 76	361 552 802 624	403791 5924	908224 18732	241605 901	1403706 197
7125	50 76 56 25	361 705 078 125	409715 5923	926956 18731	242506 900	1403509 197
7126	50 77 98 76	361 857 396 376	415638 5923	945687 18730	243406 900	1403312 197
7127	50 79 41 29	362 009 757 383	421561 5923	964417 18729	244306 900	1403115 197
7128	50 80 83 84	362 162 161 152	427484 5922	983146 18727	245206 900	1402918 197
7129	50 82 26 41	362 314 607 689	433406 5921	*001873 18725	246106 900	1402721 196
7130	50 83 69 00	362 467 097 000	439327 5922	020598 18725	247006 900	1402525 197
7131	50 85 11 61	362 619 629 091	445249 5920	039323 18723	247906 900	1402328 197
7132	50 86 54 24	362 772 203 968	451169 5921	058046 18722	248805 899	1402131 196
7133	50 87 96 89	362 924 821 637	457090 5920	076768 18721	249705 899	1401935 197
7134	50 89 39 56	363 077 482 104	463010 5919	095489 18719	250604 900	1401738 196
7135	50 90 82 25	363 230 185 375	468929 5919	114208 18718	251504 899	1401542 197
7136	50 92 24 96	363 382 931 456	474848 5919	132926 18716	252403 899	1401345 196
7137	50 93 67 69	363 535 720 353	480767 5918	151642 18716	253302 900	1401149 196
7138	50 95 10 44	363 688 552 072	486685 5918	170358 18714	254202 899	1400953 197
7139	50 96 53 21	363 841 426 619	492603 5918	189072 18712	255101 899	1400756 196
7140	50 97 96 00	363 994 344 000	498521 5917	207784 18712	256000 899	1400560 196
7141	50 99 38 81	364 147 304 221	504438 5916	226496 18710	256899 898	1400364 196
7142	51 00 81 64	364 300 307 288	510354 5917	245206 18709	257797 899	1400168 196
7143	51 02 24 49	364 453 353 207	516271 5915	263915 18707	258696 899	1399972 196
7144	51 03 67 36	364 606 441 984	522186 5916	282622 18706	259595 899	1399776 196
7145	51 05 10 25	364 759 573 625	528102 5915	301328 18705	260494 898	1399580 196
7146	51 06 53 16	364 912 748 136	534017 5914	320033 18703	261392 898	1399384 196
7147	51 07 96 09	365 065 965 523	539931 5915	338736 18703	262290 899	1399188 195
7148	51 09 39 04	365 219 225 792	545846 5913	357439 18701	263189 898	1398993 196
7149	51 10 82 01	365 372 528 949	551759 5914	376140 18699	264087 898	1398797 196
7150	51 12 25 00	365 525 875 000	557673	394839	264985	1398601
			84·	267·	19·	0·000

No. n	Square n^2	Cube n^3	Square root $\sqrt{n}$	Sq. rt. of $10n$ $\sqrt{10n}$	Cube root $\sqrt[3]{n}$	Reciprocal $\frac{1}{n}$
			84·	267·	19·	0·000
7150	51 12 25 00	365 525 875 000	557673 5913	394839 18698	264985 898	1398601
7151	51 13 68 01	365 679 263 951	563586 5913	413537 18697	265883 898	1398406 195
7152	51 15 11 04	365 832 695 808	569498 5912	432234 18696	266781 898	1398210 196
7153	51 16 54 09	365 986 170 577	575410 5912	450930 18694	267679 898	1398015 196
7154	51 17 97 16	366 139 688 264	581322 5911	469624 18694	268577 898	1397819 195
7155	51 19 40 25	366 293 248 875	587233 5911	488318 18691	269475 898	1397624 195
7156	51 20 83 36	366 446 852 416	593144 5910	507009 18691	270373 897	1397429 196
7157	51 22 26 49	366 600 498 893	599054 5910	525700 18689	271270 898	1397233 195
7158	51 23 69 64	366 754 188 312	604964 5910	544389 18688	272168 897	1397038 195
7159	51 25 12 81	366 907 920 679	610874 5909	563077 18686	273065 897	1396843 195
7160	51 26 56 00	367 061 696 000	616783 5909	581763 18685	273962 898	1396648 195
7161	51 27 99 21	367 215 514 281	622692 5908	600448 18684	274860 897	1396453 195
7162	51 29 42 44	367 369 375 528	628600 5908	619132 18683	275757 897	1396258 195
7163	51 30 85 69	367 523 279 747	634508 5908	637815 18681	276654 897	1396063 195
7164	51 32 28 96	367 677 226 944	640416 5907	656496 18680	277551 897	1395868 195
7165	51 33 72 25	367 831 217 125	646323 5907	675176 18679	278448 897	1395673 194
7166	51 35 15 56	367 985 250 296	652230 5906	693855 18677	279345 896	1395479 195
7167	51 36 58 89	368 139 326 463	658136 5906	712532 18676	280241 897	1395284 195
7168	51 38 02 24	368 293 445 632	664042 5905	731208 18675	281138 897	1395089 194
7169	51 39 45 61	368 447 607 809	669947 5906	749883 18674	282035 896	1394895 195
7170	51 40 89 00	368 601 813 000	675853 5904	768557 18672	282931 897	1394700 194
7171	51 42 32 41	368 756 061 211	681757 5904	787229 18671	283828 896	1394506 195
7172	51 43 75 84	368 910 352 448	687661 5904	805900 18669	284724 896	1394311 194
7173	51 45 19 29	369 064 686 717	693565 5904	824569 18669	285620 896	1394117 195
7174	51 46 62 76	369 219 064 024	699469 5903	843238 18667	286516 896	1393922 194
7175	51 48 06 25	369 373 484 375	705372 5902	861905 18665	287412 896	1393728 194
7176	51 49 49 76	369 527 947 776	711274 5903	880570 18665	288308 896	1393534 194
7177	51 50 93 29	369 682 454 233	717177 5901	899235 18663	289204 896	1393340 194
7178	51 52 36 84	369 837 003 752	723078 5902	917898 18662	290100 896	1393146 194
7179	51 53 80 41	369 991 596 339	728980 5901	936560 18660	290996 896	1392952 194
7180	51 55 24 00	370 146 232 000	734881 5900	955220 18659	291892 895	1392758 194
7181	51 56 67 61	370 300 910 741	740781 5900	973879 18658	292787 896	1392564 194
7182	51 58 11 24	370 455 632 568	746681 5900	992537 18655	293683 895	1392370 194
7183	51 59 54 89	370 610 397 487	752581 5899	*011194 18655	294578 896	1392176 194
7184	51 60 98 56	370 765 205 504	758480 5899	029849 18654	295474 895	1391982 194
7185	51 62 42 25	370 920 056 625	764379 5899	048503 18653	296369 895	1391788 193
7186	51 63 85 96	371 074 950 856	770278 5898	067156 18651	297264 895	1391595 194
7187	51 65 29 69	371 229 888 203	776176 5898	085807 18650	298159 895	1391401 193
7188	51 66 73 44	371 384 868 672	782074 5897	104457 18649	299054 895	1391208 194
7189	51 68 17 21	371 539 892 269	787971 5897	123106 18648	299949 895	1391014 193
7190	51 69 61 00	371 694 959 000	793868 5896	141754 18646	300844 895	1390821 194
7191	51 71 04 81	371 850 068 871	799764 5896	160400 18645	301739 894	1390627 193
7192	51 72 48 64	372 005 221 888	805660 5896	179045 18643	302633 895	1390434 193
7193	51 73 92 49	372 160 418 057	811556 5895	197688 18643	303528 894	1390241 194
7194	51 75 36 36	372 315 657 384	817451 5895	216331 18641	304422 895	1390047 193
7195	51 76 80 25	372 470 939 875	823346 5894	234972 18639	305317 894	1389854 193
7196	51 78 24 16	372 626 265 536	829240 5894	253611 18639	306211 894	1389661 193
7197	51 79 68 09	372 781 634 373	835134 5894	272250 18637	307105 895	1389468 193
7198	51 81 12 04	372 937 046 392	841028 5893	290887 18636	308000 894	1389275 193
7199	51 82 56 01	373 092 501 599	846921 5893	309523 18634	308894 894	1389082 193
7200	51 84 00 00	373 248 000 000	852814 84·	328157 268·	309788 19·	1388889 0·000

No. n	Square n^2	Cube n^3	Square root $\sqrt{n}$	Sq. rt. of 10n $\sqrt{10n}$	Cube root $\sqrt[3]{n}$	Reciprocal $\frac{1}{n}$
			84·	268·	19·	0·000
7200	51 84 00 00	373 248 000 000	852814 5892	328157 18634	309788 894	1388889 193
7201	51 85 44 01	373 403 541 601	858706 5892	346791 18632	310682 894	1388696 193
7202	51 86 88 04	373 559 126 408	864598 5892	365423 18630	311575 894	1388503 193
7203	51 88 32 09	373 714 754 427	870490 5891	384053 18630	312469 894	1388310 193
7204	51 89 76 16	373 870 425 664	876381 5890	402683 18628	313363 894	1388118 192 193
7205	51 91 20 25	374 026 140 125	882271 5891	421311 18626	314257 893	1387925 193
7206	51 92 64 36	374 181 897 816	888162 5890	439937 18626	315150 893	1387732 192
7207	51 94 08 49	374 337 698 743	894052 5889	458563 18624	316043 894	1387540 193
7208	51 95 52 64	374 493 542 912	899941 5889	477187 18623	316937 893	1387347 192
7209	51 96 96 81	374 649 430 329	905830 5889	495810 18622	317830 893	1387155 192
7210	51 98 41 00	374 805 361 000	911719 5888	514432 18620	318723 893	1386963 193
7211	51 99 85 21	374 961 334 931	917607 5888	533052 18619	319616 893	1386770 192
7212	52 01 29 44	375 117 352 128	923495 5887	551671 18618	320509 893	1386578 192
7213	52 02 73 69	375 273 412 597	929382 5887	570289 18616	321402 893	1386386 192
7214	52 04 17 96	375 429 516 344	935269 5887	588905 18615	322295 893	1386194 193
7215	52 05 62 25	375 585 663 375	941156 5886	607520 18614	323188 893	1386001 192
7216	52 07 06 56	375 741 853 696	947042 5886	626134 18613	324081 892	1385809 192
7217	52 08 50 89	375 898 087 313	952928 5886	644747 18611	324973 893	1385617 192
7218	52 09 95 24	376 054 364 232	958814 5885	663358 18610	325866 892	1385425 192
7219	52 11 39 61	376 210 684 459	964699 5884	681968 18609	326758 893	1385233 191
7220	52 12 84 00	376 367 048 000	970583 5884	700577 18607	327651 892	1385042 192
7221	52 14 28 41	376 523 454 861	976467 5884	719184 18606	328543 892	1384850 192
7222	52 15 72 84	376 679 905 048	982351 5883	737790 18605	329435 892	1384658 192
7223	52 17 17 29	376 836 398 567	988234 5883	756395 18604	330327 892	1384466 191
7224	52 18 61 76	376 992 935 424	994117 5883	774999 18602	331219 892	1384275 192
7225	52 20 06 25	377 149 515 625	*000000 5882	793601 18601	332111 892	1384083 191
7226	52 21 50 76	377 306 139 176	005882 5882	812202 18600	333003 892	1383892 192
7227	52 22 95 29	377 462 806 083	011764 5881	830802 18598	333895 892	1383700 191
7228	52 24 39 84	377 619 516 352	017645 5881	849400 18597	334787 891	1383509 192
7229	52 25 84 41	377 776 269 989	023526 5881	867997 18596	335678 892	1383317 191
7230	52 27 29 00	377 933 067 000	029407 5880	886593 18595	336570 891	1383126 191
7231	52 28 73 61	378 089 907 391	035287 5880	905188 18593	337461 892	1382935 192
7232	52 30 18 24	378 246 791 168	041167 5879	923781 18592	338353 891	1382743 191
7233	52 31 62 89	378 403 718 337	047046 5879	942373 18591	339244 891	1382552 191
7234	52 33 07 56	378 560 688 904	052925 5878	960964 18589	340135 891	1382361 191
7235	52 34 52 25	378 717 702 875	058803 5878	979553 18588	341026 891	1382170 191
7236	52 35 96 96	378 874 760 256	064681 5878	*998141 18587	341917 891	1381979 191
7237	52 37 41 69	379 031 861 053	070559 5877	*016728 18586	342808 891	1381788 191
7238	52 38 86 44	379 189 005 272	076436 5877	035314 18584	343699 891	1381597 191
7239	52 40 31 21	379 346 192 919	082313 5877	053898 18583	344590 891	1381406 191
7240	52 41 76 00	379 503 424 000	088190 5876	072481 18582	345481 890	1381215 190
7241	52 43 20 81	379 660 698 521	094066 5875	091063 18580	346371 890	1381025 190
7242	52 44 65 64	379 818 016 488	099941 5875	109643 18579	347262 890	1380834 191
7243	52 46 10 49	379 975 377 907	105816 5875	128222 18578	348152 891	1380643 190
7244	52 47 55 36	380 132 782 784	111691 5875	146800 18577	349043 890	1380453 191
7245	52 49 00 25	380 290 231 125	117566 5874	165377 18575	349933 890	1380262 190
7246	52 50 45 16	380 447 722 936	123440 5873	183952 18574	350823 890	1380072 191
7247	52 51 90 09	380 605 258 223	129313 5874	202526 18573	351713 890	1379881 190
7248	52 53 35 04	380 762 836 992	135187 5872	221099 18571	352603 890	1379691 190
7249	52 54 80 01	380 920 459 249	141059 5873	239670 18570	353493 890	1379501 191
7250	52 56 25 00	381 078 125 000	146932	258240	354383	1379310
			85·	269·	19·	0·000

No. n	Square n²	Cube n³	Square root √n	Sq. rt. of 10n √10n	Cube root ∛n	Reciprocal 1/n
			85·	269·	19·	0·000
7250	52 56 25 00	381 078 125 000	146932 $_{5872}$	258240 $_{18569}$	354383 $_{890}$	1379310 $_{190}$
7251	52 57 70 01	381 235 834 251	152804 $_{5871}$	276809 $_{18568}$	355273 $_{890}$	1379120 $_{190}$
7252	52 59 15 04	381 393 587 008	158675 $_{5872}$	295377 $_{18566}$	356163 $_{889}$	1378930 $_{190}$
7253	52 60 60 09	381 551 383 277	164547 $_{5870}$	313943 $_{18565}$	357052 $_{890}$	1378740 $_{190}$
7254	52 62 05 16	381 709 223 064	170417 $_{5871}$	332508 $_{18564}$	357942 $_{889}$	1378550 $_{190}$
7255	52 63 50 25	381 867 106 375	176288 $_{5870}$	351072 $_{18563}$	358831 $_{890}$	1378360 $_{190}$
7256	52 64 95 36	382 025 033 216	182158 $_{5869}$	369635 $_{18561}$	359721 $_{889}$	1378170 $_{190}$
7257	52 66 40 49	382 183 003 593	188027 $_{5869}$	388196 $_{18560}$	360610 $_{889}$	1377980 $_{190}$
7258	52 67 85 64	382 341 017 512	193896 $_{5869}$	406756 $_{18558}$	361499 $_{890}$	1377790 $_{190}$
7259	52 69 30 81	382 499 074 979	199765 $_{5869}$	425314 $_{18558}$	362389 $_{889}$	1377600 $_{190}$
7260	52 70 76 00	382 657 176 000	205634 $_{5868}$	443872 $_{18556}$	363278 $_{889}$	1377410 $_{189}$
7261	52 72 21 21	382 815 320 581	211502 $_{5867}$	462428 $_{18555}$	364167 $_{889}$	1377221 $_{189}$
7262	52 73 66 44	382 973 508 728	217369 $_{5867}$	480983 $_{18553}$	365056 $_{888}$	1377031 $_{189}$
7263	52 75 11 69	383 131 740 447	223236 $_{5867}$	499536 $_{18552}$	365944 $_{889}$	1376842 $_{190}$
7264	52 76 56 96	383 290 015 744	229103 $_{5866}$	518088 $_{18551}$	366833 $_{889}$	1376652 $_{190}$
7265	52 78 02 25	383 448 334 625	234969 $_{5866}$	536639 $_{18550}$	367722 $_{888}$	1376462 $_{189}$
7266	52 79 47 56	383 606 697 096	240835 $_{5866}$	555189 $_{18549}$	368610 $_{889}$	1376273 $_{189}$
7267	52 80 92 89	383 765 103 163	246701 $_{5865}$	573738 $_{18547}$	369499 $_{888}$	1376084 $_{190}$
7268	52 82 38 24	383 923 552 832	252566 $_{5865}$	592285 $_{18546}$	370387 $_{889}$	1375894 $_{189}$
7269	52 83 83 61	384 082 046 109	258431 $_{5864}$	610831 $_{18544}$	371276 $_{888}$	1375705 $_{189}$
7270	52 85 29 00	384 240 583 000	264295 $_{5864}$	629375 $_{18544}$	372164 $_{888}$	1375516 $_{189}$
7271	52 86 74 41	384 399 163 511	270159 $_{5863}$	647919 $_{18542}$	373052 $_{888}$	1375327 $_{189}$
7272	52 88 19 84	384 557 787 648	276022 $_{5864}$	666461 $_{18540}$	373940 $_{888}$	1375138 $_{190}$
7273	52 89 65 29	384 716 455 417	281886 $_{5862}$	685001 $_{18540}$	374828 $_{888}$	1374948 $_{189}$
7274	52 91 10 76	384 875 166 824	287748 $_{5863}$	703541 $_{18538}$	375716 $_{888}$	1374759 $_{189}$
7275	52 92 56 25	385 033 921 875	293611 $_{5861}$	722079 $_{18537}$	376604 $_{888}$	1374570 $_{188}$
7276	52 94 01 76	385 192 720 576	299472 $_{5862}$	740616 $_{18536}$	377492 $_{888}$	1374382 $_{189}$
7277	52 95 47 29	385 351 562 933	305334 $_{5861}$	759152 $_{18534}$	378380 $_{887}$	1374193 $_{189}$
7278	52 96 92 84	385 510 448 952	311195 $_{5861}$	777686 $_{18533}$	379267 $_{888}$	1374004 $_{189}$
7279	52 98 38 41	385 669 378 639	317056 $_{5860}$	796219 $_{18532}$	380155 $_{887}$	1373815 $_{189}$
7280	52 99 84 00	385 828 352 000	322916 $_{5860}$	814751 $_{18531}$	381042 $_{888}$	1373626 $_{188}$
7281	53 01 29 61	385 987 369 041	328776 $_{5859}$	833282 $_{18529}$	381930 $_{887}$	1373438 $_{189}$
7282	53 02 75 24	386 146 429 768	334635 $_{5859}$	851811 $_{18528}$	382817 $_{887}$	1373249 $_{188}$
7283	53 04 20 89	386 305 534 187	340494 $_{5859}$	870339 $_{18527}$	383704 $_{887}$	1373061 $_{189}$
7284	53 05 66 56	386 464 682 304	346353 $_{5858}$	888866 $_{18526}$	384591 $_{887}$	1372872 $_{188}$
7285	53 07 12 25	386 623 874 125	352211 $_{5858}$	907392 $_{18524}$	385478 $_{887}$	1372684 $_{189}$
7286	53 08 57 96	386 783 109 656	358069 $_{5858}$	925916 $_{18523}$	386365 $_{887}$	1372495 $_{188}$
7287	53 10 03 69	386 942 388 903	363927 $_{5857}$	944439 $_{18521}$	387252 $_{887}$	1372307 $_{188}$
7288	53 11 49 44	387 101 711 872	369784 $_{5857}$	962960 $_{18521}$	388139 $_{887}$	1372119 $_{189}$
7289	53 12 95 21	387 261 078 569	375641 $_{5856}$	981481 $_{18519}$	389026 $_{886}$	1371930 $_{188}$
7290	53 14 41 00	387 420 489 000	381497 $_{5856}$	*000000 $_{18518}$	389912 $_{887}$	1371742 $_{188}$
7291	53 15 86 81	387 579 943 171	387353 $_{5855}$	018518 $_{18516}$	390799 $_{886}$	1371554 $_{188}$
7292	53 17 32 64	387 739 441 088	393208 $_{5855}$	037034 $_{18516}$	391685 $_{887}$	1371366 $_{188}$
7293	53 18 78 49	387 898 982 757	399063 $_{5855}$	055550 $_{18514}$	392572 $_{886}$	1371178 $_{188}$
7294	53 20 24 36	388 058 568 184	404918 $_{5854}$	074064 $_{18513}$	393458 $_{886}$	1370990 $_{188}$
7295	53 21 70 25	388 218 197 375	410772 $_{5854}$	092577 $_{18511}$	394344 $_{886}$	1370802 $_{188}$
7296	53 23 16 16	388 377 870 336	416626 $_{5853}$	111088 $_{18511}$	395230 $_{886}$	1370614 $_{188}$
7297	53 24 62 09	388 537 587 073	422479 $_{5854}$	129599 $_{18509}$	396116 $_{886}$	1370426 $_{188}$
7298	53 26 08 04	388 697 347 592	428333 $_{5852}$	148108 $_{18507}$	397002 $_{886}$	1370238 $_{187}$
7299	53 27 54 01	388 857 151 899	434185 $_{5852}$	166615 $_{18507}$	397888 $_{886}$	1370051 $_{188}$
7300	53 29 00 00	389 017 000 000	440037	185122	398774	1369863
			85·	270·	19·	0·000

No. n	Square n^2	Cube n^3	Square root $\sqrt{n}$	Sq. rt. of 10n $\sqrt{10n}$	Cube root $\sqrt[3]{n}$	Reciprocal $\dfrac{1}{n}$
			85·	270·	19·	0·000
7300	53 29 00 00	389 017 000 000	440037 5852	185122 18505	398774 886	1369863 188
7301	53 30 46 01	389 176 891 901	445889 5852	203627 18504	399660 886	1369675 187
7302	53 31 92 04	389 336 827 608	451741 5851	222131 18503	400546 885	1369488 187
7303	53 33 38 09	389 496 807 127	457592 5850	240634 18501	401431 886	1369300 187
7304	53 34 84 16	389 656 830 464	463442 5851	259135 18500	402317 885	1369113 188
7305	53 36 30 25	389 816 897 625	469293 5850	277635 18499	403202 885	1368925 187
7306	53 37 76 36	389 977 008 616	475143 5849	296134 18497	404087 886	1368738 187
7307	53 39 22 49	390 137 163 443	480992 5849	314631 18497	404973 885	1368551 188
7308	53 40 68 64	390 297 362 112	486841 5849	333128 18495	405858 885	1368363 187
7309	53 42 14 81	390 457 604 629	492690 5848	351623 18494	406743 885	1368176 187
7310	53 43 61 00	390 617 891 000	498538 5848	370117 18492	407628 885	1367989 187
7311	53 45 07 21	390 778 221 231	504386 5847	388609 18491	408513 885	1367802 187
7312	53 46 53 44	390 938 595 328	510233 5847	407100 18491	409398 885	1367615 187
7313	53 47 99 69	391 099 013 297	516080 5847	425591 18488	410283 884	1367428 187
7314	53 49 45 96	391 259 475 144	521927 5846	444079 18488	411167 885	1367241 187
7315	53 50 92 25	391 419 980 875	527773 5846	462567 18486	412052 884	1367054 187
7316	53 52 38 56	391 580 530 496	533619 5846	481053 18485	412936 885	1366867 187
7317	53 53 84 89	391 741 124 013	539465 5845	499538 18484	413821 884	1366680 187
7318	53 55 31 24	391 901 761 432	545310 5844	518022 18482	414705 885	1366494 186
7319	53 56 77 61	392 062 442 759	551154 5845	536504 18481	415590 884	1366307 187
7320	53 58 24 00	392 223 168 000	556999 5843	554985 18480	416474 884	1366120 186
7321	53 59 70 41	392 383 937 161	562842 5844	573465 18479	417358 884	1365934 186
7322	53 61 16 84	392 544 750 248	568686 5843	591944 18477	418242 884	1365747 187
7323	53 62 63 29	392 705 607 267	574529 5843	610421 18476	419126 884	1365561 187
7324	53 64 09 76	392 866 508 224	580372 5842	628897 18475	420010 884	1365374 186
7325	53 65 56 25	393 027 453 125	586214 5842	647372 18474	420894 883	1365188 187
7326	53 67 02 76	393 188 441 976	592056 5841	665846 18472	421777 884	1365001 186
7327	53 68 49 29	393 349 474 783	597897 5841	684318 18471	422661 884	1364815 186
7328	53 69 95 84	393 510 551 552	603738 5841	702789 18470	423545 883	1364629 186
7329	53 71 42 41	393 671 672 289	609579 5840	721259 18468	424428 883	1364443 187
7330	53 72 89 00	393 832 837 000	615419 5840	739727 18468	425311 884	1364256 186
7331	53 74 35 61	393 994 045 691	621259 5840	758195 18466	426195 883	1364070 186
7332	53 75 82 24	394 155 298 368	627099 5839	776661 18465	427078 883	1363884 186
7333	53 77 28 89	394 316 595 037	632938 5838	795126 18463	427961 883	1363698 186
7334	53 78 75 56	394 477 935 704	638776 5839	813589 18462	428844 883	1363512 185
7335	53 80 22 25	394 639 320 375	644615 5837	832051 18461	429727 883	1363327 186
7336	53 81 68 96	394 800 749 056	650452 5838	850512 18460	430610 883	1363141 186
7337	53 83 15 69	394 962 221 753	656290 5837	868972 18458	431493 883	1362955 186
7338	53 84 62 44	395 123 738 472	662127 5837	887430 18458	432376 883	1362769 186
7339	53 86 09 21	395 285 299 219	667964 5836	905888 18456	433259 883	1362583 185
7340	53 87 56 00	395 446 904 000	673800 5836	924344 18454	434141 883	1362398 186
7341	53 89 02 81	395 608 552 821	679636 5835	942798 18454	435024 883	1362212 185
7342	53 90 49 64	395 770 245 688	685471 5835	961252 18452	435906 883	1362027 186
7343	53 91 96 49	395 931 982 607	691306 5835	979704 18451	436789 882	1361841 185
7344	53 93 43 36	396 093 763 584	697141 5834	998155 18450	437671 882	1361656 186
7345	53 94 90 25	396 255 588 625	702975 5834	*016605 18448	438553 882	1361470 185
7346	53 96 37 16	396 417 457 736	708809 5834	035053 18447	439435 882	1361285 185
7347	53 97 84 09	396 579 370 923	714643 5833	053500 18446	440317 882	1361100 185
7348	53 99 31 24	396 741 328 192	720476 5833	071946 18445	441199 882	1360915 186
7349	54 00 78 01	396 903 329 549	726309 5832	090391 18443	442081 882	1360729 185
7350	54 02 25 00	397 065 375 000	732141 85·	108834 271·	442963 19·	1360544 0·000

No. n	Square n²	Cube n³	Square root √n	Sq. rt. of 10n √10n	Cube root ∛n	Reciprocal 1/n
			85·	271·	19·	0·000
7350	54 02 25 00	397 065 375 000	732141 _5832_	108834 _18442_	442963 _882_	1360544 _185_
7351	54 03 72 01	397 227 464 551	737973 _5831_	127276 _18441_	443845 _881_	1360359 _185_
7352	54 05 19 04	397 389 598 208	743804 _5832_	145717 _18440_	444726 _882_	1360174 _185_
7353	54 06 66 09	397 551 775 977	749636 _5830_	164157 _18438_	445608 _881_	1359989 _185_
7354	54 08 13 16	397 713 997 864	755466 _5831_	182595 _18437_	446489 _882_	1359804 _185_
7355	54 09 60 25	397 876 263 875	761297 _5830_	201032 _18436_	447371 _881_	1359619 _185_
7356	54 11 07 36	398 038 574 016	767127 _5829_	219468 _18435_	448252 _881_	1359434 _184_
7357	54 12 54 49	398 200 928 293	772956 _5829_	237903 _18433_	449133 _881_	1359250 _185_
7358	54 14 01 64	398 363 326 712	778785 _5829_	256336 _18432_	450014 _882_	1359065 _185_
7359	54 15 48 81	398 525 769 279	784614 _5828_	274768 _18431_	450896 _881_	1358880 _184_
7360	54 16 96 00	398 688 256 000	790442 _5828_	293199 _18430_	451777 _880_	1358696 _185_
7361	54 18 43 21	398 850 786 881	796270 _5828_	311629 _18428_	452657 _880_	1358511 _184_
7362	54 19 90 44	399 013 361 928	802098 _5827_	330057 _18427_	453538 _881_	1358327 _185_
7363	54 21 37 69	399 175 981 147	807925 _5827_	348484 _18426_	454419 _881_	1358142 _184_
7364	54 22 84 96	399 338 644 544	813752 _5826_	366910 _18425_	455300 _880_	1357958 _185_
7365	54 24 32 25	399 501 352 125	819578 _5826_	385335 _18423_	456180 _881_	1357773 _184_
7366	54 25 79 56	399 664 103 896	825404 _5826_	403758 _18422_	457061 _880_	1357589 _184_
7367	54 27 26 89	399 826 899 863	831230 _5825_	422180 _18421_	457941 _881_	1357405 _185_
7368	54 28 74 24	399 989 740 032	837055 _5825_	440601 _18420_	458822 _880_	1357220 _184_
7369	54 30 21 61	400 152 624 409	842880 _5824_	459021 _18418_	459702 _880_	1357036 _184_
7370	54 31 69 00	400 315 553 000	848704 _5824_	477439 _18417_	460582 _880_	1356852 _184_
7371	54 33 16 41	400 478 525 811	854528 _5824_	495856 _18416_	461462 _880_	1356668 _184_
7372	54 34 63 84	400 641 542 848	860352 _5823_	514272 _18415_	462342 _880_	1356484 _184_
7373	54 36 11 29	400 804 604 117	866175 _5823_	532687 _18413_	463222 _880_	1356300 _184_
7374	54 37 58 76	400 967 709 624	871998 _5822_	551100 _18412_	464102 _880_	1356116 _184_
7375	54 39 06 25	401 130 859 375	877820 _5822_	569512 _18411_	464982 _880_	1355932 _184_
7376	54 40 53 76	401 294 053 376	883642 _5822_	587923 _18410_	465862 _879_	1355748 _183_
7377	54 42 01 29	401 457 291 633	889464 _5821_	606333 _18408_	466741 _880_	1355565 _184_
7378	54 43 48 84	401 620 574 152	895285 _5821_	624741 _18407_	467621 _880_	1355381 _184_
7379	54 44 96 41	401 783 900 939	901106 _5820_	643148 _18406_	468501 _879_	1355197 _183_
7380	54 46 44 00	401 947 272 000	906926 _5820_	661554 _18405_	469380 _879_	1355014 _184_
7381	54 47 91 61	402 110 687 341	912746 _5820_	679959 _18403_	470259 _880_	1354830 _184_
7382	54 49 39 24	402 274 146 968	918566 _5819_	698362 _18402_	471139 _879_	1354646 _183_
7383	54 50 86 89	402 437 650 887	924385 _5819_	716764 _18401_	472018 _879_	1354463 _183_
7384	54 52 34 56	402 601 199 104	930204 _5819_	735165 _18400_	472897 _879_	1354280 _184_
7385	54 53 82 25	402 764 791 625	936023 _5818_	753565 _18398_	473776 _879_	1354096 _183_
7386	54 55 29 96	402 928 428 456	941841 _5817_	771963 _18397_	474655 _879_	1353913 _183_
7387	54 56 77 69	403 092 109 603	947658 _5818_	790360 _18396_	475534 _878_	1353730 _184_
7388	54 58 25 44	403 255 835 072	953476 _5817_	808756 _18395_	476412 _879_	1353546 _183_
7389	54 59 73 21	403 419 604 869	959293 _5816_	827151 _18393_	477291 _879_	1353363 _183_
7390	54 61 21 00	403 583 419 000	965109 _5816_	845544 _18393_	478170 _878_	1353180 _183_
7391	54 62 68 81	403 747 277 471	970925 _5816_	863937 _18390_	479048 _879_	1352997 _183_
7392	54 64 16 64	403 911 180 288	976741 _5815_	882327 _18390_	479927 _878_	1352814 _183_
7393	54 65 64 49	404 075 127 457	982556 _5815_	900717 _18389_	480805 _878_	1352631 _183_
7394	54 67 12 36	404 239 118 984	988371 _5815_	919106 _18387_	481683 _879_	1352448 _183_
7395	54 68 60 25	404 403 154 875	994186 _5814_	937493 _18386_	482562 _878_	1352265 _183_
7396	54 70 08 16	404 567 235 136	*000000 _5814_	955879 _18384_	483440 _878_	1352082 _183_
7397	54 71 56 09	404 731 359 773	005814 _5813_	974263 _18384_	484318 _878_	1351899 _182_
7398	54 73 04 04	404 895 528 792	011627 _5813_	992647 _18382_	485196 _878_	1351717 _183_
7399	54 74 52 01	405 059 742 199	017440 _5813_	*011029 _18381_	486074 _878_	1351534 _183_
7400	54 76 00 00	405 224 000 000	023253	029410	486952	1351351
			86·	272·	19·	0·000

No. n	Square n^2	Cube n^3	Square root $\sqrt{n}$	Sq. rt. of $10n$ $\sqrt{10n}$	Cube root $\sqrt[3]{n}$	Reciprocal $\frac{1}{n}$
			86·	272·	19·	0·000
7400	54 76 00 00	405 224 000 000	023253 _5812_	029410 _18380_	486952 _877_	1351351 _182_
7401	54 77 48 01	405 388 302 201	029065 _5812_	047790 _18378_	487829 _878_	1351169 _183_
7402	54 78 96 04	405 552 648 808	034877 _5811_	066168 _18378_	488707 _878_	1350986 _182_
7403	54 80 44 09	405 717 039 827	040688 _5811_	084546 _18376_	489585 _877_	1350804 _183_
7404	54 81 92 16	405 881 475 264	046499 _5811_	102922 _18374_	490462 _878_	1350621 _182_
7405	54 83 40 25	406 045 955 125	052310 _5810_	121296 _18374_	491340 _877_	1350439 _182_
7406	54 84 88 36	406 210 479 416	058120 _5810_	139670 _18372_	492217 _877_	1350257 _183_
7407	54 86 36 49	406 375 048 143	063930 _5809_	158042 _18371_	493094 _877_	1350074 _182_
7408	54 87 84 64	406 539 661 312	069739 _5809_	176413 _18370_	493971 _878_	1349892 _182_
7409	54 89 32 81	406 704 318 929	075548 _5809_	194783 _18369_	494849 _877_	1349710 _182_
7410	54 90 81 00	406 869 021 000	081357 _5808_	213152 _18367_	495726 _877_	1349528 _182_
7411	54 92 29 21	407 033 767 531	087165 _5808_	231519 _18366_	496603 _876_	1349346 _182_
7412	54 93 77 44	407 198 558 528	092973 _5807_	249885 _18365_	497479 _877_	1349164 _182_
7413	54 95 25 69	407 363 393 997	098780 _5808_	268250 _18364_	498356 _877_	1348982 _182_
7414	54 96 73 96	407 528 273 944	104588 _5806_	286614 _18362_	499233 _877_	1348800 _182_
7415	54 98 22 25	407 693 198 375	110394 _5807_	304976 _18361_	500110 _876_	1348618 _182_
7416	54 99 70 56	407 858 167 296	116201 _5805_	323337 _18360_	500986 _877_	1348436 _182_
7417	55 01 18 89	408 023 180 713	122006 _5806_	341697 _18359_	501863 _876_	1348254 _182_
7418	55 02 67 24	408 188 238 632	127812 _5805_	360056 _18357_	502739 _876_	1348072 _181_
7419	55 04 15 61	408 353 341 059	133617 _5805_	378413 _18356_	503615 _877_	1347891 _182_
7420	55 05 64 00	408 518 488 000	139422 _5804_	396769 _18355_	504492 _876_	1347709 _182_
7421	55 07 12 41	408 683 679 461	145226 _5804_	415124 _18354_	505368 _876_	1347527 _182_
7422	55 08 60 84	408 848 915 448	151030 _5804_	433478 _18353_	506244 _876_	1347346 _182_
7423	55 10 09 29	409 014 195 967	156834 _5803_	451831 _18351_	507120 _876_	1347164 _181_
7424	55 11 57 76	409 179 521 024	162637 _5803_	470182 _18350_	507996 _876_	1346983 _182_
7425	55 13 06 25	409 344 890 625	168440 _5802_	488532 _18349_	508872 _875_	1346801 _181_
7426	55 14 54 76	409 510 304 776	174242 _5802_	506881 _18347_	509747 _876_	1346620 _181_
7427	55 16 03 29	409 675 763 483	180044 _5802_	525228 _18346_	510623 _876_	1346439 _182_
7428	55 17 51 84	409 841 266 752	185846 _5801_	543574 _18346_	511499 _875_	1346257 _181_
7429	55 19 00 41	410 006 814 589	191647 _5801_	561920 _18343_	512374 _876_	1346076 _181_
7430	55 20 49 00	410 172 407 000	197448 _5800_	580263 _18343_	513250 _875_	1345895 _181_
7431	55 21 97 61	410 338 043 991	203248 _5800_	598606 _18341_	514125 _876_	1345714 _181_
7432	55 23 46 24	410 503 725 568	209048 _5800_	616947 _18341_	515001 _875_	1345533 _181_
7433	55 24 94 89	410 669 451 737	214848 _5799_	635288 _18338_	515876 _875_	1345352 _181_
7434	55 26 43 56	410 835 222 504	220647 _5799_	653626 _18338_	516751 _875_	1345171 _181_
7435	55 27 92 25	411 001 037 875	226446 _5799_	671964 _18337_	517626 _875_	1344990 _181_
7436	55 29 40 96	411 166 897 856	232245 _5798_	690301 _18335_	518501 _875_	1344809 _181_
7437	55 30 89 69	411 332 802 453	238043 _5798_	708636 _18334_	519376 _875_	1344628 _181_
7438	55 32 38 44	411 498 751 672	243840 _5797_	726970 _18332_	520251 _874_	1344447 _180_
7439	55 33 87 21	411 664 745 519	249638 _5798_	745302 _18332_	521125 _875_	1344267 _181_
7440	55 35 36 00	411 830 784 000	255435 _5796_	763634 _18330_	522000 _875_	1344086 _181_
7441	55 36 84 81	411 996 867 121	261231 _5796_	781964 _18329_	522875 _874_	1343905 _180_
7442	55 38 33 64	412 162 994 888	267027 _5796_	800293 _18328_	523749 _875_	1343725 _180_
7443	55 39 82 49	412 329 167 307	272823 _5795_	818621 _18327_	524624 _874_	1343544 _180_
7444	55 41 31 36	412 495 384 384	278618 _5795_	836948 _18325_	525498 _874_	1343364 _181_
7445	55 42 80 25	412 661 646 125	284413 _5795_	855273 _18324_	526372 _875_	1343183 _180_
7446	55 44 29 16	412 827 952 536	290208 _5794_	873597 _18323_	527247 _874_	1343003 _180_
7447	55 45 78 09	412 994 303 623	296002 _5794_	891920 _18322_	528121 _874_	1342823 _181_
7448	55 47 27 04	413 160 699 392	301796 _5793_	910242 _18320_	528995 _874_	1342642 _180_
7449	55 48 76 01	413 327 139 849	307589 _5794_	928562 _18319_	529869 _874_	1342462 _180_
7450	55 50 25 00	413 493 625 000	313383 86·	946881 272·	530743 19·	1342282 0·000

No. n	Square n²	Cube n³	Square root √n	Sq. rt. of 10n √10n	Cube root ∛n	Reciprocal 1/n
			86·	272·	19·	0·000
7450	55 50 25 00	413 493 625 000	313383 5792	946881 18318	530743 873	1342282 180
7451	55 51 74 01	413 660 154 851	319175 5792	965199 18317	531616 874	1342102 180
7452	55 53 23 04	413 826 729 408	324967 5792	983516 18315	532490 874	1341922 180
7453	55 54 72 09	413 993 348 677	330759 5792	*001831 18315	533364 874	1341742 180
7454	55 56 21 16	414 160 012 664	336551 5791	020146 18313	534237 874	1341562 180
7455	55 57 70 25	414 326 721 375	342342 5791	038459 18312	535111 873	1341382 180
7456	55 59 19 36	414 493 474 816	348133 5790	056771 18310	535984 874	1341202 180
7457	55 60 68 49	414 660 272 993	353923 5790	075081 18310	536858 873	1341022 180
7458	55 62 17 64	414 827 115 912	359713 5789	093391 18308	537731 873	1340842 180
7459	55 63 66 81	414 994 003 579	365502 5790	111699 18307	538604 873	1340662 179
7460	55 65 16 00	415 160 936 000	371292 5788	130006 18305	539477 873	1340483 180
7461	55 66 65 21	415 327 913 181	377080 5789	148311 18305	540350 873	1340303 180
7462	55 68 14 44	415 494 935 128	382869 5788	166616 18303	541223 873	1340123 180
7463	55 69 63 69	415 662 001 847	388657 5787	184919 18302	542096 873	1339944 180
7464	55 71 12 96	415 829 113 344	394444 5787	203221 18301	542969 873	1339764 179
7465	55 72 62 25	415 996 269 625	400231 5787	221522 18299	543842 872	1339585 180
7466	55 74 11 56	416 163 470 696	406018 5787	239821 18299	544714 873	1339405 179
7467	55 75 60 89	416 330 716 563	411805 5786	258120 18297	545587 872	1339226 179
7468	55 77 10 24	416 498 007 232	417591 5785	276417 18296	546459 873	1339047 180
7469	55 78 59 61	416 665 342 709	423376 5786	294713 18294	547332 872	1338867 179
7470	55 80 09 00	416 832 723 000	429162 5785	313007 18294	548204 872	1338688 179
7471	55 81 58 41	417 000 148 111	434947 5784	331301 18292	549076 873	1338509 179
7472	55 83 07 84	417 167 618 048	440731 5784	349593 18291	549949 872	1338330 179
7473	55 84 57 29	417 335 132 817	446515 5784	367884 18290	550821 872	1338151 179
7474	55 86 06 76	417 502 692 424	452299 5783	386174 18288	551693 872	1337972 179
7475	55 87 56 25	417 670 296 875	458082 5783	404462 18288	552565 872	1337793 179
7476	55 89 05 76	417 837 946 176	463865 5783	422750 18286	553437 871	1337614 179
7477	55 90 55 29	418 005 640 333	469648 5782	441036 18285	554308 872	1337435 179
7478	55 92 04 84	418 173 379 352	475430 5782	459321 18283	555180 872	1337256 179
7479	55 93 54 41	418 341 163 239	481212 5781	477604 18283	556052 871	1337077 179
7480	55 95 04 00	418 508 992 000	486993 5781	495887 18281	556923 872	1336898 178
7481	55 96 53 61	418 676 865 641	492774 5781	514168 18280	557795 871	1336720 179
7482	55 98 03 24	418 844 784 168	498555 5780	532448 18279	558666 872	1336541 179
7483	55 99 52 89	419 012 747 587	504335 5780	550727 18277	559538 871	1336362 178
7484	56 01 02 56	419 180 755 904	510115 5779	569004 18276	560409 871	1336184 179
7485	56 02 52 25	419 348 809 125	515894 5780	587280 18275	561280 871	1336005 178
7486	56 04 01 96	419 516 907 256	521674 5778	605555 18274	562151 871	1335827 179
7487	56 05 51 69	419 685 050 303	527452 5779	623829 18273	563022 871	1335648 178
7488	56 07 01 44	419 853 238 272	533231 5778	642102 18271	563893 871	1335470 178
7489	56 08 51 21	420 021 471 169	539009 5777	660373 18271	564764 871	1335292 179
7490	56 10 01 00	420 189 749 000	544786 5777	678644 18268	565635 870	1335113 178
7491	56 11 50 81	420 358 071 771	550563 5777	696913 18267	566505 871	1334935 178
7492	56 13 00 64	420 526 439 488	556340 5776	715180 18267	567376 871	1334757 178
7493	56 14 50 49	420 694 852 157	562116 5776	733447 18265	568247 870	1334579 178
7494	56 16 00 36	420 863 309 784	567892 5776	751712 18264	569117 870	1334401 178
7495	56 17 50 25	421 031 812 375	573668 5775	769976 18263	569987 871	1334223 178
7496	56 19 00 16	421 200 359 936	579443 5775	788239 18262	570858 870	1334045 178
7497	56 20 50 09	421 368 952 473	585218 5775	806501 18260	571728 870	1333867 178
7498	56 22 00 04	421 537 589 992	590993 5774	824761 18260	572598 870	1333689 178
7499	56 23 50 01	421 706 272 499	596767 5773	843021 18258	573468 870	1333511 178
7500	56 25 00 00	421 875 000 000	602540 86·	861279 273·	574338 19·	1333333 0·000

No. n	Square n²	Cube n³	Square root √n	Sq. rt. of 10n √10n	Cube root ∛n	Reciprocal 1/n
			86·	273·	19·	0·000
7500	56 25 00 00	421 875 000 000	602540	861279	574338	1333333
7501	56 26 50 01	422 043 772 501	608314 5774	879536 18257	575208 870	1333156 177
7502	56 28 00 04	422 212 590 008	614087 5773	897791 18255	576078 870	1332978 178
7503	56 29 50 09	422 381 452 527	619859 5772	916046 18255	576948 870	1332800 178
7504	56 31 00 16	422 550 360 064	625631 5772	934299 18253	577817 869	1332623 177
			5772	18252	870	178
7505	56 32 50 25	422 719 312 625	631403 5771	952551 18250	578687 870	1332445 177
7506	56 34 00 36	422 888 310 216	637174 5771	970801 18250	579557 869	1332268 178
7507	56 35 50 49	423 057 352 843	642945 5771	989051 18248	580426 869	1332090 178
7508	56 37 00 64	423 226 440 512	648716 5771	*007299 18247	581295 870	1331913 178
7509	56 38 50 81	423 395 573 229	654486 5770	025546 18246	582165 869	1331735 177
			5770			
7510	56 40 01 00	423 564 751 000	660256 5770	043792 18245	583034 869	1331558 177
7511	56 41 51 21	423 733 973 831	666026 5770	062037 18243	583903 869	1331381 178
7512	56 43 01 44	423 903 241 728	671795 5769	080280 18242	584772 869	1331203 177
7513	56 44 51 69	424 072 554 697	677563 5768	098522 18241	585641 869	1331026 177
7514	56 46 01 96	424 241 912 744	683332 5769	116763 18240	586510 869	1330849 177
			5768			177
7515	56 47 52 25	424 411 315 875	689100 5767	135003 18239	587379 869	1330672 177
7516	56 49 02 56	424 580 764 096	694867 5767	153242 18237	588248 869	1330495 177
7517	56 50 52 89	424 750 257 413	700634 5767	171479 18236	589117 868	1330318 177
7518	56 52 03 24	424 919 795 832	706401 5767	189715 18235	589985 869	1330141 177
7519	56 53 53 61	425 089 379 359	712168 5766	207950 18234	590854 868	1329964 177
7520	56 55 04 00	425 259 008 000	717934 5765	226184 18233	591722 869	1329787 177
7521	56 56 54 41	425 428 681 761	723699 5765	244417 18231	592591 868	1329610 177
7522	56 58 04 84	425 598 400 648	729464 5765	262648 18230	593459 868	1329434 177
7523	56 59 55 29	425 768 164 667	735229 5765	280878 18229	594327 868	1329257 177
7524	56 61 05 76	425 937 973 824	740994 5764	299107 18227	595195 868	1329080 176
7525	56 62 56 25	426 107 828 125	746758 5764	317334 18227	596063 868	1328904 177
7526	56 64 06 76	426 277 727 576	752522 5763	335561 18225	596931 868	1328727 176
7527	56 65 57 29	426 447 672 183	758285 5763	353786 18224	597799 868	1328551 177
7528	56 67 07 84	426 617 661 952	764048 5762	372010 18223	598667 868	1328374 176
7529	56 68 58 41	426 787 696 889	769810 5763	390233 18222	599535 868	1328198 177
7530	56 70 09 00	426 957 777 000	775573 5761	408455 18220	600403 867	1328021 176
7531	56 71 59 61	427 127 902 291	781334 5762	426675 18219	601270 868	1327845 176
7532	56 73 10 24	427 298 072 768	787096 5761	444894 18218	602138 867	1327669 177
7533	56 74 60 89	427 468 288 437	792857 5761	463112 18217	603005 868	1327492 176
7534	56 76 11 56	427 638 549 304	798618 5760	481329 18216	603873 867	1327316 176
7535	56 77 62 25	427 808 855 375	804378 5760	499545 18214	604740 867	1327140 176
7536	56 79 12 96	427 979 206 656	810138 5759	517759 18213	605607 867	1326964 176
7537	56 80 63 69	428 149 603 153	815897 5759	535972 18212	606474 867	1326788 176
7538	56 82 14 44	428 320 044 872	821656 5759	554184 18211	607341 867	1326612 176
7539	56 83 65 21	428 490 531 819	827415 5758	572395 18209	608208 867	1326436 176
7540	56 85 16 00	428 661 064 000	833173 5758	590604 18209	609075 867	1326260 176
7541	56 86 66 81	428 831 641 421	838931 5758	608813 18207	609942 867	1326084 176
7542	56 88 17 64	429 002 264 088	844689 5757	627020 18206	610809 867	1325908 176
7543	56 89 68 49	429 172 932 007	850446 5757	645226 18204	611676 867	1325732 175
7544	56 91 19 36	429 343 645 184	856203 5756	663430 18204	612542 867	1325557 176
7545	56 92 70 25	429 514 403 625	861959 5757	681634 18202	613409 866	1325381 176
7546	56 94 21 16	429 685 207 336	867716 5757	699836 18201	614275 867	1325205 175
7547	56 95 72 09	429 856 056 323	873471 5755	718037 18201	615142 866	1325030 176
7548	56 97 23 04	430 026 950 592	879227 5756	736237 18200	616008 866	1324854 175
7549	56 98 74 01	430 197 890 149	884981 5754	754436 18199	616874 866	1324679 175
			5755	18197		
7550	57 00 25 00	430 368 875 000	890736 86·	772633 274·	617740 19·	1324503 0·000

No. n	Square n²	Cube n³	Square root √n	Sq. rt. of 10n √10n	Cube root ∛n	Reciprocal 1/n
			86·	274·	19·	0·000
7550	57 00 25 00	430 368 875 000	890736 5754	772633 18197	617740 867	1324503 175
7551	57 01 76 01	430 539 905 151	896490 5754	790830 18195	618607 866	1324328 175
7552	57 03 27 04	430 710 980 608	902244 5753	809025 18193	619473 865	1324153 176
7553	57 04 78 09	430 882 101 377	907997 5753	827218 18193	620338 866	1323977 175
7554	57 06 29 16	431 053 267 464	913750 5753	845411 18192	621204 866	1323802 175
7555	57 07 80 25	431 224 478 875	919503 5752	863603 18190	622070 866	1323627 175
7556	57 09 31 36	431 395 735 616	925255 5752	881793 18189	622936 865	1323452 176
7557	57 10 82 49	431 567 037 693	931007 5752	899982 18188	623801 866	1323276 175
7558	57 12 33 64	431 738 385 112	936759 5751	918170 18186	624667 865	1323101 175
7559	57 13 84 81	431 909 777 879	942510 5750	936356 18186	625532 866	1322926 175
7560	57 15 36 00	432 081 216 000	948260 5751	954542 18184	626398 865	1322751 175
7561	57 16 87 21	432 252 699 481	954011 5750	972726 18183	627263 865	1322576 175
7562	57 18 38 44	432 424 228 328	959761 5749	990909 18182	628128 866	1322401 174
7563	57 19 89 69	432 595 802 547	965510 5750	*009091 18180	628994 865	1322227 175
7564	57 21 40 96	432 767 422 144	971260 5748	027271 18180	629859 865	1322052 175
7565	57 22 92 25	432 939 087 125	977008 5749	045451 18178	630724 865	1321877 175
7566	57 24 43 56	433 110 797 496	982757 5748	063629 18177	631589 865	1321702 174
7567	57 25 94 89	433 282 553 263	988505 5748	081806 18176	632454 864	1321528 175
7568	57 27 46 24	433 454 354 432	994253 5747	099982 18174	633318 865	1321353 175
7569	57 28 97 61	433 626 201 009	*000000 5747	118156 18174	634183 865	1321178 174
7570	57 30 49 00	433 798 093 000	005747 5746	136330 18172	635048 864	1321004 175
7571	57 32 00 41	433 970 030 411	011493 5746	154502 18171	635912 865	1320829 174
7572	57 33 51 84	434 142 013 248	017240 5745	172673 18170	636777 864	1320655 174
7573	57 35 03 29	434 314 041 517	022985 5746	190843 18168	637641 864	1320481 175
7574	57 36 54 76	434 486 115 224	028731 5745	209011 18168	638505 865	1320306 174
7575	57 38 06 25	434 658 234 375	034476 5745	227179 18166	639370 864	1320132 174
7576	57 39 57 76	434 830 398 976	040221 5744	245345 18165	640234 864	1319958 174
7577	57 41 09 29	435 002 609 033	045965 5744	263510 18164	641098 864	1319784 175
7578	57 42 60 84	435 174 864 552	051709 5743	281674 18163	641962 864	1319609 174
7579	57 44 12 41	435 347 165 539	057452 5743	299837 18161	642826 864	1319435 174
7580	57 45 64 00	435 519 512 000	063195 5743	317998 18160	643690 864	1319261 174
7581	57 47 15 61	435 691 903 941	068938 5743	336158 18159	644554 863	1319087 174
7582	57 48 67 24	435 864 341 368	074681 5742	354317 18158	645417 864	1318913 174
7583	57 50 18 89	436 036 824 287	080423 5741	372475 18157	646281 864	1318739 174
7584	57 51 70 56	436 209 352 704	086164 5741	390632 18155	647145 863	1318565 173
7585	57 53 22 25	436 381 926 625	091905 5741	408787 18154	648008 864	1318392 174
7586	57 54 73 96	436 554 546 056	097646 5741	426941 18153	648872 863	1318218 174
7587	57 56 25 69	436 727 211 003	103387 5740	445094 18152	649735 863	1318044 174
7588	57 57 77 44	436 899 921 472	109127 5740	463246 18151	650598 863	1317870 173
7589	57 59 29 21	437 072 677 469	114867 5739	481397 18149	651461 863	1317697 174
7590	57 60 81 00	437 245 479 000	120606 5739	499546 18149	652324 863	1317523 174
7591	57 62 32 81	437 418 326 071	126345 5739	517695 18147	653187 863	1317349 173
7592	57 63 84 64	437 591 218 688	132084 5738	535842 18145	654050 863	1317176 173
7593	57 65 36 49	437 764 156 857	137822 5738	553987 18145	654913 863	1317003 174
7594	57 66 88 36	437 937 140 584	143560 5737	572132 18144	655776 863	1316829 173
7595	57 68 40 25	438 110 169 875	149297 5737	590276 18142	656639 863	1316656 174
7596	57 69 92 16	438 283 244 736	155034 5737	608418 18141	657502 862	1316482 173
7597	57 71 44 09	438 456 365 173	160771 5736	626559 18140	658364 863	1316309 173
7598	57 72 96 04	438 629 531 192	166507 5736	644699 18139	659227 862	1316136 173
7599	57 74 48 01	438 802 742 799	172243 5736	662838 18137	660089 862	1315963 174
7600	57 76 00 00	438 976 000 000	177979 87·	680975 275·	660951 19·	1315789 0·000

No. n	Square n^2	Cube n^3	Square root $\sqrt{n}$	Sq. rt. of 10n $\sqrt{10n}$	Cube root $\sqrt[3]{n}$	Reciprocal $\frac{1}{n}$
			87·	275·	19·	0·000
7600	57 76 00 00	438 976 000 000	177979 5735	680975 18136	660951 863	1315789 173
7601	57 77 52 01	439 149 302 801	183714 5735	699111 18135	661814 862	1315616 173
7602	57 79 04 04	439 322 651 208	189449 5734	717246 18134	662676 862	1315443 173
7603	57 80 56 09	439 496 045 227	195183 5734	735380 18133	663538 862	1315270 173
7604	57 82 08 16	439 669 484 864	200917 5734	753513 18132	664400 862	1315097 173
7605	57 83 60 25	439 842 970 125	206651 5733	771645 18130	665262 862	1314924 172
7606	57 85 12 36	440 016 501 016	212384 5733	789775 18129	666124 862	1314752 173
7607	57 86 64 49	440 190 077 543	218117 5733	807904 18128	666986 862	1314579 173
7608	57 88 16 64	440 363 699 712	223850 5733	826032 18127	667848 861	1314406 173
7609	57 89 68 81	440 537 367 529	229582 5732	844159 18125	668709 862	1314233 173
7610	57 91 21 00	440 711 081 000	235314 5731	862284 18125	669571 861	1314060
7611	57 92 73 21	440 884 840 131	241045 5731	880409 18123	670432 861	1313888 172
7612	57 94 25 44	441 058 644 928	246776 5731	898532 18122	671294 861	1313715 173
7613	57 95 77 69	441 232 495 397	252507 5730	916654 18121	672155 862	1313543 173
7614	57 97 29 96	441 406 391 544	258237 5730	934775 18120	673017 861	1313370 172
7615	57 98 82 25	441 580 333 375	263967 5730	952895 18118	673878 861	1313198 173
7616	58 00 34 56	441 754 320 896	269697 5729	971013 18117	674739 861	1313025 172
7617	58 01 86 89	441 928 354 113	275426 5729	989130 18116	675600 861	1312853 173
7618	58 03 39 24	442 102 433 032	281155 5728	*007246 18115	676461 861	1312680 172
7619	58 04 91 61	442 276 557 659	286883 5728	025361 18114	677322 861	1312508 172
7620	58 06 44 00	442 450 728 000	292611 5728	043475 18112	678183 861	1312336 172
7621	58 07 96 41	442 624 944 061	298339 5728	061587 18112	679044 861	1312164 172
7622	58 09 48 84	442 799 205 848	304066 5727	079699 18110	679904 861	1311992 172
7623	58 11 01 29	442 973 513 367	309793 5727	097809 18109	680765 860	1311819 173
7624	58 12 53 76	443 147 866 624	315520 5726	115918 18107	681625 861	1311647 172
7625	58 14 06 25	443 322 265 625	321246 5726	134025 18107	682486 860	1311475 172
7626	58 15 58 76	443 496 710 376	326972 5725	152132 18105	683346 861	1311303 171
7627	58 17 11 29	443 671 200 883	332697 5725	170237 18105	684207 860	1311132 172
7628	58 18 63 84	443 845 737 152	338422 5725	188342 18103	685067 860	1310960 172
7629	58 20 16 41	444 020 319 189	344147 5724	206445 18101	685927 860	1310788 172
7630	58 21 69 00	444 194 947 000	349871 5724	224546 18101	686787 860	1310616 172
7631	58 23 21 61	444 369 620 591	355595 5724	242647 18099	687647 860	1310444 172
7632	58 24 74 24	444 544 339 968	361319 5723	260746 18099	688507 860	1310273 171
7633	58 26 26 89	444 719 105 137	367042 5723	278845 18097	689367 860	1310101 172
7634	58 27 79 56	444 893 916 104	372765 5722	296942 18096	690227 860	1309929 171
7635	58 29 32 25	445 068 772 875	378487 5722	315038 18094	691087 859	1309758 172
7636	58 30 84 96	445 243 675 456	384209 5722	333132 18094	691946 860	1309586 171
7637	58 32 37 69	445 418 623 853	389931 5721	351226 18092	692806 859	1309415 172
7638	58 33 90 44	445 593 618 072	395652 5721	369318 18091	693665 860	1309243 171
7639	58 35 43 21	445 768 658 119	401373 5721	387409 18090	694525 859	1309072 171
7640	58 36 96 00	445 943 744 000	407094 5720	405499 18089	695384 859	1308901 172
7641	58 38 48 81	446 118 875 721	412814 5720	423588 18088	696243 859	1308729 171
7642	58 40 01 64	446 294 053 288	418534 5719	441676 18086	697102 860	1308558 171
7643	58 41 54 49	446 469 276 707	424253 5719	459762 18085	697962 859	1308387 171
7644	58 43 07 36	446 644 545 984	429972 5719	477847 18084	698821 859	1308216 172
7645	58 44 60 25	446 819 861 125	435691 5718	495931 18083	699680 859	1308044 171
7646	58 46 13 16	446 995 222 136	441409 5718	514014 18082	700539 858	1307873 171
7647	58 47 66 09	447 170 629 023	447127 5717	532096 18080	701397 859	1307702 171
7648	58 49 19 04	447 346 081 792	452844 5718	550176 18080	702256 859	1307531 171
7649	58 50 72 01	447 521 580 449	458562 5716	568256 18078	703115 858	1307360 170
7650	58 52 25 00	447 697 125 000	464278 87·	586334 276·	703973 19	1307190 0·000

No. n	Square n²	Cube n³	Square root √n	Sq. rt. of 10n √10n	Cube root ∛n	Reciprocal 1/n
			87·	276·	19·	0·000
7650	58 52 25 00	447 697 125 000	464278 5717	586334 18077	703973 859	1307190 171
7651	58 53 78 01	447 872 715 451	469995 5716	604411 18075	704832 858	1307019 171
7652	58 55 31 04	448 048 351 808	475711 5716	622486 18075	705690 859	1306848 171
7653	58 56 84 09	448 224 034 077	481427 5715	640561 18073	706549 858	1306677 171
7654	58 58 37 16	448 399 762 264	487142 5715	658634 18073	707407 858	1306506 170
7655	58 59 90 25	448 575 536 375	492857 5714	676707 18071	708265 858	1306336 171
7656	58 61 43 36	448 751 356 416	498571 5715	694778 18070	709123 858	1306165 170
7657	58 62 96 49	448 927 222 393	504286 5713	712848 18068	709981 858	1305995 171
7658	58 64 49 64	449 103 134 312	509999 5714	730916 18068	710839 858	1305824 171
7659	58 66 02 81	449 279 092 179	515713 5713	748984 18066	711697 858	1305653 170
7660	58 67 56 00	449 455 096 000	521426 5713	767050 18065	712555 858	1305483 170
7661	58 69 09 21	449 631 145 781	527139 5713	785115 18064	713413 858	1305313 171
7662	58 70 62 44	449 807 241 528	532851 5712	803179 18063	714271 857	1305142 170
7663	58 72 15 69	449 983 383 247	538563 5712	821242 18062	715128 858	1304972 170
7664	58 73 68 96	450 159 570 944	544275 5711	839304 18060	715986 857	1304802 171
7665	58 75 22 25	450 335 804 625	549986 5711	857364 18059	716843 858	1304631 170
7666	58 76 75 56	450 512 084 296	555697 5710	875423 18058	717701 857	1304461 170
7667	58 78 28 89	450 688 409 963	561407 5710	893481 18057	718558 857	1304290 170
7668	58 79 82 24	450 864 781 632	567117 5710	911538 18056	719415 858	1304121 170
7669	58 81 35 61	451 041 199 309	572827 5709	929594 18054	720273 857	1303951 170
7670	58 82 89 00	451 217 663 000	578536 5709	947648 18054	721130 857	1303781 170
7671	58 84 42 41	451 394 172 711	584245 5709	965702 18052	721987 857	1303611 170
7672	58 85 95 84	451 570 728 448	589954 5708	983754 18051	722844 857	1303441 170
7673	58 87 49 29	451 747 330 217	595662 5708	*001805 18050	723701 856	1303271 170
7674	58 89 02 76	451 923 978 024	601370 5707	019855 18049	724557 857	1303101 169
7675	58 90 56 25	452 100 671 875	607077 5707	037904 18047	725414 857	1302932 170
7676	58 92 09 76	452 277 411 776	612784 5707	055951 18046	726271 856	1302762 170
7677	58 93 63 29	452 454 197 733	618491 5707	073997 18045	727127 857	1302592 169
7678	58 95 16 84	452 631 029 752	624198 5706	092042 18044	727984 856	1302423 170
7679	58 96 70 41	452 807 907 839	629904 5705	110086 18043	728840 857	1302253 170
7680	58 98 24 00	452 984 832 000	635609 5705	128129 18042	729697 856	1302083 169
7681	58 99 77 61	453 161 802 241	641314 5705	146171 18042	730553 856	1301914 170
7682	59 01 31 24	453 338 818 568	647019 5705	164211 18040	731409 856	1301744 169
7683	59 02 84 89	453 515 880 987	652724 5704	182251 18040	732265 856	1301575 169
7684	59 04 38 56	453 692 989 504	658428 5704	200289 18038	733121 856	1301406 170
7685	59 05 92 25	453 870 144 125	664132 5703	218326 18037	733977 856	1301236 169
7686	59 07 45 96	454 047 344 856	669835 5703	236361 18035	734833 856	1301067 169
7687	59 08 99 69	454 224 591 703	675538 5703	254396 18035	735689 856	1300898 170
7688	59 10 53 44	454 401 884 672	681241 5702	272429 18033	736545 855	1300728 169
7689	59 12 07 21	454 579 223 769	686943 5702	290461 18032	737400 856	1300559 169
7690	59 13 61 00	454 756 609 000	692645 5702	308492 18031	738256 856	1300390 169
7691	59 15 14 81	454 934 040 371	698347 5701	326522 18030	739112 855	1300221 169
7692	59 16 68 64	455 111 517 888	704048 5701	344551 18029	739967 856	1300052 169
7693	59 18 22 49	455 289 041 557	709749 5700	362579 18028	740823 855	1299883 169
7694	59 19 76 36	455 466 611 384	715449 5700	380605 18026	741678 855	1299714 169
7695	59 21 30 25	455 644 227 375	721149 5700	398630 18025	742533 855	1299545 169
7696	59 22 84 16	455 821 889 536	726849 5699	416654 18024	743388 855	1299376 169
7697	59 24 38 09	455 999 597 873	732548 5699	434677 18023	744243 855	1299207 168
7698	59 25 92 04	456 177 352 392	738247 5699	452699 18022	745098 855	1299039 169
7699	59 27 46 01	456 355 153 099	743946 5698	470719 18020	745953 855	1298870 169
7700	59 29 00 00	456 533 000 000	749644	488739	746808	1298701
			87·	277·	19·	0·000

No. n	Square n²	Cube n³	Square root √n	Sq. rt. of 10n √10n	Cube root ∛n	Reciprocal 1/n
			87·	277·	19·	0·000
7700	59 29 00 00	456 533 000 000	749644 5698	488739 18018	746808 855	1298701 168
7701	59 30 54 01	456 710 893 101	755342 5697	506757 18018	747663 855	1298533 168
7702	59 32 08 04	456 888 832 408	761039 5697	524774 18017	748518 855	1298364 169
7703	59 33 62 09	457 066 817 927	766736 5697	542789 18015	749372 854	1298196 168
7704	59 35 16 16	457 244 849 664	772433 5696	560804 18015	750227 854	1298027 169 168
7705	59 36 70 25	457 422 927 625	778129 5696	578818 18014 18012	751081 855	1297859 169
7706	59 38 24 36	457 601 051 816	783825 5696	596830 18011	751936 854	1297690 168
7707	59 39 78 49	457 779 222 243	789521 5695	614841 18011	752790 855	1297522 169
7708	59 41 32 64	457 957 438 912	795216 5695	632851 18010	753645 854	1297353 168
7709	59 42 86 81	458 135 701 829	800911 5695 5695	650860 18009 18008	·754499 854	1297185 168
7710	59 44 41 00	458 314 011 000	806606 5694	668868 18006	755353 854	1297017 168
7711	59 45 95 21	458 492 366 431	812300 5694	686874 18005	756207 854	1296849 169
7712	59 47 49 44	458 670 768 128	817994 5693	704879 18004	757061 854	1296680 168
7713	59 49 03 69	458 849 216 097	823687 5693	722883 18003	757915 854	1296512 168
7714	59 50 57 96	459 027 710 344	829380 5693	740886 18002	758769 854	1296344 168
7715	59 52 12 25	459 206 250 875	835073 5692	758888 18001	759623 853	1296176 168
7716	59 53 66 56	459 384 837 696	840765 5692	776889 17999	760476 854	1296008 168
7717	59 55 20 89	459 563 470 813	846457 5692	794888 17999	761330 853	1295840 168
7718	59 56 75 24	459 742 150 232	852149 5691	812887 17999 17997	762183 853 854	1295672 167
7719	59 58 29 61	459 920 875 959	857840 5691 5691	830884 17996	·763037 853	1295505 168
7720	59 59 84 00	460 099 648 000	863531 5690	848880 17995	763890 854	1295337 168
7721	59 61 38 41	460 278 466 361	869221 5690	866875 17993	764744 854 853	1295169 168
7722	59 62 92 84	460 457 331 048	874911 5690	884868 17993	765597 853	1295001 168
7723	59 64 47 29	460 636 242 067	880601 5690 5689	902861 17993 17991	766450 853	1294834 167
7724	59 66 01 76	460 815 199 424	886290 5689	920852 17991 17990	767303 853	1294666 168 168
7725	59 67 56 25	460 994 203 125	891979 5689	938842 17989	768156 853	1294498 167
7726	59 69 10 76	461 173 253 176	897668 5689 5688	956831 17988	769009 853	1294331 168
7727	59 70 65 29	461 352 349 583	903356 5688	974819 17988 17987	769862 853	1294163 167
7728	59 72 19 84	461 531 492 352	909044 5688	992806 17987	770715 853	1293996 168
7729	59 73 74 41	461 710 681 489	914731 5687 5688	*010791 17985 17984	771568 852	1293828 167
7730	59 75 29 00	461 889 917 000	920419 5686	028775 17984	772420 853	1293661 167
7731	59 76 83 61	462 069 198 891	926105 5687	046759 17984 17982	773273 852	1293494 168
7732	59 78 38 24	462 248 527 168	931792 5686	064741 17981	774125 853	1293326 167
7733	59 79 92 89	462 427 901 837	937478 5685	082722 17981 17979	774978 852	1293159 167
7734	59 81 47 56	462 607 322 904	943163 5686	100701 17979	775830 852	1292992 167
7735	59 83 02 25	462 786 790 375	948849 5685	118680 17977	776682 853	1292825 167
7736	59 84 56 96	462 966 304 256	954534 5684	136657 17976	777535 852	1292658 167
7737	59 86 11 69	463 145 864 553	960218 5684	154633 17975	778387 852	1292491 167
7738	59 87 66 44	463 325 471 272	965902 5684	172608 17975 17974	779239 852	1292324 167
7739	59 89 21 21	463 505 124 419	971586 5684 5684	190582 17973	780091 852	1292157 167
7740	59 90 76 00	463 684 824 000	977270 5683	208555 17971	780943 852	1291990 167
7741	59 92 30 81	463 864 570 021	982953 5683	226526 17971	781795 851	1291823 167
7742	59 93 85 64	464 044 362 488	988636 5682	244497 17969	782646 851	1291656 167
7743	59 95 40 49	464 224 201 407	994318 5682	262466 17968	783498 852	1291489 167
7744	59 96 95 36	464 404 086 784	*000000 5682	280434 17967	784350 851	1291322 166
7745	59 98 50 25	464 584 018 625	005682 5681	298401 17966	785201 852	1291156 167
7746	60 00 05 16	464 763 996 936	011363 5681	316367 17964	786053 851	1290989 167
7747	60 01 60 09	464 944 021 723	017044 5680	334331 17964	786904 852	1290822 166
7748	60 03 15 04	465 124 092 992	022724 5681	352295 17962	787756 851	1290656 167
7749	60 04 70 01	465 304 210 749	028405 5679	370257 17961	788607 851	1290489 166
7750	60 06 25 00	465 484 375 000	034084 88·	388218 278·	789458 19·	1290323 0·000

No. n	Square n^2	Cube n^3	Square root $\sqrt{n}$	Sq. rt. of 10n $\sqrt{10n}$	Cube root $\sqrt[3]{n}$	Reciprocal $\dfrac{1}{n}$
			88·	278·	19·	0·000
7750	60 06 25 00	465 484 375 000	034084 5680	388218 17960	789458 851	1290323 167
7751	60 07 80 01	465 664 585 751	039764 5679	406178 17959	790309 851	1290156 166
7752	60 09 35 04	465 844 843 008	045443 5679	424137 17958	791160 851	1289990 167
7753	60 10 90 09	466 025 146 777	051122 5678	442095 17956	792011 851	1289823 166
7754	60 12 45 16	466 205 497 064	056800 5678	460051 17955	792862 851	1289657 166
7755	60 14 00 25	466 385 893 875	062478 5677	478006 17954	793713 851	1289491 167
7756	60 15 55 36	466 566 337 216	068155 5678	495960 17953	794564 850	1289324 166
7757	60 17 10 49	466 746 827 093	073833 5677	513913 17952	795414 851	1289158 166
7758	60 18 65 64	466 927 363 512	079510 5676	531865 17951	796265 851	1288992 166
7759	60 20 20 81	467 107 946 479	085186 5676	549816 17950	797116 850	1288826 166
7760	60 21 76 00	467 288 576 000	090862 5676	567766 17948	797966 850	1288660 166
7761	60 23 31 21	467 469 252 081	096538 5675	585714 17947	798816 851	1288494 166
7762	60 24 86 44	467 649 974 728	102213 5675	603661 17946	799667 850	1288328 166
7763	60 26 41 69	467 830 743 947	107888 5675	621607 17945	800517 850	1288162 166
7764	60 27 96 96	468 011 559 744	113563 5674	639552 17944	801367 850	1287996 166
7765	60 29 52 25	468 192 422 125	119237 5674	657496 17942	802217 850	1287830 166
7766	60 31 07 56	468 373 331 096	124911 5674	675438 17942	803067 850	1287664 166
7767	60 32 62 89	468 554 286 663	130585 5673	693380 17940	803917 850	1287498 165
7768	60 34 18 24	468 735 288 832	136258 5673	711320 17939	804767 850	1287333 166
7769	60 35 73 61	468 916 337 609	141931 5672	729259 17938	805617 850	1287167 166
7770	60 37 29 00	469 097 433 000	147603 5673	747197 17937	806467 849	1287001 165
7771	60 38 84 41	469 278 575 011	153276 5671	765134 17936	807316 850	1286836 166
7772	60 40 39 84	469 459 763 648	158947 5672	783070 17934	808166 849	1286670 165
7773	60 41 95 29	469 640 998 917	164619 5671	801004 17934	809015 850	1286505 166
7774	60 43 50 76	469 822 280 824	170290 5670	818938 17932	809865 849	1286339 165
7775	60 45 06 25	470 003 609 375	175960 5671	836870 17931	810714 849	1286174 166
7776	60 46 61 76	470 184 984 576	181631 5670	854801 17930	811563 850	1286008 165
7777	60 48 17 29	470 366 406 433	187301 5669	872731 17929	812413 849	1285843 165
7778	60 49 72 84	470 547 874 952	192970 5669	890660 17927	813262 849	1285678 166
7779	60 51 28 41	470 729 390 139	198639 5669	908587 17927	814111 849	1285512 165
7780	60 52 84 00	470 910 952 000	204308 5669	926514 17925	814960 849	1285347 165
7781	60 54 39 61	471 092 560 541	209977 5668	944439 17924	815809 849	1285182 165
7782	60 55 95 24	471 274 215 768	215645 5668	962363 17923	816658 849	1285017 165
7783	60 57 50 89	471 455 917 687	221313 5667	980286 17923	817507 848	1284852 165
7784	60 59 06 56	471 637 666 304	226980 5667	998208 17921	818355 849	1284687 165
7785	60 60 62 25	471 819 461 625	232647 5667	*016129 17919	819204 848	1284522 165
7786	60 62 17 96	472 001 303 656	238314 5666	034048 17918	820052 849	1284357 165
7787	60 63 73 69	472 183 192 403	243980 5666	051966 17918	820901 848	1284192 165
7788	60 65 29 44	472 365 127 872	249646 5665	060884 17916	821749 849	1284027 165
7789	60 66 85 21	472 547 110 069	255311 5666	087800 17915	822598 848	1283862 165
7790	60 68 41 00	472 729 139 000	260977 5664	105715 17914	823446 848	1283697 165
7791	60 69 96 81	472 911 214 671	266641 5665	123629 17912	824294 848	1283532 164
7792	60 71 52 64	473 093 337 088	272306 5664	141541 17912	825142 848	1283368 165
7793	60 73 08 49	473 275 506 257	277970 5664	159453 17910	825990 848	1283203 165
7794	60 74 64 36	473 457 722 184	283634 5663	177363 17909	826838 848	1283038 164
7795	60 76 20 25	473 639 984 875	289297 5663	195272 17908	827686 848	1282874 165
7796	60 77 76 16	473 822 294 336	294960 5663	213180 17907	828534 848	1282709 164
7797	60 79 32 09	474 004 650 573	300623 5662	231087 17906	829382 848	1282545 165
7798	60 80 88 04	474 187 053 592	306285 5662	248993 17904	830230 847	1282380 164
7799	60 82 44 01	474 369 503 399	311947 5662	266897 17904	831077 848	1282216 165
7800	60 84 00 00	474 552 000 000	317609 88·	284801 279·	831925 19·	1282051 0·000

No. n	Square n²	Cube n³	Square root √n	Sq. rt. of 10n √10n	Cube root ∛n	Reciprocal 1/n
			88·	279·	19·	0·000
7800	60 84 00 00	474 552 000 000	317609	284801	831925 847	1282051 164
7801	60 85 56 01	474 734 543 401	323270 5661	302703 17902	832772 848	1281887 164
7802	60 87 12 04	474 917 133 608	328931 5661	320604 17901	833620 847	1281723 164
7803	60 88 68 09	475 099 770 627	334591 5660	338504 17900	834467 847	1281558 165
7804	60 90 24 16	475 282 454 464	340251 5660 5660	356403 17899 17898	835314 848	1281394 164
7805	60 91 80 25	475 465 185 125	345911	374301 17896	836162 847	1281230 164
7806	60 93 36 36	475 647 962 616	351570 5659	392197 17896	837009 847	1281066 164
7807	60 94 92 49	475 830 786 943	357229 5659	410093 17894	837856 847	1280902 164
7808	60 96 48 64	476 013 658 112	362888 5659	427987 17893	838703 847	1280738 164
7809	60 98 04 81	476 196 576 129	368546 5658 5658	445880 17892	839550 846	1280574 164
7810	60 99 61 00	476 379 541 000	374204	463772 17891	840396 847	1280410 164
7811	61 01 17 21	476 562 552 731	379862 5658	481663 17890	841243 847	1280246 164
7812	61 02 73 44	476 745 611 328	385519 5657	499553 17888	842090 847	1280082 164
7813	61 04 29 69	476 928 716 797	391176 5657	517441 17888	842936 846	1279918 164
7814	61 05 85 96	477 111 869 144	396833 5657 5656	535329 17886	843783 846	1279754 163
7815	61 07 42 25	477 295 068 375	402489	553215 17885	844629 847	1279591 164
7816	61 08 98 56	477 478 314 496	408144 5655	571100 17884	845476 846	1279427 164
7817	61 10 54 89	477 661 607 513	413800 5656	588984 17883	846322 846	1279263 163
7818	61 12 11 24	477 844 947 432	419455 5655	606867 17882	847168 847	1279100 164
7819	61 13 67 61	478 028 334 259	425110 5655 5654	624749 17880	848015 846	1278936 164
7820	61 15 24 00	478 211 768 000	430764	642629 17879	848861 846	1278772 163
7821	61 16 80 41	478 395 248 661	436418 5654	660508 17879	849707 846	1278609 164
7822	61 18 36 84	478 578 776 248	442071 5653	678387 17877	850553 846	1278445 163
7823	61 19 93 29	478 762 350 767	447725 5654	696264 17876	851399 846	1278282 163
7824	61 21 49 76	478 945 972 224	453378 5653 5652	714140 17875	852244 846	1278119 164
7825	61 23 06 25	479 129 640 625	459030	732015 17873	853090 846	1277955 163
7826	61 24 62 76	479 313 355 976	464682 5652	749888 17873	853936 846	1277792 163
7827	61 26 19 29	479 497 118 283	470334 5652	767761 17871	854781 846	1277629 163
7828	61 27 75 84	479 680 927 552	475985 5651	785632 17870	855627 845	1277466 164
7829	61 29 32 41	479 864 783 789	481637 5652 5650	803502 17870	856472 846	1277302 163
7830	61 30 89 00	480 048 687 000	487287	821372 17868	857318 845	1277139 163
7831	61 32 45 61	480 232 637 191	492938 5651	839240 17866	858163 845	1276976 163
7832	61 34 02 24	480 416 634 368	498588 5650	857106 17866	859008 845	1276813 163
7833	61 35 58 89	480 600 678 537	504237 5649	874972 17865	859854 846	1276650 163
7834	61 37 15 56	480 784 769 704	509886 5649 5649	892837 17863	860699 845	1276487 163
7835	61 38 72 25	480 968 907 875	515535	910700 17862	861544 845	1276324 163
7836	61 40 28 96	481 153 093 056	521184 5649	928562 17861	862389 845	1276161 163
7837	61 41 85 69	481 337 325 253	526832 5648	946423 17860	863234 845	1275998 162
7838	61 43 42 44	481 521 604 472	532480 5648	964283 17859	864078 845	1275836 163
7839	61 44 99 21	481 705 930 719	538127 5647 5647	982142 17858	864923 845	1275673 163
7840	61 46 56 00	481 890 304 000	543774	*000000 17857	865768 844	1275510 162
7841	61 48 12 81	482 074 724 321	549421 5647	017857 17855	866612 845	1275348 163
7842	61 49 69 64	482 259 191 688	555068 5647	035712 17854	867457 844	1275185 163
7843	61 51 26 49	482 443 706 107	560714 5646	053566 17853	868301 845	1275022 162
7844	61 52 83 36	482 628 267 584	566359 5645 5646	071419 17852	869146 844	1274860 163
7845	61 54 40 25	482 812 876 125	572005	089271 17851	869990 844	1274697 162
7846	61 55 97 16	482 997 531 736	577650 5645	107122 17850	870834 844	1274535 163
7847	61 57 54 09	483 182 234 423	583294 5644	124972 17849	871678 844	1274372 162
7848	61 59 11 04	483 366 984 192	588938 5644	142821 17847	872523 844	1274210 162
7849	61 60 68 01	483 551 781 049	594582 5644 5644	160668 17847	873367 844	1274048 163
7850	61 62 25 00	483 736 625 000	600226 88·	178515 280·	874211 19·	1273885 0·000

No. n	Square n^2	Cube n^3	Square root $\sqrt{n}$	Sq. rt. of 10n $\sqrt{10n}$	Cube root $\sqrt[3]{n}$	Reciprocal $\dfrac{1}{n}$
			88·	280·	19·	0·000
7850	61 62 25 00	483 736 625 000	600226 5643	178515 17845	874211 843	1273885 162
7851	61 63 82 01	483 921 516 051	605869 5643	196360 17844	875054 844	1273723 162
7852	61 65 39 04	484 106 454 208	611512 5642	214204 17843	875898 844	1273561 162
7853	61 66 96 09	484 291 439 477	617154 5642	232047 17841	876742 844	1273399 162
7854	61 68 53 16	484 476 471 864	622796 5642	249888 17841	877586 843	1273237 163
7855	61 70 10 25	484 661 551 375	628438 5641	267729 17840	878429 844	1273074 162
7856	61 71 67 36	484 846 678 016	634079 5641	285569 17838	879273 843	1272912 162
7857	61 73 24 49	485 031 851 793	639720 5641	303407 17837	880116 844	1272750 162
7858	61 74 81 64	485 217 072 712	645361 5640	321244 17836	880960 843	1272588 161
7859	61 76 38 81	485 402 340 779	651001 5640	339080 17835	881803 843	1272427 162
7860	61 77 96 00	485 587 656 000	656641 5640	356915 17834	882646 843	1272265 162
7861	61 79 53 21	485 773 018 381	662281 5639	374749 17833	883489 843	1272103 162
7862	61 81 10 44	485 958 427 928	667920 5639	392582 17832	884332 843	1271941 162
7863	61 82 67 69	486 143 884 647	673559 5638	410414 17830	885175 843	1271779 162
7864	61 84 24 96	486 329 388 544	679197 5638	428244 17829	886018 843	1271617 161
7865	61 85 82 25	486 514 939 625	684835 5638	446073 17828	886861 843	1271456 162
7866	61 87 39 56	486 700 537 896	690473 5637	463901 17827	887704 843	1271294 161
7867	61 88 96 89	486 886 183 363	696110 5637	481728 17826	888547 842	1271133 162
7868	61 90 54 24	487 071 876 032	701747 5637	499554 17825	889389 843	1270971 161
7869	61 92 11 61	487 257 615 909	707384 5636	517379 17824	890232 843	1270810 162
7870	61 93 69 00	487 443 403 000	713020 5636	535203 17822	891075 842	1270648 161
7871	61 95 26 41	487 629 237 311	718656 5636	553025 17822	891917 842	1270487 162
7872	61 96 83 84	487 815 118 848	724292 5635	570847 17820	892759 843	1270325 161
7873	61 98 41 29	488 001 047 617	729927 5635	588667 17819	893602 842	1270164 161
7874	61 99 98 76	488 187 023 624	735562 5635	606486 17818	894444 842	1270003 162
7875	62 01 56 25	488 373 046 875	741197 5634	624304 17817	895286 842	1269841 161
7876	62 03 13 76	488 559 117 376	746831 5634	642121 17816	896128 842	1269680 161
7877	62 04 71 29	488 745 235 133	752465 5633	659937 17814	896970 842	1269519 161
7878	62 06 28 84	488 931 400 152	758098 5633	677751 17814	897812 842	1269358 161
7879	62 07 86 41	489 117 612 439	763731 5633	695565 17812	898654 842	1269197 161
7880	62 09 44 00	489 303 872 000	769364 5632	713377 17811	899496 842	1269036 161
7881	62 11 01 61	489 490 178 841	774996 5633	731188 17810	900338 842	1268875 161
7882	62 12 59 24	489 676 532 968	780629 5631	748998 17809	901179 841	1268714 161
7883	62 14 16 89	489 862 934 387	786260 5632	766807 17808	902021 841	1268553 161
7884	62 15 74 56	490 049 383 104	791892 5630	784615 17807	902862 842	1268392 161
7885	62 17 32 25	490 235 879 125	797522 5631	802422 17805	903704 841	1268231 161
7886	62 18 89 96	490 422 422 456	803153 5630	820227 17805	904545 841	1268070 161
7887	62 20 47 69	490 609 013 103	808783 5630	838032 17803	905386 842	1267909 161
7888	62 22 05 44	490 795 651 072	814413 5630	855835 17802	906228 841	1267748 160
7889	62 23 63 21	490 982 336 369	820043 5629	873637 17801	907069 841	1267588 161
7890	62 25 21 00	491 169 069 000	825672 5629	891438 17800	907910 841	1267427 160
7891	62 26 78 81	491 355 848 971	831301 5628	909238 17799	908751 841	1267267 161
7892	62 28 36 64	491 542 676 288	836929 5628	927037 17799	909592 841	1267106 161
7893	62 29 94 49	491 729 550 957	842557 5628	944834 17797	910433 841	1266945 160
7894	62 31 52 36	491 916 472 984	848185 5628	962631 17795	911274 840	1266785 161
7895	62 33 10 25	492 103 442 375	853813 5627	980426 17795	912114 841	1266624 160
7896	62 34 68 16	492 290 459 136	859440 5626	998221 17793	912955 841	1266464 160
7897	62 36 26 09	492 477 523 273	865066 5627	*016014 17792	913796 840	1266304 161
7898	62 37 84 04	492 664 634 792	870693 5626	033806 17791	914636 841	1266143 160
7899	62 39 42 01	492 851 793 699	876319 5625	051597 17789	915477 840	1265983 160
7900	62 41 00 00	493 039 000 000	881944	069386	916317	1265823
			88·	281·	19·	0·000

No. n	Square n^2	Cube n^3	Square root $\sqrt{n}$	Sq. rt. of 10n $\sqrt{10n}$	Cube root $\sqrt[3]{n}$	Reciprocal $\frac{1}{n}$
			88·	281·	19·	0·000
7900	62 41 00 00	493 039 000 000	881944 5625	069386 17789	916317 840	1265823 160
7901	62 42 58 01	493 226 253 701	887569 5625	087175 17788	917157 840	1265663 161
7902	62 44 16 04	493 413 554 808	893194 5625	104963 17786	917998 841	1265502 160
7903	62 45 74 09	493 600 903 327	898819 5624	122749 17785	918838 840	1265342 160
7904	62 47 32 16	493 788 299 264	904443 5624	140534 17784	919678 840	1265182 160
7905	62 48 90 25	493 975 742 625	910067 5623	158318 17783	920518 840	1265022 160
7906	62 50 48 36	494 163 233 416	915690 5624	176101 17782	921358 840	1264862 160
7907	62 52 06 49	494 350 771 643	921314 5622	193883 17781	922198 840	1264702 160
7908	62 53 64 64	494 538 357 312	926936 5623	211664 17780	923038 839	1264542 160
7909	62 55 22 81	494 725 990 429	932559 5622	229444 17778	923877 840	1264382 159
7910	62 56 81 00	494 913 671 000	938181 5621	247222 17778	924717 840	1264223 160
7911	62 58 39 21	495 101 399 031	943802 5622	265000 17776	925557 840	1264063 160
7912	62 59 97 44	495 289 174 528	949424 5621	282776 17775	926396 839	1263903 160
7913	62 61 55 69	495 476 997 497	955045 5620	300551 17774	927236 839	1263743 159
7914	62 63 13 96	495 664 867 944	960665 5621	318325 17773	928075 839	1263584 160
7915	62 64 72 25	495 852 785 875	966286 5620	336098 17772	928914 840	12⁄63424 160
7916	62 66 30 56	496 040 751 296	971906 5619	353870 17770	929754 839	1263264 159
7917	62 67 88 89	496 228 764 213	977525 5619	371640 17770	930593 839	1263105 160
7918	62 69 47 24	496 416 824 632	983144 5619	389410 17768	931432 839	1262945 159
7919	62 71 05 61	496 604 932 559	988763 5619	407178 17768	932271 839	1262786 160
7920	62 72 64 00	496 793 088 000	994382 5618	424946 17766	933110 839	1262626 159
7921	62 74 22 41	496 981 290 961	*000000 5618	442712 17765	933949 839	1262467 160
7922	62 75 80 84	497 169 541 448	005618 5617	460477 17764	934788 838	1262307 159
7923	62 77 39 29	497 357 839 467	011235 5617	478241 17763	935626 839	1262148 159
7924	62 78 97 76	497 546 185 024	016852 5617	496004 17761	936465 839	1261989 159
7925	62 80 56 25	497 734 578 125	022469 5616	513765 17761	937304 838	1261830 160
7926	62 82 14 76	497 923 018 776	028085 5616	531526 17759	938142 839	1261670 159
7927	62 83 73 29	498 111 506 983	033701 5616	549285 17759	938981 838	1261511 159
7928	62 85 31 84	498 300 042 752	039317 5615	567044 17757	939819 838	1261352 159
7929	62 86 90 41	498 488 626 089	044932 5615	584801 17756	940657 839	1261193 159
7930	62 88 49 00	498 677 257 000	050547 5615	602557 17755	941496 838	1261034 159
7931	62 90 07 61	498 865 935 491	056162 5614	620312 17754	942334 838	1260875 159
7932	62 91 66 24	499 054 661 568	061776 5614	638066 17752	943172 838	1260716 159
7933	62 93 24 89	499 243 435 237	067390 5614	655818 17752	944010 838	1260557 159
7934	62 94 83 56	499 432 256 504	073004 5613	673570 17750	944848 838	1260398 159
7935	62 96 42 25	499 621 125 375	078617 5613	691320 17750	945686 838	1260239 158
7936	62 98 00 96	499 810 041 856	084230 5612	709070 17748	946524 838	1260081 159
7937	62 99 59 69	499 999 005 953	089842 5612	726818 17747	947362 837	1259922 159
7938	63 01 18 44	500 188 017 672	095454 5612	744565 17746	948199 838	1259763 159
7939	63 02 77 21	500 377 077 019	101066 5612	762311 17745	949037 837	1259604 158
7940	63 04 36 00	500 566 184 000	106678 5611	780056 17744	949874 838	1259446 159
7941	63 05 94 81	500 755 338 621	112289 5610	797800 17743	950712 837	1259287 158
7942	63 07 53 64	500 944 540 888	117899 5611	815543 17741	951549 838	1259129 159
7943	63 09 12 49	501 133 790 807	123510 5610	833284 17740	952387 837	1258970 158
7944	63 10 71 36	501 323 088 384	129120 5609	851024 17740	953224 837	1258812 159
7945	63 12 30 25	501 512 433 625	134729 5610	868764 17738	954061 837	1258653 158
7946	63 13 89 16	501 701 826 536	140339 5609	886502 17737	954898 837	1258495 159
7947	63 15 48 09	501 891 267 123	145948 5608	904239 17736	955735 837	1258336 158
7948	63 17 07 04	502 080 755 392	151556 5609	921975 17735	956572 837	1258178 158
7949	63 18 66 01	502 270 291 349	157165 5608	939710 17734	957409 837	1258020 158
7950	63 20 25 00	502 459 875 000	162773 89·	957444 281·	958246 19·	1257862 0·000

No. n	Square n²	Cube n³	Square root √n	Sq. rt. of 10n √10n	Cube root ∛n	Reciprocal 1/n
			89·	281·	19·	0·000
7950	63 20 25 00	502 459 875 000	162773 5607	957444 17732	958246 837	1257862
7951	63 21 84 01	502 649 506 351	168380 5607	975176 17732	959083 837	1257703 159
7952	63 23 43 04	502 839 185 408	173987 5607	*992908 17730	959920 836	1257545 158
7953	63 25 02 09	503 028 912 177	179594 5607	010638 17729	960756 837	1257387 158
7954	63 26 61 16	503 218 686 664	185201 5606	028367 17729	961593 836	1257229 158
7955	63 28 20 25	503 408 508 875	190807 5605	046096 17727	962429 837	1257071 158
7956	63 29 79 36	503 598 378 816	196412 5606	063823 17725	963266 836	1256913 158
7957	63 31 38 49	503 788 296 493	202018 5605	081548 17725	964102 837	1256755 158
7958	63 32 97 64	503 978 261 912	207623 5605	099273 17724	964939 836	1256597 158
7959	63 34 56 81	504 168 275 079	213228 5604	116997 17723	965775 836	1256439 158
7960	63 36 16 00	504 358 336 000	218832 5604	134720 17721	966611 836	1256281 157
7961	63 37 75 21	504 548 444 681	224436 5604	152441 17720	967447 836	1256124 158
7962	63 39 34 44	504 738 601 128	230040 5603	170161 17720	968283 836	1255966 158
7963	63 40 93 69	504 928 805 347	235643 5603	187881 17718	969119 836	1255808 158
7964	63 42 52 96	505 119 057 344	241246 5603	205599 17717	969955 836	1255650 157
7965	63 44 12 25	505 309 357 125	246849 5602	223316 17716	970791 835	1255493 158
7966	63 45 71 56	505 499 704 696	252451 5602	241032 17715	971626 836	1255335 157
7967	63 47 30 89	505 690 100 063	258053 5601	258747 17713	972462 836	1255178 158
7968	63 48 90 24	505 880 543 232	263654 5602	276460 17713	973298 835	1255020 157
7969	63 50 49 61	506 071 034 209	269256 5600	294173 17711	974133 836	1254863 158
7970	63 52 09 00	506 261 573 000	274856 5601	311884 17711	974969 835	1254705 157
7971	63 53 68 41	506 452 159 611	280457 5600	329595 17709	975804 835	1254548 158
7972	63 55 27 84	506 642 794 048	286057 5599	347304 17708	976639 836	1254390 157
7973	63 56 87 29	506 833 476 317	291657 5599	365012 17707	977475 835	1254233 157
7974	63 58 46 76	507 024 206 424	297256 5599	382719 17706	978310 835	1254076 158
7975	63 60 06 25	507 214 984 375	302855 5599	400425 17705	979145 835	1253918 157
7976	63 61 65 76	507 405 810 176	308454 5599	418130 17703	979980 835	1253761 157
7977	63 63 25 29	507 596 683 833	314053 5598	435833 17703	980815 835	1253604 157
7978	63 64 84 84	507 787 605 352	319651 5597	453536 17701	981650 835	1253447 157
7979	63 66 44 41	507 978 574 739	325248 5598	471237 17701	982485 834	1253290 157
7980	63 68 04 00	508 169 592 000	330846 5597	488938 17699	983319 835	1253133 157
7981	63 69 63 61	508 360 657 141	336443 5596	506637 17698	984154 835	1252976 157
7982	63 71 23 24	508 551 770 168	342039 5597	524335 17697	984989 834	1252819 157
7983	63 72 82 89	508 742 931 087	347636 5596	542032 17696	985823 835	1252662 157
7984	63 74 42 56	508 934 139 904	353232 5595	559728 17695	986658 834	1252505 157
7985	63 76 02 25	509 125 396 625	358827 5595	577423 17694	987492 835	1252348 157
7986	63 77 61 96	509 316 701 256	364422 5595	595117 17692	988327 834	1252191 156
7987	63 79 21 69	509 508 053 803	370017 5595	612809 17692	989161 834	1252035 157
7988	63 80 81 44	509 699 454 272	375612 5594	630501 17690	989995 834	1251878 157
7989	63 82 41 21	509 890 902 669	381206 5594	648191 17690	990829 834	1251721 157
7990	63 84 01 00	510 082 399 000	386800 5593	665881 17688	991663 834	1251564 156
7991	63 85 60 81	510 273 943 271	392393 5594	683569 17687	992497 834	1251408 157
7992	63 87 20 64	510 465 535 488	397987 5592	701256 17686	993331 834	1251251 156
7993	63 88 80 49	510 657 175 657	403579 5592	718942 17685	994165 834	1251095 156
7994	63 90 40 36	510 848 863 784	409172 5592	736627 17683	994999 833	1250938 156
7995	63 92 00 25	511 040 599 875	414764 5592	754310 17683	995832 834	1250782 157
7996	63 93 60 16	511 232 383 936	420356 5591	771993 17681	996666 834	1250625 156
7997	63 95 20 09	511 424 215 973	425947 5591	789674 17681	997500 833	1250469 156
7998	63 96 80 04	511 616 095 992	431538 5591	807355 17679	998333 834	1250313 157
7999	63 98 40 01	511 808 023 999	437129 5590	825034 17678	999167 833	1250156 156
8000	64 00 00 00	512 000 000 000	442719 89·	842712 282·	*000000 20·	1250000 0·000

M

No. n	Square n^2	Cube n^3	Square root $\sqrt{n}$	Sq. rt. of $10n$ $\sqrt{10n}$	Cube root $\sqrt[3]{n}$	Reciprocal $\dfrac{1}{n}$
			89·	**282·**	**20·**	**0·000**
8000	64 00 00 00	512 000 000 000	442719	842712 17678	000000 833	1250000 156
8001	64 01 60 01	512 192 024 001	448309 5590	860390 17676	000833 834	1249844 156
8002	64 03 20 04	512 384 096 008	453899 5590	878066 17675	001667 833	1249688 157
8003	64 04 80 09	512 576 216 027	459488 5589	895741 17673	002500 833	1249531 156
8004	64 06 40 16	512 768 384 064	465077 5589	913414 17673	003333 833	1249375 156
8005	64 08 00 25	512 960 600 125	470666 5588	931087 17672	004166 833	1249219 156
8006	64 09 60 36	513 152 864 216	476254 5588	948759 17670	004999 833	1249063 156
8007	64 11 20 49	513 345 176 343	481842 5587	966429 17670	005832 832	1248907 156
8008	64 12 80 64	513 537 536 512	487429 5587	984098 17669	006664 833	1248751 156
8009	64 14 40 81	513 729 944 729	493016 5587	*001767 17669 17667	007497 833	1248595 156
8010	64 16 01 00	513 922 401 000	498603 5587	019434 17666	008330 832	1248439 155
8011	64 17 61 21	514 114 905 331	504190 5586	037100 17665	009162 833	1248284 156
8012	64 19 21 44	514 307 457 728	509776 5586	054765 17664	009995 832	1248128 156
8013	64 20 81 69	514 500 058 197	515362 5585	072429 17663	010827 833	1247972 156
8014	64 22 41 96	514 692 706 744	520947 5585	090092 17661	011660 832	1247816 155
8015	64 24 02 25	514 885 403 375	526532 5585	107753 17661	012492 832	1247661 156
8016	64 25 62 56	515 078 148 096	532117 5585	125414 17659	013324 833	1247505 156
8017	64 27 22 89	515 270 940 913	537702 5584	143073 17659	014157 832	1247349 155
8018	64 28 83 24	515 463 781 832	543286 5583	160732 17657	014989 832	1247194 156
8019	64 30 43 61	515 656 670 859	548869 5584	178389 17657 17656	015821 832	1247038 155
8020	64 32 04 00	515 849 608 000	554453 5583	196045 17655	016653 832	1246883 156
8021	64 33 64 41	516 042 593 261	560036 5582	213700 17654	017485 832	1246727 156
8022	64 35 24 84	516 235 626 648	565618 5583	231354 17653	018317 831	1246572 155
8023	64 36 85 29	516 428 708 167	571201 5582	249007 17652	019148 832	1246417 156
8024	64 38 45 76	516 621 837 824	576783 5581	266659 17650	019980 832	1246261 155
8025	64 40 06 25	516 815 015 625	582364 5582	284309 17650	020812 831	1246106 155
8026	64 41 66 76	517 008 241 576	587946 5581	301959 17649	021643 832	1245951 156
8027	64 43 27 29	517 201 515 683	593527 5580	319608 17647	022475 831	1245795 155
8028	64 44 87 84	517 394 837 952	599107 5580	337255 17646	023306 832	1245640 155
8029	64 46 48 41	517 588 208 389	604687 5580	354901 17645	024138 831	1245485 155
8030	64 48 09 00	517 781 627 000	610267 5580	372546 17644	024969 831	1245330 155
8031	64 49 69 61	517 975 093 791	615847 5579	390190 17643	025800 831	1245175 155
8032	64 51 30 24	518 168 608 768	621426 5579	407833 17642	026631 831	1245020 155
8033	64 52 90 89	518 362 171 937	627005 5578	425475 17641	027462 831	1244865 155
8034	64 54 51 56	518 555 783 304	632583 5579	443116 17640	028293 831	1244710 155
8035	64 56 12 25	518 749 442 875	638162 5577	460756 17638	029124 831	1244555 155
8036	64 57 72 96	518 943 150 656	643739 5578	478394 17638	029955 831	1244400 155
8037	64 59 33 69	519 136 906 653	649317 5577	496032 17636	030786 831	1244245 154
8038	64 60 94 44	519 330 710 872	654894 5577	513668 17635	031617 830	1244091 155
8039	64 62 55 21	519 524 563 319	660471 5576	531303 17635	032447 831	1243936 155
8040	64 64 16 00	519 718 464 000	666047 5576	548938 17633	033278 830	1243781 155
8041	64 65 76 81	519 912 412 921	671623 5576	566571 17632	034108 831	1243626 154
8042	64 67 37 64	520 106 410 088	677199 5575	584203 17631	034939 830	1243472 155
8043	64 68 98 49	520 300 455 507	682774 5575	601834 17629	035769 831	1243317 154
8044	64 70 59 36	520 494 549 184	688349 5575	619463 17629	036600 830	1243163 155
8045	64 72 20 25	520 688 691 125	693924 5574	637092 17628	037430 830	1243008 154
8046	64 73 81 16	520 882 881 336	699498 5574	654720 17626	038260 830	1242854 155
8047	64 75 42 09	521 077 119 823	705072 5574	672346 17626	039090 830	1242699 154
8048	64 77 03 04	521 271 406 592	710646 5573	689972 17624	039920 830	1242545 155
8049	64 78 64 01	521 465 741 649	716219 5573	707596 17623	040750 830	1242390 154
8050	64 80 25 00	521 660 125 000	721792	725219	041580	1242236
			89·	**283·**	**20·**	**0·000**

No. n	Square n^2	Cube n^3	Square root $\sqrt{n}$	Sq. rt. of 10n $\sqrt{10n}$	Cube root $\sqrt[3]{n}$	Reciprocal $\frac{1}{n}$
			89·	283·	20·	0·000
8050	64 80 25 00	521 660 125 000	721792 5573	725219 17622	041580 830	1242236 154
8051	64 81 86 01	521 854 556 651	727365 5572	742841 17621	042410 830	1242082 155
8052	64 83 47 04	522 049 036 608	732937 5572	760462 17620	043240 829	1241927 154
8053	64 85 08 09	522 243 564 877	738509 5572	778082 17619	044069 830	1241773 154
8054	64 86 69 16	522 438 141 464	744081 5571	795701 17618	044899 830	1241619 154
8055	64 88 30 25	522 632 766 375	749652 5571	813319 17617	045729 829	1241465 154
8056	64 89 91 36	522 827 439 616	755223 5570	830936 17615	046558 830	1241311 154
8057	64 91 52 49	523 022 161 193	760793 5570	848551 17615	047388 829	1241157 154
8058	64 93 13 64	523 216 931 112	766363 5570	866166 17613	048217 829	1241003 154
8059	64 94 74 81	523 411 749 379	771933 5570	883779 17612	049046 830	1240849 154
8060	64 96 36 00	523 606 616 000	777503 5569	901391 17612	049876 829	1240695 154
8061	64 97 97 21	523 801 530 981	783072 5569	919003 17610	050705 829	1240541 154
8062	64 99 58 44	523 996 494 328	788641 5568	936613 17609	051534 829	1240387 154
8063	65 01 19 69	524 191 506 047	794209 5568	954222 17608	052363 829	1240233 154
8064	65 02 80 96	524 386 566 144	799777 5568	971830 17606	053192 829	1240079 153
8065	65 04 42 25	524 581 674 625	805345 5567	*989436 17606	054021 828	1239926 154
8066	65 06 03 56	524 776 831 496	810912 5568	007042 17605	054849 829	1239772 154
8067	65 07 64 89	524 972 036 763	816480 5566	024647 17603	055678 829	1239618 153
8068	65 09 26 24	525 167 290 432	822046 5567	042250 17603	056507 828	1239465 154
8069	65 10 87 61	525 362 592 509	827613 5566	059853 17601	057335 829	1239311 154
8070	65 12 49 00	525 557 943 000	833179 5565	077454 17601	058164 828	1239157 153
8071	65 14 10 41	525 753 341 911	838744 5566	095055 17599	058992 829	1239004 153
8072	65 15 71 84	525 948 789 248	844310 5565	112654 17598	059821 828	1238850 154
8073	65 17 33 29	526 144 285 017	849875 5564	130252 17597	060649 828	1238697 153
8074	65 18 94 76	526 339 829 224	855439 5565	147849 17596	061477 829	1238543 153
8075	65 20 56 25	526 535 421 875	861004 5564	165445 17595	062306 828	1238390 153
8076	65 22 17 76	526 731 062 976	866568 5563	183040 17593	063134 828	1238237 154
8077	65 23 79 29	526 926 752 533	872131 5564	200633 17593	063962 828	1238083 153
8078	65 25 40 84	527 122 490 552	877695 5563	218226 17592	064790 828	1237930 153
8079	65 27 02 41	527 318 277 039	883258 5562	235818 17590	065618 828	1237777 153
8080	65 28 64 00	527 514 112 000	888820 5562	253408 17589	066446 827	1237624 153
8081	65 30 25 61	527 709 995 441	894382 5562	270997 17589	067273 828	1237471 154
8082	65 31 87 24	527 905 927 368	899944 5562	288586 17587	068101 828	1237317 153
8083	65 33 48 89	528 101 907 787	905506 5561	306173 17586	068929 827	1237164 153
8084	65 35 10 56	528 297 936 704	911067 5561	323759 17585	069756 828	1237011 153
8085	65 36 72 25	528 494 014 125	916628 5561	341344 17584	070584 827	1236858 153
8086	65 38 33 96	528 690 140 056	922189 5560	358928 17583	071411 828	1236705 153
8087	65 39 95 69	528 886 314 503	927749 5560	376511 17582	072239 827	1236552 152
8088	65 41 57 44	529 082 537 472	933309 5559	394093 17580	073066 827	1236400 153
8089	65 43 19 21	529 278 808 969	938868 5559	411673 17580	073893 827	1236247 153
8090	65 44 81 00	529 475 129 000	944427 5559	429253 17579	074720 828	1236094 153
8091	65 46 42 81	529 671 497 571	949986 5559	446832 17577	075548 827	1235941 153
8092	65 48 04 64	529 867 914 688	955545 5557	464409 17576	076375 827	1235788 153
8093	65 49 66 49	530 064 380 357	961103 5557	481985 17576	077202 827	1235636 152
8094	65 51 28 36	530 260 894 584	966660 5558	499561 17574	078029 826	1235483 153
8095	65 52 90 25	530 457 457 375	972218 5557	517135 17573	078855 827	1235330 152
8096	65 54 52 16	530 654 068 736	977775 5557	534708 17572	079682 827	1235178 152
8097	65 56 14 09	530 850 728 673	983332 5556	552280 17571	080509 826	1235025 152
8098	65 57 76 04	531 047 437 192	988888 5556	569851 17570	081335 827	1234873 153
8099	65 59 38 01	531 244 194 299	994444 5556	587421 17568	082162 827	1234720 152
8100	65 61 00 00	531 441 000 000	*000000 90·	604989 284·	082989 20·	1234568 0·000

No. n	Square n^2	Cube n^3	Square root $\sqrt{n}$	Sq. rt. of 10n $\sqrt{10n}$	Cube root $\sqrt[3]{n}$	Reciprocal $\frac{1}{n}$
			90·	284·	20·	0·000
8100	65 61 00 00	531 441 000 000	000000	604989 17568	082989 826	1234568 152
8101	65 62 62 01	531 637 854 301	005555 5555	622557 17567	083815 826	1234416 152
8102	65 64 24 04	531 834 757 208	011110 5555	640124 17567	084641 827	1234263 153
8103	65 65 86 09	532 031 708 727	016665 5554	657689 17565	085468 826	1234111 152
8104	65 67 48 16	532 228 708 864	022219 5554	675254 17563	086294 826	1233959 152 153
8105	65 69 10 25	532 425 757 625	027773 5554	692817 17562	087120 826	1233806 152
8106	65 70 72 36	532 622 855 016	033327 5553	710379 17561	087946 826	1233654 152
8107	65 72 34 49	532 820 001 043	038880 5553	727940 17560	088772 826	1233502 152
8108	65 73 96 64	533 017 195 712	044433 5553	745500 17559	089598 826	1233350 152
8109	65 75 58 81	533 214 439 029	049986 5552	763059 17558	090424 826	1233198 152
8110	65 77 21 00	533 411 731 000	055538 5552	780617 17557	091250 825	1233046 152
8111	65 78 83 21	533 609 071 631	061090 5552	798174 17556	092075 826	1232894 152
8112	65 80 45 44	533 806 460 928	066642 5551	815730 17555	092901 826	1232742 152
8113	65 82 07 69	534 003 898 897	072193 5551	833285 17553	093727 825	1232590 152
8114	65 83 69 96	534 201 385 544	077744 5551	850838 17553	094552 826	1232438 152
8115	65 85 32 25	534 398 920 875	083295 5550	868391 17551	095378 825	1232286 152
8116	65 86 94 56	534 596 504 896	088845 5550	885942 17550	096203 826	1232134 152
8117	65 88 56 89	534 794 137 613	094395 5550	903492 17550	097029 825	1231982 151
8118	65 90 19 24	534 991 819 032	099945 5549	921042 17548	097854 825	1231831 152
8119	65 91 81 61	535 189 549 159	105494 5549	938590 17547	098679 825	1231679 152
8120	65 93 44 00	535 387 328 000	111043 5548	956137 17546	099504 825	1231527 152
8121	65 95 06 41	535 585 155 561	116591 5548	973683 17545	100329 825	1231375 151
8122	65 96 68 84	535 783 031 848	122139 5548	991228 17544	101154 825	1231224 152
8123	65 98 31 29	535 980 956 867	127687 5548	*008772 17543	101979 825	1231072 151
8124	65 99 93 76	536 178 930 624	133235 5547	026315 17541	102804 825	1230921 152
8125	66 01 56 25	536 376 953 125	138782 5547	043856 17541	103629 825	1230769 151
8126	66 03 18 76	536 575 024 376	144329 5546	061397 17539	104454 824	1230618 151
8127	66 04 81 29	536 773 144 383	149875 5546	078936 17539	105278 825	1230466 151
8128	66 06 43 84	536 971 313 152	155421 5546	096475 17537	106103 824	1230315 151
8129	66 08 06 41	537 169 530 689	160967 5546	114012 17537	106927 825	1230164 152
8130	66 09 69 00	537 367 797 000	166513 5545	131549 17535	107752 824	1230012 151
8131	66 11 31 61	537 566 112 091	172058 5545	149084 17534	108576 824	1229861 151
8132	66 12 94 24	537 764 475 968	177603 5544	166618 17533	109400 825	1229710 151
8133	66 14 56 89	537 962 888 637	183147 5544	184151 17532	110225 824	1229559 151
8134	66 16 19 56	538 161 350 104	188691 5544	201683 17531	111049 824	1229407 151
8135	66 17 82 25	538 359 860 375	194235 5543	219214 17530	111873 824	1229256 151
8136	66 19 44 96	538 558 419 456	199778 5543	236744 17529	112697 824	1229105 151
8137	66 21 07 69	538 757 027 353	205321 5543	254273 17527	113521 824	1228954 151
8138	66 22 70 44	538 955 684 072	210864 5542	271800 17527	114345 824	1228803 151
8139	66 24 33 21	539 154 389 619	216406 5543	289327 17525	115169 824	1228652 151
8140	66 25 96 00	539 353 144 000	221949 5541	306852 17525	115993 823	1228501 151
8141	66 27 58 81	539 551 947 221	227490 5542	324377 17523	116816 824	1228350 151
8142	66 29 21 64	539 750 799 288	233032 5541	341900 17522	117640 824	1228199 151
8143	66 30 84 49	539 949 700 207	238573 5540	359422 17522	118464 823	1228049 150
8144	66 32 47 36	540 148 649 984	244113 5541	376944 17520	119287 824	1227898 151
8145	66 34 10 25	540 347 648 625	249654 5540	394464 17519	120111 823	1227747 151
8146	66 35 73 16	540 546 696 136	255194 5539	411983 17518	120934 823	1227596 151
8147	66 37 36 09	540 745 792 523	260733 5540	429501 17517	121757 823	1227446 150
8148	66 38 99 04	540 944 937 792	266273 5539	447018 17516	122580 824	1227295 151
8149	66 40 62 01	541 144 131 949	·271812 5538	464534 17514	123404 823	1227144 150
8150	66 42 25 00	541 343 375 000	277350 90·	482048 285·	124227 20·	1226994 0·000

No. n	Square n²	Cube n³	Square root √n	Sq. rt. of 10n √10n	Cube root ∛n	Reciprocal 1/n
			90·	285·	20·	0·000
8150	66 42 25 00	541.343 375 000	277350 5539	482048 17514	124227 823	1226994 151
8151	66 43 88 01	541 542 666 951	282889 5538	499562 17513	125050 823	1226843 150
8152	66 45 51 04	541 742 007 808	288427 5537	517075 17511	125873 823	1226693 151
8153	'66 47 14 09	541 941 397 577	293964 5538	534586 17511	126696 823	1226542 150
8154	66 48 77 16	542 140 836 264	299502 5537	552097 17509	127519 822	1226392 150
8155	66 50 40 25	542 340 323 875	305039 5536	569606 17509	128341 823	1226242 151
8156	66 52 03 36	542 539 860 416	310575 5537	587115 17507	129164 823	1226091 150
8157	66 53 66 49	542 739 445 893	316112 5535	604622 17506	129987 822	1225941 150
8158	66 55 29 64	542 939 080 312	321647 5536	622128 17505	130809 823	1225791 151
8159	66 56 92 81	543 138 763 679	327183 5535	639633 17504	131632 822	1225640 150
8160	66 58 56 00	543 338 496 000	332718 5535	657137 17503	132454 823	1225490 150
8161	66 60 19 21	543 538 277 281	338253 5535	674640 17502	133277 822	1225340 150
8162	66 61 82 44	543 738 107 528	343788 5534	692142 17501	134099 822	1225190 190
8163	66 63 45 69	543 937 986 747	349322 5534	709643 17500	134921 822	1225040 150
8164	66 65 08 96	544 137 914 944	354856 5534	727143 17498	135743 822	1224890 150
8165	66 66 72 25	544 337.892 125	360390 5533	744641 17498	136565 822	1224740 150
8166	66 68 35 56	544 537 918 296	365923 5533	762139 17496	137387 822	1224590 150
8167	66 69 98 89	544 737 993 463	371456 5532	779635 17496	138209 822	1224440 150
8168	66 71 62 24	544 938 117 632	376988 5532	797131 17494	139031 822	1224290 150
8169	66 73 25 61	545 138 290 809	382520 5532	814625 17494	139853 822	1224140 150
8170	66 74 89 00	545 338 513 000	388052 5532	832119 17492	140675 822	1223990 150
8171	66 76 52 41	545 538 784 211	393584 5531	849611 17491	141497 821	1223840 150
8172	66 78 15 84	545 739 104 448	399115 5531	867102 17490	142318 821	1223690 149
8173	66 79 79 29	545 939 473 717	404646 5530	884592 17489	143140 821	1223541 150
8174	66 81 42 76	546 139 892 024	410176 5531	902081 17488	143961 822	1223391 150
8175	66 83 06 25	546 340 359 375	415707 5529	919569 17487	144783 821	1223242 150
8176	66 84 69 76	546 540 875 776	421236 5530	937056 17486	145604 821	1223092 150
8177	66 86 33 29	546 741 441 233	426766 5529	954542 17485	146425 822	1222942 149
8178	66 87 96 84	546 942 055 752	432295 5529	972027 17483	147247 821	1222793 150
8179	66 89 60 41	547 142 719 339	437824 5528	989510 17483	148068 821	1222643 149
8180	66 91 24 00	547 343 432 000	443352 5529	*006993 17481	148889 821	1222494 150
8181	66 92 87 61	547 544 193 741	448881 5527	024474 17481	149710 821	1222344 149
8182	66 94 51 24	547 745 004 568	454408 5528	041955 17479	150531 821	1222195 149
8183	66 96 14 89	547 945 864 487	459936 5527	059434 17479	151352 821	1222046 150
8184	66 97 78 56	548 146 773 504	465463 5527	076913 17477	152173 820	1221896 149
8185	66 99 42 25	548 347 731 625	470990 5526	094390 17476	152993 821	1221747 149
8186	67 01 05 96	548 548 738 856	476516 5526	111866 17475	153814 821	1221598 149
8187	67 02 69 69	548 749 795 203	482042 5526	129341 17474	154635 820	1221449 150
8188	67 04 33 44	548 950 900 672	487568 5526	146815 17473	155455 820	1221299 149
8189	67 05 97 21	549 152 055 269	493094 5525	164288 17472	156276 820	1221150 149
8190	67 07 61 00	549 353 259 000	498619 5525	181760 17471	157096 821	1221001 149
8191	67 09 24 81	549 554 511 871	504144 5524	199231 17470	157917 820	1220852 149
8192	67 10 88 64	549 755 813 888	509668 5524	216701 17469	158737 820	1220703 149
8193	67 12 52 49	549 957 165 057	515192 5524	234170 17468	159557 820	1220554 149
8194	67 14 16 36	550 158 565 384	520716 5523	251638 17466	160377 820	1220405 149
8195	67 15 80 25	550 360 014 875	526239 5523	269104 17466	161197 820	1220256 149
8196	67 17 44 16	550 561 513 536	531762 5523	286570 17464	162017 820	1220107 148
8197	67 19 08 09	550 763 061 373	537285 5523	304034 17464	162837 820	1219959 149
8198	67 20 72 04	550 964 658 392	542808 5522	321498 17462	163657 820	1219810 149
8199	67 22 36 01	551 166 304 599	548330 5521	338960 17461	164477 820	1219661 149
8200	67 24 00 00	551 368 000 000	553851	356421	165297	1219512
			90·	286·	20·	0·000

No. n	Square n²	Cube n³	Square root √n	Sq. rt. of 10n √10n	Cube root ∛n	Reciprocal 1/n
			90·	**286·**	**20·**	**0·000**
8200	67 24 00 00	551 368 000 000	553851	356421	165297	1219512
8201	67 25 64 01	551 569 744 601	559373 [5522]	373881 [17460]	166116 [819]	1219363 [149]
8202	67 27 28 04	551 771 538 408	564894 [5521]	391341 [17460]	166936 [820]	1219215 [149]
8203	67 28 92 09	551 973 381 427	570415 [5521]	408799 [17458]	167756 [820]	1219066 [149]
8204	67 30 56 16	552 175 273 664	575935 [·5520]	426256 [17457]	168575 [819]	1218918 [148]
			[5520]	[17456]	[820]	[149]
8205	67 32 20 25	552 377 215 125	581455 [5520]	443712 [17455]	169395 [819]	1218769 [148]
8206	67 33 84 36	552 579 205 816	586975 [5520]	461167 [17455]	170214 [819]	1218621 [148]
8207	67 35 48 49	552 781 245 743	592494 [5519]	478620 [17453]	171033 [819]	1218472 [149]
8208	67 37 12 64	552 983 334 912	598013 [5519]	496073 [17453]	171852 [819]	1218324 [149]
8209	67 38 76 81	553 185 473 329	603532 [5519]	513525 [17452]	172672 [820]	1218175 [148]
			[5518]	[17451]	[819]	
8210	67 40 41 00	553 387 661 000	609050 [5518]	530976 [17449]	173491 [819]	1218027 [149]
8211	67 42 05 21	553 589 897 931	614568 [5518]	548425 [17449]	174310 [819]	1217878 [148]
8212	67 43 69 44	553 792 184 128	620086 [5518]	565874 [17447]	175129 [819]	1217730 [148]
8213	67 45 33 69	553 994 519 597	625603 [5517]	583321 [17447]	175948 [819]	1217582 [148]
8214	67 46 97 96	554 196 904 344	631120 [5517]	600768 [17447]	176766 [818]	1217434 [148]
			[5517]	[17445]	[819]	[149]
8215	67 48 62 25	554 399 338 375	636637 [5517]	618213 [17444]	177585 [819]	1217285 [148]
8216	67 50 26 56	554 601 821 696	642154 [5516]	635657 [17443]	178404 [819]	1217137 [148]
8217	67 51 90 89	554 804 354 313	647670 [5515]	653100 [17443]	179223 [818]	1216989 [148]
8218	67 53 55 24	555 006 936 232	653185 [5516]	670543 [17441]	180041 [819]	1216841 [148]
8219	67 55 19 61	555 209 567 459	658701 [5515]	687984 [17440]	180860 [818]	1216693 [148]
8220	67 56 84 00	555 412 248 000	664216 [5514]	705424 [17439]	181678 [818]	1216545 [148]
8221	67 58 48 41	555 614 977 861	669730 [5515]	722863 [17438]	182496 [819]	1216397 [148]
8222	67 60 12 84	555 817 757 048	675245 [5514]	740301 [17436]	183315 [818]	1216249 [148]
8223	67 61 77 29	556 020 585 567	680759 [5513]	757737 [17436]	184133 [818]	1216101 [148]
8224	67 63 41 76	556 223 463 424	686272 [5514]	775173 [17435]	184951 [818]	1215953 [148]
8225	67 65 06 25	556 426 390 625	691786 [5513]	792608 [17434]	185769 [818]	1215805 [147]
8226	67 66 70 76	556 629 367 176	697299 [5512]	810042 [17432]	186587 [818]	1215658 [148]
8227	67 68 35 29	556 832 393 083	702811 [5513]	827474 [17432]	187405 [818]	1215510 [148]
8228	67 69 99 84	557 035 468 352	708324 [5512]	844906 [17430]	188223 [818]	1215362 [148]
8229	67 71 64 41	557 238 592 989	713836 [5511]	862336 [17430]	189041 [818]	1215214 [147]
8230	67 73 29 00	557 441 767 000	719347 [5512]	879766 [17428]	189859 [817]	1215067 [148]
8231	67 74 93 61	557 644 990 391	724859 [5511]	897194 [17427]	190676 [818]	1214919 [147]
8232	67 76 58 24	557 848 263 168	730370 [5510]	914621 [17427]	191494 [818]	1214772 [148]
8233	67 78 22 89	558 051 585 337	735880 [5511]	932048 [17425]	192312 [817]	1214624 [147]
8234	67 79 87 56	558 254 956 904	741391 [5510]	949473 [17424]	193129 [817]	1214477 [148]
8235	67 81 52 25	558 458 377 875	746901 [5509]	966897 [17423]	193946 [818]	1214329 [147]
8236	67 83 16 96	558 661 848 256	752410 [5510]	984320 [17422]	194764 [817]	1214182 [148]
8237	67 84 81 69	558 865 368 053	757920 [5509]	*001742 [17421]	195581 [817]	1214034 [147]
8238	67 86 46 44	559 068 937 272	763429 [5508]	019163 [17420]	196398 [818]	1213887 [147]
8239	67 88 11 21	559 272 555 919	768937 [5509]	036583 [17419]	197216 [817]	1213740 [148]
8240	67 89 76 00	559 476 224 000	774446 [5508]	054002 [17418]	198033 [817]	1213592 [147]
8241	67 91 40 81	559 679 941 521	779954 [5507]	071420 [17416]	198850 [817]	1213445 [147]
8242	67 93 05 64	559 883 708 488	785461 [5508]	088836 [17416]	199667 [817]	1213298 [147]
8243	67 94 70 49	560 087 524 907	790969 [5507]	106252 [17415]	200484 [816]	1213151 [147]
8244	67 96 35 36	560 291 390 784	796476 [5506]	123667 [17413]	201300 [817]	1213003 [147]
8245	67 98 00 25	560 495 306 125	801982 [5507]	141080 [17413]	202117 [817]	1212856 [147]
8246	67 99 65 16	560 699 270 936	807489 [5506]	158493 [17411]	202934 [817]	1212709 [147]
8247	68 01 30 09	560 903 285 223	812995 [5505]	175904 [17411]	203751 [816]	1212562 [147]
8248	68 02 95 04	561 107 348 992	818500 [5506]	193315 [17409]	204567 [816]	1212415 [147]
8249	68 04 60 01	561 311 462 249	824006 [5505]	210724 [17408]	205384 [816]	1212268 [147]
8250	68 06 25 00	561 515 625 000	829511	228132	206200	1212121
			90·	**287·**	**20·**	**0·000**

No. n	Square n²	Cube n³	Square root √n	Sq. rt. of 10n √10n	Cube root ∛n	Reciprocal 1/n
			90·	287·	20·	0·000
8250	68 06 25 00	561 515 625 000	829511	228132 17408	206200 816	1212121 147
8251	68 07 90 01	561 719 837 251	835015 5504	245540 17406	207016 817	1211974 147
8252	68 09 55 04	561 924 099 008	840520 5505	262946 17405	207833 816	1211827 147
8253	58 11 20 09	562 128 410 277	846024 5504	280351 17404	208649 816	1211681 146
8254	68 12 85 16	562 332 771 064	851527 5503	297755 17403	209465 816	1211534 147
8255	68 14 50 25	562 537 181 375	857031 5504	315158 17402	210281 816	1211387 147
8256	68 16 15 36	562 741 641 216	862534 5503	332560 17401	211097 816	1211240 147
8257	68 17 80 49	562 946 150 593	868036 5502	349961 17400	211913 816	1211094 146
8258	68 19 45 64	563 150 709 512	873539 5503	367361 17400	212729 816	1210947 147
8259	68 21 10 81	563 355 317 979	879040 5501	384760 17399	213545 816	1210800 146
				17397		
8260	68 22 76 00	563 559 976 000	884542 5502	402157 17397	214361 816	1210654 147
8261	68 24 41 21	563 764 683 581	890043 5501	419554 17396	215177 815	1210507 146
8262	68 26 06 44	563 969 440 728	895544 5501	436950 17394	215992 816	1210361 147
8263	68 27 71 69	564 174 247 447	901045 5501	454344 17394	216808 815	1210214 146
8264	68 29 36 96	564 379 103 744	906545 5500	471738 17392	217623 816	1210068 147
				17392		
8265	68 31 02 25	564 584 009 625	912045 5500	489130 17392	218439 815	1209921 146
8266	68 32 67 56	564 788 965 096	917545 5500	506522 17390	219254 816	1209775 146
8267	68 34 32 89	564 994 970 163	923044 5499	523912 17389	220070 815	1209629 147
8268	68 35 98 24	565 199 024 832	928543 5499	541301 17389	220885 815	1209482 146
8269	68 37 63 61	565 404 129 109	934042 5499	558690 17387	221700 815	1209336 146
				5498		
8270	68 39 29 00	565 609 283 000	939540 5498	576077 17386	222515 815	1209190 146
8271	68 40 94 41	565 814 486 511	945038 5498	593463 17385	223330 815	1209044 146
8272	68 42 59 84	566 019 739 648	950536 5498	610848 17384	224145 815	1208897 147
8273	68 44 25 29	566 225 042 417	956033 5497	628232 17383	224960 815	1208751 146
8274	68 45 90 76	566 430 394 824	961530 5497	645615 17382	225775 815	1208605 146
				5497		
8275	68 47 56 25	566 635 796 875	967027 5496	662997 17381	226590 815	1208459 146
8276	68 49 21 76	566 841 248 576	972523 5496	680378 17380	227405 814	1208313 146
8277	68 50 87 29	567 046 749 933	978019 5496	697758 17379	228219 815	1208167 146
8278	68 52 52 84	567 252 300 952	983515 5495	715137 17379	229034 814	1208021 146
8279	68 54 18 41	567 457 901 639	989010 5495	732515 17378	229848 814	1207875 146
				17376		815
8280	68 55 84 00	567 663 552 000	994505 5495	749891 17376	230663 814	1207729 145
8281	68 57 49 61	567 869 252 041	*000000 5494	767267 17375	231477 815	1207584 146
8282	68 59 15 24	568 075 001 768	005494 5494	784642 17373	232292 814	1207438 146
8283	68 60 80 89	568 280 801 187	010988 5494	802015 17373	233106 814	1207292 146
8284	68 62 46 56	568 486 650 304	016482 5493	819388 17371	233920 814	1207146 145
8285	68 64 12 25	568 692 549 125	021975 5493	836759 17371	234734 814	1207001 146
8286	68 65 77 96	568 898 497 656	027468 5493	854130 17369	235548 814	1206855 146
8287	68 67 43 69	569 104 495 903	032961 5492	871499 17368	236362 814	1206709 145
8288	68 69 09 44	569 310 543 872	038453 5492	888867 17368	237176 814	1206564 146
8289	68 70 75 21	569 516 641 569	043945 5492	906235 17366	237990 814	1206418 145
8290	68 72 41 00	569 722 789 000	049437 5491	923601 17365	238804 814	1206273 146
8291	68 74 06 81	569 928 986 171	054928 5492	940966 17365	239618 814	1206127 145
8292	68 75 72 64	570 135 233 088	060420 5490	958330 17364	240431 813	1205982 146
8293	68 77 38 49	570 341 529 757	065910 5491	975693 17363	241245 814	1205836 146
8294	68 79 04 36	570 547 876 184	071401 5490	993055 17362	242059 813	1205691 145
				17361		
8295	68 80 70 25	570 754 272 375	076891 5489	*010416 17360	242872 813	1205546 146
8296	68 82 36 16	570 960 718 336	082380 5490	027776 17359	243685 814	1205400 145
8297	68 84 02 09	571 167 214 073	087870 5489	045135 17358	244499 813	1205255 145
8298	68 85 68 04	571 373 759 592	093359 5488	062493 17357	245312 813	1205110 146
8299	68 87 34 01	571 580 354 899	098847 5489	079850 17356	246125 814	1204964 145
8300	68 89 00 00	571 787 000 000	104336	097206	246939	1204819
			91·	288·	20·	0·000

No. n	Square n²	Cube n³	Square root √n	Sq. rt. of 10n √10n	Cube root ∛n	Reciprocal 1/n
			91·	288·	20·	0·000
8300	68 89 00 00	571 787 000 000	104336 5488	097206 17355	246939 813	1204819 145
8301	68 90 66 01	571 993 694 901	109824 5488	114561 17353	247752 813	1204674 145
8302	68 92 32 04	572 200 439 608	115312 5487	131914 17353	248565 813	1204529 145
8303	68 93 98 09	572 407 234 127	120799 5487	149267 17351	249378 813	1204384 145
8304	68 95 64 16	572 614 078 464	126286 5487	166618 17351	250191 812	1204239 145
8305	68 97 30 25	572 820 972 625	131773 5486	183969 17350	251003 813	1204094 145
8306	68 98 96 36	573 027 916 616	137259 5486	201319 17348	251816 813	1203949 145
8307	69 00 62 49	573 234 910 443	142745 5486	218667 17348	252629 812	1203804 145
8308	69 02 28 64	573 441 954 112	148231 5485	236014 17347	253441 813	1203659 145
8309	69 03 94 81	573 649 047 629	153716 5485	253361 17345	254254 813	1203514 145
8310	69 05 61 00	573 856 191 000	159201 5485	270706 17344	255067 812	1203369 144
8311	69 07 27 21	574 063 384 231	164686 5485	288050 17344	255879 812	1203225 144
8312	69 08 93 44	574 270 627 328	170171 5484	305394 17342	256691 813	1203080 145
8313	69 10 59 69	574 477 920 297	175655 5483	322736 17341	257504 812	1202935 145
8314	69 12 25·96	574 685 263 144	181138 5484	340077 17340	258316 812	1202790 144
8315	69 13 92 25	574 892 655 875	186622 5483	357417 17339	259128 812	1202646 145
8316	69 15 58 56	575 100 098 496	192105 5483	374756 17338	259940 812	1202501 145
8317	69 17 24 89	575 307 591 013	197588 5482	392094 17337	260752 812	1202357 144
8318	69 18 91 24	575 515 133 432	203070 5482	409431 17336	261564 812	1202212 144
8319	69 20 57 61	575 722 725 759	208552 5482	426767 17335	262376 812	1202068 145
8320	69 22 24 00	575 930 368 000	214034 5481	444102 17334	263188 812	1201923 144
8321	69 23 90 41	576 138 060 161	219515 5482	461436 17333	264000 812	1201779 144
8322	69 25 56 84	576 345 802 248	224997 5480	478769 17331	264812 811	1201634 144
8323	69 27 23 29	576 553 594 267	230477 5481	496100 17331	265623 812	1201490 144
8324	69 28 89 76	576 761 436 224	235958 5480	513431 17330	266435 811	1201346 145
8325	69 30 56 25	576 969 328 125	241438 5480	530761 17329	267246 812	1201201 144
8326	69 32 22 76	577 177 269 976	246918 5479	548090 17327	268058 811	1201057 144
8327	69 33 89 29	577 385 261 783	252397 5479	565417 17327	268869 811	1200913 144
8328	69 35 55 84	577 593 303 552	257876 5479	582744 17325	269681 811	1200768 145
8329	69 37 22 41	577 801 395 289	263355 5479	600069 17325	270492 811	1200624 144
8330	69 38 89 00	578 009 537 000	268834 5478	617394 17323	271303 811	1200480 144
8331	69 40 55 61	578 217 728 691	274312 5478	634717 17323	272114 811	1200336 144
8332	69 42 22 24	578 425 970 368	279790 5477	652040 17321	272925 811	1200192 144
8333	69 43 88 89	578 634 262 037	285267 5477	669361 17320	273736 811	1200048 144
8334	69 45 55 56	578 842 603 704	290744 5477	686681 17320	274547 811	1199904 144
8335	69 47 22 25	579 050 995 375	296221 5477	704001 17318	275358 811	1199760 144
8336	69 48 88 96	579 259 437 056	301698 5476	721319 17317	276169 811	1199616 144
8337	69 50 55 69	579 467 928 753	307174 5476	738636 17316	276980 810	1199472 144
8338	69 52 22 44	579 676 470 472	312650 5475	755952 17315	277790 810	1199328 143
8339	69 53 89 21	579 885 062 219	318125 5475	773267 17315	278601 811	1199185 144
8340	69 55 56 00	580 093 704 000	323600 5475	790582 17313	279412 810	1199041 144
8341	69 57 22 81	580 302 395 821	329075 5475	807895 17312	280222 810	1198897 144
8342	69 58 89 64	580 511 137 688	334550 5474	825207 17311	281033 810	1198753 143
8343	69 60 56 49	580 719 929 607	340024 5474	842518 17310	281843 810	1198610 144
8344	69 62 23 36	580 928 771 584	345498 5474	859828 17309	282653 810	1198466 144
8345	69 63 90 25	581 137 663 625	350972 5473	877137 17307	283463 811	1198322 143
8346	69 65 57 16	581 346 605 736	356445 5473	894444 17307	284274 810	1198179 144
8347	69 67 24 09	581 555 597 923	361918 5472	911751 17306	285084 810	1198035 143
8348	69 68 91 04	581 764 640 192	367390 5472	929057 17305	285894 810	1197892 144
8349	69 70 58 01	581 973 732 549	372862 5472	946362 17305	286704 810	1197748 143
8350	69 72 25 00	582 182 875 000	378334	963666	287514	1197605
			91·	288·	20·	0·000

No. n	Square n²	Cube n³	Square root √n	Sq. rt. of 10n √10n	Cube root ∛n	Reciprocal 1/n
			91·	288·	20·	0·000
8350	69 72 25 00	582 182 875 000	378334 5472	963666 17302	287514 810	1197605 144
8351	69 73 92 01	582 392 067 551	383806 5471	980968 17302	288324 809	1197461 143
8352	69 75 59 04	582 601 310 208	389277 5471	998270 17301	289133 810	1197318 143
8353	69 77 26 09	582 810 602 977	394748 5471	*015571 17299	289943 810	1197175 144
8354	69 78 93 16	583 019 945 864	400219 5470	032870 17299	290753 809	1197031 143
8355	69 80 60 25	583 229 338 875	405689 5470	050169 17297	291562 810	1196888 143
8356	69 82 27 36	583 438 782 016	411159 5470	067466 17297	292372 809	1196745 143
8357	69 83 94 49	583 648 275 293	416629 5469	084763 17295	293181 810	1196602 144
8358	69 85 61 64	583 857 818 712	422098 5469	102058 17295	293991 809	1196458 143
8359	69 87 28 81	584 067 412 279	427567 5469	119353 17293	294800 809	1196315 143
8360	69 88 96 00	584 277 056 000	433036 5468	136646 17292	295609 809	1196172 143
8361	69 90 63 21	584 486 749 881	438504 5468	153938 17292	296418 810	1196029 143
8362	69 92 30 44	584 696 493 928	443972 5468	171230 17290	297228 809	1195886 143
8363	69 93 97 69	584 906 288 ·147	449440 5467	188520 17289	298037 809	1195743 143
8364	69 95 64 96	585 116 132 544	454907 5467	205809 17288	298846 809	1195600 143
8365	69 97 32 25	585 326 027 125	460374 5467	223097 17287	299655 808	1195457 143
8366	69 98 99 56	585 535 971 896	465841 5466	240384 17287	300463 809	1195314 142
8367	70 00 66 89	585 745 966 863	471307 5466	257671 17285	301272 809	1195172 143
8368	70 02 34 24	585 956 012 032	476773 5466	274956 17284	302081 809	1195029 143
8369	70 04 01 61	586 166 107 409	482239 5465	292240 17283	302890 808	1194886 143
8370	70 05 69 00	586 376 253 000	487704 5465	309523 17282	303698 809	1194743 143
8371	70 07 36 41	586 586 448 811	493169 5465	326805 17281	304507 808	1194600 143
8372	70 09 03 84	586 796 694 848	498634 5464	344086 17280	305315 809	1194458 143
8373	70 10 71 29	587 006 991 117	504098 5464	361366 17279	306124 808	1194315 143
8374	70 12 38 76	587 217 337 624	509562 5464	378645 17278	306932 809	1194172 142
8375	70 14 06 25	587 427 734 375	515026 5464	395923 17276	307741 808	1194030 143
8376	70 15 73 76	587 638 181 376	520490 5463	413199 17276	308549 808	1193887 142
8377	70 17 41 29	587 848 678 633	525953 5462	430475 17275	309357 808	1193745 143
8378	70 19 08 84	588 059 226 152	531415 5463	447750 17274	310165 808	1193602 142
8379	70 20 76 41	588 269 823 939	536878 5462	465024 17273	310973 808	1193460 143
8380	70 22 44 00	588 480 472 000	542340 5462	482297 17271	311781 808	1193317 142
8381	70 24 11 61	588 691 170 341	547802 5461	499568 17271	312589 808	1193175 142
8382	70 25 79 24	588 901 918 968	553263 5461	516839 17270	313397 808	1193033 143
8383	70 27 46 89	589 112 717 887	558724 5461	534109 17268	314205 807	1192890 142
8384	70 29 14 56	589 323 567 104	564185 5461	551377 17268	315012 808	1192748 142
8385	70 30 82 25	589 534 466 625	569646 5460	568645 17266	315820 808	1192606 142
8386	70 32 49 96	589 745 416 456	575106 5460	585911 17266	316628 807	1192464 143
8387	70 34 17 69	589 956 416 603	580566 5459	603177 17264	317435 808	1192321 142
8388	70 35 85 44	590 167 467 072	586025 5459	620441 17264	318243 807	1192179 142
8389	70 37 53 21	590 378 567 869	591484 5459	637705 17262	319050 807	1192037 142
8390	70 39 21 00	590 589 719 000	596943 5459	654967 17262	319857 808	1191895 143
8391	70 40 88 81	590 800 920 471	602402 5458	672229 17260	320665 807	1191753 143
8392	70 42 56 64	591 012 172 288	607860 5458	689489 17259	321472 807	1191611 142
8393	70 44 24 49	591 223 474 457	613318 5457	706748 17259	322279 807	1191469 142
8394	70 45 92 36	591 434 826 984	618775 5458	724007 17257	323086 807	1191327 142
8395	70 47 60 25	591 646 229 875	624233 5457	741264 17256	323893 807	1191185 142
8396	70 49 28 16	591 857 683 136	629690 5456	758520 17255	324700 807	1191043 141
8397	70 50 96 09	592 069 186 773	635146 5456	775775 17255	325507 807	1190902 142
8398	70 52 64 04	592 280 740 792	640602 5456	793030 17253	326314 806	1190760 142
8399	70 54 32 01	592 492 345 199	646058 5456	810283 17252	327120 807	1190618 142
8400	70 56 00 00	592 704 000 000	651514 91·	827535 289·	327927 20·	1190476 0·000

No. n	Square n^2	Cube n^3	Square root $\sqrt{n}$	Sq. rt. of $10n$ $\sqrt{10n}$	Cube root $\sqrt[3]{n}$	Reciprocal $\frac{1}{n}$
			91·	289·	20·	0·000
8400	70 56 00 00	592 704 000 000	651514 5455	827535 17251	327927 807	1190476 142
8401	70 57 68 01	592 915 705 201	656969 5455	844786 17251	328734 806	1190334 142
8402	70 59 36 04	593 127 460 808	662424 5455	862036 17250	329540 807	1190193 141
8403	70 61 04 09	593 339 266 827	667879 5455	879285 17249	330347 806	1190051 142
8404	70 62 72 16	593 551 123 264	673333 5454	896533 17248	331153 807	1189910 142
			5454	17247		
8405	70 64 40 25	593 763 030 125	678787 5454	913780 17246	331960 806	1189768 142
8406	70 66 08 36	593 974 987 416	684241 5453	931026 17245	332766 806	1189626 142
8407	70 67 76 49	594 186 995 143	689694 5453	948271 17244	333572 806	1189485 141
8408	70 69 44 64	594 399 053 312	695147 5453	965515 17243	334378 807	1189343 142
8409	70 71 12 81	594 611 161 929	700600 5453	982758 17242	335185 806	1189202 141
			5452			
8410	70 72 81 00	594 823 321 000	706052 5452	*000000 17241	335991 806	1189061 141
8411	70 74 49 21	595 035 530 531	711504 5452	017241 17240	335797 805	1188919 142
8412	70 76 17 44	595 247 790 528	716956 5451	034481 17239	337602 806	1188778 141
8413	70 77 85 69	595 460 100 997	722407 5451	051720 17237	338408 806	1188637 142
8414	70 79 53 96	595 672 461 944	727858 5451	068957 17237	339214 806	1188495 142
8415	70 81 22 25	595 884 873 375	733309 5451	086194 17236	340020 806	1188354 141
8416	70 82 90 56	596 097 335 296	738760 5450	103430 17235	340826 805	1188213 141
8417	70 84 58 89	596 309 847 713	744210 5449	120665 17233	341631 806	1188072 141
8418	70 86 27 24	596 522 410 632	749659 5450	137898 17233	342437 805	1187931 141
8419	70 87 95 61	596 735 024 059	755109 5449	155131 17232	343242 806	1187790 142
8420	70 89 64 00	596 947 688 000	760558 5449	172363 17230	344048 805	1187648 141
8421	70 91 32 41	597 160 402 461	766007 5448	189593 17230	344853 805	1187507 141
8422	70 93 00 84	597 373 167 448	771455 5448	206823 17228	345658 805	1187366 141
8423	70 94 69 29	597 585 982 967	776903 5448	224051 17228	346463 806	1187225 140
8424	70 96 37 76	597 798 849 024	782351 5448	241279 17226	347269 805	1187085 140
8425	70 98 06 25	598 011 765 625	787799 5447	258505 17226	348074 805	1186944 141
8426	70 99 74 76	598 224 732 776	793246 5447	275731 17224	348879 805	1186803 141
8427	71 01 43 29	598 437 750 483	798693 5446	292955 17224	349684 805	1186662 141
8428	71 03 11 84	598 650 818 752	804139 5447	310179 17222	350489 805	1186521 141
8429	71 04 80 41	598 863 937 589	809586 5445	327401 17222	351294 804	1186380 140
8430	71 06 49 00	599 077 107 000	815031 5446	344623 17220	352098 805	1186240 141
8431	71 08 17 61	599 290 326 991	820477 5445	361843 17220	352903 805	1186099 141
8432	71 09 86 24	599 503 597 568	825922 5445	379063 17218	353708 804	1185958 141
8433	71 11 54 89	599 716 918 737	831367 5445	396281 17217	354512 805	1185818 140
8434	71 13 23 56	599 930 290 504	836812 5444	413498 17217	355317 804	1185677 141
8435	71 14 92 25	600 143 712 875	842256 5444	430715 17215	356121 805	1185536 140
8436	71 16 60 96	600 357 185 856	847700 5444	447930 17214	356926 804	1185396 140
8437	71 18 29 69	600 570 709 453	853144 5443	465144 17213	357730 804	1185255 140
8438	71 19 98 44	600 784 283 672	858587 5443	482357 17213	358534 804	1185115 140
8439	71 21 67 21	600 997 908 519	864030 5443	499570 17211	359338 805	1184975 141
8440	71 23 36 00	601 211 584 000	869473 5442	516781 17210	360143 804	1184834 140
8441	71 25 04 81	601 425 310 121	874915 5442	533991 17209	360947 804	1184694 140
8442	71 26 73 64	601 639 086 888	880357 5442	551200 17208	361751 804	1184553 140
8443	71 28 42 49	601 852 914 307	885799 5441	568408 17208	362555 804	1184413 140
8444	71 30 11 36	602 066 792 384	891240 5441	585616 17206	363359 803	1184273 140
8445	71 31 80 25	602 280 721 125	896681 5441	602822 17205	364162 804	1184133 141
8446	71 33 49 16	602 494 700 536	902122 5440	620027 17204	364966 804	1183992 140
8447	71 35 18 09	602 708 730 623	907562 5440	637231 17203	365770 803	1183852 140
8448	71 36 87 04	602 922 811 392	913002 5440	654434 17202	366573 804	1183712 140
8449	71 38 56 01	603 136 942 849	918442 5440	671636 17201	367377 804	1183572 140
8450	71 40 25 00	603 351 125 000	923882	688837	368181	1183432
			91·	290·	20·	0·000

No. n	Square n^2	Cube n^3	Square root $\sqrt{n}$	Sq. rt. of $10n$ $\sqrt{10n}$	Cube root $\sqrt[3]{n}$	Reciprocal $\dfrac{1}{n}$
			91·	290·	20·	0·000
8450	71 40 25 00	603 351 125 000	923882	688837	368181	1183432
8451	71 41 94 01	603 565 357 851	929321 ₅₄₃₉	706037 ₁₇₂₀₀	368984 ₈₀₃	1183292 ₁₄₀
8452	71 43 63 04	603 779 641 408	934759 ₅₄₃₈	723236 ₁₇₁₉₉	369787 ₈₀₃	1183152 ₁₄₀
8453	71 45 32 09	603 993 975 677	940198 ₅₄₃₉	740434 ₁₇₁₉₈	370591 ₈₀₄	1183012 ₁₄₀
8454	71 47 01 16	604 208 360 664	945636 ₅₄₃₈	757631 ₁₇₁₉₇	371394 ₈₀₃	1182872 ₁₄₀
			₅₄₃₈	₁₇₁₉₆	₈₀₃	₁₄₀
8455	71 48 70 25	604 422 796 375	951074	774827	372197 ₈₀₃	1182732
8456	71 50 39 36	604 637 282 816	956511 ₅₄₃₇	792022 ₁₇₁₉₅	373000 ₈₀₃	1182592 ₁₄₀
8457	71 52 08 49	604 851 819 993	961949 ₅₄₃₈	809216 ₁₇₁₉₄	373803 ₈₀₃	1182452 ₁₄₀
8458	71 53 77 64	605 066 407 912	967386 ₅₄₃₇	826409 ₁₇₁₉₃	374606 ₈₀₃	1182313 ₁₃₉
8459	71 55 46 81	605 281 046 579	972822 ₅₄₃₆	843601 ₁₇₁₉₂	375409 ₈₀₃	1182173 ₁₄₀
			₅₄₃₆	₁₇₁₉₀	₈₀₃	₁₄₀
8460	71 57 16 00	605 495 736 000	978258	860791	376212 ₈₀₃	1182033
8461	71 58 85 21	605 710 476 181	983694 ₅₄₃₆	877981 ₁₇₁₉₀	377015 ₈₀₃	1181893 ₁₄₀
8462	71 60 54 44	605 925 267 128	989130 ₅₄₃₆	895170 ₁₇₁₈₉	377818 ₈₀₂	1181754 ₁₃₉
8463	71 62 23 69	606 140 108 847	994565 ₅₄₃₅	912358 ₁₇₁₈₈	378620 ₈₀₃	1181614 ₁₄₀
8464	71 63 92 96	606 355 001 344	*000000 ₅₄₃₅	929545 ₁₇₁₈₇	379423 ₈₀₃	1181474 ₁₄₀
			₅₄₃₅	₁₇₁₈₆		₁₃₉
8465	71 65 62 25	606 569 944 625	005435	946731	380226	1181335
8466	71 67 31 56	606 784 938 696	010869 ₅₄₃₄	963915 ₁₇₁₈₄	381028 ₈₀₂	1181195 ₁₄₀
8467	71 69 00 89	606 999 983 563	016303 ₅₄₃₄	981099 ₁₇₁₈₄	381831 ₈₀₃	1181056 ₁₃₉
8468	71 70 70 24	607 215 079 232	021737 ₅₄₃₄	998282 ₁₇₁₈₃	382633 ₈₀₂	1180916 ₁₄₀
8469	71 72 39 61	607 430 225 709	027170 ₅₄₃₃	*015464 ₁₇₁₈₂	383435 ₈₀₂	1180777 ₁₃₉
			₅₄₃₃	₁₇₁₈₀		₁₃₉
8470	71 74 09 00	607 645 423 000	032603	032644	384237 ₈₀₃	1180638
8471	71 75 78 41	607 860 671 111	038036 ₅₄₃₃	049824 ₁₇₁₈₀	385040 ₈₀₂	1180498 ₁₄₀·
8472	71 77 47 84	608 075 970 048	043468 ₅₄₃₂	067003 ₁₇₁₇₉	385842 ₈₀₂	1180359 ₁₃₉
8473	71 79 17 29	608 291 319 817	048900 ₅₄₃₂	084180 ₁₇₁₇₇	386644 ₈₀₂	1180220 ₁₄₀
8474	71 80 86 76	608 506 720 424	054332 ₅₄₃₂	101357 ₁₇₁₇₇	387446 ₈₀₂	1180080 ₁₃₉
			₅₄₃₁	₁₇₁₇₆		
8475	71 82 56 25	608 722 171 875	059763	118533	388248 ₈₀₂	1179941
8476	71 84 25 76	608 937 674 176	065194 ₅₄₃₁	135707 ₁₇₁₇₄	389050 ₈₀₁	1179802 ₁₃₉
8477	71 85 95 29	609 153 227 333	070625 ₅₄₃₁	152881 ₁₇₁₇₄	389851 ₈₀₂	1179663 ₁₃₉
8478	71 87 64 84	609 368 831 352	076056 ₅₄₃₁	170053 ₁₇₁₇₂	390653 ₈₀₂	1179523 ₁₄₀
8479	71 89 34 41	609 584 486 239	081486 ₅₄₃₀	187225 ₁₇₁₇₂	391455 ₈₀₁	1179384 ₁₃₉
			₅₄₂₉	₁₇₁₇₁		₁₃₉
8480	71 91 04 00	609 800 192 000	086915	204396	392256 ₈₀₂	1179245
8481	71 92 73 61	610 015 948 641	092345 ₅₄₃₀	221565 ₁₇₁₆₉	393058 ₈₀₂	1179106 ₁₃₉
8482	71 94 43 24	610 231 756 168	097774 ₅₄₂₉	238734 ₁₇₁₆₉	393859 ₈₀₁	1178967 ₁₃₉
8483	71 96 12 89	610 447 614 587	103203 ₅₄₂₉	255901 ₁₇₁₆₇	394661 ₈₀₁	1178828 ₁₃₉
8484	71 97 82 56	610 663 523 904	108632 ₅₄₂₉	273068 ₁₇₁₆₇	395462 ₈₀₂	1178689 ₁₃₉
			₅₄₂₈	₁₇₁₆₅		₁₃₉
8485	71 99 52 25	610 879 484 125	114060	290233	396264 ₈₀₁	1178550
8486	72 01 21 96	611 095 495 256	119488 ₅₄₂₈	307398 ₁₇₁₆₅	397065 ₈₀₁	1178412 ₁₃₈
8487	72 02 91 69	611 311 557 303	124915 ₅₄₂₇	324561 ₁₇₁₆₃	397866 ₈₀₁	1178273 ₁₃₉
8488	72 04 61 44	611 527 670 272	130342 ₅₄₂₇	341724 ₁₇₁₆₃	398667 ₈₀₁	1178134 ₁₃₉
8489	72 06 31 21	611 743 834 169	135769 ₅₄₂₇	358885 ₁₇₁₆₁	399468 ₈₀₁	1177995 ₁₃₉
			₅₄₂₇	₁₇₁₆₁		₁₃₉
8490	72 08 01 00	611 960 049 000	141196	376046	400269 ₈₀₁	1177856
8491	72 09 70 81	612 176 314 771	146622 ₅₄₂₆	393205 ₁₇₁₅₉	401070 ₈₀₁	1177718 ₁₃₈
8492	72 11 40 64	612 392 631 488	152048 ₅₄₂₆	410364 ₁₇₁₅₉	401871 ₈₀₁	1177579 ₁₃₉
8493	72 13 10 49	612 608 999 157	157474 ₅₄₂₆	427521 ₁₇₁₅₇	402672 ₈₀₀	1177440 ₁₃₈
8494	72 14 80 36	612 825 417 784	162899 ₅₄₂₅	444677 ₁₇₁₅₆	403472 ₈₀₁	1177302 ₁₃₉
			₅₄₂₅	₁₇₁₅₆		
8495	72 16 50 25	613 041 887 375	168324	461833	404273 ₈₀₁	1177163
8496	72 18 20 16	613 258 407 936	173749 ₅₄₂₅	478987 ₁₇₁₅₄	405074 ₈₀₀	1177024 ₁₃₉
8497	72 19 90 09	613 474 979 473	179173 ₅₄₂₄	496141 ₁₇₁₅₄	405874 ₈₀₁	1176886 ₁₃₈
8498	72 21 60 04	613 691 601 992	184597 ₅₄₂₄	513293 ₁₇₁₅₂	406675 ₈₀₀	1176747 ₁₃₉
8499	72 23 30 01	613 908 275 499	190021 ₅₄₂₄	530444 ₁₇₁₅₁	407475 ₈₀₁	1176609 ₁₃₈
			₅₄₂₄	₁₇₁₅₁		₁₃₈
8500	72 25 00 00	614 125 000 000,	195445	547595	408276	1176471
			92·	291·	20·	0·000

No. n	Square n²	Cube n³	Square root √n	Sq. rt. of 10n √10n	Cube root ∛n	Reciprocal 1/n
			92·	291·	20·	0·000
8500	72 25 00 00	614 125 000 000	195445 5423	547595 17149	408276 800	1176471
8501	72 26 70 01	614 341 775 501	200868 5422	564744 17148	409076 800	1176332 139
8502	72 28 40 04	614 558 602 008	206290 5423	581892 17148	409876 800	1176194 138
8503	72 30 10 09	614 775 479 527	211713 5422	599040 17146	410676 800	1176056 138
8504	72 31 80 16	614 992 408 064	217135 5422	616186 17145	411476 800	1175917 139 138
8505	72 33 50 25	615 209 387 625	222557 5421	633331 17145	412276 800	1175779 138
8506	72 35 20 36	615 426 418 216	227978 5422	650476 17143	413076 800	1175641 138
8507	72 36 90 49	615 643 499 843	233400 5422	667619 17142	413876 800	1175503 138
8508	72 38 60 64	615 860 632 512	238820 5420	684761 17142	414676 800	1175364 139 138
8509	72 40 30 81	616 077 816 229	244241 5421 5420	701903 17140	415476 800	1175226 138
8510	72 42 01 00	616 295 051 000	249661	719043 17139	416276	1175088 138
8511	72 43 71 21	616 512 336 831	255081 5420 5420	736182 17138	417075 799 800	1174950 138
8512	72 45 41 44	616 729 673 728	260501 5420	753320 17138	417875 799	1174812 138
8513	72 47 11 69	616 947 061 697	265920 5419	770458 17136	418674 800	1174674 138
8514	72 48 81 96	617 164 500 744	271339 5419 5419	787594 17135	419474 799	1174536 138 138
8515	72 50 52 25	617 381 990 875	276758 5418	804729 17134	420273 800	1174398 138
8516	72 52 22 56	617 599 532 096	282176 5418	821863 17134	421073 799	1174260 138
8517	72 53 92 89	617 817 124 413	287594 5418	838997 17132	421872 799	1174122 138
8518	72 55 63 24	618 034 767 832	293012 5417	856129 17131	422671 799	1173985 137 138
8519	72 57 33 61	618 252 462 359	298429 5417	873260 17130	423470 799	1173847 138 138
8520	72 59 04 00	618 470 208 000	303846 5417	890390 17130	424269 800	1173709 138
8521	72 60 74 41	618 688 004 761	309263 5416	907520 17128	425069 798	1173571 138
8522	72 62 44 84	618 905 852 648	314679 5416	924648 17127	425867 799	1173433 138
8523	72 64 15 29	619 123 751 667	320095 5416	941775 17126	426666 799	1173296 137 138
8524	72 65 85 76	619 341 701 824	325511 5416	958901 17125	427465 799	1173158 137
8525	72 67 56 25	619 559 703 125	330927 5415	976026 17125	428264 799	1173021 138
8526	72 69 26 76	619 777 755 576	336342 5415	993151 17123	429063 798	1172883 138
8527	72 70 97 29	619 995 859 183	341757 5414	*010274 17122	429861 799	1172745 138
8528	72 72 67 84	620 214 013 952	347171 5414	027396 17121	430660 799	1172608 137
8529	72 74 38 41	620 432 219 889	352585 5414	044517 17120	431459 798	1172470 138 137
8530	72 76 09 00	620 650 477 000	357999 5414	061637 17120	432257 798	1172333 137
8531	72 77 79 61	620 868 785 291	363413 5413	078757 17118	433055 799	1172196 137
8532	72 79 50 24	621 087 144 768	368826 5413	095875 17117	433854 798	1172058 138
8533	72 81 20 89	621 305 555 437	374239 5412	112992 17116	434652 798	1171921 137
8534	72 82 91 56	621 524 017·304	379651 5413	130108 17115	435450 799	1171783 138 137
8535	72 84 62 25	621 742 530 375	385064 5412	147223 17114	436249 798	1171646 137
8536	72 86 32 96	621 961 094 656	390476 5411	164337 17113	437047 798	1171509 137
8537	72 88 03 69	622 179 710 153	395887 5412	181450 17113	437845 798	1171372 137
8538	72 89 74 44	622 398 376 872	401299 5411	198563 17111	438643 798	1171234 138 137
8539	72 91 45 21	622 617 094 819	406710 5410	215674 17110	439441 797	1171097 137 137
8540	72 93 16 00	622 835 864 000	412120 5411	232784 17109	440238 798	1170960 137
8541	72 94 86 81	623 054 684 421	417531 5410	249893 17108	441036 798	1170823 137
8542	72 96 57 64	623 273 556 088	422941 5410	267001 17107	441834 798	1170686 137
8543	72 98 28 49	623 492 479 007	428351 5409	284108 17107	442632 797	1170549 137
8544	72 99 99 36	623 711 453 184	433760 5409	301215 17105	443429 798	1170412 137 137
8545	73 01 70 25	623 930 478 625	439169 5409	318320 17104	444227 797	1170275 137
8546	73 03 41 16	624 149 555 336	444578 5408	335424 17103	445024 798	1170138 137
8547	73 05 12 09	624 368 683 323	449986 5409	352527 17102	445822 797	1170001 137
8548	73 06 83 04	624 587 862 592	455395 5408	369629 17101	446619 797	1169864 137
8549	73 08 54 01	624 807 093 149	460803 5407	386730 17100	447416 798	1169727 137 136
8550	73 10 25 00	625 026 375 000	466210 92·	403830 292·	448214 20·	1169591 0·000

No. n	Square n^2	Cube n^3	Square root $\sqrt{n}$	Sq. rt. of $10n$ $\sqrt{10n}$	Cube root $\sqrt[3]{n}$	Reciprocal $\dfrac{1}{n}$
			92·	292·	20·	0·000
8550	73 10 25 00	625 026 375 000	466210 5407	403830 17099	448214 797	1169591 137
8551	73 11 96 01	625 245 708 151	471617 5407	420929 17099	449011 797	1169454 137
8552	73 13 67 04	625 465 092 608	477024 5407	438028 17097	449808 797	1169317 137
8553	73 15 38 09	625 684 528 377	482431 5406	455125 17096	450605 797	1169180 136
8554	73 17 09 16	625 904 015 464	487837 5406	472221 17095	451402 797	1169044 137
8555	73 18 80 25	626 123 553 875	493243 5406	489316 17094	452199 797	1168907 137
8556	73 20 51 36	626 343 143 616	498649 5405	506410 17093	452996 796	1168770 136
8557	73 22 22 49	626 562 784 693	504054 5405	523503 17092	453792 797	1168634 137
8558	73 23 93 64	626 782 477 112	509459 5405	540595 17092	454589 797	1168497 136
8559	73 25 64 81	627 002 220 879	514864 5404	557687 17090	455386 796	1168361 137
8560	73 27 36 00	627 222 016 000	520268 5404	574777 17089	456182 797	1168224 136
8561	73 29 07 21	627 441 862 481	525672 5404	591866 17088	456979 797	1168088 137
8562	73 30 78 44	627 661 760 328	531076 5403	608954 17087	457775 797	1167951 136
8563	73 32 49 69	627 881 709 547	536479 5403	626041 17086	458572 796	1167815 136
8564	73 34 20 96	628 101 710 144	541882 5403	643127 17086	459368 797	1167679 137
8565	73 35 92 25	628 321 762 125	547285 5403	660213 17084	460165 796	1167542 136
8566	73 37 63 56	628 541 865 496	552688 5402	677297 17083	460961 796	1167406 136
8567	73 39 34 89	628 762 020 263	558090 5402	694380 17082	461757 796	1167270 136
8568	73 41 06 24	628 982 226 432	563492 5401	711462 17081	462553 796	1167134 137
8569	73 42 77 61	629 202 484 009	568893 5401	728543 17080	463349 796	1166997 136
8570	73 44 49 00	629 422 793 000	574294 5401	745623 17080	464145 796	1166861 136
8571	73 46 20 41	629 643 153 411	579695 5401	762703 17078	464941 796	1166725 136
8572	73 47 91 84	629 863 565 248	585096 5400	777981 17077	465737 796	1166589 136
8573	73 49 63 29	630 084 028 517	590496 5400	796858 17076	466533 795	1166453 136
8574	73 51 34 76	630 304 543 224	595896 5400	813934 17075	467328 796	1166317 136
8575	73 53 06 25	630 525 109 375	601296 5399	831009 17074	468124 796	1166181 136
8576	73 54 77 76	630 745 726 976	606695 5399	848083 17074	468920 795	1166045 136
8577	73 56 49 29	630 966 396 033	612094 5399	865157 17072	469715 796	1165909 136
8578	73 58 20 84	631 187 116 552	617493 5398	882229 17071	470511 795	1165773 136
8579	73 59 92 41	631 407 888 539	622891 5398	899300 17070	471306 796	1165637 136
8580	73 61 64 00	631 628 712 000	628289 5398	916370 17070	472102 795	1165501 136
8581	73 63 35 61	631 849 586 941	633687 5398	933440 17068	472897 795	1165365 136
8582	73 65 07 24	632 070 513 368	639085 5397	950508 17067	473692 795	1165230 135
8583	73 66 78 89	632 291 491 287	644482 5397	967575 17066	474487 796	1165094 136
8584	73 68 50 56	632 512 520 704	649879 5396	984641 17065	475283 795	1164958 136
8585	73 70 22 25	632 733 601 625	655275 5396	*001706 17065	476078 795	1164822 135
8586	73 71 93 96	632 954 734 056	660671 5396	018771 17063	476873 795	1164687 136
8587	73 73 65 69	633 175 918 003	666067 5396	035834 17062	477668 795	1164551 136
8588	73 75 37 44	633 397 153 472	671463 5395	052896 17062	478462 794	1164415 135
8589	73 77 09 21	633 618 440 469	676858 5395	069958 17060	479257 795	1164280 136
8590	73 78 81 00	633 839 779 000	682253 5395	087018 17059	480052 795	1164144 135
8591	73 80 52 81	634 061 169 071	687648 5394	104077 17058	480847 794	1164009 136
8592	73 82 24 64	634 282 610 688	693042 5394	121135 17058	481641 795	1163873 135
8593	73 83 96 49	634 504 103 857	698436 5393	138193 17056	482436 794	1163738 135
8594	73 85 68 36	634 725 648 584	703829 5394	155249 17055	483230 795	1163603 136
8595	73 87 40 25	634 947 244 875	709223 5393	172304 17055	484025 794	1163467 135
8596	73 89 12 16	635 168 892 736	714616 5393	189359 17053	484819 795	1163332 136
8597	73 90 84 09	635 390 592 173	720009 5392	206412 17052	485614 794	1163196 135
8598	73 92 56 04	635 612 343 192	725401 5392	223464 17052	486408 794	1163061 135
8599	73 94 28 01	635 834 145 799	730793 5392	240516 17050	487202 794	1162926 135
8600	73 96 00 00	636 056 000 000	736185 92·	257566 293·	487996 20·	1162791 0·000

No. n	Square n^2	Cube n^3	Square root $\sqrt{n}$	Sq. rt. of 10n $\sqrt{10n}$	Cube root $\sqrt[3]{n}$	Reciprocal $\frac{1}{n}$
			92·	293·	20·	0·000
8600	73 96 00 00	636 056 000 000	736185 5391	257566 17049	487996 794	1162791 135
8601	73 97 72 01	636 277 905 801	741576 5392	274615 17049	488790 794	1162656 136
8602	73 99 44 04	636 499 863 208	746968 5390	291664 17047	489584 794	1162520 135
8603	74 01 16 09	636 721 872 227	752358 5391	308711 17046	490378 794	1162385 135
8604	74 02 88 16	636 943 932 864	757749 5390	325757 17046	491172 794	1162250 135
8605	74 04 60 25	637 166 045 125	763139 5390	342803 17044	491966 794	1162115 135
8606	74 06 32 36	637 388 209 016	768529 5390	359847 17044	492760 793	1161980 135
8607	74 08 04 49	637 610 424 543	773919 5389	376891 17042	493553 794	1161845 135
8608	74 09 76 64	637 832 691 712	779308 5389	393933 17042	494347 794	1161710 135
8609	74 11 48 81	638 055 010 529	784697 5389	410975 17040	495141 793	1161575 135
8610	74 13 21 00	638 277 381 000	790086 5388	428015 17039	495934 794	1161440 135
8611	74 14 93 21	638 499 803 131	795474 5388	445054 17039	496728 793	1161305 135
8612	74 16 65 44	638 722 276 928	800862 5388	462093 17037	497521 793	1161170 135
8613	74 18 37 69	638 944 802 397	806250 5387	479130 17037	498314 794	1161036 134
8614	74 20 09 96	639 167 379 544	811637 5387	496167 17035	499108 793	1160901 135
8615	74 21 82 25	639 390 008 375	817024 5387	513202 17035	499901 793	1160766 135
8616	74 23 54 56	639 612 688 896	822411 5387	530237 17033	500694 793	1160631 134
8617	74 25 26 89	639 835 421 113	827798 5386	547270 17033	501487 793	1160497 135
8618	74 26 99 24	640 058 205 032	833184 5386	564303 17032	502280 793	1160362 135
8619	74 28 71 61	640 281 040 659	838570 5385	581335 17030	503073 793	1160227 134
8620	74 30 44 00	640 503 928 000	843955 5385	598365 17030	503866 793	1160093 135
8621	74 32 16 41	640 726 867 061	849340 5385	615395 17028	504659 793	1159958 134
8622	74 33 88 84	640 949 857 848	854725 5385	632423 17028	505452 793	1159824 135
8623	74 35 61 29	641 172 900 367	860110 5384	649451 17026	506244 793	1159689 134
8624	74 37 33 76	641 395 994 624	865494 5384	666477 17026	507037 793	1159555 135
8625	74 39 06 25	641 619 140 625	870878 5384	683503 17025	507830 792	1159420 134
8626	74 40 78 76	641 842 338 376	876262 5383	700528 17023	508622 793	1159286 134
8627	74 42 51 29	642 065 587 883	881645 5383	717551 17023	509415 792	1159152 134
8628	74 44 23 84	642 288 889 152	887028 5383	734574 17022	510207 792	1159017 134
8629	74 45 96 41	642 512 242 189	892411 5382	751596 17020	510999 793	1158883 134
8630	74 47 69 00	642 735 647 000	897793 5382	768616 17020	511792 792	1158749 135
8631	74 49 41 61	642 959 103 591	903175 5382	785636 17019	512584 792	1158614 134
8632	74 51 14 24	643 182 611 968	908557 5382	802655 17018	513376 792	1158480 134
8633	74 52 86 89	643 406 172 137	913939 5381	819673 17016	514168 792	1158346 134
8634	74 54 59 56	643 629 784 104	919320 5381	836689 17016	514960 792	1158212 134
8635	74 56 32 25	643 853 447 875	924701 5380	853705 17015	515752 792	1158078 135
8636	74 58 04 96	644 077 163 456	930081 5380	870720 17014	516544 792	1157943 134
8637	74 59 77 69	644 300 930 853	935461 5380	887734 17012	517336 792	1157809 134
8638	74 61 50 44	644 524 750 072	940841 5380	904746 17012	518128 792	1157675 134
8639	74 63 23 21	644 748 621 119	946221 5379	921758 17011	518920 791	1157541 134
8640	74 64 96 00	644 972 544 000	951600 5379	938769 17010	519711 792	1157407 134
8641	74 66 68 81	645 196 518 721	956979 5379	955779 17009	520503 792	1157273 133
8642	74 68 41 64	645 420 545 288	962358 5378	972788 17008	521295 792	1157140 134
8643	74 70 14 49	645 644 623 707	967736 5378	989796 17007	522086 791	1157006 134
8644	74 71 87 36	645 868 753 984	973114 5378	*006803 17006	522877 792	1156872 134
8645	74 73 60 25	646 092 936 125	978492 5378	023809 17004	523669 791	1156738 134
8646	74 75 33 16	646 317 170 136	983870 5377	040813 17004	524460 791	1156604 134
8647	74 77 06 09	646 541 456 023	989247 5377	057817 17003	525251 792	1156470 133
8648	74 78 79 04	646 765 793 792	994624 5376	074820 17002	526043 791	1156337 134
8649	74 80 52 01	646 990 183 449	*000000 5376	091822 17001	526834 791	1156203 134
8650	74 82 25 00	647 214 625 000	005376 93·	108823 294·	527625 20·	1156069 0·000

174

No. n	Square n²	Cube n³	Square root √n (93·)	Sq. rt. of 10n √10n (294·)	Cube root ∛n (20·)	Reciprocal 1/n (0·000)
8650	74 82 25 00	647 214 625 000	005376 (5376)	108823 (17000)	527625 (791)	1156069 (133)
8651	74 83 98 01	647 439 118 451	010752 (5376)	125823 (16999)	528416 (791)	1155936 (133)
8652	74 85 71 04	647 663 663 808	016128 (5375)	142822 (16999)	529207 (791)	1155802 (134)
8653	74 87 44 09	647 888 261 077	021503 (5375)	159821 (16997)	529998 (791)	1155669 (133)
8654	74 89 17 16	648 112 910 264	026878 (5375/5374)	176818 (16996)	530789 (790)	1155535 (134)
8655	74 90 90 25	648 337 611 375	032252 (5375)	193814 (16995)	531579 (791)	1155402 (134)
8656	74 92 63 36	648 562 364 416	037627 (5375/5374)	210809 (16994)	532370 (791)	1155268 (134)
8657	74 94 36 49	648 787 169 393	043001 (5374)	227803 (16993)	533161 (790)	1155135 (134)
8658	74 96 09 64	649 012 026 312	048375 (5374)	244796 (16992)	533951 (791)	1155001 (133)
8659	74 97 82 81	649 236 935 179	053748 (5373/5373)	261788 (16991)	534742 (790)	1154868 (134)
8660	74 99 56 00	649 461 896 000	059121 (5373)	278779 (16991)	535532 (791)	1154734 (133)
8661	75 01 29 21	649 686 908 781	064494 (5372)	295770 (16989)	536323 (790)	1154601 (133)
8662	75 03 02 44	649 911 973 528	069866 (5372)	312759 (16988)	537113 (790)	1154468 (133)
8663	75 04 75 69	650 137 090 247	075238 (5372/5372)	329747 (16987)	537903 (791)	1154335 (134)
8664	75 06 48 96	650 362 258 944	080610 (5372)	346734 (16987)	538694 (790)	1154201 (133)
8665	75 08 22 25	650 587 479 625	085982 (5371)	363721 (16985)	539484 (790)	1154068 (133)
8666	75 09 95 56	650 812 752 296	091353 (5371)	380706 (16984)	540274 (790)	1153935 (133)
8667	75 11 68 89	651 038 076 963	096724 (5370)	397690 (16984)	541064 (790)	1153802 (133)
8668	75 13 42 24	651 263 453 632	102094 (5371/5370)	414674 (16982)	541854 (790)	1153669 (133)
8669	75 15 15 61	651 488 882 309	107465 (5370)	431656 (16981)	542644 (790)	1153536 (133)
8670	75 16 89 00	651 714 363 000	112835 (5369)	448637 (16981)	543434 (789)	1153403 (133)
8671	75 18 62 41	651 939 895 711	118204 (5370)	465618 (16979)	544223 (790)	1153270 (133)
8672	75 20 35 84	652 165 480 448	123574 (5369)	482597 (16979)	545013 (790)	1153137 (133)
8673	75 22 09 29	652 391 117 217	128943 (5369/5368)	499576 (16977)	545803 (789)	1153004 (133)
8674	75 23 82 76	652 616 806 024	134312 (5368)	516553 (16977)	546592 (790)	1152871 (133)
8675	75 25 56 25	652 842 546 875	139680 (5368)	533530 (16975)	547382 (789)	1152738 (133)
8676	75 27 29 76	653 068 339 776	145048 (5368)	550505 (16975)	548171 (790)	1152605 (133)
8677	75 29 03 29	653 294 184 733	150416 (5368/5367)	567480 (16973)	548961 (789)	1152472 (133)
8678	75 30 76 84	653 520 081 752	155784 (5367)	584453 (16973)	549750 (790)	1152339 (133)
8679	75 32 50 41	653 746 030 839	161151 (5367)	601426 (16971)	550540 (789)	1152206 (132)
8680	75 34 24 00	653 972 032 000	166518 (5366)	618397 (16971)	551329 (789)	1152074 (133)
8681	75 35 97 61	654 198 085 241	171884 (5366)	635368 (16970)	552118 (789)	1151941 (133)
8682	75 37 71 24	654 424 190 568	177250 (5366)	652338 (16968)	552907 (789)	1151808 (132)
8683	75 39 44 89	654 650 347 987	182616 (5366/5365)	669306 (16968)	553696 (789)	1151676 (133)
8684	75 41 18 56	654 876 557 504	187982 (5365)	686274 (16967)	554485 (789)	1151543 (133)
8685	75 42 92 25	655 102 819 125	193347 (5365)	703241 (16965)	555274 (789)	1151410 (132)
8686	75 44 65 96	655 329 132 856	198712 (5365)	720206 (16965)	556063 (789)	1151278 (133)
8687	75 46 39 69	655 555 498 703	204077 (5365/5364)	737171 (16964)	556852 (789)	1151145 (132)
8688	75 48 13 44	655 781 916 672	209442 (5364/5363)	754135 (16961)	557641 (788)	1151013 (132)
8689	75 49 87 21	656 008 386 769	214806 (5363)	771098 (16961)	558429 (789)	1150880 (132)
8690	75 51 61 00	656 234 909 000	220169 (5364/5363)	788059 (16961)	559218 (789)	1150748 (132)
8691	75 53 34 81	656 461 483 371	225533 (5363)	805020 (16960)	560007 (788)	1150616 (133)
8692	75 55 08 64	656 688 109 888	230896 (5363)	821980 (16959)	560795 (789)	1150483 (132)
8693	75 56 82 49	656 914 788 557	236259 (5363/5362)	838939 (16958)	561584 (788)	1150351 (132)
8694	75 58 56 36	657 141 519 384	241622 (5362)	855897 (16957)	562372 (788)	1150219 (133)
8695	75 60 30 25	657 368 302 375	246984 (5362)	872854 (16956)	563160 (789)	1150086 (132)
8696	75 62 04 16	657 595 137 536	252346 (5361)	889810 (16955)	563949 (788)	1149954 (132)
8697	75 63 78 09	657 822 024 873	257707 (5362/5361)	906765 (16954)	564737 (788)	1149822 (132)
8698	75 65 52 04	658 048 964 392	263069 (5361)	923719 (16953)	565525 (788)	1149690 (132)
8699	75 67 26 01	658 275 956 099	268430 (5361)	940672 (16952)	566313 (788)	1149557 (132)
8700	75 69 00 00	658 503 000 000	273791 (93·)	957624 (294·)	567101 (20·)	1149425 (0·000)

No. n	Square n^2	Cube n^3	Square root $\sqrt{n}$	Sq. rt. of $10n$ $\sqrt{10n}$	Cube root $\sqrt[3]{n}$	Reciprocal $\frac{1}{n}$
			93·	294·	20·	0·000
8700	75 69 00 00	658 503 000 000	273791 5360	957624 16951	567101 788	1149425 132
8701	75 70 74 01	658 730 096 101	279151 5360	974575 16950	567889 788	1149293 132
8702	75 72 48 04	658 957 244 408	284511 5360	991525 16949	568677 788	1149161 132
8703	75 74 22 09	659 184 444 927	289871 5360	*008474 16949	569465 788	1149029 132
8704	75 75 96 16	659 411 697 664	295230 5359	025423 16947	570253 787	1148897 132
8705	75 77 70 25	659 639 002 625	300589 5359	042370 16946	571040 788	1148765 132
8706	75 79 44 36	659 866 359 816	305948 5359	059316 16945	571828 788	1148633 132
8707	75 81 18 49	660 093 769 243	311307 5359	076261 16945	572616 787	1148501 132
8708	75 82 92 64	660 321 230 912	316665 5358	093206 16943	573403 788	1148369 132
8709	75 84 66 81	660 548 744 829	322023 5358	110149 16942	574191 787	1148237 131
			5358			
8710	75 86 41 00	660 776 311 000	327381 5357	127091 16942	574978 788	1148106 132
8711	75 88 15 21	661 003 929 431	332738 5357	144033 16940	575766 787	1147974 132
8712	75 89 89 44	661 231 600 128	338095 5357	160973 16939	576553 787	1147842 132
8713	75 91 63 69	661 459 323 097	343452 5356	177912 16939	577340 787	1147710 131
8714	75 93 37 96	661 687 098 344	348808 5356	194851 16937	578127 788	1147579 132
8715	75 95 12 25	661 914 925 875	354164 5356	211788 16937	578915 787	1147447 132
8716	75 96 86 56	662 142 805 696	359520 5356	228725 16935	579702 787	1147315 132
8717	75 98 60 89	662 370 737 813	364876 5355	245660 16935	580489 787	1147184 131
8718	76 00 35 24	662 598 722 232	370231 5355	262595 16934	581276 786	1147052 131
8719	76 02 09 61	662 826 758 959	375586 5354	279529 16932	582062 787	1146921 132
8720	76 03 84 00	663 054 848 000	380940 5354	296461 16932	582849 787	1146789 132
8721	76 05 58 41	663 282 989 361	386294 5354	313393 16931	583636 787	1146657 132
8722	76 07 32 84	663 511 183 048	391648 5354	330324 16929	584423 786	1146526 131
8723	76 09 07 29	663 739 429 067	397002 5353	347253 16920	585209 787	1146395 132
8724	76 10 81 76	663 967 727 424	402355 5353	364182 16928	585996 787	1146263 131
8725	76 12 56 25	664 196 078 125	407708 5353	381110 16927	586783 786	1146132 132
8726	76 14 30 76	664 424 481 176	413061 5353	398037 16925	587569 787	1146000 132
8727	76 16 05 29	664 652 936 583	418414 5352	414962 16925	588356 786	1145869 131
8728	76 17 79 84	664 881 444 352	423766 5352	431887 16924	589142 786	1145738 131
8729	76 19 54 41	665 110 004 489	429118 5352 5351	448811 16923	589928 786	1145607 132
8730	76 21 29 00	665 338 617 000	434469 5351	465734 16922	590714 787	1145475 131
8731	76 23 03 61	665 567 281 891	439820 5351	482656 16921	591501 786	1145344 131
8732	76 24 78 24	665 795 999 168	445171 5351	499577 16920	592287 786	1145213 131
8733	76 26 52 89	666 024 768 837	450522 5350	516497 16919	593073 786	1145082 131
8734	76 28 27 56	666 253 590 904	455872 5350	533416 16918	593859 786	1144951 131
8735	76 30 02 25	666 482 465 375	461222 5350	550334 16917	594645 786	1144820 131
8736	76 31 76 96	666 711 392 256	466572 5349	567251 16916	595431 785	1144689 131
8737	76 33 51 69	666 940 371 553	471921 5349	584167 16916	596216 786	1144558 131
8738	76 35 26 44	667 169 403 272	477270 5349	601083 16914	597002 786	1144427 131
8739	76 37 01 21	667 398 487 419	482619 5348	617997 16913	597788 785	1144296 131
8740	76 38 76 00	667 627 624 000	487967 5348	634910 16912	598573 786	1144165 131
8741	76 40 50 81	667 856 813 021	493315 5348	651822 16912	599359 786	1144034 131
8742	76 42 25 64	668 086 054 488	498663 5348	668734 16910	600145 785	1143903 131
8743	76 44 00 49	668 315 348 407	504011 5347	685644 16909	600930 785	1143772 131
8744	76 45 75 36	668 544 694 784	509358 5347	702553 16909	601715 786	1143641 130
8745	76 47 50 25	668 774 093 625	514705 5346	719462 16907	602501 785	1143511 131
8746	76 49 25 16	669 003 544 936	520051 5347	736369 16907	603286 785	1143380 131
8747	76 51 00 09	669 233 048 723	525398 5346	753276 16905	604071 785	1143249 131
8748	76 52 75 04	669 462 604 992	530744 5345	770181 16905	604856 785	1143118 130
8749	76 54 50 01	669 692 213 749	536089 5346	787086 16903	605641 785	1142988 131
8750	76 56 25 00	669 921 875 000	541435 93·	803989 295·	606426 20·	1142857 0·000

176

No. n	Square n^2	Cube n^3	Square root $\sqrt{n}$	Sq. rt. of 10n $\sqrt{10n}$	Cube root $\sqrt[3]{n}$	Reciprocal $\dfrac{1}{n}$
			93·	295·	20·	0·000
8750	76 56 25 00	669 921 875 000	541435 5345	803989 16903	606426 785	1142857 130
8751	76 58 00 01	670 151 588 751	546780 5345	820892 16901	607211 785	1142727 130
8752	76 59 75 04	670 381 355 008	552125 5344	837793 16901	607996 785	1142596 131
8753	76 61 50 09	670 611 173 777	557469 5344	854694 16900	608781 785	1142465 130
8754	76 63 25 16	670 841 045 064	562813 5344	871594 16899	609566 785	1142335 131
8755	76 65 00 25	671 070 968 875	568157 5344	888493 16897	610351 784	1142204 130
8756	76 66 75 36	671 300 945 216	573501 5343	905390 16897	611135 785	1142074 130
8757	76 68 50 49	671 530 974 093	578844 5343	922287 16896	611920 785	1141944 131
8758	76 70 25 64	671 761 055 512	584187 5343	939183 16895	612705 784	1141813 130
8759	76 72 00 81	671 991 189 479	589529 5342	956078 16894	613489 785	1141683 130
8760	76 73 76 00	672 221 376 000	594872 5342	972972 16893	614274 784	1141553 131
8761	76 75 51 21	672 451 615 081	600214 5342	989865 16892	615058 784	1141422 130
8762	76 77 26 44	672 681 906 728	605555 5341	*006757 16891	615842 785	1141292 130
8763	76 79 01 69	672 912 250 947	610897 5341	023648 16890	616627 784	1141162 131
8764	76 80 76 96	673 142 647 744	616238 5341	040538 16889	.617411 784	1141031 130
8765	76 82 52 25	673 373 097 125	621579 5340	057427 16888	618195 784	1140901 130
8766	76 84 27 56	673 603 599 096	626919 5340	074315 16887	618979 784	1140771 130
8767	76 86 02 89	673 834 153 663	632259 5340	091202 16886	619763 784	1140641 130
8768	76 87 78 24	674 064 760 832	637599 5340	108088 16886	620547 784	1140511 130
8769	76 89 53 61	674 295 420 609	642939 5339	124974 16884	621331 784	1140381 130
8770	76 91 29 00	674 526 133 000	648278 5339	141858 16883	622115 783	1140251 130
8771	76 93 04 41	674 756 898 011	653617 5339	158741 16883	622898 784	1140121 130
8772	76 94 79 84	674 987 715 648	658956 5338	175624 16881	623682 784	1139991 130
8773	76 96 55 29	675 218 585 917	664294 5338	192505 16880	624466 783	1139861 130
8774	76 98 30 76	675 449 508 824	669632 5338	209385 16880	625249 784	1139731 130
8775	77 00 06 25	675 680 484 375	674970 5337	226265 16878	626033 783	1139601 130
8776	77 01 81 76	675 911 512 576	680307 5338	243143 16878	626816 784	1139471 130
8777	77 03 57 29	676 142 593 433	685645 5336	260021 16877	627600 783	1139341 130
8778	77 05 32 84	676 373 726 952	690981 5337	276898 16877	628383 784	1139212 129
8779	77 07 08 41	676 604 913 139	696318 5336	293773 16875	629167 783	1139082 130
8780	77 08 84 00	676 836 152 000	701654 5336	310648 16874	629950 783	1138952 130
8781	77 10 59 61	677 067 443 541	706990 5336	327522 16872	630733 783	1138822 130
8782	77 12 35 24	677 298 787 768	712326 5335	344394 16872	631516 783	1138693 129
8783	77 14 10 89	677 530 184 687	717661 5335	361266 16871	632299 783	1138563 130
8784	77 15 86 56	677 761 634 304	722996 5335	378137 16870	633082 783	1138434 129
8785	77 17 62 25	677 993 136 625	728331 5334	395007 16869	633865 783	1138304 130
8786	77 19 37 96	678 224 691 656	733665 5334	411876 16868	634648 783	1138174 129
8787	77 21 13 69	678 456 299 403	738999 5334	428744 16867	635431 783	1138045 130
8788	77 22 89 44	678 687 959 872	744333 5334	445611 16866	636214 782	1137915 129
8789	77 24 65 21	678 919 673 069	749667 5333	462477 16865	636996 783	1137786 130
8790	77 26 41 00	679 151 439 000	755000 5333	479342 16864	637779 783	1137656 129
8791	77 28 16 81	679 383 257 671	760333 5333	496206 16863	638562 782	1137527 129
8792	77 29 92 64	679 615 129 088	765665 5332	513069 16862	639344 782	1137398 129
8793	77 31 68 49	679 847 053 257	770998 5332	529931 16861	640127 782	1137268 129
8794	77 33 44 36	680 079 030 184	776330 5331	546792 16861	640909 782	1137139 129
8795	77 35 20 25	680 311 059 875	781661 5332	563653 16859	641691 783	1137010 130
8796	77 36 96 16	680 543 142 336	786993 5331	580512 16858	642474 782	1136880 129
8797	77 38 72 09	680 775 277 573	792324 5331	597370 16858	643256 782	1136751 129
8798	77 40 48 04	681 007 465 592	797655 5330	614228 16856	644038 782	1136622 129
8799	77 42 24 01	681 239 706 399	802985 5330	631084 16855	644820 782	1136493 129
8800	77 44 00 00	681 472 000 000	808315	647939	645602	1136364
			93·	296·	20·	0·000

No. n	Square n^2	Cube n^3	Square root $\sqrt{n}$	Sq. rt. of 10n $\sqrt{10n}$	Cube root $\sqrt[3]{n}$	Reciprocal $\frac{1}{n}$
			93·	296·	20·	0·000
8800	77 44 00 00	681 472 000 000	808315 5330	647939 16855	645602 782	1136364 129
8801	77 45 76 01	681 704 346 401	813645 5330	664794 16854	646384 782	1136235 130
8802	77 47 52 04	681 936 745 608	818975 5329	681648 16852	647166 782	1136105 129
8803	77 49 28 09	682 169 197 627	824304 5329	698500 16852	647948 782	1135976 129
8804	77 51 04 16	682 401 702 464	829633 5329	715352 16850	648730 782	1135847 129
8805	77 52 80 25	682 634 260 125	834962 5328	732202 16850	649512 781	1135718 129
8806	77 54 56 36	682 866 870 616	840290 5328	749052 16849	650293 782	1135589 129
8807	77 56 32 49	683 099 533 943	845618 5328	765901 16848	651075 782	1135460 128
8808	77 58 08 64	683 332 250 112	850946 5327	782749 16847	651857 781	1135332 129
8809	77 59 84 81	683 565 019 129	856273 5327	799596 16846	652638 782	1135203 129
8810	77 61 61 00	683 797 841 000	861600 5327	816442 16845	653420 781	1135074 129
8811	77 63 37 21	684 030 715 731	866927 5327	833287 16844	654201 781	1134945 129
8812	77 65 13 44	684 263 643 328	872254 5326	850131 16843	654982 782	1134816 129
8813	77 66 89 69	684 496 623 797	877580 5326	866974 16842	655764 781	1134687 128
8814	77 68 65 96	684 729 657 144	882906 5325	883816 16841	656545 781	1134559 129
8815	77 70 42 25	684 962 743 375	888231 5326	900657 16840	657326 781	1134430 129
8816	77 72 18 56	685 195 882 496	893557 5325	917497 16839	658107 781	1134301 128
8817	77 73 94 89	685 429 074 513	898882 5325	934336 16838	658888 781	1134173 129
8818	77 75 71 24	685 662 319 432	904207 5325	951174 16838	659669 781	1134044 129
8819	77 77 47 61	685 895 617 259	909531 5324	968012 16836	660450 781	1133915 128
8820	77 79 24 00	686 128 968 000	914855 5324	984848 16835	661231 781	1133787 129
8821	77 81 00 41	686 362 371 661	920179 5324	*001683 16835	662012 781	1133658 129
8822	77 82 76 84	686 595 828 248	925502 5323	018518 16833	662793 780	1133530 128
8823	77 84 53 29	686 829 337 767	930826 5323	035351 16833	663573 781	1133401 128
8824	77 86 29 76	687 062 900 224	936149 5322	052184 16832	664354 781	1133273 129
8825	77 88 06 25	687 296 515 625	941471 5322	069016 16830	665135 780	1133144 128
8826	77 89 82 76	687 530 183 976	946793 5322	085846 16830	665915 781	1133016 128
8827	77 91 59 29	687 763 905 283	952115 5322	102676 16829	666696 780	1132888 128
8828	77 93 35 84	687 997 679 552	957437 5322	119505 16829	667476 780	1132759 128
8829	77 95 12 41	688 231 506 789	962759 5321	136332 16827	668256 781	1132631 128
8830	77 96 89 00	688 465 387 000	968080 5320	153159 16826	669037 780	1132503 128
8831	77 98 65 61	688 699 320 191	973400 5321	169985 16825	669817 780	1132375 128
8832	78 00 42 24	688 933 306 368	978721 5320	186810 16824	670597 780	1132246 129
8833	78 02 18 89	689 167 345 537	984041 5320	203634 16823	671377 780	1132118 128
8834	78 03 95 56	689 401 437 704	989361 5320	220457 16822	672157 780	1131990 128
8835	78 05 72 25	689 635 582 875	994681 5319	237279 16821	672937 780	1131862 128
8836	78 07 48 96	689 869 781 056	*000000 5319	254100 16820	673717 780	1131734 128
8837	78 09 25 69	690 104 032 253	005319 5319	270920 16819	674497 780	1131606 128
8838	78 11 02 44	690 338 336 472	010638 5319	287739 16819	675277 780	1131478 128
8839	78 12 79 21	690 572 693 719	015956 5318	304558 16817	676057 779	1131350 128
8840	78 14 56 00	690 807 104 000	021274 5318	321375 16816	676836 780	1131222 128
8841	78 16 32 81	691 041 567 321	026592 5318	338191 16816	677616 780	1131094 128
8842	78 18 09 64	691 276 083 688	031909 5317	355007 16814	678395 779	1130966 128
8843	78 19 86 49	691 510 653 107	037227 5318	371821 16814	679175 780	1130838 128
8844	78 21 63 36	691 745 275 584	042544 5316	388635 16812	679954 780	1130710 128
8845	78 23 40 25	691 979 951 125	047860 5316	405447 16812	680734 779	1130582 128
8846	78 25 17 16	692 214 679 736	053176 5316	422259 16810	681513 779	1130454 127
8847	78 26 94 09	692 449 461 423	058492 5316	439069 16810	682292 780	1130327 128
8848	78 28 71 04	692 684 296 192	063808 5316	455879 16809	683072 779	1130199 128
8849	78 30 48 01	692 919 184 049	069124 5315	472688 16808	683851 779	1130071 127
8850	78 32 25 00	693 154 125 000	074439	489496	684630	1129944
			94·	297·	20·	0·000

No. n	Square n^2	Cube n^3	Square root $\sqrt{n}$	Sq. rt. of $10n$ $\sqrt{10n}$	Cube root $\sqrt[3]{n}$	Reciprocal $\dfrac{1}{n}$
			94·	297·	20·	0·000
8850	78 32 25 00	693 154 125 000	074439	489496	684630	1129944
8851	78 34 02 01	693 389 119 051	079753 ₅₃₁₄	506302 ₁₆₈₀₆	685409 ₇₇₉	1129816 ₁₂₈
8852	78 35 79 04	693 624 166 208	085068 ₅₃₁₅	523108 ₁₆₈₀₆	686188 ₇₇₉	1129688 ₁₂₈
8853	78 37 56 09	693 859 266 477	090382 ₅₃₁₄	539913 ₁₆₈₀₅	686967 ₇₇₉	1129561 ₁₂₇
8854	78 39 33 16	694 094 419 864	095696 ₅₃₁₄	556717 ₁₆₈₀₄	687746 ₇₇₉	1129433 ₁₂₈
8855	78 41 10 25	694 329 626 375	101010	573520	688525	1129305
8856	78 42 87 36	694 564 886 016	106323 ₅₃₁₃	590322 ₁₆₈₀₂	689303 ₇₇₈	1129178 ₁₂₇
8857	78 44 64 49	694 800 198 793	111636 ₅₃₁₃	607124 ₁₆₈₀₂	690082 ₇₇₉	1129050 ₁₂₈
8858	78 46 41 64	695 035 564 712	116949 ₅₃₁₃	623924 ₁₆₈₀₀	690861 ₇₇₉	1128923 ₁₂₇
8859	78 48 18 81	695 270 983 779	122261 ₅₃₁₂	640723 ₁₆₇₉₉	691639 ₇₇₈	1128796 ₁₂₇
8860	78 49 96 00	695 506 456 000	127573	657521	692418	1128668
8861	78 51 73 21	695 741 981 381	132885 ₅₃₁₂	674319 ₁₆₇₉₈	693196 ₇₇₈	1128541 ₁₂₇
8862	78 53 50 44	695 977 559 928	138196 ₅₃₁₁	691115 ₁₆₇₉₆	693975 ₇₇₈	1128413 ₁₂₈
8863	78 55 27 69	696 213 191 647	143507 ₅₃₁₁	707911 ₁₆₇₉₆	694753 ₇₇₈	1128286 ₁₂₇
8864	78 57 04 96	696 448 876 544	148818 ₅₃₁₁	724705 ₁₆₇₉₄	695531 ₇₇₉	1128159 ₁₂₇
8865	78 58 82 25	696 684 614 625	154129	741499	696310	1128032
8866	78 60 59 56	696 920 405 896	159439 ₅₃₁₀	758290 ₁₆₇₉₂	697088 ₇₇₈	1127904 ₁₂₈
8867	78 62 36 89	697 156 250 363	164749 ₅₃₁₀	775083 ₁₆₇₉₂	697866 ₇₇₈	1127777 ₁₂₇
8868	78 64 14 24	697 392 148 032	170059 ₅₃₁₀	791874 ₁₆₇₉₁	698644 ₇₇₈	1127650 ₁₂₇
8869	78 65 91 61	697 628 098 909	175368 ₅₃₀₉	808663 ₁₆₇₈₉	699422 ₇₇₈	1127523 ₁₂₇
8870	78 67 69 00	697 864 103 000	180677	825452	700200	1127396
8871	78 69 46 41	698 100 160 311	185986 ₅₃₀₉	842240 ₁₆₇₈₈	700978 ₇₇₈	1127269 ₁₂₇
8872	78 71 23 84	698 336 270 848	191295 ₅₃₀₉	859027 ₁₆₇₈₇	701756 ₇₇₈	1127142 ₁₂₇
8873	78 73 01 29	698 572 434 617	196603 ₅₃₀₈	875813 ₁₆₇₈₆	702533 ₇₇₇	1127015 ₁₂₇
8874	78 74 78 76	698 808 651 624	201911 ₅₃₀₈	892598 ₁₆₇₈₅	703311 ₇₇₈	1126888 ₁₂₇
8875	78 76 56 25	699 044 921 875	207218	909382	704089	1126761
8876	78 78 33 76	699 281 245 376	212526 ₅₃₀₈	926165 ₁₆₇₈₃	704866 ₇₇₇	1126634 ₁₂₇
8877	78 80 11 29	699 517 622 133	217833 ₅₃₀₇	942948 ₁₆₇₈₃	705644 ₇₇₈	1126507 ₁₂₇
8878	78 81 88 84	699 754 052 152	223139 ₅₃₀₆	959729 ₁₆₇₈₁	706421 ₇₇₇	1126380 ₁₂₇
8879	78 83 66 41	699 990 535 439	228446 ₅₃₀₇	976509 ₁₆₇₈₀	707199 ₇₇₈	1126253 ₁₂₇
8880	78 85 44 00	700 227 072 000	233752	993289	707976	1126126
8881	78 87 21 61	700 463 661 841	239058 ₅₃₀₆	*010067 ₁₆₇₇₈	708753 ₇₇₇	1125999 ₁₂₇
8882	78 88 99 24	700 700 304 968	244363 ₅₃₀₅	026844 ₁₆₇₇₇	709531 ₇₇₈	1125873 ₁₂₆
8883	78 90 76 89	700 937 001 387	249668 ₅₃₀₅	043621 ₁₆₇₇₇	710308 ₇₇₇	1125746 ₁₂₇
8884	78 92 54 56	701 173 751 104	254973 ₅₃₀₅	060397 ₁₆₇₇₆	711085 ₇₇₇	1125619 ₁₂₇
8885	78 94 32 25	701 410 554 125	260278	077171	711862	1125492
8886	78 96 09 96	701 647 410 456	265582 ₅₃₀₄	093945 ₁₆₇₇₄	712639 ₇₇₇	1125366 ₁₂₆
8887	78 97 87 69	701 884 320 103	270886 ₅₃₀₄	110718 ₁₆₇₇₃	713416 ₇₇₇	1125239 ₁₂₇
8888	78 99 65 44	702 121 283 072	276190 ₅₃₀₄	127490 ₁₆₇₇₂	714193 ₇₇₇	1125113 ₁₂₆
8889	79 01 43 21	702 358 299 369	281493 ₅₃₀₃	144260 ₁₆₇₇₀	714970 ₇₇₇	1124986 ₁₂₇
8890	79 03 21 00	702 595 369 000	286797	161030	715746	1124859
8891	79 04 98 81	702 832 491 971	292099 ₅₃₀₂	177799 ₁₆₇₆₉	716523 ₇₇₇	1124733 ₁₂₆
8892	79 06 76 64	703 069 668 288	297402 ₅₃₀₃	194567 ₁₆₇₆₈	717300 ₇₇₇	1124606 ₁₂₇
8893	79 08 54 49	703 306 897 957	302704 ₅₃₀₂	211334 ₁₆₇₆₇	718076 ₇₇₆	1124480 ₁₂₆
8894	79 10 32 36	703 544 180 984	308006 ₅₃₀₂	228101 ₁₆₇₆₅	718853 ₇₇₇	1124353 ₁₂₆
8895	79 12 10 25	703 781 517 375	313308	244866	719629	1124227
8896	79 13 88 16	704 018 907 136	318609 ₅₃₀₁	261630 ₁₆₇₆₄	720406 ₇₇₇	1124101 ₁₂₆
8897	79 15 66 09	704 256 350 273	323910 ₅₃₀₁	278393 ₁₆₇₆₃	721182 ₇₇₆	1123974 ₁₂₇
8898	79 17 44 04	704 493 846 792	329211 ₅₃₀₁	295156 ₁₆₇₆₃	721959 ₇₇₆	1123848 ₁₂₆
8899	79 19 22 01	704 731 396 699	334511 ₅₃₀₀	311917 ₁₆₇₆₁	722735 ₇₇₆	1123722 ₁₂₆
8900	79 21 00 00	704 969 000 000	339811	328678	723511	1123596
			94·	298·	20·	0·000

No. n	Square n²	Cube n³	Square root √n	Sq. rt. of 10n √10n	Cube root ∛n	Reciprocal 1/n
			94·	**298·**	**20·**	**0·000**
8900	79 21 00 00	704 969 000 000	339811	328678	723511	1123596
8901	79 22 78 01	705 206 656 701	345111 5300	345437 16759	724287 776	1123469 127
8902	79 24 56 04	705 444 366 808	350411 5300	362196 16759	725063 776	1123343 126
8903	79 26 34 09	705 682 130 327	355710 5299	378954 16758	725839 776	1123217 126
8904	79 28 12 16	705 919 947 264	361009 5299	395710 16756	726615 776	1123091 126
			5299	16756		126
8905	79 29 90 25	706 157 817 625	366308 5298	412466 16755	727391 776	1122965 126
8906	79 31 68 36	706 395 741 416	371606 5298	429221 16754	728167 776	1122839 127
8907	79 33 46 49	706 633 718 643	376904 5298	445975 16753	728943 776	1122712 126
8908	79 35 24 64	706 871 749 312	382202 5297	462728 16752	729718 775	1122586 126
8909	79 37 02 81	707 109 833 429	387499 5297	479480 16751	730494 776	1122460 126
			5297	16751	776	126
8910	79 38 81 00	707 347 971 000	392796 5297	496231 16750	731270 775	1122334 125
8911	79 40 59 21	707 586 162 031	398093 5297	512981 16750	732045 776	1122209 126
8912	79 42 37 44	707 824 406 528	403390 5296	529731 16748	732821 775	1122083 126
8913	79 44 15 69	708 062 704 497	408686 5296	546479 16747	733596 776	1121957 126
8914	79 45 93 96	708 301 055 944	413982 5296	563226 16747	734372 775	1121831 126
			5296	16747		126
8915	79 47 72 25	708 539 460 875	419278 5295	579973 16745	735147 775	1121705 126
8916	79 49 50 56	708 777 919 296	424573 5295	596718 16745	735922 775	1121579 126
8917	79 51 28 89	709 016 431 213	429868 5295	613463 16743	736697 775	1121453 125
8918	79 53 07 24	709 254 996 632	435163 5294	630206 16743	737472 776	1121328 126
8919	79 54 85 61	709 493 615 559	440457 5295	646949 16741	738248 775	1121202 126
8920	79 56 64 00	709 732 288 000	445752 5294	663690 16741	739023 775	1121076 125
8921	79 58 42 41	709 971 013 961	451046 5294	680431 16740	739798 775	1120951 126
8922	79 60 20 84	710 209 793 448	456339 5293	697171 16739	740572 774	1120825 126
8923	79 61 99 29	710 448 626 467	461632 5293	713910 16738	741347 775	1120699 125
8924	79 63 77 76	710 687 513 024	466925 5293	730648 16737	742122 775	1120574 126
8925	79 65 56 25	710 926 453 125	472218 5293	747385 16736	742897 775	1120448 125
8926	79 67 34 76	711 165 446 776	477511 5292	764121 16735	743672 774	1120323 126
8927	79 69 13 29	711 404 493 983	482803 5291	780856 16734	744446 775	1120197 125
8928	79 70 91 84	711 643 594 752	488094 5291	797590 16734	745221 774	1120072 125
8929	79 72 70 41	711 882 749 089	493386 5291	814324 16732	745995 775	1119946 126
8930	79 74 49 00	712 121 957 000	498677 5291	831056 16731	746770 774	1119821 126
8931	79 76 27 61	712 361 218 491	503968 5291	847787 16731	747544 774	1119695 126
8932	79 78 06 24	712 600 533 568	509259 5290	864518 16729	748318 775	1119570 125
8933	79 79 84 89	712 839 902 237	514549 5290	881247 16729	749093 774	1119445 126
8934	79 81 63 56	713 079 324 504	519839 5290	897976 16728	749867 774	1119319 125
8935	79 83 42 25	713 318 800 375	525129 5289	914704 16726	750641 774	1119194 125
8936	79 85 20 96	713 558 329 856	530418 5290	931430 16726	751415 774	1119069 125
8937	79 86 99 69	713 797 912 953	535708 5288	948156 16725	752189 774	1118944 126
8938	79 88 78 44	714 037 549 672	540996 5289	964881 16724	752963 774	1118819 126
8939	79 90 57 21	714 277 240 019	546285 5288	981605 16723	753737 774	1118693 125
8940	79 92 36 00	714 516 984 000	551573 5288	*998328 16722	754511 774	1118568 125
8941	79 94 14 81	714 756 781 621	556861 5288	015050 16721	755285 774	1118443 125
8942	79 95 93 64	714 996 632 888	562149 5287	031771 16720	756059 773	1118318 125
8943	79 97 72 49	715 236 537 807	567436 5287	048491 16719	756832 774	1118193 125
8944	79 99 51 36	715 476 496 384	572723 5287	065210 16719	757606 774	1118068 125
8945	80 01 30 25	715 716 508 625	578010 5287	081929 16717	758380 773	1117943 125
8946	80 03 09 16	715 956 574 536	583297 5286	098646 16716	759153 774	1117818 125
8947	80 04 88 09	716 196 694 123	588583 5286	115362 16716	759927 773	1117693 125
8948	80 06 67 04	716 436 867 392	593869 5286	132078 16714	760700 773	1117568 125
8949	80 08 46 01	716 677 094 349	599154 5285	148792 16714	761473 774	1117443 125
8950	80 10 25 00	716 917 375 000	604440	165506	762247	1117318
			94·	**299·**	**20·**	**0·000**

No. n	Square n²	Cube n³	Square root √n	Sq. rt. of 10n √10n	Cube root ∛n	Reciprocal 1/n
			94·	299·	20·	0·000
8950	80 10 25 00	716 917 375 000	604440 ₅₂₈₅	165506 ₁₆₇₁₃	762247 ₇₇₃	1117318 ₁₂₄
8951	80 12 04 01	717 157 709 351	609725 ₅₂₈₄	182219 ₁₆₇₁₁	763020 ₇₇₃	1117194 ₁₂₄
8952	80 13 83 04	717 398 097 408	615009 ₅₂₈₅	198930 ₁₆₇₁₁	763793 ₇₇₃	1117069 ₁₂₅
8953	80 15 62 09	717 638 539 177	620294 ₅₂₈₄	215641 ₁₆₇₁₀	764566 ₇₇₃	1116944 ₁₂₅
8954	80 17 41 16	717 879 034 664	625578 ₅₂₈₄	232351 ₁₆₇₀₉	765339 ₇₇₃	1116819 ₁₂₄
8955	80 19 20 25	718 119 583 875	630862 ₅₂₈₃	249060 ₁₆₇₀₈	766112 ₇₇₃	1116695 ₁₂₅
8956	80 20 99 36	718 360 186 816	636145 ₅₂₈₄	265768 ₁₆₇₀₇	766885 ₇₇₃	1116570 ₁₂₅
8957	80 22 78 49	718 600 843 493	641429 ₅₂₈₃	282475 ₁₆₇₀₆	767658 ₇₇₃	1116445 ₁₂₄
8958	80 24 57 64	718 841 553 912	646712 ₅₂₈₂	299181 ₁₆₇₀₆	768431 ₇₇₃	1116321 ₁₂₅
8959	80 26 36 81	719 082 318 079	651994 ₅₂₈₃	315887 ₁₆₇₀₄	769204 ₇₇₂	1116196 ₁₂₅
8960	80 28 16 00	719 323 136 000	657277 ₅₂₈₂	332591 ₁₆₇₀₃	769976 ₇₇₃	1116071 ₁₂₄
8961	80 29 95 21	719 564 007 681	662559 ₅₂₈₁	349294 ₁₆₇₀₃	770749 ₇₇₃	1115947 ₁₂₅
8962	80 31 74 44	719 804 933 128	667840 ₅₂₈₂	365997 ₁₆₇₀₁	771522 ₇₇₂	1115822 ₁₂₅
8963	80 33 53 69	720 045 912 347	673122 ₅₂₈₁	382698 ₁₆₇₀₁	772294 ₇₇₃	1115698 ₁₂₄
8964	80 35 32 96	720 286 945 344	678403 ₅₂₈₁	399399 ₁₆₆₉₉	773067 ₇₇₂	1115573 ₁₂₄
8965	80 37 12 25	720 528 032 125	683684· ₅₂₈₁	416098 ₁₆₆₉₉	773839 ₇₇₃	1115449 ₁₂₄
8966	80 38 91 56	720 769 172 696	688965 ₅₂₈₀	432797 ₁₆₆₉₈	774612 ₇₇₂	1115325 ₁₂₄
8967	80 40 70 89	721 010 367 063	694245 ₅₂₈₀	449495 ₁₆₆₉₇	775384 ₇₇₂	1115200 ₁₂₅
8968	80 42 50 24	721 251 615 232	699525 ₅₂₈₀	466192 ₁₆₆₉₆	776156 ₇₇₂	1115076 ₁₂₄
8969	80 44 29 61	721 492 917 209	704805 ₅₂₇₉	482888 ₁₆₆₉₅	776928 ₇₇₂	1114951 ₁₂₄
8970	80 46 09 00	721 734 273 000	710084 ₅₂₇₉	499583 ₁₆₆₉₄	777700 ₇₇₃	1114827 ₁₂₄
8971	80 47 88 41	721 975 682 611	715363 ₅₂₇₉	516277 ₁₆₆₉₃	778473 ₇₇₂	1114703 ₁₂₄
8972	80 49 67 84	722 217 146 048	720642 ₅₂₇₈	532970 ₁₆₆₉₂	779245 ₇₇₂	1114579 ₁₂₄
8973	80 51 47 29	722 458 663 317	725920 ₅₂₇₉	549662 ₁₆₆₉₁	780017 ₇₇₁	1114454 ₁₂₅
8974	80 53 26 76	722 700 234 424	731199 ₅₂₇₈	566353 ₁₆₆₉₁	780788 ₇₇₂	1114330 ₁₂₄
8975	80 55 06 25	722 941 859 375	736477 ₅₂₇₇	583044 ₁₆₆₈₉	781560 ₇₇₂	1114206 ₁₂₄
8976	80 56 85 76	723 183 538 176	741754 ₅₂₇₈	599733 ₁₆₆₈₈	782332 ₇₇₂	1114082 ₁₂₄
8977	80 58 65 29	723 425 270 833	747032 ₅₂₇₇	616421 ₁₆₆₈₈	783104 ₇₇₂	1113958 ₁₂₄
8978	80 60 44 84	723 667 057 352	752309 ₅₂₇₆	633109 ₁₆₆₈₇	783876 ₇₇₂	1113834 ₁₂₄
8979	80 62 24 41	723 908 897 739	757585 ₅₂₇₇	649796 ₁₆₆₈₅	784647 ₇₇₁	1113710 ₁₂₄
8980	80 64 04 00	724 150 792 000	762862 ₅₂₇₆	666481 ₁₆₆₈₅	785419 ₇₇₁	1113586 ₁₂₄
8981	80 65 83 61	724 392 740 141	768138 ₅₂₇₆	683166 ₁₆₆₈₄	786190 ₇₇₁	1113462 ₁₂₄
8982	80 67 63 24	724 634 742 168	773414 ₅₂₇₆	699850 ₁₆₆₈₃	786962 ₇₇₁	1113338 ₁₂₄
8983	80 69 42 89	724 876 798 087	778690 ₅₂₇₅	716533 ₁₆₆₈₂	787733 ₇₇₁	1113214 ₁₂₄
8984	80 71 22 56	725 118 907 904	783965 ₅₂₇₅	733215 ₁₆₆₈₁	788504 ₇₇₂	1113090 ₁₂₄
8985	80 73 02 25	725 361 071 625	789240 ₅₂₇₅	749896 ₁₆₆₈₀	789276 ₇₇₁	1112966 ₁₂₄
8986	80 74 81 96	725 603 289 256	794515 ₅₂₇₄	766576 ₁₆₆₇₉	790047 ₇₇₁	1112842 ₁₂₄
8987	80 76 61 69	725 845 560 803	799789 ₅₂₇₄	783255 ₁₆₆₇₈	790818 ₇₇₁	1112718 ₁₂₃
8988	80 78 41 44	726 087 886 272	805063 ₅₂₇₄	799933 ₁₆₆₇₈	791589 ₇₇₁	1112595 ₁₂₄
8989	80 80 21 21	726 330 265 669	810337 ₅₂₇₄	816611 ₁₆₆₇₆	792360 ₇₇₁	1112471 ₁₂₄
8990	80 82 01 00	726 572 699 000	815611 ₅₂₇₃	833287 ₁₆₆₇₅	793131 ₇₇₁	1112347 ₁₂₄
8991	80 83 80 81	726 815 186 271	820884 ₅₂₇₃	849962 ₁₆₆₇₅	793902 ₇₇₁	1112223 ₁₂₃
8992	80 85 60 64	727 057 727 488	826157 ₅₂₇₂	866637 ₁₆₆₇₄	794673 ₇₇₁	1112100 ₁₂₄
8993	80 87 40 49	727 300 322 657	831429 ₅₂₇₂	883311 ₁₆₆₇₂	795444 ₇₇₁	1111976 ₁₂₄
8994	80 89 20 36	727 542 971 784	836702 ₅₂₇₂	899983 ₁₆₆₇₂	796215 ₇₇₁	1111852 ₁₂₃
8995	80 91 00 25	727 785 674 875	841974 ₅₂₇₂	916655 ₁₆₆₇₁	796986 ₇₇₀	1111729 ₁₂₄
8996	80 92 80 16	728 028 431 936	847246 ₅₂₇₁	933326 ₁₆₆₇₀	797756 ₇₇₁	1111605 ₁₂₄
8997	80 94 60 09	728 271 242 973	852517 ₅₂₇₁	949996 ₁₆₆₆₉	798527 ₇₇₀	1111482 ₁₂₃
8998	80 96 40 04	728 514 107 992	857788 ₅₂₇₁	966665 ₁₆₆₆₈	799297 ₇₇₁	1111358 ₁₂₃
8999	80 98 20 01	728 757 026 999	863059 ₅₂₇₁	983333 ₁₆₆₆₇	800068 ₇₇₀	1111235 ₁₂₄
9000	81 00 00 00	729 000 000 000	868330	*000000	800838	1111111
			94·	300·	20·	0·000

No. n	Square n^2	Cube n^3	Square root $\sqrt{n}$	Sq. rt. of 10n $\sqrt{10n}$	Cube root $\sqrt[3]{n}$	Reciprocal $\dfrac{1}{n}$
			94·	300·	20·	0·000
9000	81 00 00 00	729 000 000 000	868330	000000	800838	1111111
9001	81 01 80 01	729 243 027 001	873600 5270	016666 16666	801609 771	1110088 123
9002	81 03 60 04	729 486 108 008	878870 5270	033331 16665	802379 770	1110864 124
9003	81 05 40 09	729 729 243 027	884140 5270	049996 16665	803149 770	1110741 123
9004	81 07 20 16	729 972 432 064	889409 5269	066659 16663	803919 770	1110618 123
			5269	16663	771	124
9005	81 09 00 25	730 215 675 125	894678 5269	083322 16661	804690 770	1110494 123
9006	81 10 80 36	730 458 972 216	899947 5269	099983 16661	805460 770	1110371 123
9007	81 12 60 49	730 702 323 343	905216 5268	116644 16660	806230 770	1110248 124
9008	81 14 40 64	730 945 728 512	910484 5268	133304 16659	807000 770	1110124 123
9009	81 16 20 81	731 189 187 729	915752 5268	149963 16657	807770 769	1110001 123
9010	81 18 01 00	731 432 701 000	921020 5267	166620 16657	808539 770	1109878 123
9011	81 19 81 21	731 676 268 331	926287 5267	183277 16656	809309 770	1109755 123
9012	81 21 61 44	731 919 889 728	931554 5267	199933 16655	810079 770	1109632 124
9013	81 23 41 69	732 163 565 197	936821 5267	216588 16655	810849 769	1109508 123
9014	81 25 21 96	732 407 294 744	942088 5266	233243 16653	811618 770	1109385 123
9015	81 27 02 25	732 651 078 375	947354 5266	249896 16652	812388 769	1109262 123
9016	81 28 82 56	732 894 916 096	952620 5265	266548 16652	813157 770	1109139 123
9017	81 30 62 89	733 138 807 913	957885 5266	283200 16650	813927 769	1109016 123
9018	81 32 43 24	733 382 753 832	963151 5265	299850 16650	814696 770	1108893 123
9019	81 34 23 61	733 626 753 859	968416 5265	316500 16648	815466 769	1108770 123
9020	81 36 04 00	733 870 808 000	973681 5264	333148 16648	816235 769	1108647 122
9021	81 37 84 41	734 114 916 261	978945 5264	349796 16647	817004 769	1108525 123
9022	81 39 64 84	734 359 078 648	984209 5264	366443 16646	817773 769	1108402 122
9023	81 41 45 29	734 603 295 167	989473 5264	383089 16645	818542 769	1108279 123
9024	81 43 25 76	734 847 565 824	994737 5263	399734 16644	819311 769	1108156 123
9025	81 45 06 25	735 091 890 625	*000000 5263	416378 16643	820080 769	1108033 123
9026	81 46 86 76	735 336 269 576	005263 5263	433021 16642	820849 769	1107910 123
9027	81 48 67 29	735 580 702 683	010526 5262	449663 16641	821618 769	1107788 123
9028	81 50 47 84	735 825 189 952	015788 5262	466304 16641	822387 769	1107665 123
9029	81 52 28 41	736 069 731 389	021050 5262	482945 16639	823156 769	1107542 122
9030	81 54 09 00	736 314 327 000	026312 5262	499584 16639	823925 768	1107420 123
9031	81 55 89 61	736 558 976 791	031574 5261	516223 16637	824693 769	1107297 123
9032	81 57 70 24	736 803 680 768	036835 5261	532860 16637	825462 768	1107174 122
9033	81 59 50 89	737 048 438 937	042096 5261	549497 16635	826230 769	1107052 122
9034	81 61 31 56	737 293 251 304	047357 5260	566132 16635	826999 768	1106929 122
9035	81 63 12 25	737 538 117 875	052617 5260	582767 16634	827767 769	1106807 123
9036	81 64 92 96	737 783 038 656	057877 5260	599401 16633	828536 768	1106684 122
9037	81 66 73 69	738 028 013 653	063137 5259	616034 16632	829304 768	1106562 123
9038	81 68 54 44	738 273 042 872	068396 5260	632666 16631	830072 769	1106439 122
9039	81 70 35 21	738 518 126 319	073656 5259	649297 16631	830841 768	1106317 122
9040	81 72 16 00	738 763 264 000	078915 5258	665928 16629	831609 768	1106195 123
9041	81 73 96 81	739 008 455 921	084173 5259	682557 16628	832377 768	1106072 122
9042	81 75 77 64	739 253 702 088	089432 5258	699185 16628	833145 768	1105950 122
9043	81 77 58 49	739 499 002 507	094690 5257	715813 16626	833913 768	1105828 122
9044	81 79 39 36	739 744 357 184	099947 5258	732439 16626	834681 768	1105705 123
9045	81 81 20 25	739 989 766 125	105205 5257	749065 16625	835449 767	1105583 122
9046	81 83 01 16	740 235 229 336	110462 5257	765690 16625	836216 768	1105461 122
9047	81 84 82 09	740 480 746 823	115719 5257	782313 16623	836984 768	1105339 122
9048	81 86 63 04	740 726 318 592	120976 5256	798936 16622	837752 768	1105217 123
9049	81 88 44 01	740 971 944 649	126232 5256	815558 16621	838520 767	1105094 122
9050	81 90 25 00	741 217 625 000	131488	832179	839287	1104972
			95·	300·	20·	0·000

No. n	Square n²	Cube n³	Square root √n	Sq. rt. of 10n √10n	Cube root ∛n	Reciprocal 1/n
			95·	300·	20·	0·000
9050	81 90 25 00	741 217 625 000	131488 5256	832179 16620	839287 768	1104972 122
9051	81 92 06 01	741 463 359 651	136744 5255	848799 16619	840055 767	1104850 122
9052	81 93 87 04	741 709 148 608	141999 5255	865418 16619	840822 768	1104728 122
9053	81 95 68 09	741 954 991 877	147254 5255	882037 16617	841590 767	1104606 122
9054	81 97 49 16	742 200 889 464	152509 5255	898654 16616	842357 767	1104484 122
9055	81 99 30 25	742 446 841 375	157764 5254	915270 16616	843124 768	1104362 122
9056	82 01 11 36	742 692 847 616	163018 5254	931886 16615	843892 767	1104240 122
9057	82 02 92 49	742 938 908 193	168272 5254	948501 16613	844659 767	1104118 122
9058	82 04 73 64	743 185 023 112	173526 5253	965114 16613	845426 767	1103996 121
9059	82 06 54 81	743 431 192 379	178779 5253	981727 16612	846193 767	1103875 122
9060	82 08 36 00	743 677 416 000	184032 5253	998339 16611	846960 767	1103753 122
9061	82 10 17 21	743 923 693 981	189285 5253	*014950 16610	847727 767	1103631 122
9062	82 11 98 44	744 170 026 328	194538 5252	031560 16609	848494 767	1103509 122
9063	82 13 79 69	744 416 413 047	199790 5252	048169 16608	849261 767	1103387 121
9064	82 15 60 96	744 662 854 144	205042 5252	064777 16607	850028 766	1103266 122
9065	82 17 42 25	744 909 349 625	210294 5251	081384 16607	850794 767	1103144 122
9066	82 19 23 56	745 155 899 496	215545 5251	097991 16605	851561 767	1103022 122
9067	82 21 04 89	745 402 503 763	220796 5251	114596 16605	852328 766	1102901 122
9068	82 22 86 24	745 649 162 432	226047 5250	131201 16603	853094 767	1102779 122
9069	82 24 67 61	745 895 875 509	231297 5251	147804 16603	853861 766	1102657 122
9070	82 26 49 00	746 142 643 000	236548 5250	164407 16602	854627 767	1102536 122
9071	82 28 30 41	746 389 464 911	241798 5250	181009 16601	855394 766	1102414 122
9072	82 30 11 84	746 636 341 248	247047 5250	197610 16599	856160 766	1102293 122
9073	82 31 93 29	746 883 272 017	252297 5249	214209 16600	856926 766	1102171 121
9074	82 33 74 76	747 130 257 224	257546 5248	230809 16598	857692 767	1102050 122
9075	82 35 56 25	747 377 296 875	262794 5249	247407 16597	858459 766	1101928 121
9076	82 37 37 76	747 624 390 976	268043 5248	264004 16596	859225 766	1101807 121
9077	82 39 19 29	747 871 539 533	273291 5248	280600 16595	859991 766	1101686 121
9078	82 41 00 84	748 118 742 552	278539 5248	297195 16595	860757 766	1101564 121
9079	82 42 82 41	748 366 000 039	283787 5247	313790 16593	861523 766	1101443 121
9080	82 44 64 00	748 613 312 000	289034 5247	330383 16593	862289 765	1101322 122
9081	82 46 45 61	748 860 678 441	294281 5247	346976 16592	863054 766	1101200 121
9082	82 48 27 24	749 108 099 368	299528 5246	363568 16591	863820 766	1101079 121
9083	82 50 08 89	749 355 574 787	304774 5246	380159 16589	864586 766	1100958 121
9084	82 51 90 56	749 603 104 704	310020 5246	396748 16589	865352 765	1100837 122
9085	82 53 72 25	749 850 689 125	315266 5246	413337 16589	866117 766	1100715 121
9086	82 55 53 96	750 098 328 056	320512 5245	429926 16587	866883 765	1100594 121
9087	82 57 35 69	750 346 021 503	325757 5245	446513 16586	867648 766	1100473 121
9088	82 59 17 44	750 593 769 472	331002 5245	463099 16585	868414 765	1100352 121
9089	82 60 99 21	750 841 571 969	336247 5244	479684 16585	869179 765	1100231 121
9090	82 62 81 00	751 089 429 000	341491 5245	496269 16583	869945 765	1100110 121
9091	82 64 62 81	751 337 340 571	346736 5244	512852 16583	870710 765	1099989 121
9092	82 66 44 64	751 585 306 688	351980 5243	529435 16581	871475 765	1099868 121
9093	82 68 26 49	751 833 327 357	357223 5243	546016 16581	872240 765	1099747 121
9094	82 70 08 36	752 081 402 584	362466 5243	562597 16580	873005 765	1099626 121
9095	82 71 90 25	752 329 532 375	367709 5243	579177 16579	873770 765	1099505 121
9096	82 73 72 16	752 577 716 736	372952 5243	595756 16578	874535 765	1099384 121
9097	82 75 54 09	752 825 955 673	378195 5242	612334 16577	875300 765	1099263 120
9098	82 77 36 04	753 074 249 192	383437 5242	628911 16576	876065 765	1099143 121
9099	82 79 18 01	753 322 597 299	388679 5241	645487 16576	876830 765	1099022 121
9100	82 81 00 00	753 571 000 000	393920 95·	662063 301·	877595 20·	1098901 0·000

No. n	Square n²	Cube n³	Square root √n	Sq. rt. of 10n √10n	Cube root ∛n	Reciprocal 1/n
			95·	301·	20·	0·000
9100	82 81 00 00	753 571 000 000	393920	662063	877595	1098901
9101	82 82 82 01	753 819 457 301	399161 5241	678637 16574	878360 765	1098780 121
9102	82 84 64 04	754 067 969 208	404402 5241	695210 16573	879124 764	1098660 120
9103	82 86 46 09	754 316 535 727	409643 5241	711783 16573	879889 765	1098539 121
9104	82 88 28 16	754 565 156 864	414884 5241	728355 16572	880653 764	1098418 121
			5240	16570	765	120
9105	82 90 10 25	754 813 832 625	420124 5240	744925 16570	881418 764	1098298 121
9106	82 91 92 36	755 062 563 016	425364 5239	761495 16569	882182 765	1098177 121
9107	82 93 74 49	755 311 348 043	430603 5239	778064 16568	882947 764	1098056 120
9108	82 95 56 64	755 560 187 712	435842 5239	794632 16567	883711 764	1097936 120
9109	82 97 38 81	755 809 082 029	441081 5239	811199 16566	884475 764	1097815 120
9110	82 99 21 00	756 058 031 000	446320 5238	827765 16566	885239 765	1097695 121
9111	83 01 03 21	756 307 034 631	451558 5239	844331 16564	886004 764	1097574 121
9112	83 02 85 44	756 556 092 928	456797 5237	860895 16564	886768 764	1097454 121
9113	83 04 67 69	756 805 205 897	462034 5238	877459 16562	887532 764	1097333 120
9114	83 06 49 96	757 054 373 544	467272 5237	894021 16562	888296 764	1097213 120
9115	83 08 32 25	757 303 595 875	472509 5237	910583 16561	889060 764	1097093 121
9116	83 10 14 56	757 552 872 896	477746 5237	927144 16559	889824 763	1096972 120
9117	83 11 96 89	757 802 204 613	482983 5236	943703 16559	890587 764	1096852 120
9118	83 13 79 24	758 051 591 032	488219 5236	960262 16558	891351 764	1096732 120
9119	83 15 61 61	758 301 032 159	493455 5236	976820 16557	892115 764	1096611 120
9120	83 17 44 00	758 550 528 000	498691 5236	*993377 16557	892879 763	1096491 120
9121	83 19 26 41	758 800 078 561	503927 5235	009934 16555	893642 764	1096371 120
9122	83 21 08 84	759 049 683 848	509162 5235	026489 16554	894406 763	1096251 120
9123	83 22 91 29	759 299 343 867	514397 5234	043043 16554	895169 764	1096131 120
9124	83 24 73 76	759 549 058 624	519631 5235	059597 16552	895933 763	1096011 121
9125	83 26 56 25	759 798 828 125	524866 5234	076149 16552	896696 763	1095890 120
9126	83 28 38 76	760 048 652 376	530100 5234	092701 16551	897459 764	1095770 120
9127	83 30 21 29	760 298 531 383	535334 5233	109252 16550	898223 763	1095650 120
9128	83 32 03 84	760 548 465 152	540567 5234	125802 16549	898986 763	1095530 120
9129	83 33 86 41	760 798 453 689	545801 5232	142351 16548	899749 763	1095410 120
9130	83 35 69 00	761 048 497 000	551033 5233	158899 16547	900512 763	1095290 120
9131	83 37 51 61	761 298 595 091	556266 5233	175446 16546	901275 763	1095170 120
9132	83 39 34 24	761 548 747 968	561499 5232	191992 16545	902038 763	1095050 120
9133	83 41 16 89	761 798 955 637	566731 5231	208537 16545	902801 763	1094930 119
9134	83 42 99 56	762 049 218 104	571962 5232	225082 16543	903564 763	1094811 120
9135	83 44 82 25	762 299 535 375	577194 5231	241625 16543	904327 762	1094691 120
9136	83 46 64 96	762 549 907 456	582425 5231	258168 16541	905089 763	1094571 120
9137	83 48 47 69	762 800 334 353	587656 5231	274709 16541	905852 763	1094451 120
9138	83 50 30 44	763 050 816 072	592887 5230	291250 16540	906615 762	1094331 119
9139	83 52 13 21	763 301 352 619	598117 5230	307790 16539	907377 763	1094212 120
9140	83 53 96 00	763 551 944 000	603347 5230	324329 16538	908140 762	1094092 120
9141	83 55 78 81	763 802 590 221	608577 5230	340867 16537	908902 763	1093972 119
9142	83 57 61 64	764 053 291 288	613807 5229	357404 16537	909665 762	1093853 120
9143	83 59 44 49	764 304 047 207	619036 5229	373941 16535	910427 763	1093733 120
9144	83 61 27 36	764 554 857 984	624265 5228	390476 16535	911190 762	1093613 119
9145	83 63 10 25	764 805 723 625	629493 5229	407011 16533	911952 762	1093494 120
9146	83 64 93 16	765 056 644 136	634722 5228	423544 16533	912714 762	1093374 119
9147	83 66 76 09	765 307 619 523	639950 5228	440077 16531	913476 762	1093255 120
9148	83 68 59 04	765 558 649 792	645178 5227	456608 16531	914238 762	1093135 119
9149	83 70 42 01	765 809 734 949	650405 5227	473139 16530	915000 762	1093016 120
9150	83 72 25 00	766 060 875 000	655632	489669	915762	1092896
			95·	302·	20·	0·000

No. n	Square n²	Cube n³	Square root √n	Sq. rt. of 10n √10n	Cube root ∛n	Reciprocal 1/n
			95·	302·	20·	0·000
9150	83 72 25 00	766 060 875 000	655632 5227	489669 16529	915762 762	1092896 119
9151	83 74 08 01	766 312 069 951	660859 5227	506198 16528	916524 762	1092777 120
9152	83 75 91 04	766 563 319 808	666086 5226	522726 16528	917286 762	1092657 119
9153	83 77 74 09	766 814 624 577	671312 5226	539254 16526	918048 762	1092538 119
9154	83 79 57 16	767 065 984 264	676538 5226	555780 16525	918810 761	1092419 120
9155	83 81 40 25	767 317 398 875	681764 5226	572305 16525	919571 762	1092299 119
9156	83 83 23 36	767 568 868 416	686990 5225	588830 16524	920333 762	1092180 119
9157	83 85 06 49	767 820 392 893	692215 5225	605354 16522	921095 761	1092061 120
9158	83 86 89 64	768 071 972 312	697440 5225	621876 16522	921856 762	1091941 119
9159	83 88 72 81	768 323 606 679	702665 5224	638398 16521	922618 761	1091822 119
9160	83 90 56 00	768 575 296 000	707889 5224	654919 16520	923379 762	1091703 119
9161	83 92 39 21	768 827 040 281	713113 5224	671439 16519	924141 761	1091584 119
9162	83 94 22 44	769 078 839 528	718337 5223	687958 16518	924902 761	1091465 119
9163	83 96 05 69	769 330 693 747	723560 5224	704476 16518	925663 761	1091346 119
9164	83 97 88 96	769 582 602 944	728784 5222	720994 16516	926424 761	1091227 120
9165	83 99 72 25	769 834 567 125	734006 5223	737510 16516	927185 762	1091107 119
9166	84 01 55 56	770 086 586 296	739229 5223	754026 16514	927947 761	1090988 119
9167	84 03 38 89	770 338 660 463	744452 5222	770540 16514	928708 761	1090869 119
9168	84 05 22 24	770 590 789 632	749674 5221	787054 16513	929469 761	1090750 119
9169	84 07 05 61	770 842 973 809	754895 5222	803567 16512	930230 760	1090631 118
9170	84 08 89 00	771 095 213 000	760117 5221	820079 16511	930990 761	1090513 119
9171	84 10·72 41	771 347 507 211	765338 5221	836590 16510	931751 761	1090394 119
9172	84 12 55 84	771 599 856 448	770559 5221	853100 16509	932512 761	1090275 119
9173	84 14 39 29	771 852 260 717	775780 5220	869609 16508	933273 760	1090156 119
9174	84 16 22 76	772 104 720 024	781000 5220	886117 16508	934033 761	1090037 119
9175	84 18 06 25	772 357 234 375	786220 5220	902625 16506	934794 761	1089918 119
9176	84 19 89 76	772 609 803 776	791440 5220	919131 16506	935555 760	1089799 118
9177	84 21 73 29	772 862 428 233	796660 5219	935637 16504	936315 760	1089681 119
9178	84 23 56 84	773 115 107 752	801879 5219	952141 16504	937075 761	1089562 119
9179	84 25 40 41	773 367 842 339	807098 5219	968645 16503	937836 760	1089443 118
9180	84 27 24 00	773 620 632 000	812317 5218	*985148 16502	938596 760	1089325 119
9181	84 29 07 61	773 873 476 741	817535 5218	*001650 16501	939356 761	1089206 119
9182	84 30 91 24	774 126 376 568	822753 5218	018151 16500	940117 760	1089087 118
9183	84 32 74 89	774 379 331 487	827971 5217	034651 16500	940877 760	1088969 119
9184	84 34 58 56	774 632 341 504	833188 5218	051151 16498	941637 760	1088850 118
9185	84 36 42 25	774 885 406 625	838406 5217	.067649 16498	942397 760	1088732 119
9186	84 38 25 96	775 138 526 856	843623 5216	084147 16496	943157 760	1088613 118
9187	84 40 09 69	775 391 702 203	848839 5217	100643 16496	943917 760	1088495 119
9188	84 41 93 44	775 644 932 672	854056 5216	117139 16495	944677 760	1088376 118
9189	84 43 77 21	775 898 218 269	859272 5216	133634 16494	945437 759	1088258 119
9190	84 45 61 00	776 151 559 000	864488 5215	150128 16493	946196 760	1088139 118
9191	84 47 44 81	776 404 954 871	869703 5216	166621 16492	946956 760	1088021 118
9192	84 49 28 64	776 658 405 888	874919 5215	183113 16491	947716 759	1087903 119
9193	84 51 12 49	776 911 912 057	880134 5214	199604 16491	948475 760	1087784 118
9194	84 52 96 36	777 165 473 384	885348 5215	216095 16489	949235 759	1087666 118
9195	84 54 80 25	777 419 089 875	890563 5214	232584 16489	949994 760	1087548 119
9196	84 56 64 16	777 672 761 536	895777 5214	249073 16487	950754 759	1087429 118
9197	84 58 48 09	777 926 488 373	900991 5213	265560 16487	951513 760	1087311 118
9198	84 60 32 04	778 180 270 392	906204 5213	282047 16486	952273 759	1087193 118
9199	84 62 16 01	778 434 107 599	911417 5213	298533 16485	953032 759	1087075 118
9200	84 64 00 00	778 688 000 000	916630 95·	315018 303·	953791 20·	1086957 0·000

No. n	Square n^2	Cube n^3	Square root $\sqrt{n}$	Sq. rt. of 10n $\sqrt{10n}$	Cube root $\sqrt[3]{n}$	Reciprocal $\frac{1}{n}$
			95·	303·	20·	0·000
9200	84 64 00 00	778 688 000 000	916630	315018 16484	953791	1086957
9201	84 65 84 01	778 941 947 601	921843 5213	331502 16483	954550 759	1086838 119
9202	84 67 68 04	779 195 950 408	927056 5213	347985 16482	955309 759	1086720 118
9203	84 69 52 09	779 450 008 427	932268 5212	364467 16482	956068 759	1086602 118
9204	84 71 36 16	779 704 121 664	937480 5212 / 5211	380949 16480	956827 759 / 759	1086484 118 / 118
9205	84 73 20 25	779 958 290 125	942691 5212	397429 16480	957586 759	1086366
9206	84 75 04 36	780 212 513 816	947903 5211	413909 16478	958345 759	1086248 118
9207	84 76 88 49	780 466 792 743	953114 5210	430387 16478	959104 759	1086130 118
9208	84 78 72 64	780 721 126 912	958324 5211	446865 16477	959863 759	1086012 118
9209	84 80 56 81	780 975 516 329	963535 5210	463342 16476	960622 759 / 758	1085894 118 / 118
9210	84 82 41 00	781 229 961 000	968745 5210	479818 16475	961380	1085776
9211	84 84 25 21	781 484 460 931	973955 5209	496293 16474	962139 759	1085658 118
9212	84 86 09 44	781 739 016 128	979164 5210	512767 16474	962897 758	1085541 117
9213	84 87 93 69	781 993 626 597	984374 5209	529241 16472	963656 759	1085423 118
9214	84 89 77 96	782 248 292 344	989583 5209	545713 16472	964414 758 / 759	1085305 118 / 118
9215	84 91 62 25	782 503 013 375	*994792 5208	562185 16470	965173 758	1085187
9216	84 93 46 56	782 757 789 696	*000000 5208	578655 16470	965931 758	1085069 118
9217	84 95 30 89	783 012 621 313	005208 5208	595125 16469	966689 759	1084952 117
9218	84 97 15 24	783 267 508 232	010416 5208	611594 16468	967448 758	1084834 118
9219	84 98 99 61	783 522 450 459	015624 5207	628062 16467	968206 758 / 758	1084716 118 / 117
9220	85 00 84 00	783 777 448 000	020831 5207	644529 16466	968964 758	1084599
9221	85 02 68 41	784 032 500 861	026038 5207	660995 16465	969722 758	1084481 118
9222	85 04 52 84	784 287 609 048	031245 5206	677460 16465	970480 758	1084363 118
9223	85 06 37 29	784 542 772 567	036451 5207	693925 16463	971238 758	1084246 117
9224	85 08 21 76	784 797 991 424	041658 5206	710388 16463	971996 758	1084128 118 / 117
9225	85 10 06 25	785 053 265 625	046864 5205	726851 16462	972754 758	1084011
9226	85 11 90 76	785 308 595 176	052069 5206	743313 16461	973512 758	1083893 118
9227	85 13 75 29	785 563 980 083	057275 5205	759774 16459	974269 757	1083776 117
9228	85 15 59 84	785 819 420 352	062480 5204	776233 16459	975027 758	1083658 118
9229	85 17 44 41	786 074 915 989	067684 5205	792692 16459	975785 758 / 757	1083541 117 / 117
9230	85 19 29 00	786 330 467 000	072889 5204	809151 16457	976542 758	1083424
9231	85 21 13 61	786 586 073 391	078093 5204	825608 16456	977300 758	1083306 118
9232	85 22 98 24	786 841 735 168	083297 5204	842064 16456	978057 757	1083189 117
9233	85 24 82 89	787 097 452 337	088501 5203	858520 16454	978815 758	1083072 117
9234	85 26 67 56	787 353 224 904	093704 5203	874974 16454	979572 757	1082954 118 / 117
9235	85 28 52 25	787 609 052 875	098907 5203	891428 16453	980329 758	1082837
9236	85 30 36 96	787 864 936 256	104110 5203	907881 16452	981087 757	1082720 117
9237	85 32 21 69	788 120 875 053	109313 5202	924333 16451	981844 757	1082603 117
9238	85 34 06 44	788 376 869 272	114515 5202	940784 16450	982601 757	1082485 118
9239	85 35 91 21	788 632 918 919	119717 5202	957234 16449	983358 757 / 757	1082368 117 / 117
9240	85 37 76 00	788 889 024 000	124919 5201	973683 16448	984115 757	1082251
9241	85 39 60 81	789 145 184 521	130120 5201	990131 16448	984872 757	1082134 117
9242	85 41 45 64	789 401 400 488	135321 5201	*006579 16446	985629 757	1082017 117
9243	85 43 30 49	789 657 671 907	140522 5201	023025 16446	986386 757	1081900 117
9244	85 45 15 36	789 913 998 784	145723 5200	039471 16445	987143 756	1081783 117
9245	85 47 00 25	790 170 381 125	150923 5200	055916 16444	987899 757	1081666
9246	85 48 85 16	790 426 818 936	156123 5200	072360 16443	988656 757	1081549 117
9247	85 50 70 09	790 683 312 223	161323 5199	088803 16442	989413 757	1081432 117
9248	85 52 55 04	790 939 860 992	166522 5199	105245 16442	990169 756	1081315 117
9249	85 54 40 01	791 196 465 249	171721 5199 / 5199	121686 16441	990926 757 / 756	1081198 117 / 117
9250	85 56 25 00	791 453 125 000	176920	138127	991682	1081081
			96·	304·	20·	0·000

No. n	Square n²	Cube n³	Square root √n	Sq. rt. of 10n √10n	Cube root ∛n	Reciprocal 1/n
			96·	304·	20·	0·000
9250	85 56 25 00	791 453 125 000	176920	138127	991682	1081081
9251	85 58 10 01	791 709 840 251	182119 ^{5199}	154566 ^{16439}	992439 ^{757}	1080964 ^{117}
9252	85 59 95 04	791 966 611 008	187317 ^{5198}	171005 ^{16439}	993195 ^{756}	1080847 ^{117}
9253	85 61 80 09	792 223 437 277	192515 ^{5198}	187442 ^{16437}	993951 ^{757}	1080731 ^{117}
9254	85 63 65 16	792 480 319 064	197713 ^{5198}	203879 ^{16437}	994708 ^{756}	1080614 ^{117}
9255	85 65 50 25	792 737 256 375	202911 ^{5197}	220315 ^{16436}	995464 ^{756}	1080497 ^{117}
9256	85 67 35 36	792 994 249 216	208108 ^{5197}	236750 ^{16435}	996220 ^{756}	1080380 ^{117}
9257	85 69 20 49	793 251 297 593	213305 ^{5196}	253184 ^{16434}	996976 ^{756}	1080264 ^{116}
9258	85 71 05 64	793 508 401 512	218501 ^{5197}	269617 ^{16433}	997732 ^{756}	1080147 ^{117}
9259	85 72 90 81	793 765 560 979	223698 ^{5196}	286050 ^{16433}	998488 ^{756}	1080030 ^{117}
9260	85 74 76 00	794 022 776 000	228894 ^{5196}	302481 ^{16431}	*999244 ^{756}	1079914 ^{116}
9261	85 76 61 21	794 280 046 581	234090 ^{5196}	318912 ^{16431}	*000000 ^{756}	1079797 ^{117}
9262	85 78 46 44	794 537 372 728	239285 ^{5195}	335341 ^{16429}	000756 ^{756}	1079680 ^{117}
9263	85 80 31 69	794 794 754 447	244480 ^{5195}	351770 ^{16429}	001512 ^{755}	1079564 ^{117}
9264	85 82 16 96	795 052 191 744	249675 ^{5195}	368198 ^{16428}	002267 ^{756}	1079447 ^{116}
9265	85 84 02 25	795 309 684 625	254870 ^{5195}	384625 ^{16427}	003023 ^{756}	1079331 ^{117}
9266	85 85 87 56	795 567 233 096	260064 ^{5194}	401051 ^{16426}	003779 ^{756}	1079214 ^{117}
9267	85 87 72 89	795 824 837 163	265259 ^{5195}	417477 ^{16426}	004534 ^{755}	1079098 ^{116}
9268	85 89 58 24	796 082 496 832	270452 ^{5193}	433901 ^{16424}	005290 ^{756}	1078981 ^{117}
9269	85 91 43 61	796 340 212 109	275646 ^{5194}	450324 ^{16423}	006045 ^{755}	1078865 ^{116}
9270	85 93 29 00	796 597 983 000	280839 ^{5193}	466747 ^{16423}	006801 ^{755}	1078749 ^{116}
9271	85 95 14 41	796 855 809 511	286032 ^{5193}	483169 ^{16422}	007556 ^{755}	1078632 ^{117}
9272	85 96 99 84	797 113 691 648	291225 ^{5193}	499589 ^{16420}	008311 ^{755}	1078516 ^{116}
9273	85 98 85 29	797 371 629 417	296417 ^{5192}	516009 ^{16420}	009066 ^{756}	1078400 ^{116}
9274	86 00 70 76	797 629 622 824	301610 ^{5193}	532428 ^{16419}	009822 ^{755}	1078283 ^{117}
9275	86 02 56 25	797 887 671 875	306801 ^{5191}	548847 ^{16419}	010577 ^{755}	1078167 ^{116}
9276	86 04 41 76	798 145 776 576	311993 ^{5192}	565264 ^{16417}	011332 ^{755}	1078051 ^{116}
9277	86 06 27 29	798 403 936 933	317184 ^{5191}	581680 ^{16416}	012087 ^{755}	1077935 ^{116}
9278	86 08 12 84	798 662 152 952	322375 ^{5191}	598096 ^{16416}	012842 ^{755}	1077818 ^{117}
9279	86 09 98 41	798 920 424 639	327566 ^{5191}	614510 ^{16414}	013597 ^{755}	1077702 ^{116}
9280	86 11 84 00	799 178 752 000	332757 ^{5190}	630924 ^{16414}	014351 ^{755}	1077586 ^{116}
9281	86 13 69 61	799 437 135 041	337947 ^{5190}	647337 ^{16413}	015106 ^{755}	1077470 ^{116}
9282	86 15 55 24	799 695 573 768	343137 ^{5190}	663749 ^{16412}	015861 ^{755}	1077354 ^{116}
9283	86 17 40 89	799 954 068 187	348326 ^{5190}	680160 ^{16411}	016616 ^{755}	1077238 ^{116}
9284	86 19 26 56	800 212 618 304	353516 ^{5189}	696570 ^{16410}	017370 ^{755}	1077122 ^{116}
9285	86 21 12 25	800 471 224 125	358705 ^{5189}	712980 ^{16410}	018125 ^{754}	1077006 ^{116}
9286	86 22 97 96	800 729 885 656	363894 ^{5188}	729388 ^{16408}	018879 ^{755}	1076890 ^{116}
9287	86 24 83 69	800 988 602 903	369082 ^{5188}	745796 ^{16408}	019634 ^{754}	1076774 ^{116}
9288	86 26 69 44	801 247 375 872	374270 ^{5188}	762202 ^{16406}	020388 ^{754}	1076658 ^{116}
9289	86 28 55 21	801 506 204 569	379458 ^{5188}	778608 ^{16406}	021143 ^{755}	1076542 ^{116}
9290	86 30 41 00	801 765 089 000	384646 ^{5187}	795013 ^{16405}	021897 ^{754}	1076426 ^{116}
9291	86 32 26 81	802 024 029 171	389833 ^{5188}	811417 ^{16404}	022651 ^{754}	1076310 ^{116}
9292	86 34 12 64	802 283 025 088	395021 ^{5186}	827820 ^{16403}	023405 ^{754}	1076195 ^{115}
9293	86 35 98 49	802 542 076 757	400207 ^{5187}	844223 ^{16403}	024160 ^{755}	1076079 ^{116}
9294	86 37 84 36	802 801 184 184	405394 ^{5186}	860624 ^{16401}	024914 ^{754}	1075963 ^{116}
9295	86 39 70 25	803 060 347 375	410580 ^{5186}	877024 ^{16400}	025668 ^{754}	1075847 ^{116}
9296	86 41 56 16	803 319 566 336	415766 ^{5186}	893424 ^{16399}	026422 ^{754}	1075731 ^{115}
9297	86 43 42 09	803 578 841 073	420952 ^{5186}	909823 ^{16398}	027176 ^{754}	1075616 ^{116}
9298	86 45 28 04	803 838 171 592	426138 ^{5185}	926221 ^{16397}	027930 ^{753}	1075500 ^{116}
9299	86 47 14 01	804 097 557 899	431323 ^{5185}	942618 ^{16396}	028683 ^{754}	1075384 ^{115}
9300	86 49 00 00	804 357 000 000	436508	959014	029437	1075269
			96·	304·	21·	0·000

No. n	Square n²	Cube n³	Square root √n	Sq. rt. of 10n √10n	Cube root ∛n	Reciprocal 1/n
			96·	304·	21·	0·000
9300	86 49 00 00	804 357 000 000	436508 5184	959014 16395	029437 754	1075269 116
9301	86 50 86 01	804 616 497 901	441692 5185	975409 16394	030191 754	1075153 116
9302	86 52 72 04	804 876 051 608	446877 5184	991803 16394	030945 754	1075038 115
9303	86 54 58 09	805 135 661 127	452061 5183	*008197 16392	031698 753	1074922 115
9304	86 56 44 16	805 395 326 464	457244 5184	024589 16392	032452 754	1074807 116
			5184		753	
9305	86 58 30 25	805 655 047 625	462428 5183	040981 16391	033205 754	1074691 115
9306	86 60 16 36	805 914 824 616	467611 5183	057372 16390	033959 753	1074576 115
9307	86 62 02 49	806 174 657 443	472794 5183	073762 16389	034712 753	1074460 116
9308	86 63 88 64	806 434 546 112	477977 5182	090151 16388	035465 754	1074345 115
9309	86 65 74 81	806 694 490 629	483159 5182	106539 16387	036219 753	1074229 116
9310	86 67 61 00	806 954 491 000	488341 5182	122926 16386	036972 753	1074114 116
9311	86 69 47 21	807 214 547 231	493523 5182	139312 16386	037725 753	1073998 115
9312	86 71 33 44	807 474 659 328	498705 5181	155698 16385	038478 753	1073883 115
9313	86 73 19 69	807 734 827 297	503886 5181	172083 16383	039231 753	1073768 115
9314	86 75 05 96	807 995 051 144	509067 5181	188466 16383	039984 753	1073653 116
9315	86 76 92 25	808 255 330 875	514248 5180	204849 16382	040737 753	1073537 115
9316	86 78 78 56	808 515 666 496	519428 5180	221231 16381	041490 753	1073422 115
9317	86 80 64 89	808 776 058 013	524608 5180	237612 16381	042243 753	1073307 115
9318	86 82 51 24	809 036 505 432	529788 5180	253993 16379	042996 753	1073192 115
9319	86 84 37 61	809 297 008 759	534968 5179	270372 16378	043749 752	1073077 116
9320	86 86 24 00	809 557 568 000	540147 5179	286750 16378	044501 753	1072961 115
9321	86 88 10 41	809 818 183 161	545326 5179	303128 16377	045254 752	1072846 115
9322	86 89 96 84	810 078 854 248	550505 5178	319505 16376	046006 753	1072731 115
9323	86 91 83 29	810 339 581 267	555683 5179	335881 16375	046759 752	1072616 115
9324	86 93 69 76	810 600 364 224	560862 5178	352256 16374	047511 753	1072501 115
9325	86 95 56 25	810 861 203 125	566040 5177	368630 16373	048264 752	1072386 115
9326	86 97 42 76	811 122 097 976	571217 5178	385003 16372	049016 753	1072271 115
9327	86 99 29 29	811 383 048 783	576395 5177	401375 16372	049769 752	1072156 115
9328	87 01 15 84	811 644 055 552	581572 5177	417747 16370	050521 752	1072041 115
9329	87 03 02 41	811 905 118 289	586749 5176	434117 16370	051273 752	1071926 115
9330	87 04 89 00	812 166 237 000	591925 5176	450487 16369	052025 752	1071811 115
9331	87 06 75 61	812 427 411 691	597101 5176	466856 16368	052777 752	1071696 115
9332	87 08 62 24	812 688 642 368	602277 5176	483224 16367	053529 752	1071582 114
9333	87 10 48 89	812 949 929 037	607453 5176	499591 16366	054281 752	1071467 115
9334	87 12 35 56	813 211 271 704	612629 5175	515957 16365	055033 752	1071352 115
9335	87 14 22 25	813 472 670 375	617804 5175	532322 16365	055785 752	1071237 114
9336	87 16 08 96	813 734 125 056	622979 5174	548687 16363	056537 752	1071123 115
9337	87 17 95 69	813 995 635 753	628153 5175	565050 16363	057289 752	1071008 115
9338	87 19 82 44	814 257 202 472	633328 5174	581413 16362	058040 751	1070893 115
9339	87 21 69 21	814 518 825 219	638502 5173	597775 16361	058792 752	1070778 114
9340	87 23 56 00	814 780 504 000	643675 5174	614136 16360	059544 751	1070664 115
9341	87 25 42 81	815 042 238 821	648849 5173	630496 16359	060295 752	1070549 114
9342	87 27 29 64	815 304 029 688	654022 5173	646855 16358	061047 751	1070435 115
9343	87 29 16 49	815 565 876 607	659195 5173	663213 16358	061798 752	1070320 115
9344	87 31 03 36	815 827 779 584	664368 5172	679571 16356	062550 751	1070205 114
9345	87 32 90 25	816 089 738 625	669540 5172	695927 16356	063301 751	1070091 115
9346	87 34 77 16	816 351 753 736	674712 5172	712283 16355	064052 752	1069976 114
9347	87 36 64 09	816 613 824 923	679884 5172	728638 16354	064804 751	1069862 114
9348	87 38 51 04	816 875 952 192	685056 5171	744992 16353	065555 751	1069748 115
9349	87 40 38 01	817 138 135 549	690227 5171	761345 16352	066306 751	1069633 114
9350	87 42 25 00	817 400 375 000	695398	777697	067057	1069519
			96·	305·	21·	0·000

No. n	Square n^2	Cube n^3	Square root $\sqrt{n}$	Sq. rt. of $10n$ $\sqrt{10n}$	Cube root $\sqrt[3]{n}$	Reciprocal $\dfrac{1}{n}$
			96·	305·	21·	0·000
9350	87 42 25 00	817 400 375 000	695398 5171	777697 16351	067057 751	1069519 115
9351	87 44 12 01	817 662 670 551	700569 5170	794048 16351	067808 751	1069404 114
9352	87 45 99 04	817 925 022 208	705739 5170	810399 16349	068559 751	1069290 114
9353	87 47 86 09	818 187 429 977	710909 5170	826748 16349	069310 751	1069176 115
9354	87 49 73 16	818 449 893 864	716079 5170	843097 16348	070061 751	1069061 114
9355	87 51 60 25	818 712 413 875	721249 5169	859445 16347	070812 750	1068947 114
9356	87 53 47 36	818 974 990 016	726418 5169	875792 16346	071562 751	1068833 114
9357	87 55 34 49	819 237 622 293	731587 5169	892138 16345	072313 751	1068719 115
9358	87 57 21 64	819 500 310 712	736756 5169	908483 16344	073064 750	1068604 114
9359	87 59 08 81	819 763 055 279	741925 5168	924827 16344	073814 751	1068490 114
9360	87 60 96 00	820 025 856 000	747093 5168	941171 16342	074565 750	1068376 114
9361	87 62 83 21	820 288 712 881	752261 5168	957513 16342	075315 751	1068262 114
9362	87 64 70 44	820 551 625 928	757429 5167	973855 16341	076066 750	1068148 114
9363	87 66 57 69	820 814 595 147	762596 5167	990196 16340	076816 751	1068034 114
9364	87 68 44 96	821 077 620 544	767763 5167	*006536 16339	077567 750	1067920 114
9365	87 70 32 25	821 340 702 125	772930 5167	022875 16338	078317 750	1067806 114
9366	87 72 19 56	821 603 839 896	778097 5166	039213 16338	079067 750	1067692 114
9367	87 74 06 89	821 867 033 863	783263 5166	055551 16336	079817 750	1067578 114
9368	87 75 94 24	822 130 284 032	788429 5166	071887 16336	080567 750	1067464 114
9369	87 77 81 61	822 393 590 409	793595 5165	088223 16334	081317 750	1067350 114
9370	87 79 69 00	822 656 953 000	798760 5166	104557 16334	082067 750	1067236 114
9371	87 81 56 41	822 920 371 811	803926 5164	120891 16333	082817 750	1067122 114
9372	87 83 43 84	823 183 846 848	809090 5165	137224 16332	083567 750	1067008 114
9373	87 85 31 29	823 447 378 117	814255 5165	153556 16331	084317 750	1066894 114
9374	87 87 18 76	823 710 965 624	819420 5164	169887 16331	085067 750	1066780 113
9375	87 89 06 25	823 974 609 375	824584 5163	186218 16329	085817 749	1066667 114
9376	87 90 93 76	824 238 309 376	829747 5164	202547 16329	086566 750	1066553 114
9377	87 92 81 29	824 502 065 633	834911 5163	218876 16328	087316 750	1066439 114
9378	87 94 68 84	824 765 878 152	840074 5163	235204 16327	088066 749	1066325 113
9379	87 96 56 41	825 029 746 939	845237 5163	251531 16326	088815 750	1066212 114
9380	87 98 44 00	825 293 672 000	850400 5163	267857 16325	089565 749	1066098 114
9381	88 00 31 61	825 557 653 341	855563 5162	284182 16324	090314 749	1065984 113
9382	88 02 19 24	825 821 690 968	860725 5162	300506 16323	091063 750	1065871 114
9383	88 04 06 89	826 085 784 887	865887 5161	316829 16323	091813 749	1065757 113
9384	88 05 94 56	826 349 935 104	871048 5162	333152 16322	092562 749	1065644 114
9385	88 07 82 25	826 614 141 625	876210 5161	349474 16320	093311 749	1065530 113
9386	88 09 69 96	826 878 404 456	881371 5161	365794 16320	094060 749	1065417 114
9387	88 11 57 69	827 142 723 603	886532 5160	382114 16319	094809 749	1065303 113
9388	88 13 45 44	827 407 099 072	891692 5160	398433 16319	095558 749	1065190 114
9389	88 15 33 21	827 671 530 869	896852 5160	414752 16317	096307 749	1065076 113
9390	88 17 21 00	827 936 019 000	902012 5160	431069 16316	097056 749	1064963 114
9391	88 19 08 81	828 200 563 471	907172 5160	447385 16316	097805 749	1064849 113
9392	88 20 96 64	828 465 164 288	912332 5159	463701 16315	098554 749	1064736 113
9393	88 22 84 49	828 729 821 457	917491 5159	480016 16314	099303 749	1064623 114
9394	88 24 72 36	828 994 534 984	922650 5158	496330 16312	100052 748	1064509 113
9395	88 26 60 25	829 259 304 875	927808 5159	512642 16313	100800 749	1064396 113
9396	88 28 48 16	829 524 131 136	932967 5158	528955 16311	101549 749	1064283 114
9397	88 30 36 09	829 789 013 773	938125 5157	545266 16310	102298 748	1064169 113
9398	88 32 24 04	830 053 952 792	943282 5158	561576 16310	103046 749	1064056 113
9399	88 34 12 01	830 318 948 199	948440 5157	577886 16308	103795 748	1063943 113
9400	88 36 00 00	830 584 000 000	953597 96·	594194 306·	104543 21·	1063830 0·000

No. n	Square n^2	Cube n^3	Square root $\sqrt{n}$	Sq. rt. of 10n $\sqrt{10n}$	Cube root $\sqrt[3]{n}$	Reciprocal $\frac{1}{n}$
			96·	306·	21·	0·000
9400	88 36 00 00.	830 584 000 000	953597 5157	594194 16308	104543 748	1063830 113
9401	88 37 88 01	830 849 108 201	958754 5157	610502 16307	105291 749	1063717 114
9402	88 39 76 04	831 114 272 808	963911 5156	626809 16307 16306	106040 748	1063603 113
9403	88 41 64 09	831 379 493 827	969067 5156	643115 16305	106788 748	1063490 113
9404	88 43 52 16	831 644 771 264	974223 5156	659420 16305	107536 748	1063377 113
9405	88 45 40 25	831 910 105 125	979379 5156	675725 16303	108284 748	1063264 113
9406	88 47 28 36	832 175 495 416	984535 5155	692028 16303	109032 748	1063151 113
9407	88 49 16 49	832 440 942 143	989690 5155	708331 16301	109780 748	1063038 113
9408	88 51 04 64	832 706 445 312	994845 5155	724632 16301	110528 748	1062925 113
9409	88 52 92 81	832 972 004 929	*000000 5155	740933 16300	111276 748	1062812 113
9410	88 54 81 00	833 237 621 000	005155 5154	757233 16299	112024 748	1062699 113
9411	88 56 69 21	833 503 293 531	010309 5154	773532 16298	112772 748	1062586 113
9412	88 58 57 44	833 769 022 528	015463 5154	789830 16298	113520 748	1062473 112
9413	88 60 45 69	834 034 807 997	020616 5153	806128 16296	114268 747	1062361 113
9414	88 62 33 96	834 300 649 944	025770 5154 5153	822424 16296	115015 748	1062248 113
9415	88 64 22 25	834 566 548 375	030923 5153	838720 16295	115763 747	1062135 113
9416	88 66 10 56	834 832 503 296	036076 5152	855015 16294	116510 748	1062022 113
9417	88 67 98 89	835 098 514 713	041228 5153	871309 16294 16293	117258 747	1061909 112
9418	88 69 87 24	835 364 582 632	046381 5153	887602 16293	118005 748	1061797 113
9419	88 71 75 61	835 630 707 059	051533 5151	903894 16292	118753 747	1061684 113
9420	88 73 64 00	835 896 888 000	056684 5152	920185 16291	119500 747	1061571 113
9421	88 75 52 41	836 163 125 461	061836 5152	936476 16291	120247 748	1061458 112
9422	88 77 40 84	836 429 419 448	066987 5151	952765 16289	120995 747	1061346 112
9423	88 79 29 29	836 695 769 967	072138 5151	969054 16289 16288	121742 747	1061233 112
9424	88 81 17 76	836 962 177 024	077289 5150	985342 16287	122489 747	1061121 113
9425	88 83 06 25	837 228 640 625	082439 5150	*001629 16286	123236 747	1061008 113
9426	88 84 94 76	837 495 160 776	087589 5150	017915 16285	123983 747	1060895 112
9427	88 86 83 29	837 761 737 483	092739 5150	034200 16284	124730 747	1060783 113
9428	88 88 71 84	838 028 370 752	097889 5149	050484 16284	125477 747	1060670 112
9429	88 90 60 41	838 295 060 589	103038 5149	066768 16283	126224 747	1060558 113
9430	88 92 49 00	838 561 807 000	108187 5149	083051 16281	126971 747	1060445 112
9431	88 94 37 61	838 828 609 991	113336 5149	099332 16281	127718 746	1060333 112
9432	88 96 26 24	839 095 469 568	118484 5148	115613 16280	128464 747	1060221 113
9433	88 98 14 89	839 362 385 737	123633 5147	131893 16280	129211 747	1060108 112
9434	89 00 03 56	839 629 358 504	128780 5148	148173 16278	129958 746	1059996 113
9435	89 01 92 25	839 896 387 875	133928 5148	164451 16278	130704 747	1059883 112
9436	89 03 80 96	840 163 473 856	139076 5147	180729 16276	131451 746	1059771 112
9437	89 05 69 69	840 430 616 453	144223 5147	197005 16276	132197 746	1059659 112
9438	89 07 58 44	840 697 815 672	149370 5146	213281 16275	132943 747	1059547 113
9439	89 09 47 21	840 965 071 519	154516 5146	229556 16274	133690 746	1059434 112
9440	89 11 36 00	841 232 384 000	159662 5146	245830 16273	134436 746	1059322 112
9441	89 13 24 81	841 499 753 121	164808 5146	262103 16272	135182 747	1059210 112
9442	89 15 13 64	841 767 178 888	169954 5146	278375 16272	135929 746	1059098 113
9443	89 17 02 49	842 034 661 307	175100 5145	294647 16270	136675 746	1058985 112
9444	89 18 91 36	842 302 200 384	180245 5145	310917 16270	137421 746	1058873 112
9445	89 20 80 25	842 569 796 125	185390 5145	327187 16269	138167 746	1058761 112
9446	89 22 69 16	842 837 448 536	190535 5144	343456 16268	138913 746	1058649 112
9447	89 24 58 09	843 105 157 623	195679 5144	359724 16267	139659 746	1058537 112
9448	89 26 47 04	843 372 923 392	200823 5144	375991 16267	140405 745	1058425 112
9449	89 28 36 01	843 640 745 849	205967 5143	392258 16265	141150 745	1058313 112
9450	89 30 25 00	843 908 625 000	211110	408523	141896	1058201
			97·	307·	21·	0·000

No. n	Square n²	Cube n³	Square root √n	Sq. rt. of 10n √10n	Cube root ∛n	Reciprocal 1/n
			97·	307·	21·	0·000
9450	89 30 25 00	843 908 625 000	211110 [5144]	408523 [16265]	141896 [746]	1058201 [112]
9451	89 32 14 01	844 176 560 851	216254 [5144]	424788 [16263]	142642 [746]	1058089 [112]
9452	89 34 03 04	844 444 553 408	221397 [5143]	441051 [16263]	143388 [745]	1057977 [112]
9453	89 35 92 09	844 712 602 677	226540 [5143]	457314 [16262]	144133 [746]	1057865 [112]
9454	89 37 81 16	844 980 708 664	231682 [5142]	473576 [16261]	144879 [745]	1057753 [112]
9455	89 39 70 25	845 248 871 375	236824 [5142]	489837 [16261]	145624 [746]	1057641 [111]
9456	89 41 59 36	845 517 090 816	241966 [5142]	506098 [16259]	146370 [746]	1057530 [112]
9457	89 43 48 49	845 785 366 993	247108 [5141]	522357 [16258]	147115 [745]	1057418 [112]
9458	89 45 37 64	846 053 699 912	252249 [5141]	538615 [16258]	147860 [746]	1057306 [112]
9459	89 47 26 81	846 322 089 579	257390 [5141]	554873 [16257]	148606 [745]	1057194 [112]
9460	89 49 16 00	846 590 536 000	262531 [5141]	571130 [16256]	149351 [745]	1057082 [111]
9461	89 51 05 21	846 859 039 181	267672 [5140]	587386 [16255]	150096 [745]	1056971 [111]
9462	89 52 94 44	847 127 599 128	272812 [5140]	603641 [16254]	150841 [745]	1056859 [112]
9463	89 54 83 69	847 396 215 847	277952 [5140]	619895 [16254]	151586 [745]	1056747 [112]
9464	89 56 72 96	847 664 889 344	283092 [5140]	636149 [16252]	152331 [745]	1056636 [112]
9465	89 58 62 25	847 933 619 625	288232 [5139]	652401 [16252]	153076 [745]	1056524 [112]
9466	89 60 51 56	848 202 406 696	293371 [5139]	668653 [16251]	153821 [745]	1056412 [111]
9467	89 62 40 89	848 471 250 563	298510 [5138]	684904 [16250]	154566 [745]	1056301 [112]
9468	89 64 30 24	848 740 151 232	303648 [5139]	701154 [16249]	155311 [745]	1056189 [111]
9469	89 66 19 61	849 009 108 709	308787 [5138]	717403 [16248]	156056 [745]	1056078 [112]
9470	89 68 09 00	849 278 123 000	313925 [5138]	733651 [16247]	156801 [744]	1055966 [111]
9471	89 69 98 41	849 547 194 111	319063 [5138]	749898 [16247]	157545 [745]	1055855 [111]
9472	89 71 87 84	849 816 322 048	324200 [5137]	766145 [16246]	158290 [744]	1055743 [111]
9473	89 73 77 29	850 085 506 817	329338 [5138]	782391 [16244]	159034 [744]	1055632 [112]
9474	89 75 66 76	850 354 748 424	334475 [5137]	798635 [16244]	159779 [744]	1055520 [111]
9475	89 77 56 25	850 624 046 875	339612 [5136]	814879 [16244]	160523 [745]	1055409 [111]
9476	89 79 45 76	850 893 402 176	344748 [5136]	831123 [16242]	161268 [745]	1055298 [111]
9477	89 81 35 29	851 162 814 333	349884 [5136]	847365 [16241]	162012 [744]	1055186 [112]
9478	89 83 24 84	851 432 283 352	355020 [5136]	863606 [16241]	162756 [745]	1055075 [111]
9479	89 85 14 41	851 701 809 239	360156 [5136]	879847 [16239]	163501 [744]	1054964 [112]
9480	89 87 04 00	851 971 392 000	365292 [5135]	896086 [16239]	164245 [744]	1054852 [111]
9481	89 88 93 61	852 241 031 641	370427 [5135]	912325 [16238]	164989 [744]	1054741 [111]
9482	89 90 83 24	852 510 728 168	375562 [5134]	928563 [16237]	165733 [744]	1054630 [111]
9483	89 92 72 89	852 780 481 587	380696 [5135]	944800 [16236]	166477 [744]	1054519 [111]
9484	89 94 62 56	853 050 291 904	385831 [5134]	961036 [16236]	167221 [744]	1054407 [111]
9485	89 96 52 25	853 320 159 125	390965 [5133]	977272 [16234]	167965 [744]	1054296 [111]
9486	89 98 41 96	853 590 083 256	396098 [5134]	*993506 [16234]	168709 [744]	1054185 [111]
9487	90 00 31 69	853 860 064 303	401232 [5134]	*009740 [16233]	169453 [744]	1054074 [111]
9488	90 02 21 44	854 130 102 272	406365 [5133]	025973 [16232]	170197 [743]	1053963 [111]
9489	90 04 11 21	854 400 197 169	411498 [5133]	042205 [16231]	170940 [744]	1053852 [111]
9490	90 06 01 00	854 670 349 000	416631 [5132]	058436 [16230]	171684 [744]	1053741 [111]
9491	90 07 90 81	854 940 557 771	421763 [5133]	074666 [16230]	172428 [743]	1053630 [111]
9492	90 09 80 64	855 210 823 488	426896 [5132]	090896 [16228]	173171 [744]	1053519 [111]
9493	90 11 70 49	855 481 146 157	432028 [5131]	107124 [16228]	173915 [743]	1053408 [111]
9494	90 13 60 36	855 751 525 784	437159 [5132]	123352 [16227]	174658 [744]	1053297 [111]
9495	90 15 50 25	856 021 962 375	442291 [5131]	139579 [16226]	175402 [743]	1053186 [111]
9496	90 17 40 16	856 292 455 936	447422 [5131]	155805 [16225]	176145 [743]	1053075 [111]
9497	90 19 30 09	856 563 006 473	452553 [5130]	172030 [16224]	176888 [744]	1052964 [111]
9498	90 21 20 04	856 833 613 992	457683 [5130]	188254 [16224]	177632 [743]	1052853 [111]
9499	90 23 10 01	857 104 278 499	462813 [5130]	204478 [16222]	178375 [743]	1052742 [110]
9500	90 25 00 00	857 375 000 000	467943	220700	179118	1052632
			97·	308·	21·	0·000

No. n	Square n^2	Cube n^3	Square root $\sqrt{n}$	Sq. rt. of 10n $\sqrt{10n}$	Cube root $\sqrt[3]{n}$	Reciprocal $\frac{1}{n}$
			97·	308·	21·	0·000
9500	90 25 00 00	857 375 000 000	467943 5130	220700 16222	179118 743	1052632
9501	90 26 90 01	857 645 778 501	473073 5130	236922 16222	179861 743	1052521 III
9502	90 28 80 04	857 916 614 008	478203 5129	253143 16221	180604 743	1052410 III
9503	90 30 70 09	858 187 506 527	483332 5129	269363 16220	181347 743	1052299 III
9504	90 32 60 16	858 458 456 064	488461 5129	285582 16219	182090 743	1052189 110
			5129	16218	743	III
9505	90 34 50 25	858 729 462 625	493590 5128	301800 16218	182833 743	1052078
9506	90 36 40 36	859 000 526 216	498718 5128	318018 16216	183576 743	1051967 110
9507	90 38 30 49	859 271 646 843	503846 5128	334234 16216	184319 742	1051857 III
9508	90 40 20 64	859 542 824 512	508974 5128	350450 16215	185061 743	1051746 III
9509	90 42 10 81	859 814 059 229	514102 5127	366665 16214	185804 743	1051635 III
9510	90 44 01 00	860 085 351 000	519229 5127	382879 16213	186547 742	1051525
9511	90 45 91 21	860 356 699 831	524356 5127	399092 16212	187289 743	1051414 III
9512	90 47 81 44	860 628 105 728	529483 5126	415304 16212	188032 742	1051304 110
9513	90 49 71 69	860 899 568 697	534609 5126	431516 16211	188774 743	1051193 110
9514	90 51 61 96	861 171 088 744	539735 5126	447727 16209	189517 742	1051083 III
9515	90 53 52 25	861 442 665 875	544861 5126	463936 16209	190259 742	1050972
9516	90 55 42 56	861 714 300 096	549987 5126	480145 16208	191001 743	1050862 110
9517	90 57 32 89	861 986 991 413	555113 5125	496353 16208	191744 742	1050751 III
9518	90 59 23 24	862 257 739 832	560238 5125	512561 16206	192486 742	1050641 110
9519	90 61 13 61	862 529 545 359	565363 5124	528767 16205	193228 742	1050531 110
9520	90 63 04 00	862 801 408 000	570487 5125	544972 16205	193970 742	1050420
9521	90 64 94 41	863 073 327 761	575612 5124	561177 16204	194712 742	1050310 110
9522	90 66 84 84	863 345 304 648	580736 5124	577381 16203	195454 742	1050200 110
9523	90 68 75 29	863 617 338 667	585860 5123	593584 16202	196196 742	1050089 III
9524	90 70 65 76	863 889 429 824	590983 5123	609786 16201	196938 742	1049979 110
9525	90 72 56 25	864 161 578 125	596106 5124	625987 16201	197680 742	1049869
9526	90 74 46 76	864 433 783 576	601230 5122	642188 16200	198422 741	1049759 110
9527	90 76 37 29	864 706 046 183	606352 5123	658387 16199	199163 742	1049648 III
9528	90 78 27 84	864 978 365 952	611475 5122	674586 16199	199905 742	1049538 110
9529	90 80 18 41	865 250 742 889	616597 5122	690784 16198	200647 741	1049428 110
			5122	16197	741	110
9530	90 82 09 00	865 523 177 000	621719 5122	706981 16196	201388 742	1049318
9531	90 83 99 61	865 795 668 291	626841 5122	723177 16196	202130 741	1049208 110
9532	90 85 90 24	866 068 216 768	631962 5121	739372 16195	202871 741	1049098 110
9533	90 87 80 89	866 340 822 437	637083 5121	755567 16193	203613 741	1048988 110
9534	90 89 71 56	866 613 485 304	642204 5121	771760 16193	204354 741	1048878 110
9535	90 91 62 25	866 886 205 375	647325 5120	787953 16192	205095 742	1048768
9536	90 93 52 96	867 158 982 656	652445 5120	804145 16191	205837 741	1048658 110
9537	90 95 43 69	867 431 817 153	657505 5120	820336 16190	206578 741	1048548 110
9538	90 97 34 44	867 704 708 872	662685 5119	836526 16190	207319 741	1048438 110
9539	90 99 25 21	867 977 657 819	667804 5120	852716 16188	208060 741	1048328 110
9540	91 01 16 00	868 250 664 000	672924 5119	868904 16188	208801 741	1048218
9541	91 03 06 81	868 523 727 421	678043 5118	885092 16187	209542 741	1048108 110
9542	91 04 97 64	868 796 848 088	683161 5119	901279 16186	210283 741	1047998 110
9543	91 06 88 49	869 070 026 007	688280 5118	917465 16185	211024 741	1047889 109
9544	91 08 79 36	869 343 261 184	693398 5118	933650 16184	211765 741	1047779 110
9545	91 10 70 25	869 616 553 625	698516 5118	949834 16184	212506 741	1047669
9546	91 12 61 16	869 889 903 336	703634 5117	966018 16182	213247 740	1047559 110
9547	91 14 52 09	870 163 310 323	708751 5117	982200 16182	213987 741	1047449 110
9548	91 16 43 04	870 436 774 592	713868 5117	*998382 16182	214728 741	1047340 109
9549	91 18 34 01	870 710 296 149	718985 5116	*014563 16181	215469 740	1047230 110
				16180		
9550	91 20 25 00	870 983 875 000	724101	030743	216209	1047120
			97·	309·	21·	0·000

No. n	Square n^2	Cube n^3	Square root $\sqrt{n}$	Sq. rt. of $10n$ $\sqrt{10n}$	Cube root $\sqrt[3]{n}$	Reciprocal $\dfrac{1}{n}$
			97·	309·	21·	0·000
9550	91 20 25 00	870 983 875 000	724101 5117	030743 16179	216209 741	1047120 109
9551	91 22 16 01	871 257 511 151	729218 5116	046922 16178	216950 741	1047011 109
9552	91 24 07 04	871 531 204 608	734334 5116	063100 16178	217690 741	1046901 109
9553	91 25 98 09	871 804 955 377	739450 5115	079278 16177	218431 740	1046792 110
9554	91 27 89 16	872 078 763 464	744565 5115	095455 16175	219171 740	1046682 110
9555	91 29 80 25	872 352 628 875	749680 5115	111630 16175	219911 741	1046572 109
9556	91 31 71 36	872 626 551 616	754795 5115	127805 16174	220652 740	1046463 110
9557	91 33 62 49	872 900 531 693	759910 5114	143979 16174	221392 740	1046353 109
9558	91 35 53 64	873 174 569 112	765024 5115	160153 16172	222132 740	1046244 109
9559	91 37 44 81	873 448 663 879	770139 5113	176325 16172	222872 740	1046135 110
9560	91 39 36 00	873 722 816 000	775252 5114	192497 16170	223612 740	1046025 109
9561	91 41 27 21	873 997 025 481	780366 5113	208667 16170	224352 740	1045916 110
9562	91 43 18 44	874 271 292 328	785479 5114	224837 16169	225092 740	1045806 109
9563	91 45 09 69	874 545 616 547	790593 5112	241006 16169	225832 740	1045697 109
9564	91 47 00 96	874 819 998 144	795705 5113	257175 16167	226572 739	1045588 110
9565	91 48 92 25	875 094 437 125	800818 5112	273342 16166	227311 740	1045478 109
9566	91 50 83 56	875 368 933 496	805930 5112	289508 16166	228051 740	1045369 109
9567	91 52 74 89	875 643 487 263	811042 5112	305674 16165	228791 739	1045260 109
9568	91 54 66 24	875 918 098 432	816154 5112	321839 16164	229530 740	1045151 110
9569	91 56 57 61	876 192 767 009	821266 5111	338003 16163	230270 740	1045041 109
9570	91 58 49 00	876 467 493 000	826377 5111	354166 16162	231010 739	1044932 109
9571	91 60 40 41	876 742 276 411	831488 5110	370328 16162	231749 739	1044823 109
9572	91 62 31 84	877 017 117 248	836598 5111	386490 16160	232488 740	1044714 109
9573	91 64 23 29	877 292 015 517	841709 5110	402650 16160	233228 739	1044605 109
9574	91 66 14 76	877 566 971 224	846819 5110	418810 16159	233967 739	1044496 110
9575	91 68 06 25	877 841 984 375	851929 5110	434969 16158	234706 740	1044386 109
9576	91 69 97 76	878 117 054 976	857039 5109	451127 16157	235446 739	1044277 109
9577	91 71 89 29	878 392 183 033	862148 5109	467284 16157	236185 739	1044168 109
9578	91 73 80 84	878 667 368 552	867257 5109	483441 16155	236924 739	1044059 109
9579	91 75 72 41	878 942 611 539	872366 5108	499596 16155	237663 739	1043950 109
9580	91 77 64 00	879 217 912 000	877474 5109	515751 16154	238402 739	1043841 109
9581	91 79 55 61	879 493 269 941	882583 5108	531905 16153	239141 739	1043732 109
9582	91 81 47 24	879 768 685 368	887691 5108	548058 16152	239880 739	1043623 108
9583	91 83 38 89	880 044 158 287	892799 5107	564210 16151	240619 739	1043515 109
9584	91 85 30 56	880 319 688 704	897906 5107	580361 16151	241358 738	1043406 109
9585	91 87 22 25	880 595 276 625	903013 5107	596512 16149	242096 739	1043297 109
9586	91 89 13 96	880 870 922 056	908120 5107	612661 16149	242835 739	1043188 109
9587	91 91 05 69	881 146 625 003	913227 5106	628810 16148	243574 738	1043079 109
9588	91 92 97 44	881 422 385 472	918333 5106	644958 16147	244312 739	1042970 108
9589	91 94 89 21	881 698 203 469	923439 5106	661105 16146	245051 738	1042862 109
9590	91 96 81 00	881 974 079 000	928545 5106	677251 16146	245789 739	1042753 109
9591	91 98 72 81	882 250 012 071	933651 5105	693397 16144	246528 738	1042644 109
9592	92 00 64 64	882 526 002 688	938756 5105	709541 16144	247266 738	1042535 108
9593	92 02 56 49	882 802 050 857	943861 5105	725685 16143	248004 739	1042427 109
9594	92 04 48 36	883 078 156 584	948966 5105	741828 16143	248743 738	1042318 109
9595	92 06 40 25	883 354 319 875	954071 5104	757970 16141	249481 738	1042209 108
9596	92 08 32 16	883 630 540 736	959175 5104	774111 16141	250219 738	1042101 109
9597	92 10 24 09	883 906 819 173	964279 5104	790252 16139	250957 738	1041992 108
9598	92 12 16 04	884 183 155 192	969383 5103	806391 16139	251695 738	1041884 109
9599	92 14 08 01	884 459 548 799	974486 5104	822530 16138	252433 738	1041775 108
9600	92 16 00 00	884 736 000 000	979590 97·	838668 309·	253171 21·	1041667 0·000

No. n	Square n²	Cube n³	Square root √n	Sq. rt. of 10n √10n	Cube root ∛n	Reciprocal 1/n
			97·	309·	21·	0·000
9600	92 16 00 00	884 736 000 000	979590 5103	838668 16137	253171 738	1041667 109
9601	92 17 92 01	885 012 508 801	984693 5102	854805 16136	253909 738	1041558 108
9602	92 19 84 04	885 289 075 208	989795 5103	870941 16135	254647 738	1041450 109
9603	92 21 76 09	885 565 699 227	994898 5102	887076 16135	255385 738	1041341 108
9604	92 23 68 16	885 842 380 864	*000000 5102	903211 16133	256123 738	1041233 109
9605	92 25 60 25	886 119 120 125	005102 5102	919344 16133	256861 737	1041124 108
9606	92 27 52 36	886 395 917 016	010204 5101	935477 16132	257598 738	1041016 108
9607	92 29 44 49	886 672 771 543	015305 5101	951609 16131	258336 737	1040908 108
9608	92 31 36 64	886 949 683 712	020406 5101	967740 16131	259073 738	1040799 109
9609	92 33 28 81	887 226 653 529	025507 5100	983871 16129	259811 737	1040691 108
9610	92 35 21 00	887 503 681 000	030607 5101	*000000 16129	260548 738	1040583 109
9611	92 37 13 21	887 780 766 131	035708 5100	016129 16127	261286 737	1040474 108
9612	92 39 05 44	888 057 908 928	040808 5100	032256 16127	262023 738	1040366 108
9613	92 40 97 69	888 335 109 397	045908 5099	048383 16126	262761 737	1040258 108
9614	92 42 89 96	888 612 367 544	051007 5099	064509 16126	263498 737	1040150 108
9615	92 44 82 25	888 889 683 375	056106 5099	080635 16124	264235 737	1040042 109
9616	92 46 74 56	889 167 056 896	061205 5099	096759 16124	264972 737	1039933 108
9617	92 48 66 89	889 444 488 113	066304 5099	112883 16122	265709 737	1039825 108
9618	92 50 59 24	889 721 977 032	071403 5098	129005 16122	266446 737	1039717 108
9619	92 52 51 61	889 999 523 659	076501 5098	145127 16121	267183 737	1039609 108
9620	92 54 44 00	890 277 128 000	081599 5097	161248 16121	267920 737	1039501 108
9621	92 56 36 41	890 554 790 061	086696 5098	177369 16119	268657 737	1039393 108
9622	92 58 28 84	890 832 509 848	091794 5097	193488 16119	269394 737	1039285 108
9623	92 60 21 29	891 110 287 367	096891 5097	209607 16117	270131 737	1039177 108
9624	92 62 13 76	891 388 122 624	101988 5096	225724 16117	270868 736	1039069 108
9625	92 64 06 25	891 666 015 625	107084 5097	241841 16116	271604 737	1038961 108
9626	92 65 98 76	891 943 966 376	112181 5096	257957 16115	272341 737	1038853 108
9627	92 67 91 29	892 221 974 883	117277 5096	274072 16115	273078 736	1038745 108
9628	92 69 83 84	892 500 041 152	122373 5095	290187 16113	273814 737	1038637 108
9629	92 71 76 41	892 778 165 189	127468 5095	306300 16113	274551 736	1038529 107
9630	92 73 69 00	893 056 347 000	132563 5095	322413 16112	275287 736	1038422 108
9631	92 75 61 61	893 334 586 591	137658 5095	338525 16111	276023 737	1038314 108
9632	92 77 54 24	893 612 883 968	142753 5095	354636 16110	276760 736	1038206 108
9633	92 79 46 89	893 891 239 137	147848 5094	370746 16109	277496 736	1038098 108
9634	92 81 39 56	894 169 652 104	152942 5094	386855 16109	278232 737	1037990 107
9635	92 83 32 25	894 448 122 875	158036 5094	402964 16108	278969 736	1037883 108
9636	92 85 24 96	894 726 651 456	163130 5093	419072 16106	279705 736	1037775 108
9637	92 87 17 69	895 005 237 853	168223 5093	435178 16106	280441 736	1037667 107
9638	92 89 10 44	895 283 882 072	173316 5093	451284 16106	281177 736	1037560 108
9639	92 91 03 21	895 562 584 119	178409 5093	467390 16104	281913 736	1037452 108
9640	92 92 96 00	895 841 344 000	183502 5092	483494 16103	282649 736	1037344 107
9641	92 94 88 81	896 120 161 721	188594 5092	499597 16103	283385 736	1037237 108
9642	92 96 81 64	896 399 037 288	193686 5092	515700 16102	284121 735	1037129 107
9643	92 98 74 49	896 677 970 707	198778 5092	531802 16101	284856 736	1037022 108
9644	93 00 67 36	896 956 961 984	203870 5091	547903 16100	285592 736	1036914 108
9645	93 02 60 25	897 236 011 125	208961 5091	564003 16099	286328 735	1036807 108
9646	93 04 53 16	897 515 118 136	214052 5091	580102 16099	287063 736	1036699 107
9647	93 06 46 09	897 794 283 023	219143 5090	596201 16098	287799 735	1036592 108
9648	93 08 39 04	898 073 505 792	224233 5091	612299 16096	288534 736	1036484 107
9649	93 10 32 01	898 352 786 449	229324 5090	628395 16096	289270 735	1036377 108
9650	93 12 25 00	898 632 125 000	234414	644491	290005	1036269
			98·	310·	21·	0·000

No. n	Square n^2	Cube n^3	Square root $\sqrt{n}$	Sq. rt. of $10n$ $\sqrt{10n}$	Cube root $\sqrt[3]{n}$	Reciprocal $\dfrac{1}{n}$
			98·	310·	21·	0·000
9650	93 12 25 00	898 632 125 000	234414 5089	644491 16095	290005 736	1036269 107
9651	93 14 18 01	898 911 521 451	239503 5089	660586 16095	290741 735	1036162 107
9652	93 16 11 04	899 190 975 808	244593 5090	676681 16093	291476 735	1036055 108
9653	93 18 04 09	899 470 488 077	249682 5089	692774 16093	292211 736	1035947 107
9654	93 19 97 16	899 750 058 264	254771 5089	708867 16092	292947 735	1035840 107
9655	93 21 90 25	900 029 686 375	259860 5088	724959 16091	293682 735	1035733 107
9656	93 23 83 36	900 309 372 416	264948 5088	741050 16090	294417 735	1035626 108
9657	93 25 76 49	900 589 116 393	270036 5088	757140 16089	295152 735	1035518 107
9658	93 27 69 64	900 868 918 312	275124 5088	773229 16089	295887 735	1035411 107
9659	93 29 62 81	901 148 778 179	280212 5087	789318 16087	296622 735	1035304 107
9660	93 31 56 00	901 428 696 000	285299 5087	805405 16087	297357 735	1035197 107
9661	93 33 49 21	901 708 671 781	290386 5087	821492 16086	298092 735	1035090 108
9662	93 35 42 44	901 988 705 528	295473 5087	837578 16085	298827 735	1034982 107
9663	93 37 35 69	902 268 797 247	300560 5086	853663 16085	299561 734	1034875 107
9664	93 39 28 96	902 548 946 944	305646 5086	869748 16083	300296 735	1034768 107
9665	93 41 22 25	902 829 154 625	310732 5086	885831 16083	301031 734	1034661 107
9666	93 43 15 56	903 109 420 296	315818 5085	901914 16082	301765 735	1034554 107
9667	93 45 08 89	903 389 743 963	320903 5085	917996 16081	302500 734	1034447 107
9668	93 47 02 24	903 670 125 632	325988 5085	934077 16080	303234 735	1034340 107
9669	93 48 95 61	903 950 565 309	331073 5085	950157 16079	303969 734	1034233 107
9670	93 50 89 00	904 231 063 000	336158 5085	966236 16079	304703 735	1034126 107
9671	93 52 82 41	904 511 618 711	341243 5084	982315 16077	305438 734	1034019 107
9672	93 54 75 84	904 792 232 448	346327 5084	998392 16077	306172 734	1033912 107
9673	93 56 69 29	905 072 904 217	351411 5083	*014469 16076	306906 735	1033805 106
9674	93 58 62 76	905 353 634 024	356494 5084	030545 16075	307641 734	1033699 107
9675	93 60 56 25	905 634 421 875	361578 5083	046620 16075	308375 734	1033592 107
9676	93 62 49 76	905 915 267 776	366661 5083	062695 16073	309109 734	1033485 107
9677	93 64 43 29	906 196 171 733	371744 5083	078768 16073	309843 734	1033378 107
9678	93 66 36 84	906 477 133 752	376827 5082	094841 16072	310577 734	1033271 106
9679	93 68 30 41	906 758 153 839	381909 5082	110913 16071	311311 734	1033165 107
9680	93 70 24 00	907 039 232 000	386991 5082	126984 16070	312045 734	1033058 107
9681	93 72 17 61	907 320 368 241	392073 5081	143054 16069	312779 734	1032951 107
9682	93 74 11 24	907 601 562 568	397154 5082	159123 16069	313512 733	1032844 106
9683	93 76 04 89	907 882 814 987	402236 5081	175192 16068	314246 734	1032738 107
9684	93 77 98 56	908 164 125 504	407317 5081	191260 16066	314980 734	1032631 106
9685	93 79 92 25	908 445 494 125	412398 5080	207326 16066	315714 733	1032525 107
9686	93 81 85 96	908 726 920 856	417478 5080	223392 16066	316447 734	1032418 107
9687	93 83 79 69	909 008 405 703	422558 5080	239458 16064	317181 733	1032311 106
9688	93 85 73 44	909 289 948 672	427638 5080	255522 16064	317914 734	1032205 107
9689	93 87 67 21	909 571 549 769	432718 5080	271586 16062	318648 733	1032098 106
9690	93 89 61 00	909 853 209 000	437798 5079	287648 16062	319381 733	1031992 107
9691	93 91 54 81	910 134 926 371	442877 5079	303710 16061	320114 734	1031885 107
9692	93 93 48 64	910 416 701 888	447956 5078	319771 16061	320848 733	1031779 107
9693	93 95 42 49	910 698 535 557	453034 5079	335832 16059	321581 733	1031672 106
9694	93 97 36 36	910 980 427 384	458113 5078	351891 16059	322314 733	1031566 106
9695	93 99 30 25	911 262 377 375	463191 5078	367950 16057	323047 733	1031460 107
9696	94 01 24 16	911 544 385 536	468269 5078	384007 16057	323780 733	1031353 106
9697	94 03 18 09	911 826 451 873	473347 5077	400064 16056	324513 734	1031247 107
9698	94 05 12 04	912 108 576 392	478424 5077	416120 16056	325247 732	1031140 106
9699	94 07 06 01	912 390 759 099	483501 5077	432176 16054	325979 733	1031034 106
9700	94 09 00 00	912 673 000 000	488578 98·	448230 311·	326712 21·	1030928 0·000

No. n	Square n^2	Cube n^3	Square root $\sqrt{n}$	Sq. rt. of 10n $\sqrt{10n}$	Cube root $\sqrt[3]{n}$	Reciprocal $\frac{1}{n}$
			98·	311·	21·	0·000
9700	94 09 00 00	912 673 000 000	488578	448230 16054	326712 733	1030928
9701	94 10 94 01	912 955 299 101	493655 5077	464284 16054	327445 733	1030822 106
9702	94 12 88 04	913 237 656 408	498731 5076	480336 16052	328178 733	1030715 107
9703	94 14 82 09	913 520 071 927	503807 5076	496388 16052	328911 733	1030609 106
9704	94 16 76 16	913 802 545 664	508883 5076 5075	512440 16052 16050	329643 732 733	1030503 106 106
9705	94 18 70 25	914 085 077 625	513958	528490 16049	330376 733	1030397
9706	94 20 64 36	914 367 667 816	519034 5076	544539 16049	331109 733	1030291 106
9707	94 22 58 49	914 650 316 243	524109 5075	560588 16049	331841 732	1030184 107
9708	94 24 52 64	914 933 022 912	529183 5074	576636 16048	332574 733	1030078 106
9709	94 26 46 81	915 215 787 829	534258 5075 5074	592683 16047 16046	333306 732 733	1029972 106 106
9710	94 28 41 00	915 498 611 000	539332	608729	334039	1029866
9711	94 30 35 21	915 781 492 431	544406 5074	624774 16045	334771 732	1029760 106
9712	94 32 29 44	916 064 432 128	549480 5074	640819 16045	335503 732	1029654 106
9713	94 34 23 69	916 347 430 097	554553 5073	656863 16044	336235 732	1029548 106
9714	94 36 17 96	916 630 486 344	559627 5074 5073	672905 16042 16043	336968 733 732	1029442 106
9715	94 38 12 25	916 913 600 875	564700	688948	337700	1029336
9716	94 40 06 56	917 196 773 696	569772 5072	704989 16041	338432 732	1029230 106
9717	94 42 00 89	917 480 004 813	574845 5073	721029 16040	339164 732	1029124 106
9718	94 43 95 24	917 763 294 232	579917 5072	737069 16040	339896 732	1029018 106
9719	94 45 89 61	918 046 641 959	584989 5072 5071	753107 16038 16038	340628 732	1028912 106 105
9720	94 47 84 00	918 330 048 000	590060	769145	341360	1028807
9721	94 49 78 41	918 613 512 361	595132 5072	785182 16037	342092 732	1028701 106
9722	94 51 72 84	918 897 035 048	600203 5071	801219 16037 16035	342823 731	1028595 106
9723	94 53 67 29	919 180 616 067	605274 5071	817254 16035	343555 732	1028489 106
9724	94 55 61 76	919 464 255 424	610344 5070 5071	833289 16035 16034	344287 732	1028383 106 105
9725	94 57 56 25	919 747 953 125	615415	849323	345019	1028278
9726	94 59 50 76	920 031 709 176	620485 5070	865356 16033	345750 731	1028172 106
9727	94 61 45 29	920 315 523 583	625554 5069	881388 16032	346482 732	1028066 106
9728	94 63 39 84	920 599 396 352	630624 5069	897419 16031	347213 731	1027961 105
9729	94 65 34 41	920 883 327 489	635693 5069 5069	913450 16031 16029	347945 732 731	1027855 106
9730	94 67 29 00	921 167 317 000	640762	929479 16029	348676	1027749
9731	94 69 23 61	921 451 364 891	645831 5069	945508 16028	349407 731	1027644 105
9732	94 71 18 24	921 735 471 168	650900 5069 5068	961536 16027	350139 732	1027538 106
9733	94 73 12 89	922 019 635 837	655968 5068	977563 16027	350870 731	1027432 106
9734	94 75 07 56	922 303 858 904	661036 5068 5068	993590 16025	351601 731	1027327 105 106
9735	94 77 02 25	922 588 140 375	666104	*009615 16025	352332 731	1027221
9736	94 78 96 96	922 872 480 256	671171 5067	025640 16024	353063 731	1027116 105
9737	94 80 91 69	923 156 878 553	676238 5067	041664 16023	353794 731	1027010 106
9738	94 82 86 44	923 441 335 272	681305 5067	057687 16022	354525 731	1026905 105
9739	94 84 81 21	923 725 850 419	686372 5067 5066	073709 16022	355256 731	1026799 106 105
9740	94 86 76 00	924 010 424 000	691438	089731	355987	1026694
9741	94 88 70 81	924 295 056 021	696504 5066	105751 16020	356718 731	1026589 105
9742	94 90 65 64	924 579 746 488	701570 5066	121771 16019	357449 731	1026483 106
9743	94 92 60 49	924 864 495 407	706636 5066 5065	137790 16018	358180 731	1026378 105
9744	94 94 55 36	925 149 302 784	711701 5066 5065	153808 16018	358910 730 731	1026273 105 106
9745	94 96 50 25	925 434 168 625	716767	169826	359641	1026167
9746	94 98 45 16	925 719 092 936	721831 5064 5065	185842 16016	360372 731	1026062 105
9747	95 00 40 09	926 004 075 723	726896 5064	201858 16016	361102 730	1025957 105
9748	95 02 35 04	926 289 116 992	731960 5064	217873 16015	361833 731 730	1025851 106
9749	95 04 30 01	926 574 216 749	737024 5064	233887 16014 16013	362563 730	1025746 105 105
9750	95 06 25 00	926 859 375 000	742088	249900	363293	1025641
			98·	312·	21·	0·000

No. n	Square n^2	Cube n^3	Square root $\sqrt{n}$	Sq. rt. of $10n$ $\sqrt{10n}$	Cube root $\sqrt[3]{n}$	Reciprocal $\dfrac{1}{n}$
			98·	312·	21·	0·000
9750	95 06 25 00	926 859 375 000	742088 5064	249900 16012	363293 731	1025641 105
9751	95 08 20 01	927 144 591 751	747152 5063	265912 16012	364024 730	1025536 105
9752	95 10 15 04	927 429 867 008	752215 5063	281924 16011	364754 730	1025431 105
9753	95 12 10 09	927 715 200 777	757278 5063	297935 16010	365484 730	1025326 106
9754	95 14 05 16	928 000 593 064	762341 5063	313945 16009	366214 731	1025220 105
9755	95 16 00 25	928 286 043 875	767404 5062	329954 16008	366945 730	1025115 105
9756	95 17 95 36	928 571 553 216	772466 5062	345962 16008	367675 730	1025010 105
9757	95 19 90 49	928 857 121 093	777528 5062	361970 16006	368405 730	1024905 105
9758	95 21 85 64	929 142 747 512	782590 5061	377976 16006	369135 730	1024800 105
9759	95 23 80 81	929 428 432 479	787651 5061	393982 16005	369865 730	1024695 105
9760	95 25 76 00	929 714 176 000	792712 5061	409987 16004	370595 729	1024590 105
9761	95 27 71 21	929 999 978 081	797773 5061	425991 16004	371324 730	1024485 105
9762	95 29 66 44	930 285 838 728	802834 5060	441995 16002	372054 730	1024380 105
9763	95 31 61 69	930 571 757 947	807894 5061	457997 16002	372784 730	1024275 105
9764	95 33 56 96	930 857 735 744	812955 5060	473999 16001	373514 729	1024170 104
9765	95 35 52 25	931 143 772 125	818015 5059	490000 16000	374243 730	1024066 105
9766	95 37 47 56	931 429 867 096	823074 5060	506000 15999	374973 729	1023961 105
9767	95 39 42 89	931 716 020 663	828134 5059	521999 15999	375702 730	1023856 105
9768	95 41 38 24	932 002 232 832	833193 5059	537998 15997	376432 729	1023751 105
9769	95 43 33 61	932 288 503 609	838252 5058	553995 15997	377161 730	1023646 105
9770	95 45 29 00	932 574 833 000	843310 5059	569992 15996	377891 729	1023541 104
9771	95 47 24 41	932 861 221 011	848369 5058	585988 15995	378620 729	1023437 105
9772	95 49 19 84	933 147 667 648	853427 5058	601983 15995	379349 730	1023332 105
9773	95 51 15 29	933 434 172 917	858485 5057	617978 15993	380079 729	1023227 104
9774	95 53 10 76	933 720 736 824	863542 5058	633971 15993	380808 729	1023123 105
9775	95 55 06 25	934 007 359 375	868600 5057	649964 15992	381537 729	1023018 105
9776	95 57 01 76	934 294 040 576	873657 5057	665956 15991	382266 729	1022913 105
9777	95 58 97 29	934 580 780 433	878714 5056	681947 15990	382995 729	1022809 105
9778	95 60 92 84	934 867 578 952	883770 5056	697937 15990	383724 729	1022704 105
9779	95 62 88 41	935 154 436 139	888826 5057	713927 15988	384453 729	1022599 104
9780	95 64 84 00	935 441 352 000	893883 5055	729915 15988	385182 729	1022495 105
9781	95 66 79 61	935 728 326 541	898938 5056	745903 15987	385911 729	1022390 104
9782	95 68 75 24	936 015 359 768	903994 5055	761890 15986	386640 728	1022286 104
9783	95 70 70 89	936 302 451 687	909049 5055	777876 15986	387368 729	1022181 104
9784	95 72 66 56	936 589 602 304	914104 5055	793862 15984	388097 729	1022077 105
9785	95 74 62 25	936 876 811 625	919159 5054	809846 15984	388826 728	1021972 104
9786	95 76 57 96	937 164 079 656	924213 5055	825830 15983	389554 729	1021868 104
9787	95 78 53 69	937 451 406 403	929268 5054	841813 15982	390283 728	1021764 105
9788	95 80 49 44	937 738 791 872	934322 5053	857795 15981	391011 729	1021659 104
9789	95 82 45 21	938 026 236 069	939375 5054	873776 15981	391740 728	1021555 105
9790	95 84 41 00	938 313 739 000	944429 5053	889757 15980	392468 729	1021450 104
9791	95 86 36 81	938 601 300 671	949482 5053	905737 15978	393197 728	1021346 104
9792	95 88 32 64	938 888 921 088	954535 5053	921715 15978	393925 728	1021242 104
9793	95 90 28 49	939 176 600 257	959588 5052	937693 15978	394653 728	1021138 105
9794	95 92 24 36	939 464 338 184	964640 5052	953671 15976	395381 729	1021033 104
9795	95 94 20 25	939 752 134 875	969692 5052	969647 15976	396110 728	1020929 104
9796	95 96 16 16	940 039 990 336	974744 5052	985623 15974	396838 728	1020825 104
9797	95 98 12 09	940 327 904 573	979796 5051	*001597 15974	397566 728	1020721 105
9798	96 00 08 04	940 615 877 592	984847 5051	017571 15974	398294 728	1020616 104
9799	96 02 04 01	940 903 909 399	989898 5051	033545 15972	399022 728	1020512 104
9800	96 04 00 00	941 192 000 000	994949 98·	049517 313·	399750 21·	1020408 0·000

No. n	Square n²	Cube n³	Square root √n	Sq. rt. of 10n √10n	Cube root ∛n	Reciprocal 1/n
			98·	313·	21·	0·000
9800	96 04 00 00	941 192 000 000	994949 5051	049517 15971	399750 727	1020408 104
9801	96 05 96 01	941 480 149 401	*000000 5050	065488 15971	400477 728	1020304 104
9802	96 07 92 04	941 768 357 608	005050 5050	081459 15970	401205 728	1020200 104
9803	96 09 88 09	942 056 624 627	010100 5050	097429 15969	401933 728	1020096 104
9804	96 11 84 16	942 344 950 464	015150 5050	113398 15968	402661 727	1019992 104
9805	96 13 80 25	942 633 335 125	020200 5049	129366 15968	403388 728	1019888 104
9806	96 15 76 36	942 921 778 616	025249 5049	145334 15966	404116 728	1019784 104
9807	96 17 72 49	943 210 280 943	030298 5049	161300 15966	404844 727	1019680 104
9808	96 19 68 64	943 498 842 112	035347 5049	177266 15965	405571 728	1019576 104
9809	96 21 64 81	943 787 462 129	040396 5048	193231 15964	406299 727	1019472 104
9810	96 23 61 00	944 076 141 000	045444 5048	209195 15964	407026 727	1019368 104
9811	96 25 57 21	944 364 878 731	050492 5048	225159 15962	407753 728	1019264 104
9812	96 27 53 44	944 653 675 328	055540 5048	241121 15962	408481 727	1019160 104
9813	96 29 49 69	944 942 530 797	060588 5047	257083 15961	409208 727	1019056 103
9814	96 31 45 96	945 231 445 144	065635 5047	273044 15960	409935 727	1018953 104
9815	96 33 42 25	945 520 418 375	070682 5047	289004 15959	410662 727	1018849 104
9816	96 35 38 56	945 809 450 496	075729 5046	304963 15959	411389 727	1018745 104
9817	96 37 34 89	946 098 541 513	080775 5046	320922 15957	412116 727	1018641 104
9818	96 39 31 24	946 387 691 432	085821 5046	336879 15957	412843 727	1018537 104
9819	96 41 27 61	946 676 900 259	090867 5046	352836 15956	413570 727	1018434 103
9820	96 43 24 00	946 966 168 000	095913 5046	368792 15956	414297 727	1018330 104
9821	96 45 20 41	947 255 494 661	100959 5045	384748 15954	415024 727	1018226 104
9822	96 47 16 84	947 544 880 248	106004 5045	400702 15954	415751 727	1018123 103
9823	96 49 13 29	947 834 324 767	111049 5045	416656 15952	416478 727	1018019 104
9824	96 51 09 76	948 123 828 224	116094 5044	432608 15952	417205 726	1017915 103
9825	96 53 06 25	948 413 390 625	121138 5044	448560 15952	417931 727	1017812 104
9826	96 55 02 76	948 703 011 976	126182 5044	464512 15950	418658 726	1017708 104
9827	96 56 99 29	948 992 692 283	131226 5044	480462 15949	419384 727	1017605 103
9828	96 58 95 84	949 282 431 552	136270 5043	496411 15949	420111 726	1017501 104
9829	96 60 92 41	949 572 229 789	141313 5043	512360 15948	420837 727	1017397 103
9830	96 62 89 00	949 862 087 000	146356 5043	528308 15947	421564 726	1017294 103
9831	96 64 85 61	950 152 003 191	151399 5043	544255 15947	422290 727	1017191 103
9832	96 66 82 24	950 441 978 368	156442 5042	560202 15945	423017 726	1017087 103
9833	96 68 78 89	950 732 012 537	161484 5043	576147 15945	423743 726	1016984 104
9834	96 70 75 56	951 022 105 704	166527 5042	592092 15944	424469 726	1016880 103
9835	96 72 72 25	951 312 257 875	171569 5041	608036 15943	425195 726	1016777 104
9836	96 74 68 96	951 602 469 056	176610 5042	623979 15942	425921 726	1016673 103
9837	96 76 65 69	951 892 739 253	181652 5041	639921 15942	426647 726	1016570 103
9838	96 78 62 44	952 183 068 472	186693 5041	655862 15941	427373 726	1016467 104
9839	96 80 59 21	952 473 456 719	191734 5041	671803 15941	428099 726	1016363 104
9840	96 82 56 00	952 763 904 000	196774 5040	687743 15939	428825 726	1016260 103
9841	96 84 52 81	953 054 410 321	201814 5041	703682 15938	429551 726	1016157 103
9842	96 86 49 64	953 344 975 688	206855 5039	719620 15937	430277 726	1016054 104
9843	96 88 46 49	953 635 600 107	211894 5040	735557 15937	431003 726	1015950 103
9844	96 90 43 36	953 926 283 584	216934 5039	751494 15936	431729 725	1015847 103
9845	96 92 40 25	954 217 026 125	221973 5039	767430 15935	432454 726	1015744 103
9846	96 94 37 16	954 507 827 736	227012 5039	783365 15934	433180 726	1015641 103
9847	96 96 34 09	954 798 688 423	232051 5039	799299 15933	433906 725	1015538 103
9848	96 98 31 04	955 089 608 192	237090 5038	815232 15933	434631 726	1015435 103
9849	97 00 28 01	955 380 587 049	242128 5038	831165 15932	435357 725	1015332 103
9850	97 02 25 00	955 671 625 000	247166	847097	436082	1015228
			99·	313·	21·	0·000

No. n	Square n^2	Cube n^3	Square root $\sqrt{n}$		Sq. rt. of 10n $\sqrt{10n}$		Cube root $\sqrt[3]{n}$		Reciprocal $\dfrac{1}{n}$	
			99·		313·		21·		0·000	
9850	97 02 25 00	955 671 625 000	247166	5038	847097	15930	436082	725	1015228	103
9851	97 04 22 01	955 962 722 051	252204	5038	863027	15931	436807	726	1015125	103
9852	97 06 19 04	956 253 878 208	257242	5037	878958	15929	437533	725	1015022	103
9853	97 08 16 09	956 545 093 477	262279	5037	894887	15928	438258	725	1014919	103
9854	97 10 13 16	956 836 367 864	267316	5037	910815	15928	438983	725	1014816	103
9855	97 12 10 25	957 127 701 375	272353	5036	926743	15927	439708	726	1014713	103
9856	97 14 07 36	957 419 094 016	277389	5036	942670	15926	440434	725	1014610	103
9857	97 16 04 49	957 710 545 793	282425	5036	958596	15925	441159	725	1014507	102
9858	97 18 01 64	958 002 056 712	287461	5036	974521	15925	441884	725	1014405	103
9859	97 19 98 81	958 293 626 779	292497	5036	990446	15923	442609	725	1014302	103
9860	97 21 96 00	958 585 256 000	297533	5035	*006369	15923	443334	725	1014199	103
9861	97 23 93 21	958 876 944 381	302568	5035	022292	15922	444059	724	1014096	103
9862	97 25 90 44	959 168 691 928	307603	5035	038214	15921	444783	725	1013993	103
9863	97 27 87 69	959 460 498 647	312638	5034	054135	15921	445508	725	1013890	102
9864	97 29 84 96	959 752 364 544	317672	5034	070056	15919	446233	725	1013788	103
9865	97 31 82 25	960 044 289 625	322706	5034	085975	15919	446958	724	1013685	103
9866	97 33 79 56	960 336 273 896	327740	5034	101894	15918	447682	725	1013582	103
9867	97 35 76 89	960 628 317 363	332774	5034	117812	15917	448407	725	1013479	102
9868	97 37 74 24	960 920 420 032	337808	5033	133729	15917	449132	724	1013377	103
9869	97 39 71 61	961 212 581 909	342841	5033	149646	15915	449856	725	1013274	103
9870	97 41 69 00	961 504 803 000	347874	5032	165561	15915	450581	724	1013171	102
9871	97 43 66 41	961 797 083 311	352906	5033	181476	15914	451305	724	1013069	103
9872	97 45 63 84	962 089 422 848	357939	5032	197390	15913	452029	725	1012966	103
9873	97 47 61 29	962 381 821 617	362971	5032	213303	15913	452754	724	1012863	102
9874	97 49 58 76	962 674 279 624	368003	5032	229216	15911	453478	724	1012761	103
9875	97 51 56 25	962 966 796 875	373035	5031	245127	15911	454202	724	1012658	102
9876	97 53 53 76	963 259 373 376	378066	5031	261038	15910	454926	724	1012556	103
9877	97 55 51 29	963 552 009 133	383097	5031	276948	15909	455650	724	1012453	102
9878	97 57 48 84	963 844 704 152	388128	5031	292857	15908	456374	725	1012351	103
9879	97 59 46 41	964 137 458 439	393159	5030	308765	15908	457099	723	1012248	102
9880	97 61 44 00	964 430 272 000	398189	5030	324673	15907	457822	724	1012146	103
9881	97 63 41 61	964 723 144 841	403219	5030	340580	15906	458546	724	1012043	102
9882	97 65 39 24	965 016 076 968	408249	5030	356486	15905	459270	724	1011941	102
9883	97 67 36 89	965 309 068 387	413279	5029	372391	15904	459994	724	1011839	103
9884	97 69 34 56	965 602 119 104	418308	5029	388295	15903	460718	724	1011736	102
9885	97 71 32 25	965 895 229 125	423337	5029	404198	15903	461442	723	1011634	103
9886	97 73 29 96	966 188 398 456	428366	5029	420101	15902	462165	724	1011531	102
9887	97 75 27 69	966 481 627 103	433395	5028	436003	15901	462889	724	1011429	102
9888	97 77 25 44	966 774 915 072	438423	5028	451904	15900	463613	723	1011327	102
9889	97 79 23 21	967 068 262 369	443451	5028	467804	15900	464336	724	1011225	103
9890	97 81 21 00	967 361 669 000	448479	5028	483704	15899	465060	723	1011122	102
9891	97 83 18 81	967 655 134 971	453507	5027	499603	15897	465783	723	1011020	102
9892	97 85 16 64	967 948 660 288	458534	5027	515500	15897	466506	723	1010918	102
9893	97 87 14 49	968 242 244 957	463561	5027	531397	15897	467230	723	1010816	102
9894	97 89 12 36	968 535 888 984	468588	5027	547294	15895	467953	723	1010714	103
9895	97 91 10 25	968 829 592 375	473615	5026	563189	15895	468676	723	1010611	102
9896	97 93 08 16	969 123 355 136	478641	5026	579084	15894	469399	724	1010509	102
9897	97 95 06 09	969 417 177 273	483667	5026	594978	15893	470123	723	1010407	102
9898	97 97 04 04	969 711 058 792	488693	5025	610871	15892	470846	723	1010305	102
9899	97 99 02 01	970 004 999 699	493718	5026	626763	15891	471569	723	1010203	102
9900	98 01 00 00	970 299 000 000	498744 99·		642654 314·		472292 21·		1010101 0·000	

No. n	Square n^2	Cube n^3	Square root $\sqrt{n}$	Sq. rt. of 10n $\sqrt{10n}$	Cube root $\sqrt[3]{n}$	Reciprocal $\dfrac{1}{n}$
			99·	314·	21·	0·000
9900	98 01 00 00	970 299 000 000	498744 5025	642654 15891	472292 723	1010101 102
9901	98 02 98 01	970 593 059 701	503769 5025	658545 15890	473015 723	1009999 102
9902	98 04 96 04	970 887 178 808	508794 5024	674435 15889	473738 722	1009897 102
9903	98 06 94 09	971 181 357 327	513818 5024	690324 15888	474460 723	1009795 102
9904	98 08 92 16	971 475 595 264	518842 5024	706212 15888	475183 723	1009693 102
9905	98 10 90 25	971 769 892 625	523866 5024	722100 15886	475906 723	1009591 102
9906	98 12 88 36	972 064 249 416	528890 5024	737986 15886	476629 722	1009489 102
9907	98 14 86 49	972 358 665 643	533914 5023	753872 15885	477351 723	1009387 102
9908	98 16 84 64	972 653 141 312	538937 5023	769757 15884	478074 722	1009285 101
9909	98 18 82 81	972 947 676 429	543960 5023	785641 15884	478796 723	1009184 102
9910	98 20 81 00	973 242 271 000	548983 5022	801525 15882	479519 722	1009082 102
9911	98 22 79 21	973 536 925 031	554005 5023	817407 15882	480241 723	1008980 102
9912	98 24 77 44	973 831 638 528	559028 5022	833289 15881	480964 722	1008878 102
9913	98 26 75 69	974 126 411 497	564050 5022	849170 15880	481686 723	1008776 101
9914	98 28 73 96	974 421 243 944	569072 5021	865050 15880	482409 722	1008675 102
9915	98 30 72 25	974 716 135 875	574093 5021	880930 15878	483131 722	1008573 102
9916	98 32 70 56	975 011 087 296	579114 5021	896808 15878	483853 722	1008471 102
9917	98 34 68 89	975 306 098 213	584135 5021	912686 15877	484575 722	1008369 101
9918	98 36 67 24	975 601 168 632	589156 5021	928563 15877	485297 722	1008268 102
9919	98 38 65 61	975 896 298 559	594177 5020	944440 15875	486019 722	1008166 101
9920	98 40 64 00	976 191 488 000	599197 5020	960315 15875	486741 722	1008065 102
9921	98 42 62 41	976 486 736 961	604217 5020	976190 15873	487463 722	1007963 102
9922	98 44 60 84	976 782 045 448	609237 5019	992063 15873	488185 722	1007861 101
9923	98 46 59 29	977 077 413 467	614256 5019	*007936 15873	488907 722	1007760 102
9924	98 48 57 76	977 372 841 024	619275 5019	023809 15871	489629 722	1007658 101
9925	98 50 56 25	977 668 328 125	624294 5019	039680 15871	490351 722	1007557 102
9926	98 52 54 76	977 963 874 776	629313 5018	055551 15869	491073 721	1007455 101
9927	98 54 53 29	978 259 480 983	634331 5019	071420 15869	491794 722	1007354 102
9928	98 56 51 84	978 555 146 752	639350 5018	087289 15860	492516 721	1007252 101
9929	98 58 50 41	978 850 872 089	644368 5017	103158 15867	493237 722	1007151 102
9930	98 60 49 00	979 146 657 000	649385 5018	119025 15867	493959 721	1007049 101
9931	98 62 47 61	979 442 501 491	654403 5017	134892 15866	494680 722	1006948 101
9932	98 64 46 24	979 738 405 568	659420 5017	150758 15865	495402 721	1006847 103
9933	98 66 44 89	980 034 369 237	664437 5017	166623 15864	496123 722	1006745 101
9934	98 68 43 56	980 330 392 504	669454 5016	182487 15863	496845 721	1006644 101
9935	98 70 42 25	980 626 475 375	674470 5016	198350 15863	497566 721	1006543 102
9936	98 72 40 96	980 922 617 856	679486 5016	214213 15862	498287 721	1006441 101
9937	98 74 39 69	981 218 819 953	684502 5016	230075 15861	499008 722	1006340 101
9938	98 76 38 44	981 515 081 672	689518 5015	245936 15860	499730 721	1006239 102
9939	98 78 37 21	981 811 403 019	694533 5016	261796 15859	500451 721	1006137 101
9940	98 80 36 00	982 107 784 000	699549 5015	277655 15859	501172 721	1006036 101
9941	98 82 34 81	982 404 224 621	704564 5014	293514 15858	501893 721	1005935 101
9942	98 84 33 64	982 700 724 888	709578 5015	309372 15857	502614 721	1005834 101
9943	98 86 32 49	982 997 284 807	714593 5014	325229 15856	503335 720	1005733 101
9944	98 88 31 36	983 293 904 384	719607 5014	341085 15856	504055 721	1005632 102
9945	98 90 30 25	983 590 583 625	724621 5014	356941 15854	504776 721	1005530 101
9946	98 92 29 16	983 887 322 536	729635 5013	372795 15854	505497 721	1005429 101
9947	98 94 28 09	984 184 121 123	734648 5013	388649 15853	506218 720	1005328 101
9948	98 96 27 04	984 480 979 392	739661 5013	404502 15852	506938 721	1005227 101
9949	98 98 26 01	984 777 897 349	744674 5013	420354 15852	507659 721	1005126 101
9950	99 00 25 00	985 074 875 000	749687 99·	436206 315·	508380 21·	1005025 0·000

No. n	Square n²	Cube n³	Square root √n	Sq. rt. of 10n √10n	Cube root ∛n	Reciprocal 1/n
			99·	315·	21·	0·000
9950	99 00 25 00	985 074 875 000	749687 5012	436206 15851	508380 720	1005025 101
9951	99 02 24 01	985 371 912 351	754699 5012	452057 15849	509100 721	1004924 101
9952	99 04 23 04	985 669 009 408	759711 5012	467906 15850	509821 720	1004823 101
9953	99 06 22 09	985 966 166 177	764723 5012	483756 15848	510541 720	1004722 101
9954	99 08 21 16	986 263 382 664	769735 5011	499604 15847	511261 721	1004621 101
9955	99 10 20 25	986 560 658 875	774746 5011	515451 15847	511982 720	1004520 101
9956	99 12 19 36	986 857 994 816	779757 5011	531298 15846	512702 720	1004419 100
9957	99 14 18 49	987 155 390 493	784768 5011	547144 15845	513422 720	1004319 100
9958	99 16 17 64	987 452 845 912	789779 5010	562989 15845	514142 721	1004218 101
9959	99 18 16 81	987 750 361 079	794789 5011	578833 15844	514863 720	1004117 101
9960	99 20 16 00	988 047 936 000	799800 5010	594677 15842	515583 720	1004016 101
9961	99 22 15 21	988 345 570 681	804810 5009	610519 15842	516303 720	1003915 101
9962	99 24 14 44	988 643 265 128	809819 5010	626361 15842	517023 720	1003814 100
9963	99 26 13 69	988 941 019 347	814829 5009	642203 15840	517743 720	1003714 101
9964	99 28 12 96	989 238 833 344	819838 5009	658043 15839	518463 719	1003613 101
9965	99 30 12 25	989 536 707 125	824847 5008	673882 15839	519182 720	1003512 100
9966	99 32 11 56	989 834 640 696	829855 5009	689721 15838	519902 720	1003412 101
9967	99 34 10 89	990 132 634 063	834864 5008	705559 15837	520622 720	1003311 101
9968	99 36 10 24	990 430 687 232	839872 5008	721396 15837	521342 719	1003210 100
9969	99 38 09 61	990 728 800 209	844880 5007	737233 15835	522061 720	1003110 101
9970	99 40 09 00	991 026 973 000	849887 5008	753068 15835	522781 720	1003009 101
9971	99 42 08 41	991 325 205 611	854895 5007	768903 15834	523501 719	1002908 101
9972	99 44 07 84	991 623 498 048	859902 5007	784737 15833	524220 720	1002808 101
9973	99 46 07 29	991 921 850 317	864909 5006	800570 15832	524940 719	1002707 100
9974	99 48 06 76	992 220 262 424	869915 5007	816402 15832	525659 719	1002607 101
9975	99 50 06 25	992 518 734 375	874922 5006	832234 15831	526378 720	1002506 100
9976	99 52 05 76	992 817 266 176	879928 5006	848065 15830	527098 719	1002406 100
9977	99 54 05 29	993 115 857 833	884934 5005	863895 15829	527817 719	1002305 101
9978	99 56 04 84	993 414 509 352	889939 5006	879724 15828	528536 719	1002205 100
9979	99 58 04 41	993 713 220 739	894945 5005	895552 15828	529255 719	1002104 100
9980	99 60 04 00	994 011 992 000	899950 5005	911380 15827	529974 719	1002004 100
9981	99 62 03 61	994 310 823 141	904955 5004	927207 15826	530693 720	1001904 101
9982	99 64 03 24	994 609 714 168	909959 5005	943033 15825	531413 719	1001803 100
9983	99 66 02 89	994 908 665 087	914964 5004	958858 15825	532132 718	1001703 100
9984	99 68 02 56	995 207 675 904	919968 5004	974683 15823	532850 719	1001603 101
9985	99 70 02 25	995 506 746 625	924972 5003	*990506 15823	533569 719	1001502 100
9986	99 72 01 96	995 805 877 256	929975 5004	006329 15822	534288 719	1001402 100
9987	99 74 01 69	996 105 067 803	934979 5003	022151 15821	535007 719	1001302 101
9988	99 76 01 44	996 404 318 272	939982 5003	037972 15821	535726 718	1001201 100
9989	99 78 01 21	996 703 628 669	944985 5002	053793 15820	536444 719	1001101 100
9990	99 80 01 00	997 002 999 000	949987 5003	069613 15818	537163 719	1001001 100
9991	99 82 00 81	997 302 429 271	954990 5002	085431 15819	537882 718	1000901 100
9992	99 84 00 64	997 601 919 488	959992 5002	101250 15817	538600 719	1000801 100
9993	99 86 00 49	997 901 469 657	964994 5001	117067 15816	539319 718	1000700 100
9994	99 88 00 36	998 201 079 784	969995 5002	132883 15816	540037 719	1000600 100
9995	99 90 00 25	998 500 749 875	974997 5001	148699 15815	540756 718	1000500 100
9996	99 92 00 16	998 800 479 936	979998 5001	164514 15814	541474 718	1000400 100
9997	99 94 00 09	999 100 269 973	984999 5000	180328 15814	542192 719	1000300 100
9998	99 96 00 04	999 400 119 992	989999 5001	196142 15812	542911 718	1000200 100
9999	99 98 00 01	999 700 029 999	995000 5000	211954 15812	543629 718	1000100 100
10000	100 00 00 00	1000 000 000 000	*000000 100·	227766 316·	544347 21·	1000000 0·000

No. n	Square n²	Cube n³	Square root √n	Sq. rt. of 10n √10n	Cube root ∛n	Reciprocal 1/n
			100·	316·	21·	0.0000
10000	100 00 00 00	1000 000 000 000	000000 $_{5000}$	227766 $_{15811}$	544347 $_{718}$	
10001	100 02 00 01	1000 300 030 001	005000 $_{4999}$	243577 $_{15810}$	545065 $_{718}$	9999000 $_{1000}$
10002	100 04 00 04	1000 600 120 008	009999 $_{5000}$	259387 $_{15810}$	545783 $_{718}$	9998000 $_{1000}$
10003	100 06 00 09	1000 900 270 027	014999 $_{4999}$	275197 $_{15808}$	546501 $_{718}$	9997001 $_{999}$
10004	100 08 00 16	1001 200 480 064	019998 $_{4999}$	291005 $_{15808}$	547219 $_{718}$	9996002 $_{999}$
10005	100 10 00 25	1001 500 750 125	024997 $_{4999}$	306813 $_{15807}$	547937 $_{718}$	9995002 $_{998}$
10006	100 12 00 36	1001 801 080 216	029996 $_{4998}$	322620 $_{15806}$	548655 $_{718}$	9994004 $_{999}$
10007	100 14 00 49	1002 101 470 343	034994 $_{4998}$	338426 $_{15806}$	549373 $_{718}$	9993005 $_{999}$
10008	100 16 00 64	1002 401 920 512	039992 $_{4998}$	354232 $_{15805}$	550091 $_{717}$	9992006 $_{998}$
10009	100 18 00 81	1002 702 430 729	044990 $_{4998}$	370037 $_{15803}$	550808 $_{718}$	9991008 $_{998}$
10010	100 20 01 00	1003 003 001 000	049988 $_{4997}$	385840 $_{15803}$	551526 $_{718}$	9990010 $_{998}$
10011	100 22 01 21	1003 303 631 331	054985 $_{4997}$	401643 $_{15803}$	552244 $_{717}$	9989012 $_{998}$
10012	100 24 01 44	1003 604 321 728	059982 $_{4997}$	417446 $_{15801}$	552961 $_{718}$	9988014 $_{997}$
10013	100 26 01 69	1003 905 072 197	064979 $_{4997}$	433247 $_{15801}$	553679 $_{717}$	9987017 $_{997}$
10014	100 28 01 96	1004 205 882 744	069976 $_{4996}$	449048 $_{15800}$	554396 $_{718}$	9986020 $_{998}$
10015	100 30 02 25	1004 506 753 375	074972 $_{4996}$	464848 $_{15799}$	555114 $_{717}$	9985022 $_{996}$
10016	100 32 02 56	1004 807 684 096	079968 $_{4996}$	480647 $_{15798}$	555831 $_{717}$	9984026 $_{997}$
10017	100 34 02 89	1005 108 674 913	084964 $_{4996}$	496445 $_{15798}$	556548 $_{718}$	9983029 $_{997}$
10018	100 36 03 24	1005 409 725 832	089960 $_{4995}$	512243 $_{15797}$	557266 $_{717}$	9982032 $_{996}$
10019	100 38 03 61	1005 710 836 859	094955 $_{4995}$	528040 $_{15796}$	557983 $_{717}$	9981036 $_{996}$
10020	100 40 04 00	1006 012 008 000	099950 $_{4995}$	543836 $_{15795}$	558700 $_{717}$	9980040 $_{996}$
10021	100 42 04 41	1006 313 239 261	104945 $_{4995}$	559631 $_{15794}$	559417 $_{718}$	9979044 $_{996}$
10022	100 44 04 84	1006 614 530 648	109940 $_{4994}$	575425 $_{15794}$	560135 $_{717}$	9978048 $_{995}$
10023	100 46 05 29	1006 915 882 167	114934 $_{4994}$	591219 $_{15793}$	560852 $_{717}$	9977053 $_{996}$
10024	100 48 05 76	1007 217 293 824	119928 $_{4994}$	607012 $_{15792}$	561569 $_{717}$	9976057 $_{995}$
10025	100 50 06 25	1007 518 765 625	124922 $_{4994}$	622804 $_{15791}$	562286 $_{717}$	9975062 $_{995}$
10026	100 52 06 76	1007 820 297 576	129916 $_{4993}$	638595 $_{15791}$	563003 $_{716}$	9974067 $_{994}$
10027	100 54 07 29	1008 121 889 683	134909 $_{4993}$	654386 $_{15789}$	563719 $_{717}$	9973073 $_{995}$
10028	100 56 07 84	1008 423 541 952	139902 $_{4993}$	670175 $_{15789}$	564436 $_{717}$	9972078 $_{994}$
10029	100 58 08 41	1008 725 254 389	144895 $_{4993}$	685964 $_{15788}$	565153 $_{717}$	9971084 $_{994}$
10030	100 60 09 00	1009 027 027 000	149888 $_{4992}$	701752 $_{15788}$	565870 $_{716}$	9970090 $_{994}$
10031	100 62 09 61	1009 328 859 791	154880 $_{4992}$	717540 $_{15786}$	566586 $_{717}$	9969096 $_{994}$
10032	100 64 10 24	1009 630 752 768	159872 $_{4992}$	733326 $_{15786}$	567303 $_{717}$	9968102 $_{993}$
10033	100 66 10 89	1009 932 705 937	164864 $_{4992}$	749112 $_{15785}$	568020 $_{716}$	9967109 $_{994}$
10034	100 68 11 56	1010 234 719 304	169856 $_{4991}$	764897 $_{15784}$	568736 $_{717}$	9966115 $_{993}$
10035	100 70 12 25	1010 536 792 875	174847 $_{4991}$	780681 $_{15784}$	569453 $_{716}$	9965122 $_{993}$
10036	100 72 12 96	1010 838 926 656	179838 $_{4991}$	796465 $_{15782}$	570169 $_{717}$	9964129 $_{993}$
10037	100 74 13 69	1011 141 120 653	184829 $_{4991}$	812247 $_{15782}$	570886 $_{716}$	9963136 $_{992}$
10038	100 76 14 44	1011 443 374 872	189820 $_{4990}$	828029 $_{15781}$	571602 $_{716}$	9962144 $_{992}$
10039	100 78 15 21	1011 745 689 319	194810 $_{4990}$	843810 $_{15780}$	572318 $_{716}$	9961152 $_{993}$
10040	100 80 16 00	1012 048 064 000	199800 $_{4990}$	859590 $_{15780}$	573034 $_{717}$	9960159 $_{992}$
10041	100 82 16 81	1012 350 498 921	204790 $_{4990}$	875370 $_{15779}$	573751 $_{716}$	9959167 $_{991}$
10042	100 84 17 64	1012 652 994 088	209780 $_{4989}$	891149 $_{15777}$	574467 $_{716}$	9958176 $_{992}$
10043	100 86 18 49	1012 955 549 507	214769 $_{4990}$	906926 $_{15778}$	575183 $_{716}$	9957184 $_{991}$
10044	100 88 19 36	1013 258 165 184	219759 $_{4988}$	922704 $_{15776}$	575899 $_{716}$	9956193 $_{991}$
10045	100 90 20 25	1013 560 841 125	224747 $_{4989}$	938480 $_{15775}$	576615 $_{716}$	9955202 $_{991}$
10046	100 92 21 16	1013 863 577 336	229736 $_{4989}$	954255 $_{15775}$	577331 $_{716}$	9954211 $_{991}$
10047	100 94 22 09	1014 166 373 823	234725 $_{4988}$	970030 $_{15774}$	578047 $_{716}$	9953220 $_{991}$
10048	100 96 23 04	1014 469 230 592	239713 $_{4988}$	985804 $_{15773}$	578763 $_{716}$	9952229 $_{990}$
10049	100 98 24 01	1014 772 147 649	244701 $_{4987}$	*001577 $_{15773}$	579479 $_{715}$	9951239 $_{990}$
10050	101 00 25 00	1015 075 125 000	249688	017350	580194	9950249
			100·	317·	21·	0.0000

No. n	Square n^2	Cube n^3	Square root $\sqrt{n}$	Sq. rt. of $10n$ $\sqrt{10n}$	Cube root $\sqrt[3]{n}$	Reciprocal $\dfrac{1}{n}$
			100·	317·	21·	0·0000
10050	101 00 25 00	1015 075 125 000	249688 4988	017350 15771	580194 716	9950249 2990
10051	101 02 26 01	1015 378 162 651	254676 4987	033121 15771	580910 716	9949259 990
10052	101 04 27 04	1015 681 260 608	259663 4987	048892 15770	581626 716	9948269 990
10053	101 06 28 09	1015 984 418 877	264650 4986	064662 15769	582342 715	9947279 990
10054	101 08 29 16	1016 287 637 464	269636 4987	080431 15769	583057 716	9946290 989
10055	101 10 30 25	1016 590 916 375	274623 4986	096200 15768	583773 715	9945301 989
10056	101 12 31 36	1016 894 255 616	279609 4986	111968 15767	584488 715	9944312 989
10057	101 14 32 49	1017 197 655 193	284595 4986	127735 15766	585204 715	9943323 989
10058	101 16 33 64	1017 501 115 112	289581 4985	143501 15765	585919 715	9942334 988
10059	101 18 34 81	1017 804 635 379	294566 4985	159266 15765	586634 716	9941346 988
10060	101 20 36 00	1018 108 216 000	299551 4985	175031 15763	587350 715	9940358 988
10061	101 22 37 21	1018 411 856 981	304536 4985	190794 15763	588065 715	9939370 988
10062	101 24 38 44	1018 715 558 328	309521 4984	206557 15763	588780 715	9938382 988
10063	101 26 39 69	1019 019 320 047	314505 4985	222320 15761	589495 715	9937394 987
10064	101 28 40 96	1019 323 142 144	319490 4984	238081 15761	590210 716	9936407 987
10065	101 30 42 25	1019 627 024 625	324474 4983	253842 15759	590926 715	9935420 987
10066	101 32 43 56	1019 930 967 496	329457 4984	269601 15760	591641 715	9934433 987
10067	101 34 44 89	1020 234 970 763	334441 4983	285361 15758	592356 714	9933446 987
10068	101 36 46 24	1020 539 034 432	339424 4983	301119 15757	593070 715	9932459 986
10069	101 38 47 61	1020 843 158 509	344407 4983	316876 15757	593785 715	9931473 986
10070	101 40 49 00	1021 147 343 000	349390 4982	332633 15756	594500 715	9930487 986
10071	101 42 50 41	1021 451 587 911	354372 4982	348389 15755	595215 715	9929501 986
10072	101 44 51 84	1021 755 893 248	359354 4982	364144 15755	595930 714	9928515 986
10073	101 46 53 29	1022 060 259 017	364336 4982	379899 15753	596644 715	9927529 985
10074	101 48 54 76	1022 364 685 224	369318 4981	395652 15753	597359 715	9926544 986
10075	101 50 56 25	1022 669 171 875	374299 4982	411405 15752	598074 714	9925558 985
10076	101 52 57 76	1022 973 718 976	379281 4981	427157 15751	598788 715	9924573 985
10077	101 54 59 29	1023 278 326 533	384262 4980	442908 15751	599503 714	9923588 984
10078	101 56 60 84	1023 582 994 552	389242 4980	458659 15749	600217 715	9922604 985
10079	101 58 62 41	1023 887 723 039	394223 4980	474408 15749	600932 714	9921619 984
10080	101 60 64 00	1024 192 512 000	399203 4980	490157 15748	601646 714	9920635 984
10081	101 62 65 61	1024 497 361 441	404183 4980	505905 15748	602360 715	9919651 984
10082	101 64 67 24	1024 802 271 368	409163 4979	521653 15746	603075 714	9918667 984
10083	101 66 68 89	1025 107 241 787	414142 4980	537399 15746	603789 714	9917683 983
10084	101 68 70 56	1025 412 272 704	419122 4979	553145 15745	604503 714	9916700 984
10085	101 70 72 25	1025 717 364 125	424101 4978	568890 15744	605217 714	9915716 983
10086	101 72 73 96	1026 022 516 056	429079 4979	584634 15744	605931 714	9914733 983
10087	101 74 75 69	1026 327 728 503	434058 4978	600377 15742	606645 714	9913750 982
10088	101 76 77 44	1026 633 001 472	439036 4978	616120 15742	607359 714	9912768 983
10089	101 78 79 21	1026 938 334 969	444014 4978	631862 15741	608073 714	9911785 982
10090	101 80 81 00	1027 243 729 000	448992 4978	647603 15741	608787 714	9910803 982
10091	101 82 82 81	1027 549 183 571	453970 4977	663344 15739	609501 714	9909821 982
10092	101 84 84 64	1027 854 698 688	458947 4977	679083 15739	610215 713	9908839 982
10093	101 86 86 49	1028 160 274 357	463924 4977	694822 15738	610928 714	9907857 982
10094	101 88 88 36	1028 465 910 584	468901 4976	710560 15737	611642 714	9906875 981
10095	101 90 90 25	1028 771 607 375	473877 4976	726297 15737	612356 713	9905894 981
10096	101 92 92 16	1029 077 364 736	478853 4977	742034 15735	613069 714	9904913 981
10097	101 94 94 09	1029 383 182 673	483830 4975	757769 15735	613783 713	9903932 981
10098	101 96 96 04	1029 689 061 192	488805 4976	773504 15734	614496 714	9902951 981
10099	101 98 98 01	1029 995 000 299	493781 4975	789238 15734	615210 713	9901970 980
10100	102 01 00 00	1030 301 000 000	498756	804972	615923	9900990
			100·	317·	21·	0·0000

No. n	Square n^2	Cube n^3	Square root $\sqrt{n}$	Sq. rt. of $10n$ $\sqrt{10n}$	Cube root $\sqrt[3]{n}$	Reciprocal $\dfrac{1}{n}$
			100·	317·	21·	0·0000
10100	102 01 00 00	1030 301 000 000	498756	804972	615923	9900990
10101	102 03 02 01	1030 607 060 301	503731 $_{4975}$	820704 $_{15732}$	616637 $_{714}$	9900010 $_{980}$
10102	102 05 04 04	1030 913 181 208	508706 $_{4975}$	836436 $_{15732}$	617350 $_{713}$	9899030 $_{980}$
10103	102 07 06 09	1031 219 362 727	513681 $_{4974}$	852167 $_{15731}$	618063 $_{713}$	9898050 $_{980}$
10104	102 09 08 16	1031 525 604 864	518655 $_{4974}$	867897 $_{15730}$	618777 $_{714}$	9897070 $_{980}$
10105	102 11 10 25	1031 831 907 625	523629 $_{4974}$	883627 $_{15730}$	619490 $_{713}$	9896091 $_{979}$
10106	102 13 12 36	1032 138 271 016	528603 $_{4974}$	899355 $_{15728}$	620203 $_{713}$	9895112 $_{979}$
10107	102 15 14 49	1032 444 695 043	533576 $_{4973}$	915083 $_{15728}$	620916 $_{713}$	9894133 $_{979}$
10108	102 17 16 64	1032 751 179 712	538550 $_{4974}$	930810 $_{15727}$	621629 $_{713}$	9893154 $_{979}$
10109	102 19 18 81	1033 057 725 029	543523 $_{4973}$	946536 $_{15726}$	622342 $_{713}$	9892175 $_{979}$
10110	102 21 21 00	1033 364 331 000	548496 $_{4973}$	962262 $_{15726}$	623055 $_{713}$	9891197 $_{978}$
10111	102 23 23 21	1033 670 997 631	553468 $_{4972}$	977987 $_{15725}$	623768 $_{713}$	9890219 $_{978}$
10112	102 25 25 44	1033 977 724 928	558441 $_{4973}$	993711 $_{15724}$	624481 $_{713}$	9889241 $_{978}$
10113	102 27 27 69	1034 284 512 897	563413 $_{4972}$	*009434 $_{15723}$	625194 $_{712}$	9888263 $_{978}$
10114	102 29 29 96	1034 591 361 544	568385 $_{4972}$	025156 $_{15722}$	625906 $_{713}$	9887285 $_{978}$
10115	102 31 32 25	1034 898 270 875	573356 $_{4971}$	040878 $_{15722}$	626619 $_{713}$	9886307 $_{977}$
10116	102 33 34 56	1035 205 240 896	578328 $_{4972}$	056599 $_{15721}$	627332 $_{712}$	9885330 $_{977}$
10117	102 35 36 89	1035 512 271 613	583299 $_{4971}$	072319 $_{15720}$	628044 $_{713}$	9884353 $_{977}$
10118	102 37 39 24	1035 819 363 032	588270 $_{4971}$	088038 $_{15719}$	628757 $_{712}$	9883376 $_{977}$
10119	102 39 41 61	1036 126 515 159	593240 $_{4970}$	103757 $_{15719}$	629469 $_{713}$	9882399 $_{977}$
10120	102 41 44 00	1036 433 728 000	598211 $_{4971}$	119474 $_{15717}$	630182 $_{712}$	9881423 $_{976}$
10121	102 43 46 41	1036 741 001 561	603181 $_{4970}$	135191 $_{15717}$	630894 $_{713}$	9880447 $_{976}$
10122	102 45 48 84	1037 048 335 848	608151 $_{4970}$	150908 $_{15715}$	631607 $_{712}$	9879470 $_{977}$
10123	102 47 51 29	1037 355 730 867	613120 $_{4969}$	166623 $_{15715}$	632319 $_{712}$	9878495 $_{975}$
10124	102 49 53 76	1037 663 186 624	618090 $_{4970}$	182338 $_{15714}$	633031 $_{713}$	9877519 $_{976}$
10125	102 51 56 25	1037 970 703 125	623059 $_{4969}$	198052 $_{15713}$	633744 $_{712}$	9876543 $_{975}$
10126	102 53 58 76	1038 278 280 376	628028 $_{4969}$	213765 $_{15712}$	634456 $_{712}$	9875568 $_{975}$
10127	102 55 61 29	1038 585 918 383	632997 $_{4968}$	229477 $_{15711}$	635168 $_{712}$	9874593 $_{975}$
10128	102 57 63 84	1038 893 617 152	637965 $_{4968}$	245188 $_{15711}$	635880 $_{712}$	9873618 $_{975}$
10129	102 59 66 41	1039 201 376 689	642933 $_{4968}$	260899 $_{15710}$	636592 $_{712}$	9872643 $_{975}$
10130	102 61 69 00	1039 509 197 000	647901 $_{4968}$	276609 $_{15709}$	637304 $_{712}$	9871668 $_{974}$
10131	102 63 71 61	1039 817 078 091	652869 $_{4967}$	292318 $_{15709}$	638016 $_{712}$	9870694 $_{974}$
10132	102 65 74 24	1040 125 019 968	657836 $_{4967}$	308027 $_{15708}$	638728 $_{712}$	9869720 $_{974}$
10133	102 67 76 89	1040 433 022 637	662803 $_{4967}$	323735 $_{15706}$	639440 $_{712}$	9868746 $_{974}$
10134	102 69 79 56	1040 741 086 104	667770 $_{4967}$	339441 $_{15707}$	640152 $_{711}$	9867772 $_{974}$
10135	102 71 82 25	1041 049 210 375	672737 $_{4967}$	355148 $_{15705}$	640863 $_{712}$	9866798 $_{973}$
10136	102 73 84 96	1041 357 395 456	677704 $_{4966}$	370853 $_{15705}$	641575 $_{712}$	9865825 $_{973}$
10137	102 75 87 69	1041 665 641 353	682670 $_{4966}$	386558 $_{15703}$	642287 $_{711}$	9864852 $_{974}$
10138	102 77 90 44	1041 973 948 072	687636 $_{4966}$	402261 $_{15703}$	642998 $_{712}$	9863878 $_{972}$
10139	102 79 93 21	1042 282 315 619	692602 $_{4965}$	417964 $_{15703}$	643710 $_{712}$	9862906 $_{973}$
10140	102 81 96 00	1042 590 744 000	697567 $_{4965}$	433667 $_{15701}$	644422 $_{711}$	9861933 $_{973}$
10141	102 83 98 81	1042 899 233 221	702532 $_{4965}$	449368 $_{15701}$	645133 $_{712}$	9860960 $_{972}$
10142	102 86 01 64	1043 207 783 288	707497 $_{4965}$	465069 $_{15700}$	645845 $_{711}$	9859988 $_{972}$
10143	102 88 04 49	1043 516 394 207	712462 $_{4964}$	480769 $_{15699}$	646556 $_{711}$	9859016 $_{972}$
10144	102 90 07 36	1043 825 065 984	717426 $_{4965}$	496468 $_{15698}$	647267 $_{712}$	9858044 $_{972}$
10145	102 92 10 25	1044 133 798 625	722391 $_{4964}$	512166 $_{15698}$	647979 $_{711}$	9857072 $_{971}$
10146	102 94 13 16	1044 442 592 136	727355 $_{4964}$	527864 $_{15697}$	648690 $_{711}$	9856101 $_{971}$
10147	102 96 16 09	1044 751 446 523	732319 $_{4963}$	543561 $_{15696}$	649401 $_{711}$	9855130 $_{972}$
10148	102 98 19 04	1045 060 361 792	737282 $_{4963}$	559257 $_{15695}$	650112 $_{711}$	9854158 $_{970}$
10149	103 00 22 01	1045 369 337 949	742245 $_{4963}$	574952 $_{15694}$	650823 $_{711}$	9853188 $_{971}$
10150	103 02 25 00	1045 678 375 000	747208	590646	651534	9852217
			100·	318·	21·	0·0000

No. n	Square n^2	Cube n^3	Square root $\sqrt{n}$	Sq. rt. of $10n$ $\sqrt{10n}$	Cube root $\sqrt[3]{n}$	Reciprocal $\frac{1}{n}$
			100·	318·	21·	0·0000
10150	103 02 25 00	1045 678 375 000	747208 4963	590646 15694	651534 711	9852217 971
10151	103 04 28 01	1045 987 472 951	752171 4963	606340 15693	652245 711	9851246 970
10152	103 06 31 04	1046 296 631 808	757134 4962	622033 15692	652956 711	9850276 970
10153	103 08 34 09	1046 605 851 577	762096 4962	637725 15692	653667 711	9849306 970
10154	103 10 37 16	1046 915 132 264	767058 4962	653417 15690	654378 711	9848336 970
10155	103 12 40 25	1047 224 473 875	772020 4961	669107 15690	655089 711	9847366 970
10156	103 14 43 36	1047 533 876 416	776681 4962	684797 15689	655800 711	9846396 969
10157	103 16 46 49	1047 843 339 893	781943 4961	700486 15689	656511 710	9845427 969
10158	103 18 49 64	1048 152 864 312	786904 4961	716175 15687	657221 711	9844458 969
10159	103 20 52 81	1048 462 449 679	791865 4960	731862 15687	657932 711	9843489 969
10160	103 22 56 00	1048 772 096 000	796825 4961	747549 15686	658643 710	9842520 969
10161	103 24 59 21	1049 081 803 281	801786 4961	763235 15685	659353 711	9841551 968
10162	103 26 62 44	1049 391 571 528	806746 4960	778920 15685	660064 710	9840583 969
10163	103 28 65 69	1049 701 400 747	811706 4959	794605 15683	660774 711	9839614 968
10164	103 30 68 96	1050 011 290 944	816665 4960	810288 15683	661485 710	9838646 968
10165	103 32 72 25	1050 321 242 125	821625 4959	825971 15682	662195 710	9837678 967
10166	103 34 75 56	1050 631 254 296	826584 4959	841653 15682	662905 711	9836711 968
10167	103 36 78 89	1050 941 327 463	831543 4958	857335 15680	663616 710	9835743 967
10168	103 38 82 24	1051 251 461 632	836501 4959	873015 15680	664326 710	9834776 967
10169	103 40 85 61	1051 561 656 809	841460 4958	888695 15679	665036 710	9833809 967
10170	103 42 89 00	1051 871 913 000	846418 4958	904374 15679	665746 710	9832842 967
10171	103 44 92 41	1052 182 230 211	851376 4957	920053 15677	666456 710	9831875 967
10172	103 46 95 84	1052 492 608 448	856333 4958	935730 15677	667166 710	9830908 966
10173	103 48 99 29	1052 803 047 717	861291 4957	951407 15676	667876 710	9829942 966
10174	103 51 02 76	1053 113 548 024	866248 4957	967083 15675	668586 710	9828976 966
10175	103 53 06 25	1053 424 109 375	871205 4957	982758 15675	669296 710	9828010 966
10176	103 55 09 76	1053 734 731 776	876162 4956	998433 15673	670006 710	9827044 966
10177	103 57 13 29	1054 045 415 233	881118 4956	*014106 15673	670716 710	9826078 965
10178	103 59 16 84	1054 356 159 752	886074 4956	029779 15672	671426 709	9825113 965
10179	103 61 20 41	1054 666 965 339	891030 4956	045451 15672	672135 710	9824148 965
10180	103 63 24 00	1054 977 832 000	895986 4956	061123 15670	672845 710	9823183 965
10181	103 65 27 61	1055 288 759 741	900942 4955	076793 15670	673555 709	9822218 965
10182	103 67 31 24	1055 599 748 568	905897 4955	092463 15669	674264 709	9821253 964
10183	103 69 34 89	1055 910 798 487	910852 4954	108132 15668	674974 709	9820289 964
10184	103 71 38 56	1056 221 909 504	915806 4955	123800 15668	675683 710	9819324 964
10185	103 73 42 25	1056 533 081 625	920761 4954	139468 15667	676393 709	9818360 964
10186	103 75 45 96	1056 844 314 856	925715 4954	155135 15666	677102 709	9817396 963
10187	103 77 49 69	1057 155 609 203	930669 4954	170801 15665	677811 710	9816433 964
10188	103 79 53 44	1057 466 964 672	935623 4954	186466 15664	678521 709	9815469 963
10189	103 81 57 21	1057 778 381 269	940577 4953	202130 15664	679230 709	9814506 963
10190	103 83 61 00	1058 089 859 000	945530 4953	217794 15663	679939 709	9813543 963
10191	103 85 64 81	1058 401 397 871	950483 4953	233457 15662	680648 710	9812580 963
10192	103 87 68 64	1058 712 997 888	955436 4952	249119 15661	681358 709	9811617 963
10193	103 89 72 49	1059 024 659 057	960388 4953	264780 15661	682067 709	9810654 962
10194	103 91 76 36	1059 336 381 384	965341 4952	280441 15660	682776 709	9809692 962
10195	103 93 80 25	1059 648 164 875	970293 4951	296101 15659	683485 709	9808730 962
10196	103 95 84 16	1059 960 009 536	975244 4952	311760 15658	684194 708	9807768 962
10197	103 97 88 09	1060 271 915 373	980196 4951	327418 15658	684902 709	9806806 962
10198	103 99 92 04	1060 583 882 392	985147 4952	343076 15656	685611 709	9805844 961
10199	104 01 96 01	1060 895 910 599	990099 4950	358732 15656	686320 709	9804883 961
10200	104 04 00 00	1061 208 000 000	995049	374388	687029	9803922
			100·	319·	21·	0·0000

No. n	Square n²	Cube n³	Square root √n	Sq. rt. of 10n √10n	Cube root ∛n	Reciprocal 1/n
			100·	319·	21·	0·0000
10200	104 04 00 00	1061 208 000 000	995049 4951	374388 15656	687029 709	9803922 962
10201	104 06 04 01	1061 520 150 601	*000000 4950	390044 15654	687738 709	9802960 960
10202	104 08 08 04	1061 832 362 408	004950 4951	405698 15654	688446 709	9802000 960
10203	104 10 12 09	1062 144 635 427	009901 4949	421352 15653	689155 709	9801039 961
10204	104 12 16 16	1062 456 969 664	014850 4950	437005 15652	689863 709	9800078 961 960
10205	104 14 20 25	1062 769 365 125	019800 4949	452657 15651	690572 708	9799118 960
10206	104 16 24 36	1063 081 821 816	024749 4950	468308 15651	691280 709	9798158 960
10207	104 18 28 49	1063 394 339 743	029699 4949	483959 15650	691989 708	9797198 960
10208	104 20 32 64	1063 706 918 912	034648 4949	499609 15649	692697 709	9796238 960
10209	104 22 36 81	1064 019 559 329	039596 4948 4949	515258 15648	693406 709	9795279 959 960
10210	104 24 41 00	1064 332 261 000	044545 4948	530906 15648	694114 708	9794319 959
10211	104 26 45 21	1064 645 023 931	049493 4948	546554 15647	694822 708	9793360 959
10212	104 28 49 44	1064 957 848 128	054441 4947	562201 15646	695530 708	9792401 959
10213	104 30 53 69	1065 270 733 597	059388 4948	577847 15645	696238 708	9791442 958
10214	104 32 57 96	1065 583 680 344	064336 4947	593492 15644	696946 709	9790484 959
10215	104 34 62 25	1065 896 688 375	069283 4947	609136 15644	697655 708	9789525 958
10216	104 36 66 56	1066 209 757 696	074230 4947	624780 15643	698363 708	9788567 958
10217	104 38 70 89	1066 522 888 313	079177 4947	640423 15642	699071 707	9787609 958
10218	104 40 75 24	1066 836 080 232	084123 4946	656065 15642	699778 708	9786651 958
10219	104 42 79 61	1067 149 333 459	089070 4947 4946	671707 15640	700486 708	9785693 957
10220	104 44 84 00	1067 462 648 000	094016 4945	687347 15640	701194 708	9784736 958
10221	104 46 88 41	1067 776 023 861	098961 4946	702987 15639	701902 708	9783778 957
10222	104 48 92 84	1068 089 461 048	103907 4945	718626 15639	702610 707	9782821 957
10223	104 50 97 29	1068 402 959 567	108852 4945	734265 15637	703317 708	9781864 957
10224	104 53 01 76	1068 716 519 424	113797 4945	749902 15637	704025 708	9780908 957
10225	104 55 06 25	1069 030 140 625	118742 4945	765539 15636	704733 707	9779951 956
10226	104 57 10 76	1069 343 823 176	123687 4944	781175 15635	705440 708	9778995 956
10227	104 59 15 29	1069 657 567 083	128631 4944	796810 15635	706148 707	9778039 956
10228	104 61 19 84	1069 971 372 352	133575 4944	812445 15634	706855 707	9777083 956
10229	104 63 24 41	1070 285 238 989	138519 4944 4943	828079 15633	707562 708	9776127 956
10230	104 65 29 00	1070 599 167 000	143462 4944	843712 15632	708270 707	9775171 955
10231	104 67 33 61	1070 913 156 391	148406 4943	859344 15632	708977 707	9774216 956
10232	104 69 38 24	1071 227 207 168	153349 4943	874976 15630	709684 708	9773260 955
10233	104 71 42 89	1071 541 319 337	158292 4942	890606 15630	710392 707	9772305 955
10234	104 73 47 56	1071 855 492 904	163234 4943	906236 15629	711099 707	9771350 955
10235	104 75 52 25	1072 169 727 875	168177 4942	921865 15629	711806 707	9770396 955
10236	104 77 56 96	1072 484 024 256	173119 4942	937494 15628	712513 707	9769441 955
10237	104 79 61 69	1072 798 382 053	178061 4942	953122 15626	713220 707	9768487 954
10238	104 81 66 44	1073 112 801 272	183003 4942	968748 15627	713927 707	9767533 954
10239	104 83 71 21	1073 427 281 919	187944 4941	984375 15625	714634 707	9766579 954
10240	104 85 76 00	1073 741 824 000	192885 4941	*000000 15625	715341 707	9765625 954
10241	104 87 80 81	1074 056 427 521	197826 4941	015625 15623	716048 707	9764671 954
10242	104 89 85 64	1074 371 092 488	202767 4940	031248 15624	716755 706	9763718 953
10243	104 91 90 49	1074 685 818 907	207707 4940	046872 15622	717461 707	9762765 953
10244	104 93 95 36	1075 000 606 784	212647 4940	062494 15621	718168 707	9761812 953
10245	104 96 00 25	1075 315 456 125	217587 4940	078115 15621	718875 706	9760859 953
10246	104 98 05 16	1075 630 366 936	222527 4940	093736 15620	719581 707	9759906 953
10247	105 00 10 09	1075 945 339 223	227467 4939	109356 15620	720288 706	9758954 952
10248	105 02 15 04	1076 260 372 992	232406 4939	124976 15618	720994 707	9758002 952
10249	105 04 20 01	1076 575 468 249	237345 4939	140594 15618	721701 706	9757049 951
10250	105 06 25 00	1076 890 625 000	242284 101·	156212 320·	722407 21·	9756098 0·0000

No. n	Square n^2	Cube n^3	Square root $\sqrt{n}$	Sq. rt. of $10n$ $\sqrt{10n}$	Cube root $\sqrt[3]{n}$	Reciprocal $\dfrac{1}{n}$
			101·	320·	21·	0·0000
10250	105 06 25 00	1076 890 625 000	242284 $_{4938}$	156212 $_{15617}$	722407 $_{707}$	9756098 $_{952}$
10251	105 08 30 01	1077 205 843 251	247222 $_{4938}$	171829 $_{15616}$	723114 $_{706}$	9755146 $_{952}$
10252	105 10 35 04	1077 521 123 008	252160 $_{4939}$	187445 $_{15616}$	723820 $_{706}$	9754194 $_{951}$
10253	105 12 40 09	1077 836 464 277	257099 $_{4938}$	203061 $_{15614}$	724526 $_{707}$	9753243 $_{951}$
10254	105 14 45 16	1078 151 867 064	262036 $_{4938}$	218675 $_{15614}$	725233 $_{706}$	9752292 $_{951}$
10255	105 16 50 25	1078 467 331 375	266974 $_{4937}$	234289 $_{15613}$	725939 $_{706}$	9751341 $_{951}$
10256	105 18 55 36	1078 782 857 216	271911 $_{4937}$	249902 $_{15613}$	726645 $_{706}$	9750390 $_{951}$
10257	105 20 60 49	1079 098 444 593	276848 $_{4937}$	265515 $_{15612}$	727351 $_{706}$	9749439 $_{951}$
10258	105 22 65 64	1079 414 093 512	281785 $_{4937}$	281127 $_{15610}$	728057 $_{706}$	9748489 $_{950}$
10259	105 24 70 81	1079 729 803 979	286722 $_{4936}$	296737 $_{15611}$	728763 $_{706}$	9747539 $_{950}$
10260	105 26 76 00	1080 045 576 000	291658 $_{4936}$	312348 $_{15609}$	729469 $_{706}$	9746589 $_{950}$
10261	105 28 81 21	1080 361 409 581	296594 $_{4936}$	327957 $_{15609}$	730175 $_{706}$	9745639 $_{950}$
10262	105 30 86 44	1080 677 304 728	301530 $_{4936}$	343566 $_{15607}$	730881 $_{706}$	9744689 $_{950}$
10263	105 32 91 69	1080 993 261 447	306466 $_{4935}$	359173 $_{15608}$	731587 $_{706}$	9743740 $_{949}$
10264	105 34 96 96	1081 309 279 744	311401 $_{4935}$	374781 $_{15606}$	732293 $_{706}$	9742790 $_{950}$
10265	105 37 02 25	1081 625 359 625	316336 $_{4935}$	390387 $_{15605}$	732999 $_{705}$	9741841 $_{949}$
10266	105 39 07 56	1081 941 501 096	321271 $_{4935}$	405992 $_{15605}$	733704 $_{706}$	9740892 $_{949}$
10267	105 41 12 89	1082 257 704 163	326206 $_{4934}$	421597 $_{15605}$	734410 $_{706}$	9739944 $_{948}$
10268	105 43 18 24	1082 573 968 832	331140 $_{4935}$	437201 $_{15604}$	735116 $_{705}$	9738995 $_{949}$
10269	105 45 23 61	1082 890 295 109	336075 $_{4933}$	452805 $_{15602}$	735821 $_{706}$	9738047 $_{948}$
10270	105 47 29 00	1083 206 683 000	341008 $_{4934}$	468407 $_{15602}$	736527 $_{705}$	9737098 $_{948}$
10271	105 49 34 41	1083 523 132 511	345942 $_{4934}$	484009 $_{15601}$	737232 $_{706}$	9736150 $_{948}$
10272	105 51 39 84	1083 839 643 648	350876 $_{4933}$	499610 $_{15600}$	737938 $_{705}$	9735202 $_{947}$
10273	105 53 45 29	1084 156 216 417	355809 $_{4933}$	515210 $_{15600}$	738643 $_{705}$	9734255 $_{948}$
10274	105 55 50 76	1084 472 850 824	360742 $_{4933}$	530810 $_{15598}$	739348 $_{706}$	9733307 $_{947}$
10275	105 57 56 25	1084 789 546 875	365675 $_{4932}$	546408 $_{15598}$	740054 $_{705}$	9732360 $_{947}$
10276	105 59 61 76	1085 106 304 576	370607 $_{4932}$	562006 $_{15598}$	740759 $_{705}$	9731413 $_{947}$
10277	105 61 67 29	1085 423 123 933	375539 $_{4932}$	577604 $_{15596}$	741464 $_{705}$	9730466 $_{947}$
10278	105 63 72 84	1085 740 004 952	380471 $_{4932}$	593200 $_{15596}$	742169 $_{705}$	9729519 $_{946}$
10279	105 65 78 41	1086 056 947 639	385403 $_{4932}$	608796 $_{15595}$	742874 $_{705}$	9728573 $_{947}$
10280	105 67 84 00	1086 373 952 000	390335 $_{4931}$	624391 $_{15594}$	743579 $_{705}$	9727626 $_{946}$
10281	105 69 89 61	1086 691 018 041	395266 $_{4931}$	639985 $_{15593}$	744284 $_{705}$	9726680 $_{946}$
10282	105 71 95 24	1087 008 145 768	400197 $_{4931}$	655578 $_{15593}$	744989 $_{705}$	9725734 $_{946}$
10283	105 74 00 89	1087 325 335 187	405128 $_{4931}$	671171 $_{15592}$	745694 $_{705}$	9724788 $_{945}$
10284	105 76 06 56	1087 642 586 304	410059 $_{4930}$	686763 $_{15591}$	746399 $_{705}$	9723843 $_{946}$
10285	105 78 12 25	1087 959 899 125	414989 $_{4930}$	702354 $_{15591}$	747104 $_{705}$	9722897 $_{945}$
10286	105 80 17 96	1088 277 273 656	419919 $_{4930}$	717945 $_{15589}$	747809 $_{705}$	9721952 $_{945}$
10287	105 82 23 69	1088 594 709 903	424849 $_{4930}$	733534 $_{15589}$	748514 $_{704}$	9721007 $_{945}$
10288	105 84 29 44	1088 912 207 872	429779 $_{4929}$	749123 $_{15588}$	749218 $_{705}$	9720062 $_{944}$
10289	105 86 35 21	1089 229 767 569	434708 $_{4929}$	764711 $_{15588}$	749923 $_{705}$	9719118 $_{945}$
10290	105 88 41 00	1089 547 389 000	439637 $_{4929}$	780299 $_{15586}$	750628 $_{704}$	9718173 $_{944}$
10291	105 90 46 81	1089 865 072 171	444566 $_{4929}$	795885 $_{15586}$	751332 $_{705}$	9717229 $_{944}$
10292	105 92 52 64	1090 182 817 088	449495 $_{4928}$	811471 $_{15585}$	752037 $_{705}$	9716284 $_{945}$
10293	105 94 58 49	1090 500 623 757	454423 $_{4928}$	827056 $_{15585}$	752741 $_{705}$	9715341 $_{943}$
10294	105 96 64 36	1090 818 492 184	459351 $_{4928}$	842641 $_{15583}$	753446 $_{704}$	9714397 $_{944}$
10295	105 98 70 25	1091 136 422 375	464279 $_{4928}$	858224 $_{15583}$	754150 $_{704}$	9713453 $_{943}$
10296	106 00 76 16	1091 454 414 336	469207 $_{4928}$	873807 $_{15582}$	754854 $_{705}$	9712510 $_{944}$
10297	106 02 82 09	1091 772 468 073	474135 $_{4927}$	889389 $_{15581}$	755559 $_{704}$	9711566 $_{944}$
10298	106 04 88 04	1092 090 583 592	479062 $_{4927}$	904970 $_{15581}$	756263 $_{704}$	9710623 $_{943}$
10299	106 06 94 01	1092 408 760 899	483989 $_{4927}$	920551 $_{15580}$	756967 $_{704}$	9709681 $_{942}$
10300	106 09 00 00	1092 727 000 000	488916	936131	757671	9708738 $_{943}$
			101·	320·	21·	0·0000

No. n	Square n^2	Cube n^3	Square root $\sqrt{n}$	Sq. rt. of $10n$ $\sqrt{10n}$	Cube root $\sqrt[3]{n}$	Reciprocal $\frac{1}{n}$
			101·	320·	21·	0·0000
10300	106 09 00 00	1092 727 000 000	488916 4926	936131 15579	757671 704	9708738 943
10301	106 11 06 01	1093 045 300 901	493842 4926	951710 15579	758375 704	9707795 943
10302	106 13 12 04	1093 363 663 608	498768 4927	967288 15578	759079 704	9706853 942
10303	106 15 18 09	1093 682 088 127	503695 4925	982866 15576	759783 704	9705911 942
10304	106 17 24 16	1094 000 574 464	508620 4926	998442 15576	760487 704	9704969 942
10305	106 19 30 25	1094 319 122 625	513546 4925	*014018 15576	761191 704	9704027 941
10306	106 21 36 36	1094 637 732 616	518471 4925	029594 15574	761895 704	9703086 942
10307	106 23 42 49	1094 956 404 443	523396 4925	045168 15574	762599 704	9702144 941
10308	106 25 48 64	1095 275 138 112	528321 4925	060742 15573	763303 703	9701203 941
10309	106 27 54 81	1095 593 933 629	533246 4924	076315 15572	764006 704	9700262 941
10310	106 29 61 00	1095 912 791 000	538170 4924	091887 15572	764710 704	9699321 941
10311	106 31 67 21	1096 231 710 231	543094 4924	107459 15570	765414 703	9698380 941
10312	106 33 73 44	1096 550 691 328	548018 4924	123029 15570	766117 704	9697440 940
10313	106 35 79 69	1096 869 734 297	552942 4923	138599 15570	766821 704	9696500 941
10314	106 37 85 96	1097 188 839 144	557865 4923	154169 15568	767525 703	9695559 940
10315	106 39 92 25	1097 508 005 875	562788 4923	169737 15568	768228 703	9694619 939
10316	106 41 98 56	1097 827 234 496	567711 4923	185305 15567	768931 703	9693680 940
10317	106 44 04 89	1098 146 525 013	572634 4923	200872 15566	769635 703	9692740 939
10318	106 46 11 24	1098 465 877 432	577557 4922	216438 15565	770338 703	9691801 939
10319	106 48 17 61	1098 785 291 759	582479 4922	232003 15565	771041 704	9690862 940
10320	106 50 24 00	1099 104 768 000	587401 4922	247568 15564	771745 703	9689922 938
10321	106 52 30 41	1099 424 306 161	592323 4921	263132 15563	772448 703	9688984 939
10322	106 54 36 84	1099 743 906 248	597244 4921	278695 15563	773151 703	9688045 939
10323	106 56 43 29	1100 063 568 267	602165 4921	294258 15561	773854 703	9687106 938
10324	106 58 49 76	1100 383 292 224	607086 4921	309819 15561	774557 703	9686168 938
10325	106 60 56 25	1100 703 078 125	612007 4921	325380 15560	775260 703	9685230 938
10326	106 62 62 76	1101 022 925 976	616928 4920	340940 15560	775963 703	9684292 938
10327	106 64 69 29	1101 342 835 783	621848 4920	356500 15559	776666 703	9683354 937
10328	106 66 75 84	1101 662 807 552	626768 4920	372059 15557	777369 703	9682417 938
10329	106 68 82 41	1101 982 841 289	631688 4920	387616 15558	778072 703	9681479 937
10330	106 70 89 00	1102 302 937 000	636608 4919	403174 15556	778775 702	9680542 937
10331	106 72 95 61	1102 623 094 691	641527 4919	418730 15556	779477 703	9679605 937
10332	106 75 02 24	1102 943 314 368	646446 4919	434286 15555	780180 703	9678668 936
10333	106 77 08 89	1103 263 596 037	651365 4919	449841 15554	780883 703	9677732 937
10334	106 79 15 56	1103 583 939 704	656284 4918	465395 15553	781585 703	9676795 936
10335	106 81 22 25	1103 904 345 375	661202 4918	480948 15553	782288 702	9675859 936
10336	106 83 28 96	1104 224 813 056	666120 4918	496501 15552	782990 703	9674923 936
10337	106 85 35 69	1194 545 342 753	671038 4918	512053 15551	783693 702	9673987 936
10338	106 87 42 44	1104 865 934 472	675956 4917	527604 15550	784395 703	9673051 936
10339	106 89 49 21	1105 186 588 219	680873 4918	543154 15550	785098 702	9672115 935
10340	106 91 56 00	1105 507 304 000	685791 4917	558704 15549	785800 702	9671180 935
10341	106 93 62 81	1105 828 081 821	690708 4916	574253 15548	786502 703	9670245 935
10342	106 95 69 64	1106 148 921 688	695624 4917	589801 15547	787205 702	9669310 935
10343	106 97 76 49	1106 469 823 607	700541 4916	605348 15547	787907 702	9668375 935
10344	106 99 83 36	1106 790 787 584	705457 4916	620895 15546	788609 702	9667440 934
10345	107 01 90 25	1107 111 813 625	710373 4916	636441 15545	789311 702	9666506 935
10346	107 03 97 16	1107 432 901 736	715289 4915	651986 15544	790013 702	9665571 934
10347	107 06 04 09	1107 754 051 923	720204 4916	667530 15544	790715 702	9664637 934
10348	107 08 11 04	1108 075 264 192	725120 4915	683074 15543	791417 702	9663703 934
10349	107 10 18 01	1108 396 538 549	730035 4915	698617 15542	792119 702	9662769 933
10350	107 12 25 00	1108 717 875 000	734950	714159	792821	9661836
			101·	321·	21·	0·0000

No. n	Square n^2	Cube n^3	Square root $\sqrt{n}$	Sq. rt. of $10n$ $\sqrt{10n}$	Cube root $\sqrt[3]{n}$	Reciprocal $\dfrac{1}{n}$
			101·	321·	21·	0·0000
10350	107 12 25 00	1108 717 875 000	734950 4914	714159 15541	792821 702	9661836 934
10351	107 14 32 01	1109 039 273 551	739864 4915	729700 15541	793523 702	9660902 934
10352	107 16 39 04	1109 360 734 208	744779 4914	745241 15540	794225 701	9659969 933
10353	107 18 46 09	1109 682 256 977	749693 4914	760781 15539	794926 702	9659036 933
10354	107 20 53 16	1110 003 841 864	754607 4913	776320 15538	795628 702	9658103 933
						933
10355	107 22 60 25	1110 325 488 875	759520 4914	791858 15538	796330 701	9657170 932
10356	107 24 67 36	1110 647 198 016	764434 4913	807398 15537	797031 702	9656238 932
10357	107 26 74 49	1110 968 969 293	769347 4913	822933 15536	797733 701	9655306 932
10358	107 28 81 64	1111 290 802 712	774260 4913	838469 15535	798434 702	9654373 933
10359	107 30 88 81	1111 612 698 279	779173 4912	854004 15535	799136 701	9653441 932
						931
10360	107 32 96 00	1111 934 656 000	784085 4912	869539 15534	799837 702	9652510 932
10361	107 35 03 21	1112 256 675 881	788997 4912	885073 15533	800539 702	9651578 932
10362	107 37 10 44	1112 578 757 928	793909 4912	900606 15532	801240 701	9650647 931
10363	107 39 17 69	1112 900 902 147	798821 4912	916138 15532	801941 702	9649715 931
10364	107 41 24 96	1113 223 108 544	803733 4911	931670 15531	802643 701	9648784 931
						930
10365	107 43 32 25	1113 545 377 125	808644 4911	947201 15530	803344 701	9647853 930
10366	107 45 39 56	1113 867 707 896	813555 4911	962731 15529	804045 701	9646923 931
10367	107 47 46 89	1114 190 100 863	818466 4910	978260 15529	804746 701	9645992 930
10368	107 49 54 24	1114 512 556 032	823376 4911	993789 15528	805447 701	9645062 930
10369	107 51 61 61	1114 835 073 409	828287 4910	*009317 15527	806148 701	9644132 930
						930
10370	107 53 69 00	1115 157 653 000	833197 4910	024844 15526	806849 701	9643202 930
10371	107 55 76 41	1115 480 294 811	838107 4909	040370 15526	807550 701	9642272 930
10372	107 57 83 84	1115 802 998 848	843016 4910	055896 15525	808251 701	9641342 930
10373	107 59 91 29	1116 125 765 117	847926 4909	071421 15524	808952 701	9640413 929
10374	107 61 98 76	1116 448 593 624	852835 4909	086945 15523	809653 700	9639483 929
						929
10375	107 64 06 25	1116 771 484 375	857744 4909	102468 15523	810353 701	9638554 929
10376	107 66 13 76	1117 094 437 376	862653 4908	117991 15522	811054 701	9637625 928
10377	107 68 21 29	1117 417 452 633	867561 4908	133513 15521	811755 700	9636697 929
10378	107 70 28 84	1117 740 530 152	872469 4908	149034 15520	812455 701	9635768 928
10379	107 72 36 41	1118 063 669 939	877377 4908	164554 15520	813156 700	9634840 929
						929
10380	107 74 44 00	1118 386 872 000	882285 4908	180074 15519	813856 701	9633911 928
10381	107 76 51 61	1118 710 136 341	887193 4907	195593 15518	814557 700	9632983 928
10382	107 78 59 24	1119 033 462 968	892100 4907	211111 15518	815257 701	9632055 928
10383	107 80 66 89	1119 356 851 887	897007 4907	226628 15517	815958 700	9631128 927
10384	107 82 74 56	1119 680 303 104	901914 4906	242145 15516	816658 700	9630200 928
						927
10385	107 84 82 25	1120 003 816 625	906820 4907	257661 15515	817358 701	9629273 927
10386	107 86 89 96	1120 327 392 456	911727 4906	273176 15514	818059 700	9628346 927
10387	107 88 97 69	1120 651 030 603	916633 4905	288690 15514	818759 700	9627419 927
10388	107 91 05 44	1120 974 731 072	921538 4906	304204 15513	819459 700	9626492 926
10389	107 93 13 21	1121 298 493 869	926444 4905	319717 15512	820159 700	9625566 927
						926
10390	107 95 21 00	1121 622 319 000	931349 4906	335229 15512	820859 700	9624639 926
10391	107 97 28 81	1121 946 206 471	936255 4904	350741 15510	821559 700	9623713 926
10392	107 99 36 64	1122 270 156 288	941159 4905	366251 15510	822259 700	9622787 926
10393	108 01 44 49	1122 594 168 457	946064 4905	381761 15509	822959 700	9621861 926
10394	108 03 52 36	1122 918 242 984	950969 4904	397270 15509	823659 700	9620935 925
						925
10395	108 05 60 25	1123 242 379 875	955873 4904	412779 15508	824359 700	9620010 926
10396	108 07 68 16	1123 566 579 136	960777 4904	428287 15507	825059 700	9619084 925
10397	108 09 76 09	1123 890 840 773	965681 4903	443794 15506	825759 699	9618159 925
10398	108 11 84 04	1124 215 164 792	970584 4903	459300 15505	826458 700	9617234 925
10399	108 13 92 01	1124 539 551 199	975487 4903	474805 15505	827158 700	9616309 924
						924
10400	108 16 00 00	1124 864 000 000	980390 101·	490310 322·	827858 21·	9615385 0·0000

No. n	Square n^2	Cube n^3	Square root $\sqrt{n}$	Sq. rt. of $10n$ $\sqrt{10n}$	Cube root $\sqrt[3]{n}$	Reciprocal $\dfrac{1}{n}$
			101·	322·	21·	0·0000
10400	108 16 00 00	1124 864 000 000	980390 4903	490310 15504	827858 699	9615385 925
10401	108 18 08 01	1125 188 511 201	985293 4903	505814 15503	828557 700	9614460 924
10402	108 20 16 04	1125 513 084 808	990196 4902	521317 15503	829257 699	9613536 924
10403	108 22 24 09	1125 837 720 827	995098 4902	536820 15501	829956 700	9612612 924
10404	108 24 32 16	1126 162 419 264	*000000 4902	552321 15501	830656 700	9611688 924
10405	108 26 40 25	1126 487 180 125	004902 4901	567822 15501	831355 700	9610764 924
10406	108 28 48 36	1126 812 003 416	009803 4901	583323 15499	832055 699	9609840 923
10407	108 30 56 49	1127 136 889 143	014705 4901	598822 15499	832754 699	9608917 923
10408	108 32 64 64	1127 461 837 312	019606 4901	614321 15498	833453 699	9607994 923
10409	108 34 72 81	1127 786 847 929	024507 4901	629819 15497	834152 700	9607071 923
10410	108 36 81 00	1128 111 921 000	029408 4900	645316 15497	834852 699	9606148 923
10411	108 38 89 21	1128 437 056 531	034308 4900	660813 15495	835551 699	9605225 922
10412	108 40 97 44	1128 762 254 528	039208 4900	676308 15495	836250 699	9604303 923
10413	108 43 05 69	1129 087 514 997	044108 4900	691803 15495	836949 699	9603380 922
10414	108 45 13 96	1129 412 837 944	049008 4899	707298 15493	837648 699	9602458 922
10415	108 47 22 25	1129 738 223 375	053907 4900	722791 15493	838347 699	9601536 922
10416	108 49 30 56	1130 063 671 296	058807 4899	738284 15492	839046 699	9600614 921
10417	108 51 38 89	1130 389 181 713	063706 4898	753776 15491	839745 698	9599693 922
10418	108 53 47 24	1130 714 754 632	068604 4899	769267 15491	840443 699	9598771 921
10419	108 55 55 61	1131 040 390 059	073503 4898	784758 15490	841142 699	9597850 921
10420	108 57 64 00	1131 366 088 000	078401 4898	800248 15489	841841 699	9596929 921
10421	108 59 72 41	1131 691 848 461	083299 4898	815737 15488	842540 698	9596008 921
10422	108 61 80 84	1132 017 671 448	088197 4898	831225 15488	843238 699	9595087 920
10423	108 63 89 29	1132 343 556 967	093095 4897	846713 15487	843937 698	9594167 921
10424	108 65 97 76	1132 669 505 024	097992 4897	862200 15486	844635 699	9593246 920
10425	108 68 06 25	1132 995 515 625	102889 4897	877686 15485	845334 698	9592326 920
10426	108 70 14 76	1133 321 588 776	107786 4897	893171 15485	846032 699	9591406 920
10427	108 72 23 29	1133 647 724 483	112683 4896	908656 15484	846731 698	9590486 919
10428	108 74 31 84	1133 973 922 752	117579 4896	924140 15483	847429 699	9589567 919
10429	108 76 40 41	1134 300 183 589	122475 4896	939623 15482	848128 698	9588647 919
10430	108 78 49 00	1134 626 507 000	127371 4896	955105 15482	848826 698	9587728 919
10431	108 80 57 61	1134 952 892 991	132267 4896	970587 15481	849524 698	9586809 919
10432	108 82 66 24	1135 279 341 568	137163 4895	986068 15480	850222 698	9585890 919
10433	108 84 74 89	1135 605 852 737	142058 4895	*001548 15479	850920 699	9584971 919
10434	108 86 83 56	1135 932 426 504	146953 4895	017027 15479	851619 698	9584052 918
10435	108 88 92 25	1136 259 062 875	151848 4894	032506 15478	852317 698	9583134 919
10436	108 91 00 96	1136 585 761 856	156742 4895	047984 15477	853015 698	9582215 918
10437	108 93 09 69	1136 912 523 453	161637 4894	063461 15477	853713 698	9581297 918
10438	108 95 18 44	1137 239 347 672	166531 4894	078938 15475	854411 697	9580379 917
10439	108 97 27 21	1137 566 234 519	171425 4893	094413 15475	855108 698	9579462 918
10440	108 99 36 00	1137 893 184 000	176318 4894	109888 15475	855806 698	9578544 917
10441	109 01 44 81	1138 220 196 121	181212 4893	125363 15473	856504 698	9577627 918
10442	109 03 53 64	1138 547 270 888	186105 4893	140836 15473	857202 698	9576709 917
10443	109 05 62 49	1138 874 408 307	190998 4892	156309 15472	857900 697	9575792 916
10444	109 07 71 36	1139 201 608 384	195890 4893	171781 15471	858597 698	9574876 917
10445	109 09 80 25	1139 528 871 125	200783 4892	187252 15471	859295 697	9573959 917
10446	109 11 89 16	1139 856 196 536	205675 4892	202723 15470	859992 698	9573042 916
10447	109 13 98 09	1140 183 584 623	210567 4892	218193 15469	860690 697	9572126 916
10448	109 16 07 04	1140 511 035 392	215459 4891	233662 15468	861387 698	9571210 916
10449	109 18 16 01	1140 838 548 849	220350 4892	249130 15468	862085 697	9570294 916
10450	109 20 25 00	1141 166 125 000	225242 102·	264598 323·	862782 21·	9569378 0·0000

No. n	Square n^2	Cube n^3	Square root $\sqrt{n}$	Sq. rt. of $10n$ $\sqrt{10n}$	Cube root $\sqrt[3]{n}$	Reciprocal $\dfrac{1}{n}$
			102·	323·	21·	0·0000
10450	109 20 25 00	1141 166 125 000	225242 $_{4891}$	264598 $_{15466}$	862782 $_{698}$	9569378 $_{916}$
10451	109 22 34 01	1141 493 763 851	230133 $_{4890}$	280064 $_{15466}$	863480 $_{697}$	9568462 $_{915}$
10452	109 24 43 04	1141 821 465 408	235023 $_{4891}$	295530 $_{15466}$	864177 $_{697}$	9567547 $_{915}$
10453	109 26 52 09	1142 149 229 677	239914 $_{4890}$	310996 $_{15464}$	864874 $_{697}$	9566632 $_{916}$
10454	109 28 61 16	1142 477 056 664	244804 $_{4890}$	326460 $_{15464}$	865571 $_{698}$	9565716 $_{914}$
10455	109 30 70 25	1142 804 946 375	249694 $_{4890}$	341924 $_{15463}$	866269 $_{697}$	9564802 $_{915}$
10456	109 32 79 36	1143 132 898 816	254584 $_{4890}$	357387 $_{15463}$	866966 $_{697}$	9563887 $_{915}$
10457	109 34 88 49	1143 460 913 993	259474 $_{4889}$	372850 $_{15461}$	867663 $_{697}$	9562972 $_{914}$
10458	109 36 97 64	1143 788 991 912	264363 $_{4889}$	388311 $_{15461}$	868360 $_{697}$	9562058 $_{914}$
10459	109 39 06 81	1144 117 132 579	269252 $_{4889}$	403772 $_{15461}$	869057 $_{697}$	9561144 $_{915}$
10460	109 41 16 00	1144 445 336 000	274141 $_{4889}$	419233 $_{15459}$	869754 $_{697}$	9560229 $_{913}$
10461	109 43 25 21	1144 773 602 181	279030 $_{4889}$	434692 $_{15459}$	870451 $_{697}$	9559316 $_{914}$
10462	109 45 34 44	1145 101 931 128	283919 $_{4888}$	450151 $_{15458}$	871148 $_{696}$	9558402 $_{914}$
10463	109 47 43 69	1145 430 322 847	288807 $_{4888}$	465609 $_{15457}$	871844 $_{697}$	9557488 $_{913}$
10464	109 49 52 96	1145 758 777 344	293695 $_{4888}$	481066 $_{15456}$	872541 $_{697}$	9556575 $_{913}$
10465	109 51 62 25	1146 087 294 625	298583 $_{4887}$	496522 $_{15456}$	873238 $_{697}$	9555662 $_{913}$
10466	109 53 71 56	1146 415 874 696	303470 $_{4887}$	511978 $_{15455}$	873935 $_{696}$	9554749 $_{913}$
10467	109 55 80 89	1146 744 517 563	308357 $_{4887}$	527433 $_{15454}$	874631 $_{697}$	9553836 $_{913}$
10468	109 57 90 24	1147 073 223 232	313244 $_{4887}$	542887 $_{15454}$	875328 $_{696}$	9552923 $_{912}$
10469	109 59 99 61	1147 401 991 709	318131 $_{4887}$	558341 $_{15453}$	876024 $_{697}$	9552011 $_{913}$
10470	109 62 09 00	1147 730 823 000	323018 $_{4886}$	573794 $_{15452}$	876721 $_{696}$	9551098 $_{912}$
10471	109 64 18 41	1148 059 717 111	327904 $_{4886}$	589246 $_{15451}$	877417 $_{697}$	9550186 $_{912}$
10472	109 66 27 84	1148 388 674 048	332790 $_{4886}$	604697 $_{15451}$	878114 $_{696}$	9549274 $_{912}$
10473	109 68 37 29	1148 717 693 817	337676 $_{4886}$	620148 $_{15450}$	878810 $_{697}$	9548362 $_{911}$
10474	109 70 46 76	1149 046 776 424	342562 $_{4885}$	635598 $_{15449}$	879507 $_{696}$	9547451 $_{912}$
10475	109 72 56 25	1149 375 921 875	347447 $_{4886}$	651047 $_{15448}$	880203 $_{696}$	9546539 $_{911}$
10476	109 74 65 76	1149 705 130 176	352333 $_{4885}$	666495 $_{15448}$	880899 $_{696}$	9545628 $_{911}$
10477	109 76 75 29	1150 034 401 333	357218 $_{4884}$	681943 $_{15447}$	881595 $_{696}$	9544717 $_{911}$
10478	109 78 84 84	1150 363 735 352	362102 $_{4885}$	697390 $_{15446}$	882291 $_{697}$	9543806 $_{911}$
10479	109 80 94 41	1150 693 132 239	366987 $_{4884}$	712836 $_{15445}$	882988 $_{696}$	9542895 $_{910}$
10480	109 83 04 00	1151 022 592 000	371871 $_{4884}$	728281 $_{15445}$	883684 $_{696}$	9541985 $_{911}$
10481	109 85 13 61	1151 352 114 641	376755 $_{4884}$	743726 $_{15444}$	884380 $_{696}$	9541074 $_{910}$
10482	109 87 23 24	1151 681 700 168	381639 $_{4884}$	759170 $_{15443}$	885076 $_{696}$	9540164 $_{910}$
10483	109 89 32 89	1152 011 348 587	386523 $_{4883}$	774613 $_{15442}$	885772 $_{695}$	9539254 $_{910}$
10484	109 91 42 56	1152 341 059 904	391406 $_{4883}$	790055 $_{15442}$	886467 $_{696}$	9538344 $_{910}$
10485	109 93 52 25	1152 670 834 125	396289 $_{4883}$	805497 $_{15441}$	887163 $_{696}$	9537434 $_{909}$
10486	109 95 61 96	1153 000 671 256	401172 $_{4883}$	820938 $_{15440}$	887859 $_{696}$	9536525 $_{909}$
10487	109 97 71 69	1153 330 571 303	406055 $_{4882}$	836378 $_{15440}$	888555 $_{696}$	9535616 $_{909}$
10488	109 99 81 44	1153 660 534 272	410937 $_{4882}$	851818 $_{15440}$	889251 $_{695}$	9534706 $_{910}$
10489	110 01 91 21	1153 990 560 169	415819 $_{4882}$	867257 $_{15438}$	889946 $_{696}$	9533797 $_{909}$
10490	110 04 01 00	1154 320 649 000	420701 $_{4882}$	882695 $_{15437}$	890642 $_{695}$	9532888 $_{908}$
10491	110 06 10 81	1154 650 800 771	425583 $_{4881}$	898132 $_{15437}$	891337 $_{696}$	9531980 $_{909}$
10492	110 08 20 64	1154 981 015 488	430464 $_{4881}$	913569 $_{15436}$	892033 $_{695}$	9531071 $_{908}$
10493	110 10 30 49	1155 311 293 157	435345 $_{4881}$	929005 $_{15435}$	892728 $_{696}$	9530163 $_{908}$
10494	110 12 40 36	1155 641 633 784	440226 $_{4881}$	944440 $_{15434}$	893424 $_{695}$	9529255 $_{908}$
10495	110 14 50 25	1155 972 037 375	445107 $_{4881}$	959874 $_{15434}$	894119 $_{696}$	9528347 $_{908}$
10496	110 16 60 16	1156 302 503 936	449988 $_{4880}$	975308 $_{15433}$	894815 $_{695}$	9527439 $_{908}$
10497	110 18 70 09	1156 633 033 473	454868 $_{4880}$	*990741 $_{15432}$	895510 $_{695}$	9526531 $_{907}$
10498	110 20 80 04	1156 963 625 992	459748 $_{4880}$	*006173 $_{15432}$	896205 $_{696}$	9525624 $_{907}$
10499	110 22 90 01	1157 294 281 499	464628 $_{4880}$	021604 $_{15431}$	896901 $_{695}$	9524717 $_{907}$
10500	110 25 00 00	1157 625 000 000	469508	037035	897596	9523810
			102·	324·	21·	0·0000

211

No. n	Square n^2	Cube n^3	Square root $\sqrt{n}$	Sq. rt. of $10n$ $\sqrt{10n}$	Cube root $\sqrt[3]{n}$	Reciprocal $\dfrac{1}{n}$
			102·	324·	21·	0·0000
10500	110 25 00 00	1157 625 000 000	469508 4879	037035 15430	897596 695	9523810 907
10501	110 27 10 01	1157 955 781 501	474387 4879	052465 15430	898291 695	9522903 907
10502	110 29 20 04	1158 286 626 008	479266 4879	067894 15429	898986 695	9521996 907
10503	110 31 30 09	1158 617 533 527	484145 4879	083323 15429	899681 695	9521089 907
10504	110 33 40 16	1158 948 504 064	489024 4878	098750 15427	900376 695	9520183 906
10505	110 35 50 25	1159 279 537 625	493902 4878	114177 15427	901071 695	9519277 907
10506	110 37 60 36	1159 610 634 216	498780 4878	129604 15425	901766 695	9518370 905
10507	110 39 70 49	1159 941 793 843	503658 4878	145029 15425	902461 695	9517465 906
10508	110 41 80 64	1160 273 016 512	508536 4878	160454 15424	903156 694	9516559 906
10509	110 43 90 81	1160 604 302 229	513414 4877	175878 15424	903850 695	9515653 905
10510	110 46 01 00	1160 935 651 000	518291 4877	191302 15422	904545 695	9514748 905
10511	110 48 11 21	1161 267 062 831	523168 4877	206724 15422	905240 694	9513843 905
10512	110 50 21 44	1161 598 537 728	528045 4877	222146 15421	905934 695	9512938 905
10513	110 52 31 69	1161 930 075 697	532922 4876	237567 15421	906629 695	9512033 905
10514	110 54 41 96	1162 261 676 744	537798 4876	252988 15419	907324 694	9511128 905
10515	110 56 52 25	1162 593 340 875	542674 4876	268407 15419	908018 695	9510223 904
10516	110 58 62 56	1162 925 068 096	547550 4876	283826 15419	908713 694	9509319 904
10517	110 60 72 89	1163 256 858 413	552426 4875	299245 15417	909407 694	9508415 904
10518	110 62 83 24	1163 588 711 832	557301 4875	314662 15417	910101 695	9507511 904
10519	110 64 93 61	1163 920 628 359	562176 4875	330079 15416	910796 694	9506607 904
10520	110 67 04 00	1164 252 608 000	567051 4875	345495 15415	911490 694	9505703 903
10521	110 69 14 41	1164 584 650 761	571926 4874	360910 15415	912184 695	9504800 903
10522	110 71 24 84	1164 916 756 648	576800 4875	376325 15413	912879 694	9503897 903
10523	110 73 35 29	1165 248 925 667	581675 4874	391738 15414	913573 694	9502993 903
10524	110 75 45 76	1165 581 157 824	586549 4874	407152 15412	914267 694	9502090 902
10525	110 77 56 25	1165 913 453 125	591423 4873	422564 15412	914961 694	9501188 903
10526	110 79 66 76·	1166 245 811 576	596296 4874	437976 15410	915655 694	9500285 903
10527	110 81 77 29	1166 578 233 183	601170 4873	453386 15411	916349 694	9499383 903
10528	110 83 87 84	1166 910 717 952	606043 4873	468797 15409	917043 694	9498480 902
10529	110 85 98 41	1167 243 265 889	610916 4872	484206 15409	917737 694	9497578 902
10530	110 88 09 00	1167 575 877 000	615788 4873	499615 15408	918431 694	9496676 902
10531	110 90 19 61	1167 908 551 291	620661 4872	515023 15407	919125 693	9495774 901
10532	110 92 30 24	1168 241 288 768	625533 4872	530430 15407	919818 694	9494873 902
10533	110 94 40 89	1168 574 089 437	630405 4872	545837 15405	920512 694	9493971 901
10534	110 96 51 56	1168 906 953 304	635277 4871	561242 15405	921206 693	9493070 901
10535	110 98 62 25	1169 239 880 375	640148 4871	576647 15405	921899 694	9492169 901
10536	111 00 72 96	1169 572 870 656	645019 4871	592052 15403	922593 694	9491268 901
10537	111 02 83 69	1169 905 924 153	649890 4871	607455 15403	923287 693	9490367 900
10538	111 04 94 44	1170 239 040 872	654761 4871	622858 15403	923980 694	9489467 901
10539	111 07 05 21	1170 572 220 819	659632 4870	638260 15402	924674 693	9488566 901
10540	111 09 16 00	1170 905 464 000	664502 4870	653662 15400	925367 693	9487666 900
10541	111 11 26 81	1171 238 770 421	669372 4870	669062 15400	926060 693	9486766 900
10542	111 13 37 64	1171 572 140 088	674242 4870	684462 15399	926754 693	9485866 900
10543	111 15 48 49	1171 905 573 007	679112 4869	699861 15399	927447 693	9484966 899
10544	111 17 59 36	1172 239 069 184	683981 4869	715260 15398	928140 693	9484067 900
10545	111 19 70 25	1172 572 628 625	688850 4869	730658 15397	928833 694	9483167 899
10546	111 21 81 16	1172 906 251 336	693719 4869	746055 15396	929527 693	9482268 899
10547	111 23 92 09	1173 239 937 323	698588 4869	761451 15395	930220 693	9481369 899
10548	111 26 03 04	1173 573 686 592	703457 4868	776846 15395	930913 693	9480470 898
10549	111 28 14 01	1173 907 499 149	708325 4868	792241 15394	931606 693	9479572 899
10550	111 30 25 00	1174 241 375 000	713193 102·	807635 324·	932299 21·	9478673 0·0000

No. n	Square n^2	Cube n^3	Square root $\sqrt{n}$	Sq. rt. of $10n$ $\sqrt{10n}$	Cube root $\sqrt[3]{n}$	Reciprocal $\dfrac{1}{n}$
			102·	324·	21·	0·0000
10550	111 30 25 00	1174 241 375 000	713193 $_{4868}$	807635 $_{15394}$	932299 $_{693}$	9478673 $_{898}$
10551	111 32 36 01	1174 575 314 151	718061 $_{4867}$	823029 $_{15392}$	932992 $_{693}$	9477775 $_{899}$
10552	111 34 47 04	1174 909 316 608	722928 $_{4868}$	838421 $_{15392}$	933685 $_{692}$	9476876 $_{898}$
10553	111 36 58 09	1175 243 382 377	727796 $_{4867}$	853813 $_{15392}$	934377 $_{693}$	9475978 $_{897}$
10554	111 38 69 16	1175 577 511 464	732663 $_{4867}$	869204 $_{15391}$	935070 $_{693}$	9475081 $_{898}$
10555	111 40 80 25	1175 911 703 875	737530 $_{4866}$	884595 $_{15390}$	935763 $_{693}$	9474183 $_{898}$
10556	111 42 91 36	1176 245 959 616	742396 $_{4867}$	899985 $_{15389}$	936456 $_{692}$	9473285 $_{897}$
10557	111 45 02 49	1176 580 278 693	747263 $_{4866}$	915374 $_{15388}$	937148 $_{693}$	9472388 $_{897}$
10558	111 47 13 64	1176 914 661 112	752129 $_{4866}$	930762 $_{15387}$	937841 $_{693}$	9471491 $_{897}$
10559	111 49 24 81	1177 249 106 879	756995 $_{4866}$	946149 $_{15387}$	938534 $_{692}$	9470594 $_{897}$
10560	111 51 36 00	1177 583 616 000	761861 $_{4865}$	961536 $_{15386}$	939226 $_{693}$	9469697 $_{897}$
10561	111 53 47 21	1177 918 188 481	766726 $_{4865}$	976922 $_{15386}$	939919 $_{692}$	9468800 $_{896}$
10562	111 55 58 44	1178 252 824 328	771591 $_{4865}$	992308 $_{15384}$	940611 $_{692}$	9467904 $_{897}$
10563	111 57 69 69	1178 587 523 547	776456 $_{4865}$	*007692 $_{15384}$	941304 $_{692}$	9467007 $_{896}$
10564	111 59 80 96	1178 922 286 144	781321 $_{4865}$	023076 $_{15383}$	941996 $_{692}$	9466111 $_{896}$
10565	111 61 92 25	1179 257 112 125	786186 $_{4864}$	038459 $_{15383}$	942688 $_{693}$	9465215 $_{895}$
10566	111 64 03 56	●179 592 001 496	791050 $_{4864}$	053842 $_{15381}$	943381 $_{692}$	9464320 $_{896}$
10567	111 66 14 89	1179 926 954 263	795914 $_{4864}$	069223 $_{15381}$	944073 $_{692}$	9463424 $_{896}$
10568	111 68 26 24	1180 261 970 432	800778 $_{4864}$	084604 $_{15381}$	944765 $_{692}$	9462528 $_{895}$
10569	111 70 37 61	1180 597 050 009	805642 $_{4863}$	099985 $_{15379}$	945457 $_{692}$	9461633 $_{895}$
10570	111 72 49 00	1180 932 193 000	810505 $_{4864}$	115364 $_{15379}$	946149 $_{692}$	9460738 $_{895}$
10571	111 74 60 41	1181 267 399 411	815369 $_{4862}$	130743 $_{15378}$	946841 $_{692}$	9459843 $_{895}$
10572	111 76 71 84	1181 602 669 248	820231 $_{4863}$	146121 $_{15377}$	947533 $_{692}$	9458948 $_{894}$
10573	111 78 83 29	1181 938 002 517	825094 $_{4863}$	161498 $_{15377}$	948225 $_{692}$	9458054 $_{895}$
10574	111 80 94 76	1182 273 399 224	829957 $_{4862}$	176875 $_{15376}$	948917 $_{692}$	9457159 $_{894}$
10575	111 83 06 25	1182 608 859 375	834819 $_{4862}$	192251 $_{15375}$	949609 $_{692}$	9456265 $_{894}$
10576	111 85 17 76	1182 944 382 976	839681 $_{4862}$	207626 $_{15374}$	950301 $_{692}$	9455371 $_{894}$
10577	111 87 29 29	1183 279 970 033	844543 $_{4861}$	223000 $_{15374}$	950993 $_{692}$	9454477 $_{894}$
10578	111 89 40 84	1183 615 620 552	849404 $_{4862}$	238374 $_{15373}$	951685 $_{691}$	9453583 $_{894}$
10579	111 91 52 41	1183 951 334 539	854266 $_{4861}$	253747 $_{15372}$	952376 $_{692}$	9452689 $_{893}$
10580	111 93 64 00	1184 287 112 000	859127 $_{4861}$	269119 $_{15372}$	953068 $_{692}$	9451796 $_{893}$
10581	111 95 75 61	1184 622 952 941	863988 $_{4861}$	284491 $_{15371}$	953760 $_{691}$	9450903 $_{894}$
10582	111 97 87 24	1184 958 857 368	868849 $_{4860}$	299862 $_{15370}$	954451 $_{692}$	9450009 $_{892}$
10583	111 99 98 89	1185 294 825 287	873709 $_{4860}$	315232 $_{15369}$	955143 $_{691}$	9449117 $_{893}$
10584	112 02 10 56	1185 630 856 704	878569 $_{4860}$	330601 $_{15369}$	955834 $_{692}$	9448224 $_{893}$
10585	112 04 22 25	1185 966 951 625	883429 $_{4860}$	345970 $_{15368}$	956526 $_{691}$	9447331 $_{892}$
10586	112 06 33 96	1186 303 110 056	888289 $_{4859}$	361338 $_{15367}$	957217 $_{692}$	9446439 $_{893}$
10587	112 08 45 69	1186 639 332 003	893148 $_{4860}$	376705 $_{15366}$	957909 $_{691}$	9445546 $_{892}$
10588	112 10 57 44	1186 975 617 472	898008 $_{4859}$	392071 $_{15366}$	958600 $_{691}$	9444654 $_{892}$
10589	112 12 69 21	1187 311 966 469	902867 $_{4859}$	407437 $_{15365}$	959291 $_{691}$	9443762 $_{891}$
10590	112 14 81 00	1187 648 379 000	907726 $_{4858}$	422802 $_{15364}$	959982 $_{692}$	9442871 $_{892}$
10591	112 16 92 81	1187 984 855 071	912584 $_{4859}$	438166 $_{15364}$	960674 $_{691}$	9441979 $_{891}$
10592	112 19 04 64	1188 321 394 688	917443 $_{4858}$	453530 $_{15363}$	961365 $_{691}$	9441088 $_{892}$
10593	112 21 16 49	1188 657 997 857	922301 $_{4858}$	468893 $_{15362}$	962056 $_{691}$	9440196 $_{891}$
10594	112 23 28 36	1188 994 664 584	927159 $_{4857}$	484255 $_{15361}$	962747 $_{691}$	9439305 $_{891}$
10595	112 25 40 25	1189 331 394 875	932016 $_{4858}$	499616 $_{15361}$	963438 $_{691}$	9438414 $_{890}$
10596	112 27 52 16	1189 668 188 736	936874 $_{4857}$	514977 $_{15360}$	964129 $_{691}$	9437524 $_{891}$
10597	112 29 64 09	1190 005 046 173	941731 $_{4857}$	530337 $_{15359}$	964820 $_{691}$	9436633 $_{890}$
10598	112 31 76 04	1190 341 967 192	946588 $_{4857}$	545696 $_{15358}$	965511 $_{691}$	9435743 $_{891}$
10599	112 33 88 01	1190 678 951 799	951445 $_{4856}$	561054 $_{15358}$	966202 $_{690}$	9434852 $_{890}$
10600	112 36 00 00	1191 016 000 000	956301	576412	966892	9433962
			102·	325·	21·	0·0000

No. n	Square n^2	Cube n^3	Square root $\sqrt{n}$	Sq. rt. of 10n $\sqrt{10n}$	Cube root $\sqrt[3]{n}$	Reciprocal $\dfrac{1}{n}$
			102·	325·	21·	0·0000
10600	112 36 00 00	1191 016 000 000	956301 4857	576412 15357	966892 691	9433962 890
10601	112 38 12 01	1191 353 111 801	961158 4856	591769 15356	967583 691	9433072 889
10602	112 40 24 04	1191 690 287 208	966014 4856	607125 15356	968274 691	9432183 890
10603	112 42 36 09	1192 027 526 227	970870 4855	622481 15356	968965 691	9431293 889
10604	112 44 48 16	1192 364 828 864	975725 4856	637836 15355	969655 690	9430404 890
				15354	691	
10605	112 46 60 25	1192 702 195 125	980581 4855	653190 15353	970346 690	9429514 889
10606	112 48 72 36	1193 039 625 016	985436 4855	668543 15353	971036 691	9428625 889
10607	112 50 84 49	1193 377 118 543	990291 4855	683896 15352	971727 690	9427736 888
10608	112 52 96 64	1193 714 675 712	995146 4854	699248 15351	972417 691	9426848 889
10609	112 55 08 81	1194 052 296 529	*000000 4854	714599 15350	973108 690	9425959 888
10610	112 57 21 00	1194 389 981 000	004854 4854	729949 15350	973798 690	9425071 889
10611	112 59 33 21	1194 727 729 131	009708 4854	745299 15349	974488 691	9424182 888
10612	112 61 45 44	1195 065 540 928	014562 4854	760648 15349	975179 690	9423294 888
10613	112 63 57 69	1195 403 416 397	019416 4853	775997 15347	975869 690	9422406 887
10614	112 65 69 96	1195 741 355 544	024269 4853	791344 15347	976559 690	9421519 888
10615	112 67 82 25	1196 079 358 375	029122 4853	806691 15346	977249 690	9420631 887
10616	112 69 94 56	1196 417 424 896	033975 4853	822037 15346	977939 690	9419744 887
10617	112 72 06 89	1196 755 555 113	038828 4852	837383 15344	978629 690	9418857 887
10618	112 74 19 24	1197 093 749 032	043680 4852	852727 15344	979319 690	9417969 886
10619	112 76 31 61	1197 432 006 659	048532 4852	868071 15344	980009 690	9417083 887
10620	112 78 44 00	1197 770 328 000	053384 4852	883415 15342	980699 690	9416196 887
10621	112 80 56 41	1198 108 713 061	058236 4851	898757 15342	981389 690	9415309 886
10622	112 82 68 84	1198 447 161 848	063087 4852	914099 15341	982079 690	9414423 886
10623	112 84 81 29	1198 785 674 367	067939 4851	929440 15341	982769 690	9413537 886
10624	112 86 93 76	1199 124 250 624	072790 4851	944781 15339	983459 689	9412651 886
10625	112 89 06 25	1199 462 890 625	077641 4850	960120 15339	984148 690	9411765 886
10626	112 91 18 76	1199 801 594 376	082491 4851	975459 15338	984838 690	9410879 886
10627	112 93 31 29	1200 140 361 883	087342 4850	990797 15338	985528 690	9409993 885
10628	112 95 43 84	1200 479 193 152	092192 4850	*006135 15337	986217 690	9409108 885
10629	112 97 56 41	1200 818 088 189	097042 4849	021472 15336	986907 689	9408223 885
10630	112 99 69 00	1201 157 047 000	101891 4850	036808 15335	987596 690	9407338 885
10631	113 01 81 61	1201 496 069 591	106741 4849	052143 15335	988286 689	9406453 885
10632	113 03 94 24	1201 835 155 968	111590 4849	067478 15334	988975 690	9405568 884
10633	113 06 06 89	1202 174 306 137	116439 4849	082812 15333	989665 689	9404684 885
10634	113 08 19 56	1202 513 520 104	121288 4848	098145 15332	990354 689	9403799 884
10635	113 10 32 25	1202 852 797 875	126136 4849	113477 15332	991043 689	9402915 884
10636	113 12 44 96	1203 192 139 456	130985 4848	128809 15331	991732 690	9402031 884
10637	113 14 57 69	1203 531 544 853	135833 4848	144140 15330	992422 689	9401147 884
10638	113 16 70 44	1203 871 014 072	140681 4847	159470 15330	993111 689	9400263 883
10639	113 18 83 21	1204 210 547 119	145528 4848	174800 15329	993800 689	9399380 884
10640	113 20 96 00	1204 550 144 000	150376 4847	190129 15328	994489 689	9398496 883
10641	113 23 08 81	1204 889 804 721	155223 4847	205457 15327	995178 689	9397613 883
10642	113 25 21 64	1205 229 529 288	160070 4847	220784 15327	995867 689	9396730 883
10643	113 27 34 49	1205 569 317 707	164917 4846	236111 15326	996556 689	9395847 883
10644	113 29 47 36	1205 909 169 984	169763 4846	251437 15325	997245 689	9394964 882
10645	113 31 60 25	1206 249 086 125	174609 4846	266762 15325	997934 689	9394082 883
10646	113 33 73 16	1206 589 066 136	179455 4846	282087 15323	998623 688	9393199 882
10647	113 35 86 09	1206 929 110 023	184301 4846	297410 15323	999311 689	9392317 882
10648	113 37 99 04	1207 269 217 792	189147 4845	312733 15323	*000000 689	9391435 882
10649	113 40 12 01	1207 609 389 449	193992 4845	328056 15321	000689 688	9390553 882
10650	113 42 25 00	1207 949 625 000	198837	343377	001377	9389671
			103·	326·	22·	0·0000

No. n	Square n^2	Cube n^3	Square root $\sqrt{n}$	Sq. rt. of $10n$ $\sqrt{10n}$	Cube root $\sqrt[3]{n}$	Reciprocal $\dfrac{1}{n}$
			103·	326·	22·	0·0000
10650	113 42 25 00	1207 949 625 000	198837 $_{4845}$	343377 $_{15321}$	001377 $_{689}$	9389671 $_{881}$
10651	113 44 38 01	1208 289 924 451	203682 $_{4845}$	358698 $_{15321}$	002066 $_{688}$	9388790 $_{882}$
10652	113 46 51 04	1208 630 287 808	208527 $_{4844}$	374019 $_{15319}$	002754 $_{689}$	9387908 $_{881}$
10653	113 48 64 09	1208 970 715 077	213371 $_{4844}$	389338 $_{15319}$	003443 $_{688}$	9387027 $_{881}$
10654	113 50 77 16	1209 311 206 264	218215 $_{4844}$	404657 $_{15318}$	004131 $_{689}$	9386146 $_{881}$
10655	113 52 90 25	1209 651 761 375	223059 $_{4844}$	419975 $_{15317}$	004820 $_{688}$	9385265 $_{881}$
10656	113 55 03 36	1209 992 380 416	227903 $_{4844}$	435292 $_{15317}$	005508 $_{689}$	9384384 $_{880}$
10657	113 57 16 49	1210 333 063 393	232747 $_{4843}$	450609 $_{15316}$	006197 $_{688}$	9383504 $_{881}$
10658	113 59 29 64	1210 673 810 312	237590 $_{4843}$	465925 $_{15315}$	006885 $_{688}$	9382623 $_{880}$
10659	113 61 42 81	1211 014 621 179	242433 $_{4843}$	481240 $_{15314}$	007573 $_{688}$	9381743 $_{880}$
10660	113 63 56 00	1211 355 496 000	247276 $_{4843}$	496554 $_{15314}$	008261 $_{689}$	9380863 $_{880}$
10661	113 65 69 21	1211 696 434 781	252119 $_{4842}$	511868 $_{15313}$	008950 $_{688}$	9379983 $_{880}$
10662	113 67 82 44	1212 037 437 528	256961 $_{4842}$	527181 $_{15312}$	009638 $_{688}$	9379103 $_{879}$
10663	113 69 95 69	1212 378 504 247	261803 $_{4842}$	542493 $_{15312}$	010326 $_{688}$	9378224 $_{880}$
10664	113 72 08 96	1212 719 634 944	266645 $_{4842}$	557805 $_{15311}$	011014 $_{688}$	9377344 $_{879}$
10665	113 74 22 25	1213 060 829 625	271487 $_{4841}$	573116 $_{15310}$	011702 $_{688}$	9376465 $_{879}$
10666	113 76 35 56	1213 402 088 296	276328 $_{4842}$	588426 $_{15309}$	012390 $_{688}$	9375586 $_{879}$
10667	113 78 48 89	1213 743 410 963	281170 $_{4841}$	603735 $_{15309}$	013078 $_{687}$	9374707 $_{879}$
10668	113 80 62 24	1214 084 797 632	286011 $_{4840}$	619044 $_{15308}$	013765 $_{688}$	9373828 $_{878}$
10669	113 82 75 61	1214 426 248 309	290851 $_{4841}$	634352 $_{15307}$	014453 $_{688}$	9372950 $_{879}$
10670	113 84 89 00	1214 767 763 000	295692 $_{4840}$	649659 $_{15307}$	015141 $_{688}$	9372071 $_{878}$
10671	113 87 02 41	1215 109 341 711	300532 $_{4841}$	664966 $_{15306}$	015829 $_{688}$	9371193 $_{878}$
10672	113 89 15 84	1215 450 984 448	305373 $_{4839}$	680272 $_{15305}$	016517 $_{687}$	9370315 $_{878}$
10673	113 91 29 29	1215 792 691 217	310212 $_{4840}$	695577 $_{15304}$	017204 $_{688}$	9369437 $_{878}$
10674	113 93 42 76	1216 134 462 024	315052 $_{4840}$	710881 $_{15304}$	017892 $_{687}$	9368559 $_{878}$
10675	113 95 56 25	1216 476 296 875	319892 $_{4839}$	726185 $_{15303}$	018579 $_{688}$	9367681 $_{877}$
10676	113 97 69 76	1216 818 195 776	324731 $_{4839}$	741488 $_{15302}$	019267 $_{687}$	9366804 $_{877}$
10677	113 99 83 29	1217 160 158 733	329570 $_{4839}$	756790 $_{15302}$	019954 $_{688}$	9365927 $_{877}$
10678	114 01 96 84	1217 502 185 752	334409 $_{4838}$	772092 $_{15302}$	020642 $_{687}$	9365050 $_{877}$
10679	114 04 10 41	1217 844 276 839	339247 $_{4838}$	787393 $_{15301}$	021329 $_{688}$	9364173 $_{877}$
10680	114 06 24 00	1218.186 432 000	344085 $_{4839}$	802693 $_{15299}$	022017 $_{687}$	9363296 $_{877}$
10681	114 08 37 61	1218 528 651 241	348924 $_{4837}$	817992 $_{15299}$	022704 $_{687}$	9362419 $_{876}$
10682	114 10 51 24	1218 870 934 568	353761 $_{4838}$	833291 $_{15298}$	023391 $_{687}$	9361543 $_{877}$
10683	114 12 64 89	1219 213 281 987	358599 $_{4837}$	848589 $_{15297}$	024078 $_{687}$	9360666 $_{876}$
10684	114 14 78 56	1219 555 693 504	363436 $_{4838}$	863886 $_{15297}$	024765 $_{688}$	9359790 $_{876}$
10685	114 16 92 25	1219 898 169 125	368274 $_{4837}$	879183 $_{15295}$	025453 $_{687}$	9358914 $_{875}$
10686	114 19 05 96	1220 240 708 856	373111 $_{4836}$	894478 $_{15295}$	026140 $_{687}$	9358039 $_{876}$
10687	114 21 19 69	1220 583 312 703	377947 $_{4837}$	909773 $_{15295}$	026827 $_{687}$	9357163 $_{876}$
10688	114 23 33 44	1220 925 980 672	382784 $_{4836}$	925068 $_{15294}$	027514 $_{687}$	9356287 $_{875}$
10689	114 25 47 21	1221 268 712 769	387620 $_{4836}$	940362 $_{15292}$	028201 $_{687}$	9355412 $_{875}$
10690	114 27 61 00	1221 611 509 000	392456 $_{4836}$	955654 $_{15293}$	028888 $_{687}$	9354537 $_{875}$
10691	114 29 74 81	1221 954 369 371	397292 $_{4836}$	970947 $_{15291}$	029575 $_{686}$	9353662 $_{875}$
10692	114 31 88 64	1222 297 293 888	402128 $_{4835}$	*986238 $_{15291}$	030261 $_{687}$	9352787 $_{875}$
10693	114 34 02 49	1222 640 282 557	406963 $_{4835}$	*001529 $_{15291}$	030948 $_{687}$	9351912 $_{874}$
10694	114 36.16 36	1222 983 335 384	411798 $_{4835}$	016819 $_{15290}$	031635 $_{687}$	9351038 $_{874}$
10695	114 38 30 25	1223 326 452 375	416633 $_{4835}$	032109 $_{15288}$	032322 $_{686}$	9350164 $_{875}$
10696	114 40 44 16	1223 669 633 536	421468 $_{4834}$	047397 $_{15288}$	033008 $_{687}$	9349289 $_{874}$
10697	114 42 58 09	1224 012 878 873	426302 $_{4835}$	062685 $_{15287}$	033695 $_{687}$	9348415 $_{873}$
10698	114 44 72 04	1224 356 188 392	431137 $_{4834}$	077972 $_{15287}$	034382 $_{686}$	9347542 $_{874}$
10699	114 46 86 01	1224 699 562 099	435971 $_{4833}$	093259 $_{15286}$	035068 $_{687}$	9346668 $_{874}$
10700	114 49 00 00	1225 043 000 000	440804 103·	108545 327·	035755 22·	9345794 0·0000

215

No. n	Square n²	Cube n³	Square root √n	Sq. rt. of 10n √10n	Cube root ∛n	Reciprocal 1/n
			103.	327.	22.	0.0000
10700	114 49 00 00	1225 043 000 000	440804 4834	108545 15285	035755 686	9345794 873
10701	114 51 14 01	1225 386 502 101	445638 4833	123830 15284	036441 686	9344921 873
10702	114 53 28 04	1225 730 068 408	450471 4833	139114 15284	037127 687	9344048 873
10703	114 55 42 09	1226 073 698 927	455304 4833	154398 15283	037814 686	9343175 873
10704	114 57 56 16	1226 417 393 664	460137 4833	169681 15282	038500 686	9342302 873
10705	114 59 70 25	1226 761 152 625	464970 4832	184963 15281	039186 687	9341429 872
10706	114 61 84 36	1227 104 975 816	469802 4833	200244 15281	039873 686	9340557 873
10707	114 63 98 49	1227 448 863 243	474635 4832	215525 15280	040559 686	9339684 872
10708	114 66 12 64	1227 792 814 912	479467 4831	230805 15280	041245 686	9338812 872
10709	114 68 26 81	1228 136 830 829	484298 4832	246085 15278	041931 686	9337940 872
10710	114 70 41 00	1228 480 911 000	489130 4831	261363 15278	042617 686	9337068 872
10711	114 72 55 21	1228 825 055 431	493961 4831	276641 15278	043303 686	9336196 871
10712	114 74 69 44	1229 169 264 128	498792 4831	291919 15276	043989 686	9335325 872
10713	114 76 83 69	1229 513 537 097	503623 4831	307195 15276	044675 686	9334453 871
10714	114 78 97 96	1229 857 874 344	508454 4830	322471 15275	045361 686	9333582 871
10715	114 81 12 25	1230 202 275 875	513284 4830	337746 15274	046047 686	9332711 871
10716	114 83 26 56	1230 546 741 696	518114 4830	353020 15274	046733 685	9331840 871
10717	114 85 40 89	1230 891 271 813	522944 4830	368294 15273	047418 686	9330969 870
10718	114 87 55 24	1231 235 866 232	527774 4830	383567 15272	048104 686	9330099 871
10719	114 89 69 61	1231 580 524 959	532604 4829	398839 15272	048790 685	9329228 870
10720	114 91 84 00	1231 925 248 000	537433 4829	414111 15271	049475 686	9328358 870
10721	114 93 98 41	1232 270 035 361	542262 4829	429382 15270	050161 686	9327488 870
10722	114 96 12 84	1232 614 887 048	547091 4828	444652 15269	050847 685	9326618 870
10723	114 98 27 29	1232 959 803 067	551919 4829	459921 15269	051532 686	9325748 869
10724	115 00 41 76	1233 304 783 424	556748 4828	475190 15268	052218 685	9324879 870
10725	115 02 56 25	1233 649 828 125	561576 4828	490458 15267	052903 685	9324009 869
10726	115 04 70 76	1233 994 937 176	566404 4828	505725 15267	053588 686	9323140 869
10727	115 06 85 29	1234 340 110 583	571232 4827	520992 15266	054274 685	9322271 869
10728	115 08 99 84	1234 685 348 352	576059 4827	536258 15265	054959 685	9321402 869
10729	115 11 14 41	1235 030 650 489	580886 4827	551523 15264	055644 685	9320533 869
10730	115 13 29 00	1235 376 017 000	585713 4827	566787 15264	056329 686	9319664 868
10731	115 15 43 61	1235 721 447 891	590540 4827	582051 15263	057015 685	9318796 868
10732	115 17 58 24	1236 066 943 168	595367 4826	597314 15262	057700 685	9317928 868
10733	115 19 72 89	1236 412 502 837	600193 4826	612576 15262	058385 685	9317060 868
10734	115 21 87 56	1236 758 126 904	605019 4826	627838 15261	059070 685	9316192 868
10735	115 24 02 25	1237 103 815 375	609845 4826	643099 15260	059755 685	9315324 868
10736	115 26 16 96	1237 449 568 256	614671 4825	658359 15259	060440 685	9314456 867
10737	115 28 31 69	1237 795 385 553	619496 4825	673618 15259	061125 685	9313589 868
10738	115 30 46 44	1238 141 267 272	624321 4825	688877 15258	061810 684	9312721 867
10739	115 32 61 21	1238 487 213 419	629146 4825	704135 15257	062494 685	9311854 867
10740	115 34 76 00	1238 833 224 000	633971 4825	719392 15257	063179 685	9310987 867
10741	115 36 90 81	1239 179 299 021	638796 4824	734649 15256	063864 685	9310120 867
10742	115 39 05 64	1239 525 438 488	643620 4824	749905 15255	064549 684	9309253 866
10743	115 41 20 49	1239 871 642 407	648444 4824	765160 15254	065233 685	9308387 867
10744	115 43 35 36	1240 217 910 784	653268 4824	780414 15254	065918 685	9307520 866
10745	115 45 50 25	1240 564 243 625	658092 4823	795668 15253	066603 684	9306654 866
10746	115 47 65 16	1240 910 640 936	662915 4823	810921 15252	067287 685	9305788 866
10747	115 49 80 09	1241 257 102 723	667738 4823	826173 15252	067972 684	9304922 865
10748	115 51 95 04	1241 603 628 992	672561 4823	841425 15251	068656 684	9304057 866
10749	115 54 10 01	1241 950 219 749	677384 4823	856676 15250	069340 685	9303191 865
10750	115 56 25 00	1242 296 875 000	682207	871926	070025	9302326
			103.	327.	22.	0.0000

No. n	Square n^2	Cube n^3	Square root $\sqrt{n}$	Sq. rt. of 10n $\sqrt{10n}$	Cube root $\sqrt[3]{n}$	Reciprocal $\dfrac{1}{n}$
			103.	327.	22.	0·0000
10750	115 56 25 00	1242 296 875 000	682207 $_{4822}$	871926 $_{15250}$	070025 $_{684}$	9302326 $_{866}$
10751	115 58 40 01	1242 643 594 751	687029 $_{4822}$	887176 $_{15249}$	070709 $_{684}$	9301460 $_{865}$
10752	115 60 55 04	1242 990 379 008	691851 $_{4822}$	902425 $_{15248}$	071393 $_{685}$	9300595 $_{865}$
10753	115 62 70 09	1243 337 227 777	696673 $_{4822}$	917673 $_{15247}$	072078 $_{684}$	9299730 $_{864}$
10754	115 64 85 16	1243 684 141 064	701495 $_{4821}$	932920 $_{15247}$	072762 $_{684}$	9298866 $_{865}$
10755	115 67 00 25	1244 031 118 875	706316 $_{4821}$	948167 $_{15246}$	073446 $_{684}$	9298001 $_{865}$
10756	115 69 15 36	1244 378 161 216	711137 $_{4821}$	963413 $_{15245}$	074130 $_{684}$	9297136 $_{864}$
10757	115 71 30 49	1244 725 268 093	715958 $_{4821}$	978658 $_{15244}$	074814 $_{684}$	9296272 $_{864}$
10758	115 73 45 64	1245 072 439 512	720779 $_{4821}$	993902 $_{15244}$	075498 $_{684}$	9295408 $_{864}$
10759	115 75 60 81	1245 419 675 479	725600 $_{4820}$	*009146 $_{15243}$	076182 $_{684}$	9294544 $_{864}$
10760	115 77 76 00	1245 766 976 000	730420 $_{4820}$	024389 $_{15243}$	076866 $_{684}$	9293680 $_{863}$
10761	115 79 91 21	1246 114 341 081	735240 $_{4820}$	039632 $_{15241}$	077550 $_{684}$	9292817 $_{864}$
10762	115 82 06 44	1246 461 770 728	740060 $_{4819}$	054873 $_{15241}$	078234 $_{684}$	9291953 $_{863}$
10763	115 84 21 69	1246 809 264 947	744879 $_{4820}$	070114 $_{15241}$	078918 $_{683}$	9291090 $_{863}$
10764	115 86 36 96	1247 156 823 744	749699 $_{4819}$	085355 $_{15239}$	079601 $_{684}$	9290227 $_{863}$
10765	115 88 52 25	1247 504 447 125	754518 $_{4819}$	100594 $_{15239}$	080285 $_{684}$	9289364 $_{863}$
10766	115 90 67 56	1247 852 135 096	759337 $_{4819}$	115833 $_{15238}$	080969 $_{683}$	9288501 $_{863}$
10767	115 92 82 89	1248 199 887 663	764156 $_{4818}$	131071 $_{15238}$	081652 $_{684}$	9287638 $_{862}$
10768	115 94 98 24	1248 547 704 832	768974 $_{4818}$	146309 $_{15237}$	082336 $_{684}$	9286776 $_{863}$
10769	115 97 13 61	1248 895 586 609	773792 $_{4819}$	161546 $_{15236}$	083020 $_{683}$	9285913 $_{862}$
10770	115 99 29 00	1249 243 533 000	778611 $_{4817}$	176782 $_{15235}$	083703 $_{684}$	9285051 $_{862}$
10771	116 01 44 41	1249 591 544 011	783428 $_{4818}$	192017 $_{15235}$	084387 $_{683}$	9284189 $_{862}$
10772	116 03 59 84	1249 939 619 648	788246 $_{4817}$	207252 $_{15234}$	085070 $_{683}$	9283327 $_{862}$
10773	116 05 75 29	1250 287 759 917	793063 $_{4818}$	222486 $_{15233}$	085753 $_{684}$	9282465 $_{861}$
10774	116 07 90 76	1250 635 964 824	797881 $_{4816}$	237719 $_{15232}$	086437 $_{683}$	9281604 $_{862}$
10775	116 10 06 25	1250 984 234 375	802697 $_{4817}$	252951 $_{15232}$	087120 $_{683}$	9280742 $_{861}$
10776	116 12 21 76	1251 332 568 576	807514 $_{4817}$	268183 $_{15231}$	087803 $_{684}$	9279881 $_{861}$
10777	116 14 37 29	1251 680 967 433	812331 $_{4816}$	283414 $_{15231}$	088487 $_{683}$	9279020 $_{861}$
10778	116 16 52 84	1252 029 430 952	817147 $_{4816}$	298645 $_{15229}$	089170 $_{683}$	9278159 $_{861}$
10779	116 18 68 41	1252 377 959 139	821963 $_{4816}$	313874 $_{15229}$	089853 $_{683}$	9277298 $_{860}$
10780	116 20 84 00	1252 726 552 000	826779 $_{4815}$	329103 $_{15228}$	090536 $_{683}$	9276438 $_{861}$
10781	116 22 99 61	1253 075 209 541	831594 $_{4816}$	344331 $_{15228}$	091219 $_{683}$	9275577 $_{860}$
10782	116 25 15 24	1253 423 931 768	836410 $_{4815}$	359559 $_{15227}$	091902 $_{683}$	9274717 $_{860}$
10783	116 27 30 89	1253 772 718 687	841225 $_{4815}$	374786 $_{15226}$	092585 $_{683}$	9273857 $_{860}$
10784	116 29 46 56	1254 121 570 304	846040 $_{4815}$	390012 $_{15225}$	093268 $_{683}$	9272997 $_{860}$
10785	116 31 62 25	1254 470 486 625	850855 $_{4814}$	405237 $_{15225}$	093951 $_{683}$	9272137 $_{859}$
10786	116 33 77 96	1254 819 467 656	855669 $_{4814}$	420462 $_{15224}$	094634 $_{682}$	9271278 $_{859}$
10787	116 35 93 69	1255 168 513 403	860483 $_{4814}$	435686 $_{15224}$	095316 $_{683}$	9270418 $_{859}$
10788	116 38 09 44	1255 517 623 872	865297 $_{4814}$	450910 $_{15222}$	095999 $_{683}$	9269559 $_{859}$
10789	116 40 25 21	1255 866 799 069	870111 $_{4814}$	466132 $_{15222}$	096682 $_{683}$	9268700 $_{859}$
10790	116 42 41 00	1256 216 039 000	874925 $_{4813}$	481354 $_{15221}$	097365 $_{682}$	9267841 $_{859}$
10791	116 44 56 81	1256 565 343 671	879738 $_{4813}$	496575 $_{15221}$	098047 $_{683}$	9266982 $_{859}$
10792	116 46 72 64	1256 914 713 088	884551 $_{4813}$	511796 $_{15220}$	098730 $_{682}$	9266123 $_{858}$
10793	116 48 88 49	1257 264 147 257	889364 $_{4813}$	527016 $_{15219}$	099412 $_{683}$	9265265 $_{859}$
10794	116 51 04 36	1257 613 646 184	894177 $_{4812}$	542235 $_{15218}$	100095 $_{682}$	9264406 $_{858}$
10795	116 53 20 25	1257 963 209 875	898989 $_{4813}$	557453 $_{15218}$	100777 $_{683}$	9263548 $_{858}$
10796	116 55 36 16	1258 312 838 336	903802 $_{4812}$	572671 $_{15217}$	101460 $_{682}$	9262690 $_{858}$
10797	116 57 52 09	1258 662 531 573	908614 $_{4812}$	587888 $_{15216}$	102142 $_{682}$	9261832 $_{858}$
10798	116 59 68 04	1259 012 289 592	913426 $_{4811}$	603104 $_{15216}$	102824 $_{683}$	9260974 $_{857}$
10799	116 61 84 01	1259 362 112 399	918237 $_{4811}$	618320 $_{15215}$	103507 $_{682}$	9260117 $_{858}$
10800	116 64 00 00	1259 712 000 000	923048 103·	633535 328·	104189 22·	9259259 0·0000

No. n	Square n^2	Cube n^3	Square root $\sqrt{n}$	Sq. rt. of 10n $\sqrt{10n}$	Cube root $\sqrt[3]{n}$	Reciprocal $\frac{1}{n}$
			103.	328.	22.	0.0000
10800	116 64 00 00	1259 712 000 000	923048 4812	633535 15214	104189 682	9259259 857
10801	116 66 16 01	1260 061 952 401	927860 4811	648749 15214	104871 682	9258402 857
10802	116 68 32 04	1260 411 969 608	932671 4810	663962 15213	105553 682	9257545 857
10803	116 70 48 09	1260 762 051 627	937481 4810	679175 15213	106235 683	9256688 857
10804	116 72 64 16	1261 112 198 464	942292 4811	694387 15212	106918 682	9255831 856
10805	116 74 80 25	1261 462 410 125	947102 4810	709598 15211	107600 682	9254975 857
10806	116 76 96 36	1261 812 686 616	951912 4810	724809 15211	108282 682	9254118 856
10807	116 79 12 49	1262 163 027 943	956722 4810	740019 15210	108964 682	9253262 856
10808	116 81 28 64	1262 513 434 112	961531 4809	755228 15209	109645 682	9252406 856
10809	116 83 44 81	1262 863 905 129	966341 4810	770437 15209	110327 682	9251550 856
10810	116 85 61 00	1263 214 441 000	971150 4809	785644 15208	111009 682	9250694 856
10811	116 87 77 21	1263 565 041 731	975959 4809	800852 15206	111691 682	9249838 855
10812	116 89 93 44	1263 915 707 328	980767 4808	816058 15206	112373 681	9248983 856
10813	116 92 09 69	1264 266 437 797	985576 4809	831264 15206	113054 682	9248127 855
10814	116 94 25 96	1264 617 233 144	990384 4808	846469 15205	113736 682	9247272 855
10815	116 96 42 25	1264 968 093 375	995192 4808	861673 15204	114418 681	9246417 855
10816	116 98 58 56	1265 319 018 496	*000000 4808	876877 15204	115099 682	9245562 855
10817	117 00 74 89	1265 670 008 513	004808 4808	892080 15203	115781 682	9244707 855
10818	117 02 91 24	1266 021 063 432	009615 4807	907282 15202	116462 682	9243853 854
10819	117 05 07 61	1266 372 183 259	014422 4807	922483 15201	117144 681	9242998 855
10820	117 07 24 00	1266 723 368 000	019229 4807	937684 15201	117825 682	9242144 854
10821	117 09 40 41	1267 074 617 661	024036 4807	952884 15200	118507 681	9241290 854
10822	117 11 56 84	1267 425 932 248	028842 4806	968084 15200	119188 681	9240436 854
10823	117 13 73 29	1267 777 311 767	033648 4806	983282 15198	119869 681	9239582 853
10824	117 15 89 76	1268 128 756 224	038454 4806	998480 15198	120550 682	9238729 854
10825	117 18 06 25	1268 480 265 625	043260 4806	*013678 15198	121232 681	9237875 853
10826	117 20 22 76	1268 831 839 976	048066 4806	028874 15196	121913 681	9237022 853
10827	117 22 39 29	1269 183 479 283	052871 4805	044070 15196	122594 681	9236169 853
10828	117 24 55 84	1269 535 183 552	057676 4805	059265 15195	123275 681	9235316 853
10829	117 26 72 41	1269 886 952 789	062481 4805	074460 15195	123956 681	9234463 853
10830	117 28 89 00	1270 238 787 000	067286 4804	089653 15193	124637 681	9233610 852
10831	117 31 05 61	1270 590 686 191	072090 4805	104847 15194	125318 681	9232758 853
10832	117 33 22 24	1270 942 650 368	076895 4804	120039 15192	125999 681	9231905 852
10833	117 35 38 89	1271 294 679 537	081699 4804	135231 15192	126680 680	9231053 852
10834	117 37 55 56	1271 646 773 704	086502 4803	150422 15191	127360 681	9230201 852
10835	117 39 72 25	1271 998 932 875	091306 4804	165612 15190	128041 681	9229349 851
10836	117 41 88 96	1272 351 157 056	096109 4803	180801 15189	128722 681	9228498 852
10837	117 44 05 69	1272 703 446 253	100913 4804	195990 15189	129403 680	9227646 851
10838	117 46 22 44	1273 055 800 472	105716 4803	211178 15188	130083 681	9226795 851
10839	117 48 39 21	1273 408 219 719	110518 4803	226366 15188	130764 680	9225943 851
10840	117 50 56 00	1273 760 704 000	115321 4803	241553 15187	131444 681	9225092 851
10841	117 52 72 81	1274 113 253 321	120123 4802	256739 15186	132125 681	9224241 851
10842	117 54 89 64	1274 465 867 688	124925 4802	271924 15185	132806 680	9223391 850
10843	117 57 06 49	1274 818 547 107	129727 4802	287109 15185	133486 680	9222540 851
10844	117 59 23 36	1275 171 291 584	134528 4801	302293 15184	134166 681	9221689 851
10845	117 61 40 25	1275 524 101 125	139330 4802	317476 15183	134847 680	9220839 850
10846	117 63 57 16	1275 876 975 736	144131 4801	332659 15183	135527 680	9219989 850
10847	117 65 74 09	1276 229 915 423	148932 4801	347840 15181	136207 681	9219139 850
10848	117 67 91 04	1276 582 920 192	153733 4801	363022 15182	136888 680	9218289 850
10849	117 70 08 01	1276 935 990 049	158533 4800	378202 15180	137568 680	9217439 850
10850	117 72 25 00	1277 289 125 000	163333	393382	138248	9216590 849
			104.	329.	22.	0.0000

No. n	Square n^2	Cube n^3	Square root $\sqrt{n}$	Sq. rt. of 10n $\sqrt{10n}$	Cube root $\sqrt[3]{n}$	Reciprocal $\dfrac{1}{n}$
			104·	329·	22·	0·0000
10850	117 72 25 00	1277 289 125 000	163333 $_{4800}$	393382 $_{15179}$	138248 $_{680}$	9216590 $_{850}$
10851	117 74 42 01	1277 642 325 051	168133 $_{4800}$	408561 $_{15178}$	138928 $_{680}$	9215740 $_{849}$
10852	117 76 59 04	1277 995 590 208	172933 $_{4800}$	423739 $_{15178}$	139608 $_{680}$	9214891 $_{849}$
10853	117 78 76 09	1278 348 920 477	177733 $_{4799}$	438917 $_{15177}$	140288 $_{680}$	9214042 $_{849}$
10854	117 80 93 16	1278 702 315 864	182532 $_{4799}$	454094 $_{15176}$	140968 $_{680}$	9213193 $_{848}$
10855	117 83 10 25	1279 055 776 375	187331 $_{4799}$	469270 $_{15176}$	141648 $_{680}$	9212345 $_{849}$
10856	117 85 27 36	1279 409 302 016	192130 $_{4799}$	484446 $_{15175}$	142328 $_{680}$	9211496 $_{848}$
10857	117 87 44 49	1279 762 892 793	196929 $_{4798}$	499621 $_{15175}$	143008 $_{680}$	9210648 $_{849}$
10858	117 89 61 64	1280 116 548 712	201727 $_{4799}$	514795 $_{15174}$	143688 $_{679}$	9209799 $_{848}$
10859	117 91 78 81	1280 470 269 779	206526 $_{4798}$	529968 $_{15173}$	144367 $_{680}$	9208951 $_{848}$
10860	117 93 96 00	1280 824 056 000	211324 $_{4798}$	545141 $_{15172}$	145047 $_{680}$	9208103 $_{848}$
10861	117 96 13 21	1281 177 907 381	216122 $_{4797}$	560313 $_{15172}$	145727 $_{679}$	9207255 $_{847}$
10862	117 98 30 44	1281 531 823 928	220919 $_{4798}$	575485 $_{15170}$	146406 $_{680}$	9206408 $_{848}$
10863	118 00 47 69	1281 885 805 647	225717 $_{4797}$	590655 $_{15170}$	147086 $_{680}$	9205560 $_{847}$
10864	118 02 64 96	1282 239 852 544	230514 $_{4797}$	605825 $_{15169}$	147766 $_{679}$	9204713 $_{847}$
10865	118 04 82 25	1282 593 964 625	235311 $_{4796}$	620994 $_{15169}$	148445 $_{680}$	9203866 $_{847}$
10866	118 06 99 56	1282 948 141 896	240107 $_{4797}$	636163 $_{15168}$	149125 $_{680}$	9203019 $_{847}$
10867	118 09 16 89	1283 302 384 363	244904 $_{4796}$	651331 $_{15167}$	149804 $_{679}$	9202172 $_{847}$
10868	118 11 34 24	1283 656 692 032	249700 $_{4796}$	666498 $_{15167}$	150483 $_{680}$	9201325 $_{847}$
10869	118 13 51 61	1284 011 064 909	254496 $_{4796}$	681665 $_{15165}$	151163 $_{679}$	9200478 $_{846}$
10870	118 15 69 00	1284 365 503 000	259292 $_{4796}$	696830 $_{15166}$	151842 $_{679}$	9199632 $_{846}$
10871	118 17 86 41	1284 720 006 311	264088 $_{4795}$	711996 $_{15164}$	152521 $_{680}$	9198786 $_{846}$
10872	118 20 03 84	1285 074 574 848	268883 $_{4795}$	727160 $_{15164}$	153201 $_{679}$	9197940 $_{846}$
10873	118 22 21 29	1285 429 208 617	273678 $_{4795}$	742324 $_{15163}$	153880 $_{679}$	9197094 $_{846}$
10874	118 24 38 76	1285 783 907 624	278473 $_{4795}$	757487 $_{15162}$	154559 $_{679}$	9196248 $_{846}$
10875	118 26 56 25	1286 138 671 875	283268 $_{4795}$	772649 $_{15162}$	155238 $_{679}$	9195402 $_{845}$
10876	118 28 73 76	1286 493 501 376	288063 $_{4794}$	787811 $_{15160}$	155917 $_{679}$	9194557 $_{845}$
10877	118 30 91 29	1286 848 396 133	292857 $_{4794}$	802971 $_{15161}$	156596 $_{679}$	9193712 $_{846}$
10878	118 33 08 84	1287 203 356 152	297651 $_{4794}$	818132 $_{15159}$	157275 $_{679}$	9192866 $_{845}$
10879	118 35 26 41	1287 558 381 439	302445 $_{4793}$	833291 $_{15159}$	157954 $_{679}$	9192021 $_{845}$
10880	118 37 44 00	1287 913 472 000	307238 $_{4794}$	848450 $_{15158}$	158633 $_{679}$	9191176 $_{844}$
10881	118 39 61 61	1288 268 627 841	312032 $_{4793}$	863608 $_{15158}$	159312 $_{679}$	9190332 $_{845}$
10882	118 41 79 24	1288 623 848 968	316825 $_{4793}$	878766 $_{15156}$	159991 $_{678}$	9189487 $_{844}$
10883	118 43 96 89	1288 979 135 387	321618 $_{4793}$	893922 $_{15156}$	160669 $_{679}$	9188643 $_{844}$
10884	118 46 14 56	1289 334 487 104	326411 $_{4792}$	909078 $_{15156}$	161348 $_{679}$	9187799 $_{844}$
10885	118 48 32 25	1289 689 904 125	331203 $_{4793}$	924234 $_{15154}$	162027 $_{679}$	9186955 $_{844}$
10886	118 50 49 96	1290 045 386 456	335996 $_{4792}$	939388 $_{15154}$	162706 $_{678}$	9186111 $_{844}$
10887	118 52 67 69	1290 400 934 103	340788 $_{4792}$	954542 $_{15154}$	163384 $_{679}$	9185267 $_{844}$
10888	118 54 85 44	1290 756 547 072	345580 $_{4791}$	969696 $_{15152}$	164063 $_{678}$	9184423 $_{843}$
10889	118 57 03 21	1291 112 225 369	350371 $_{4792}$	984848 $_{15152}$	164741 $_{679}$	9183580 $_{844}$
10890	118 59 21 00	1291 467 969 000	355163 $_{4791}$	*000000 $_{15151}$	165420 $_{678}$	9182736 $_{843}$
10891	118 61 38 81	1291 823 777 971	359954 $_{4791}$	015151 $_{15151}$	166098 $_{679}$	9181893 $_{843}$
10892	118 63 56 64	1292 179 652 288	364745 $_{4791}$	030302 $_{15149}$	166777 $_{678}$	9181050 $_{843}$
10893	118 65 74 49	1292 535 591 957	369536 $_{4790}$	045451 $_{15149}$	167455 $_{678}$	9180207 $_{842}$
10894	118 67 92 36	1292 891 596 984	374326 $_{4791}$	060600 $_{15149}$	168133 $_{679}$	9179365 $_{843}$
10895	118 70 10 25	1293 247 667 375	379117 $_{4790}$	075749 $_{15148}$	168812 $_{678}$	9178522 $_{842}$
10896	118 72 28 16	1293 603 803 136	383907 $_{4790}$	090897 $_{15147}$	169490 $_{678}$	9177680 $_{842}$
10897	118 74 46 09	1293 960 004 273	388697 $_{4790}$	106044 $_{15146}$	170168 $_{678}$	9176838 $_{842}$
10898	118 76 64 04	1294 316 270 792	393486 $_{4789}$	121190 $_{15146}$	170846 $_{678}$	9175996 $_{842}$
10899	118 78 82 01	1294 672 602 699	398276 $_{4789}$	136335 $_{15145}$	171524 $_{678}$	9175154 $_{842}$
10900	118 81 00 00	1295 029 000 000	403065 104·	151480 330·	172202 22·	9174312 0·0000

No. n	Square n²	Cube n³	Square root √n	Sq. rt. of 10n √10n	Cube root ∛n	Reciprocal 1/n
			104·	330·	22·	0·0000
10900	118 81 00 00	1295 029 000 000	403065 4789	151480 15145	172202 678	9174312 842
10901	118 83 18 01	1295 385 462 701	407854 4789	166625 15145	172880 678	9173470 841
10902	118 85 36 04	1295 741 990 808	412643 4788	181768 15143	173558 678	9172629 841
10903	118 87 54 09	1296 098 584 327	417431 4789	196911 15143	174236 678	9171788 841
10904	118 89 72 16	1296 455 243 264	422220 4788	212053 15142	174914 678	9170946 841
10905	118 91 90 25	1296 811 967 625	427008 4788	227195 15140	175592 678	9170105 840
10906	118 94 08 36	1297 168 757 416	431796 4788	242335 15140	176270 678	9169265 841
10907	118 96 26 49	1297 525 612 643	436584 4787	257475 15140	176948 677	9168424 841
10908	118 98 44 64	1297 882 533 312	441371 4787	272615 15138	177625 678	9167583 840
10909	119 00 62 81	1298 239 519 429	446158 4787	287753 15138	178303 678	9166743 840
10910	119 02 81 00	1298 596 571 000	450945 4787	302891 15138	178981 677	9165903 840
10911	119 04 99 21	1298 953 688 031	455732 4787	318029 15136	179658 678	9165063 840
10912	119 07 17 44	1299 310 870 528	460519 4786	333165 15136	180336 677	9164223 840
10913	119 09 35 69	1299 668 118 497	465305 4786	348301 15135	181013 678	9163383 840
10914	119 11 53 96	1300 025 431 944	470091 4786	363436 15135	181691 677	9162544 839
10915	119 13 72 25	1300 382 810 875	474877 4786	378571 15134	182368 678	9161704 839
10916	119 15 90 56	1300 740 255 296	479663 4786	393705 15133	183046 677	9160865 839
10917	119 18 08 89	1301 097 765 213	484449 4785	408838 15132	183723 677	9160026 839
10918	119 20 27 24	1301 455 340 632	489234 4785	423970 15132	184400 678	9159187 839
10919	119 22 45 61	1301 812 981 559	494019 4785	439102 15131	185078 677	9158348 839
10920	119 24 64 00	1302 170 688 000	498804 4784	454233 15130	185755 677	9157509 838
10921	119 26 82 41	1302 528 459 961	503588 4785	469363 15130	186432 677	9156671 839
10922	119 29 00 84	1302 886 297 448	508373 4784	484493 15129	187109 677	9155832 838
10923	119 31 19 29	1303 244 200 467	513157 4784	499622 15128	187786 678	9154994 838
10924	119 33 37 76	1303 602 169 024	517941 4784	514750 15128	188464 677	9154156 838
10925	119 35 56 25	1303 960 203 125	522725 4783	529878 15126	189141 677	9153318 838
10926	119 37 74 76	1304 318 302 776	527508 4784	545004 15127	189818 677	9152480 838
10927	119 39 93 29	1304 676 467 983	532292 4783	560131 15125	190495 676	9151643 837
10928	119 42 11 84	1305 034 698 752	537075 4783	575256 15125	191171 677	9150805 838
10929	119 44 30 41	1305 392 995 089	541858 4782	590381 15124	191848 677	9149968 837
10930	119 46 49 00	1305 751 357 000	546640 4783	605505 15124	192525 677	9149131 837
10931	119 48 67 61	1306 109 784 491	551423 4782	620629 15122	193202 677	9148294 837
10932	119 50 86 24	1306 468 277 568	556205 4782	635751 15122	193879 676	9147457 837
10933	119 53 04 89	1306 826 836 237	560987 4782	650873 15122	194555 677	9146620 836
10934	119 55 23 56	1307 185 460 504	565769 4781	665995 15120	195232 677	9145784 837
10935	119 57 42 25	1307 544 150 375	570550 4782	681115 15120	195909 676	9144947 836
10936	119 59 60 96	1307 902 905 856	575332 4781	696235 15120	196585 677	9144111 836
10937	119 61 79 69	1308 261 726 953	580113 4781	711355 15118	197262 676	9143275 836
10938	119 63 98 44	1308 620 613 672	584894 4780	726473 15118	197938 677	9142439 836
10939	119 66 17 21	1308 979 566 019	589674 4781	741591 15117	198615 676	9141603 835
10940	119 68 36 00	1309 338 584 000	594455 4780	756708 15117	199291 677	9140768 836
10941	119 70 54 81	1309 697 667 621	599235 4780	771825 15115	199968 677	9139932 836
10942	119 72 73 64	1310 056 816 888	604015 4780	786940 15116	200644 676	9139097 835
10943	119 74 92 49	1310 416 031 807	608795 4780	802056 15114	201320 676	9138262 835
10944	119 77 11 36	1310 775 312 384	613575 4779	817170 15114	201996 677	9137427 835
10945	119 79 30 25	1311 134 658 625	618354 4779	832284 15113	202673 676	9136592 835
10946	119 81 49 16	1311 494 070 536	623133 4779	847397 15112	203349 676	9135757 835
10947	119 83 68 09	1311 853 548 123	627912 4779	862509 15112	204025 676	9134923 834
10948	119 85 87 04	1312 213 091 392	632691 4778	877621 15112	204701 676	9134088 835
10949	119 88 06 01	1312 572 700 349	637469 4779	892732 15111	205377 676	9133254 834
10950	119 90 25 00	1312 932 375 000	642248 104·	907842 330·	206053 22·	9132420 0·0000

No. n	Square n^2	Cube n^3	Square root $\sqrt{n}$	Sq. rt. of $10n$ $\sqrt{10n}$	Cube root $\sqrt[3]{n}$	Reciprocal $\dfrac{1}{n}$
			104·	330·	22·	0·0000
10950	119 90 25 00	1312 932 375 000	642248 $_{4778}$	907842 $_{15110}$	206053 $_{676}$	9132420 $_{834}$
10951	119 92 44 01	1313 292 115 351	647026 $_{4778}$	922952 $_{15109}$	206729 $_{676}$	9131586 $_{834}$
10952	119 94 63 04	1313 651 921 408	651804 $_{4777}$	938061 $_{15108}$	207405 $_{676}$	9130752 $_{833}$
10953	119 96 82 09	1314 011 793 177	656581 $_{4778}$	953169 $_{15107}$	208081 $_{676}$	9129919 $_{834}$
10954	119 99 01 16	1314 371 730 664	661359 $_{4777}$	968276 $_{15107}$	208757 $_{675}$	9129085 $_{833}$
10955	120 01 20 25	1314 731 733 875	666136 $_{4777}$	983383 $_{15106}$	209432 $_{676}$	9128252 $_{833}$
10956	120 03 39 36	1315 091 802 816	670913 $_{4777}$	998489 $_{15106}$	210108 $_{676}$	9127419 $_{833}$
10957	120 05 58 49	1315 451 937 493	675690 $_{4776}$	*013595 $_{15105}$	210784 $_{676}$	9126586 $_{833}$
10958	120 07 77 64	1315 812 137 912	680466 $_{4777}$	028700 $_{15104}$	211460 $_{675}$	9125753 $_{833}$
10959	120 09 96 81	1316 172 404 079	685243 $_{4776}$	043804 $_{15103}$	212135 $_{676}$	9124920 $_{832}$
10960	120 12 16 00	1316 532 736 000	690019 $_{4776}$	058907 $_{15103}$	212811 $_{675}$	9124088 $_{833}$
10961	120 14 35 21	1316 893 133 681	694795 $_{4775}$	074010 $_{15102}$	213486 $_{676}$	9123255 $_{832}$
10962	120 16 54 44	1317 253 597 128	699570 $_{4776}$	089112 $_{15101}$	214162 $_{675}$	9122423 $_{832}$
10963	120 18 73 69	1317 614 126 347	704346 $_{4775}$	104213 $_{15101}$	214837 $_{676}$	9121591 $_{832}$
10964	120 20 92 96	1317 974 721 344	709121 $_{4775}$	119314 $_{15100}$	215513 $_{675}$	9120759 $_{832}$
10965	120 23 12 25	1318 335 382 125	713896 $_{4775}$	134414 $_{15099}$	216188 $_{676}$	9119927 $_{832}$
10966	120 25 31 56	1318 696 108 696	718671 $_{4774}$	149513 $_{15099}$	216864 $_{675}$	9119095 $_{831}$
10967	120 27 50 89	1319 056 901 063	723445 $_{4775}$	164612 $_{15098}$	217539 $_{675}$	9118264 $_{831}$
10968	120 29 70 24	1319 417 759 232	728220 $_{4774}$	179710 $_{15097}$	218214 $_{675}$	9117433 $_{832}$
10969	120 31 89 61	1319 778 683 209	732994 $_{4774}$	194807 $_{15096}$	218889 $_{675}$	9116601 $_{831}$
10970	120 34 09 00	1320 139 673 000	737768 $_{4774}$	209903 $_{15096}$	219564 $_{676}$	9115770 $_{831}$
10971	120 36 28 41	1320 500 728 611	742542 $_{4773}$	224999 $_{15095}$	220240 $_{675}$	9114939 $_{830}$
10972	120 38 47 84	1320 861 850 048	747315 $_{4773}$	240094 $_{15095}$	220915 $_{675}$	9114109 $_{831}$
10973	120 40 67 29	1321 223 037 317	752088 $_{4773}$	255189 $_{15093}$	221590 $_{675}$	9113278 $_{830}$
10974	120 42 86 76	1321 584 290 424	756861 $_{4773}$	270282 $_{15093}$	222265 $_{675}$	9112448 $_{831}$
10975	120 45 06 25	1321 945 609 375	761634 $_{4773}$	285375 $_{15093}$	222940 $_{675}$	9111617 $_{830}$
10976	120 47 25 76	1322 306 994 176	766407 $_{4772}$	300468 $_{15092}$	223615 $_{675}$	9110787 $_{830}$
10977	120 49 45 29	1322 668 444 833	771179 $_{4772}$	315560 $_{15091}$	224290 $_{674}$	9109957 $_{830}$
10978	120 51 64 84	1323 029 961 352	775951 $_{4772}$	330651 $_{15090}$	224964 $_{675}$	9109127 $_{829}$
10979	120 53 84 41	1323 391 543 739	780723 $_{4772}$	345741 $_{15090}$	225639 $_{675}$	9108298 $_{830}$
10980	120 56 04 00	1323 753 192 000	785495 $_{4772}$	360831 $_{15088}$	226314 $_{675}$	9107468 $_{829}$
10981	120 58 23 61	1324 114 906 141	790267 $_{4771}$	375919 $_{15089}$	226989 $_{674}$	9106639 $_{829}$
10982	120 60 43 24	1324 476 686 168	795038 $_{4771}$	391008 $_{15087}$	227663 $_{675}$	9105810 $_{830}$
10983	120 62 62 89	1324 838 532 087	799809 $_{4771}$	406095 $_{15087}$	228338 $_{675}$	9104980 $_{829}$
10984	120 64 82 56	1325 200 443 904	804580 $_{4771}$	421182 $_{15086}$	229013 $_{674}$	9104151 $_{828}$
10985	120 67 02 25	1325 562 421 625	809351 $_{4770}$	436268 $_{15086}$	229687 $_{675}$	9103323 $_{829}$
10986	120 69 21 96	1325 924 465 256	814121 $_{4770}$	451354 $_{15085}$	230362 $_{674}$	9102494 $_{828}$
10987	120 71 41 69	1326 286 574 803	818891 $_{4770}$	466439 $_{15084}$	231036 $_{675}$	9101666 $_{829}$
10988	120 73 61 44	1326 648 750 272	823661 $_{4770}$	481523 $_{15083}$	231711 $_{674}$	9100837 $_{828}$
10989	120 75 81 21	1327 010 991 669	828431 $_{4770}$	496606 $_{15083}$	232385 $_{675}$	9100009 $_{828}$
10990	120 78 01 00	1327 373 299 000	833201	511689 $_{15082}$	233060 $_{674}$	9099181 $_{828}$
10991	120 80 20 81	1327 735 672 271	837970 $_{4769}$	526771 $_{15082}$	233734 $_{674}$	9098353 $_{828}$
10992	120 82 40 64	1328 098 111 488	842739 $_{4769}$	541853 $_{15080}$	234408 $_{674}$	9097525 $_{827}$
10993	120 84 60 49	1328 460 616 657	847508 $_{4769}$	556933 $_{15080}$	235082 $_{675}$	9096698 $_{828}$
10994	120 86 80 36	1328 823 187 784	852277 $_{4769}$	572013 $_{15080}$	235757 $_{674}$	9095870 $_{827}$
10995	120 89 00 25	1329 185 824 875	857046 $_{4768}$	587093 $_{15078}$	236431 $_{674}$	9095043 $_{827}$
10996	120 91 20 16	1329 548 527 936	861814 $_{4768}$	602171 $_{15078}$	237105 $_{674}$	9094216 $_{827}$
10997	120 93 40 09	1329 911 296 973	866582 $_{4768}$	617249 $_{15078}$	237779 $_{674}$	9093389 $_{827}$
10998	120 95 60 04	1330 274 131 992	871350 $_{4767}$	632327 $_{15076}$	238453 $_{674}$	9092562 $_{826}$
10999	120 97 80 01	1330 637 032 999	876117 $_{4768}$	647403 $_{15076}$	239127 $_{674}$	9091736 $_{827}$
11000	121 00 00 00	1331 000 000 000	880885 104·	662479 331·	239801 22·	9090909 · 0·0000

221

No. n	Square n^2	Cube n^3	Square root $\sqrt{n}$	Sq. rt. of $10n$ $\sqrt{10n}$	Cube root $\sqrt[3]{n}$	Reciprocal $\dfrac{1}{n}$
			104·	331·	22·	0·0000
11000	121 00 00 00	1331 000 000 000	880885 4767	662479 15075	239801 674	9090909 826
11001	121 02 20 01	1331 363 033 001	885652 4767	677554 15075	240475 674	9090083 827
11002	121 04 40 44	1331 726 132 008	890419 4767	692629 15074	241149 674	9089256 826
11003	121 06 60 09	1332 089 297 027	895186 4766	707703 15073	241823 673	9088430 825
11004	121 08 80 16	1332 452 528 064	899952 4767	722776 15072	242496 674	9087605 826
11005	121 11 00 25	1332 815 825 125	904719 4766	737848 15072	243170 674	9086779 826
11006	121 13 20 36	1333 179 188 216	909485 4766	752920 15071	243844 673	9085953 825
11007	121 15 40 49	1333 542 617 343	914251 4765	767991 15071	244517 674	9085128 826
11008	121 17 60 64	1333 906 112 512	919016 4766	783062 15069	245191 674	9084302 825
11009	121 19 80 81	1334 269 673 729	923782 4765	798131 15069	245865 673	9083477 825
11010	121 22 01 00	1334 633 301 000	928547 4765	813200 15069	246538 674	9082652 825
11011	121 24 21 21	1334 996 994 331	933312 4765	828269 15068	247212 673	9081827 824
11012	121 26 41 44	1335 360 753 728	938077 4765	843337 15067	247885 674	9081003 825
11013	121 28 61 69	1335 724 579 197	942842 4764	858404 15066	248559 673	9080178 824
11014	121 30 81 96	1336 088 470 744	947606 4764	873470 15066	249232 673	9079354 825
11015	121 33 02 25	1336 452 428 375	952370 4764	888536 15064	249905 674	9078529 824
11016	121 35 22 56	1336 816 452 096	957134 4764	903600 15065	250579 673	9077705 824
11017	121 37 42 89	1337 180 541 913	961898 4763	918665 15063	251252 673	9076881 824
11018	121 39 63 24	1337 544 697 832	966661 4764	933728 15063	251925 673	9076057 823
11019	121 41 83 61	1337 908 919 859	971425 4763	948791 15062	252598 673	9075234 824
11020	121 44 04 00	1338 273 208 000	976188 4763	963853 15062	253271 674	9074410 823
11021	121 46 24 41	1338 637 562 261	980951 4762	978915 15061	253945 673	9073587 823
11022	121 48 44 84	1339 001 982 648	985713 4763	993976 15060	254618 673	9072764 824
11023	121 50 65 29	1339 366 469 167	990476 4762	*009036 15060	255291 673	9071940 822
11024	121 52 85 76	1339 731 021 824	995238 4762	024096 15058	255964 672	9071118 823
11025	121 55 06 25	1340 095 640 625	*000000 4762	039154 15058	256636 673	9070295 823
11026	121 57 26 76	1340 460 325 576	004762 4761	054212 15058	257309 673	9069472 822
11027	121 59 47 29	1340 825 076 683	009523 4762	069270 15057	257982 673	9068650 823
11028	121 61 67 84	1341 189 893 952	014285 4761	084327 15056	258655 673	9067827 822
11029	121 63 88 41	1341 554 777 389	019046 4761	099383 15055	259328 673	9067005 822
11030	121 66 09 00	1341 919 727 000	023807 4761	114438 15055	260001 672	9066183 822
11031	121 68 29 61	1342 284 742 791	028568 4760	129493 15054	260673 673	9065361 821
11032	121 70 50 24	1342 649 824 768	033328 4760	144547 15053	261346 673	9064540 822
11033	121 72 70 89	1343 014 972 937	038088 4760	159600 15053	262019 672	9063718 821
11034	121 74 91 56	1343 380 187 304	042848 4760	174653 15052	262691 673	9062897 822
11035	121 77 12 25	1343 745 467 875	047608 4760	189705 15051	263364 672	9062075 821
11036	121 79 32 96	1344 110 814 656	052368 4759	204756 15051	264036 673	9061254 821
11037	121 81 53 69	1344 476 227 653	057127 4760	219807 15050	264709 672	9060433 821
11038	121 83 74 44	1344 841 706 872	061887 4759	234857 15050	265381 672	9059612 820
11039	121 85 95 21	1345 207 252 319	066646 4758	249906 15049	266053 673	9058792 821
11040	121 88 16 00	1345 572 864 000	071404 4759	264955 15047	266726 672	9057971 820
11041	121 90 36 81	1345 938 541 921	076163 4758	280002 15048	267398 672	9057151 821
11042	121 92 57 64	1346 304 286 088	080921 4758	295050 15046	268070 672	9056330 820
11043	121 94 78 49	1346 670 096 507	085679 4758	310096 15046	268742 673	9055510 820
11044	121 96 99 36	1347 035 973 184	090437 4758	325142 15045	269415 672	9054690 819
11045	121 99 20 25	1347 401 916 125	095195 4757	340187 15045	270087 672	9053871 820
11046	122 01 41 16	1347 767 925 336	099952 4758	355232 15043	270759 672	9053051 820
11047	122 03 62 09	1348 134 000 823	104710 4757	370275 15044	271431 672	9052231 819
11048	122 05 83 04	1348 500 142 592	109467 4757	385319 15042	272103 672	9051412 819
11049	122 08 04 01	1348 866 350 649	114224 4756	400361 15042	272775 672	9050593 819
11050	122 10 25 00	1349 232 625 000	118980 105·	415403 332·	273447 22·	9049774 0·0000

No. n	Square n^2	Cube n^3	Square root $\sqrt{n}$	Sq. rt. of 10n $\sqrt{10n}$	Cube root $\sqrt[3]{n}$	Reciprocal $\frac{1}{n}$
			105·	332·	22·	0·0000
11050	122 10 25 00	1349 232 625 000	118980 4757	415403 15041	273447 672	9049774 819
11051	122 12 46 01	1349 598 965 651	123737 4756	430444 15040	274119 671	9048955 819
11052	122 14 67 04	1349 965 372 608	128493 4756	445484 15040	274790 672	9048136 819
11053	122 16 88 09	1350 331 845 877	133249 4756	460524 15039	275462 672	9047317 818
11054	122 19 09 16	1350 698 385 464	138005 4755	475563 15038	276134 672	9046499 818
11055	122 21 30 25	1351 064 991 375	142760 4755	490601 15038	276806 671	9045681 818
11056	122 23 51 36	1351 431 663 616	147515 4756	505639 15037	277477 672	9044863 819
11057	122 25 72 49	1351 798 402 193	152271 4754	520676 15036	278149 672	9044044 817
11058	122 27 93 64	1352 165 207 112	157025 4755	535712 15036	278821 671	9043227 818
11059	122 30 14 81	1352 532 078 379	161780 4755	550748 15035	279492 672	9042409 818
11060	122 32 36 00	1352 899 016 000	166535 4754	565783 15034	280164 671	9041591 817
11061	122 34 57 21	1353 266 019 981	171289 4754	580817 15034	280835 672	9040774 817
11062	122 36 78 44	1353 633 090 328	176043 4754	595851 15033	281507 671	9039957 818
11063	122 38 99 69	1354 000 227 047	180797 4753	610884 15032	282178 671	9039139 817
11064	122 41 20 96	1354 367 430 144	185550 4754	625916 15032	282849 672	9038322 816
11065	122 43 42 25	1354 734 699 625	190304 4753	640948 15030	283521 671	9037506 817
11066	122 45 63 56	1355 102 035 496	195057 4753	655978 15031	284192 671	9036689 817
11067	122 47 84 89	1355 469.437 763	199810 4753	671009 15029	284863 671	9035872 816
11068	122 50 06 24	1355 836 906 432	204563 4752	686038 15029	285534 671	9035056 816
11069	122 52 27 61	1356 204 441 509	209315 4753	701067 15028	286205 672	9034240 816
11070	122 54 49 00	1356 572 043 000	214068 4752	716095 15028	286877 671	9033424 816
11071	122 56 70 41	1356 939 710 911	218820 4752	731123 15026	287548 671	9032608 816
11072	122 58 91 84	1357 307 445 248	223572 4751	746149 15027	288219 671	9031792 816
11073	122 61 13 29	1357 675 246 017	228323 4752	761176 15025	288890 671	9030976 815
11074	122 63 34 76	1358 043 113 224	233075 4751	776201 15025	289561 670	9030161 816
11075	122 65 56 25	1358 411 046 875	237826 4751	791226 15024	290231 671	9029345 815
11076	122 67 77 76	1358 779 046 976	242577 4751	806250 15023	290902 671	9028530 815
11077	122 69 99 29	1359 147 113 533	247328 4750	821273 15023	291573 671	9027715 815
11078	122 72 20 84	1359 515 246 552	252078 4751	836296 15022	292244 671	9026900 815
11079	122 74 42 41	1359 883 446 039	256829 4750	851318 15022	292915 670	9026085 814
11080	122 76 64 00	1360 251 712 000	261579 4750	866340 15020	293585 671	9025271 815
11081	122 78 85 61	1360 620 044 441	266329 4750	881360 15020	294256 671	9024456 814
11082	122 81 07 24	1360 988 443 368	271079 4749	896380 15020	294927 670	9023642 814
11083	122 83 28 89	1361 356 908 787	275828 4750	911400 15018	295597 671	9022828 814
11084	122 85 50 56	1361 725 440 704	280578 4749	926418 15018	296268 670	9022014 814
11085	122 87 72 25	1362 094 039 125	285327 4749	941436 15018	296938 671	9021200 814
11086	122 89 93 96	1362 462 704 056	290076 4748	956454 15016	297609 670	9020386 814
11087	122 92 15 69	1362 831 435 503	294824 4749	971470 15016	298279 671	9019572 813
11088	122 94 37 44	1363 200 233 472	299573 4748	986486 15015	298950 670	9018759 813
11089	122 96 59 21	1363 569 097 969	304321 4748	*001501 15015	299620 670	9017946 813
11090	122 98 81 00	1363 938 029 000	309069 4748	016516 15014	300290 670	9017133 813
11091	123 01 02 81	1364 307 026 571	313817 4748	031530 15013	300960 671	9016320 813
11092	123 03 24 64	1364 676 090 688	318564 4747	046543 15013	301631 670	9015507 813
11093	123 05 46 49	1365 045 221 357	323312 4747	061556 15012	302301 670	9014694 813
11094	123 07 68 36	1365 414 418 584	328059 4747	076568 15011	302971 670	9013881 812
11095	123 09 90 25	1365 783 682 375	332806 4747	091579 15011	303641 670	9013069 812
11096	123 12 12 16	1366 153 012 736	337553 4746	106590 15009	304311 670	9012257 812
11097	123 14 34 09	1366 522 409 673	342299 4747	121599 15010	304981 670	9011445 812
11098	123 16 56 04	1366 891 873 192	347046 4746	136609 15008	305651 670	9010633 812
11099	123 18 78 01	1367 261 403 299	351792 4746	151617 15008	306321 670	9009821 812
11100	123 21 00 00	1367 631 090 000	356538	166625	306991	9009009
			105·	333·	22·	0·0000

No. n	Square n²	Cube n³	Square root √n	Sq. rt. of 10n √10n	Cube root ∛n	Reciprocal 1/n
			105.	333.	22.	0.0000
11100	123 21 00 00	1367 631 000 000	356538 4745	166625 15007	306991 670	9009009 812
11101	123 23 22 01	1368 000 663 301	361283 4746	181632 15007	307661 670	9008197 811
11102	123 25 44 04	1368 370 393 208	366029 4745	196639 15005	308331 670	9007386 811
11103	123 27 66 09	1368 740 189 727	370774 4745	211644 15006	309001 669	9006575 811
11104	123 29 88 16	1369 110 052 864	375519 4745	226650 15004	309670 670	9005764 811
11105	123 32 10 25	1369 479 982 625	380264 4744	241654 15004	310340 670	9004953 811
11106	123 34 32 36	1369 849 979 016	385008 4745	256658 15003	311010 669	9004142 811
11107	123 36 54 49	1370 220 042 043	389753 4744	271661 15002	311679 670	9003331 810
11108	123 38 76 64	1370 590 171 712	394497 4744	286663 15002	312349 669	9002521 811
11109	123 40 98 81	1370 960 368 029	399241 4744	301665 15001	313018 670	9001710 810
11110	123 43 21 00	1371 330 631 000	403985 4743	316666 15001	313688 669	9000900 810
11111	123 45 43 21	1371 700 960 631	408728 4744	331667 14999	314357 670	9000090 810
11112	123 47 65 44	1372 071 356 928	413472 4743	346666 14999	315027 669	8999280 810
11113	123 49 87 69	1372 441 819 897	418215 4743	361665 14999	315696 669	8998470 809
11114	123 52 09 96	1372 812 349 544	422958 4742	376664 14998	316365 670	8997661 810
11115	123 54 32 25	1373 182 945 875	427700 4743	391662 14997	317035 669	8996851 809
11116	123 56 54 56	1373 553 608 896	432443 4742	406659 14996	317704 669	8996042 809
11117	123 58 76 89	1373 924 338 613	437185 4742	421655 14996	318373 669	8995233 810
11118	123 60 99 24	1374 295 135 032	441927 4742	436651 14995	319042 670	8994423 808
11119	123 63 21 61	1374 665 998 159	446669 4742	451646 14994	319712 669	8993615 809
11120	123 65 44 00	1375 036 928 000	451411 4741	466640 14994	320381 669	8992806 809
11121	123 67 66 41	1375 407 924 561	456152 4741	481634 14993	321050 669	8991997 808
11122	123 69 88 84	1375 778 987 848	460893 4741	496627 14992	321719 669	8991189 809
11123	123 72 11 29	1376 150 117 867	465634 4741	511619 14992	322388 669	8990380 808
11124	123 74 33 76	1376 521 314 624	470375 4741	526611 14991	323057 668	8989572 808
11125	123 76 56 25	1376 892 578 125	475116 4740	541602 14990	323725 669	8988764 808
11126	123 78 78 76	1377 263 908 376	479856 4740	556592 14990	324394 669	8987956 808
11127	123 81 01 29	1377 635 305 383	484596 4740	571582 14988	325063 669	8987148 807
11128	123 83 23 84	1378 006 769 152	489336 4740	586570 14989	325732 669	8986341 808
11129	123 85 46 41	1378 378 299 689	494076 4739	601559 14987	326401 668	8985533 807
11130	123 87 69 00	1378 749 897 000	498815 4739	616546 14987	327069 669	8984726 807
11131	123 89 91 61	1379 121 561 091	503554 4740	631533 14987	327738 669	8983919 807
11132	123 92 14 24	1379 493 291 968	508294 4738	646520 14985	328407 668	8983112 807
11133	123 94 36 89	1379 865 089 637	513032 4739	661505 14985	329075 669	8982305 807
11134	123 96 59 56	1380 236 954 104	517771 4738	676490 14984	329744 668	8981498 806
11135	123 98 82 25	1380 608 885 375	522509 4739	691474 14984	330412 669	8980692 807
11136	124 01 04 96	1380 980 883 456	527248 4738	706458 14983	331081 668	8979885 806
11137	124 03 27 69	1381 352 948 353	531986 4737	721441 14982	331749 668	8979079 806
11138	124 05 50 44	1381 725 080 072	536723 4738	736423 14981	332417 669	8978273 806
11139	124 07 73 21	1382 097 278 619	541461 4737	751404 14981	333086 668	8977467 806
11140	124 09 96 00	1382 469 544 000	546198 4738	766385 14981	333754 668	8976661 806
11141	124 12 18 81	1382 841 876 221	550936 4737	781366 14979	334422 669	8975855 806
11142	124 14 41 64	1383 214 275 288	555673 4737	796345 14979	335091 668	8975049 805
11143	124 16 64 49	1383 586 741 207	560409 4737	811324 14978	335759 668	8974244 805
11144	124 18 87 36	1383 959 273 984	565146 4736	826302 14978	336427 668	8973439 806
11145	124 21 10 25	1384 331 873 625	569882 4736	841280 14976	337095 668	8972633 805
11146	124 23 33 16	1384 704 540 136	574618 4736	856256 14977	337763 668	8971828 804
11147	124 25 56 09	1385 077 273 523	579354 4736	871233 14975	338431 668	8971024 805
11148	124 27 79 04	1385 450 073 792	584090 4735	886208 14975	339099 668	8970219 805
11149	124 30 02 01	1385 822 940 949	588825 4735	901183 14974	339767 668	8969414 804
11150	124 32 25 00	1386 195 875 000	593560	916157	340435	8968610
			105.	333.	22.	0.0000

No. n	Square n^2	Cube n^3	Square root $\sqrt{n}$	Sq. rt. of 10n $\sqrt{10n}$	Cube root $\sqrt[3]{n}$	Reciprocal $\frac{1}{n}$
			105.	333.	22.	0.0000
11150	124 32 25 00	1386 195 875 000	593560 (4735)	916157 (14974)	340435 (668)	8968610 (804)
11151	124 34 48 01	1386 568 875 951	598295 (4735)	931131 (14972)	341103 (668)	8967806 (805)
11152	124 36 71 04	1386 941 943 808	603030 (4735)	946103 (14973)	341771 (667)	8967001 (804)
11153	124 38 94 09	1387 315 078 577	607765 (4734)	961076 (14973)	342438 (668)	8966197 (803)
11154	124 41 17 16	1387 688 280 264	612499 (4734)	976047 (14971)	343106 (668)	8965394 (804)
11155	124 43 40 25	1388 061 548 875	617233 (4734)	991018 (14971)	343774 (667)	8964590 (804)
11156	124 45 63 36	1388 434 884 416	621967 (4734)	*005988 (14970)	344441 (668)	8963786 (803)
11157	124 47 86 49	1388 808 286 893	626701 (4734)	020957 (14969)	345109 (668)	8962983 (803)
11158	124 50 09 64	1389 181 756 312	631435 (4733)	035926 (14969)	345777 (667)	8962180 (804)
11159	124 52 32 81	1389 555 292 679	636168 (4733)	050894 (14968)	346444 (668)	8961376 (803)
11160	124 54 56 00	1389 928 896 000	640901 (4733)	065862 (14968)	347112 (667)	8960573 (802)
11161	124 56 79 21	1390 302 566 281	645634 (4733)	080829 (14967)	347779 (667)	8959771 (803)
11162	124 59 02 44	1390 676 303 528	650367 (4732)	095795 (14966)	348446 (668)	8958968 (803)
11163	124 61 25 69	1391 050 107 747	655099 (4733)	110760 (14965)	349114 (667)	8958165 (802)
11164	124 63 48 96	1391 423 978 944	659832 (4732)	125725 (14965)	349781 (668)	8957363 (802)
11165	124 65 72 25	1391 797 917 125	664564 (4731)	140689 (14964)	350449 (667)	8956561 (802)
11166	124 67 95 56	1392 171 922 296	669295 (4732)	155652 (14963)	351116 (667)	8955759 (802)
11167	124 70 18 89	1392 545 994 463	674027 (4732)	170615 (14963)	351783 (667)	8954957 (802)
11168	124 72 42 24	1392 920 133 632	678759 (4731)	185577 (14962)	352450 (667)	8954155 (802)
11169	124 74 65 61	1393 294 339 809	683490 (4731)	200539 (14962)	353117 (667)	8953353 (802)
11170	124 76 89 00	1393 668 613 000	688221 (4731)	215499 (14960)	353784 (667)	8952551 (801)
11171	124 79 12 41	1394 042 953 211	692952 (4730)	230459 (14960)	354451 (667)	8951750 (801)
11172	124 81 35 84	1394 417 360 448	697682 (4730)	245419 (14959)	355118 (667)	8950949 (801)
11173	124 83 59 29	1394 791 834 717	702412 (4731)	260378 (14958)	355785 (667)	8950148 (801)
11174	124 85 82 76	1395 166 376 024	707143 (4730)	275336 (14957)	356452 (667)	8949347 (801)
11175	124 88 06 25	1395 540 984 375	711873 (4729)	290293 (14957)	357119 (667)	8948546 (801)
11176	124 90 29 76	1395 915 659 776	716602 (4730)	305250 (14956)	357786 (667)	8947745 (800)
11177	124 92 53 29	1396 290 402 233	721332 (4729)	320206 (14955)	358453 (667)	8946945 (801)
11178	124 94 76 84	1396 665 211 752	726061 (4729)	335161 (14955)	359120 (666)	8946144 (800)
11179	124 97 00 41	1397 040 088 339	730790 (4729)	350116 (14954)	359786 (667)	8945344 (800)
11180	124 99 24 00	1397 415 032 000	735519 (4729)	365070 (14953)	360453 (667)	8944544 (800)
11181	125 01 47 61	1397 790 042 741	740248 (4728)	380023 (14953)	361120 (666)	8943744 (800)
11182	125 03 71 24	1398 165 120 568	744976 (4728)	394976 (14952)	361786 (667)	8942944 (800)
11183	125 05 94 89	1398 540 265 487	749704 (4729)	409928 (14951)	362453 (667)	8942144 (799)
11184	125 08 18 56	1398 915 477 504	754433 (4727)	424879 (14951)	363120 (666)	8941345 (800)
11185	125 10 42 25	1399 290 756 625	759160 (4728)	439830 (14950)	363786 (667)	8940545 (799)
11186	125 12 65 96	1399 666 102 856	763888 (4727)	454780 (14950)	364453 (666)	8939746 (799)
11187	125 14 89 69	1400 041 516 203	768615 (4728)	469730 (14948)	365119 (666)	8938947 (799)
11188	125 17 13 44	1400 416 996 672	773343 (4727)	484678 (14948)	365785 (667)	8938148 (799)
11189	125 19 37 21	1400 792 544 269	778070 (4726)	499626 (14948)	366452 (666)	8937349 (799)
11190	125 21 61 00	1401 168 159 000	782796 (4727)	514574 (14946)	367118 (666)	8936550 (798)
11191	125 23 84 81	1401 543 840 871	787523 (4726)	529520 (14946)	367784 (666)	8935752 (798)
11192	125 26 08 64	1401 919 589 888	792249 (4726)	544466 (14946)	368450 (667)	8934954 (799)
11193	125 28 32 49	1402 295 406 057	796975 (4726)	559412 (14944)	369117 (666)	8934155 (798)
11194	125 30 56 36	1402 671 289 384	801701 (4726)	574356 (14944)	369783 (666)	8933357 (798)
11195	125 32 80 25	1403 047 239 875	806427 (4726)	589300 (14944)	370449 (666)	8932559 (798)
11196	125 35 04 16	1403 423 257 536	811153 (4725)	604244 (14943)	371115 (666)	8931761 (797)
11197	125 37 28 09	1403 799 342 373	815878 (4725)	619187 (14942)	371781 (666)	8930964 (798)
11198	125 39 52 04	1404 175 494 392	820603 (4725)	634129 (14941)	372447 (666)	8930166 (797)
11199	125 41 76 01	1404 551 713 599	825328 (4724)	649070 (14941)	373113 (666)	8929369 (798)
11200	125 44 00 00	1404 928 000 000	830052	664011	373779	8928571
			105.	334.	22.	0.0000

Ω

No. n	Square n^2	Cube n^3	Square root $\sqrt{n}$	Sq. rt. of $10n$ $\sqrt{10n}$	Cube root $\sqrt[3]{n}$	Reciprocal $\frac{1}{n}$
			105·	334·	22·	0·0000
11200	125 44 00 00	1404 928 000 000	830052 $_{4725}$	664011 $_{14940}$	373779 $_{666}$	8928571 $_{797}$
11201	125 46 24 01	1405 304 353 601	834777 $_{4724}$	678951 $_{14939}$	374445 $_{666}$	8927774 $_{797}$
11202	125 48 48 04	1405 680 774 408	839501 $_{4724}$	693890 $_{14939}$	375111 $_{665}$	8926977 $_{797}$
11203	125 50 72 09	1406 057 262 427	844225 $_{4724}$	708829 $_{14938}$	375776 $_{666}$	8926180 $_{797}$
11204	125 52 96 16	1406 433 817 664	848949 $_{4724}$	723767 $_{14937}$	376442 $_{666}$	8925384 $_{797}$
11205	125 55 20 25	1406 810 440 125	853673 $_{4723}$	738704 $_{14937}$	377108 $_{665}$	8924587 $_{796}$
11206	125 57 44 36	1407 187 129 816	858396 $_{4723}$	753641 $_{14936}$	377773 $_{666}$	8923791 $_{796}$
11207	125 59 68 49	1407 563 886 743	863119 $_{4723}$	768577 $_{14935}$	378439 $_{666}$	8922995 $_{797}$
11208	125 61 92 64	1407 940 710 912	867842 $_{4723}$	783512 $_{14935}$	379105 $_{665}$	8922198 $_{796}$
11209	125 64 16 81	1408 317 602 329	872565 $_{4722}$	798447 $_{14934}$	379770 $_{666}$	8921402 $_{795}$
11210	125 66 41 00	1408 694 561 000	877287 $_{4723}$	813381 $_{14933}$	380436 $_{665}$	8920607 $_{796}$
11211	125 68 65 21	1409 071 586 931	882010 $_{4722}$	828314 $_{14933}$	381101 $_{666}$	8919811 $_{796}$
11212	125 70 89 44	1409 448 680 128	886732 $_{4722}$	843247 $_{14932}$	381767 $_{665}$	8919015 $_{795}$
11213	125 73 13 69	1409 825 840 597	891454 $_{4722}$	858179 $_{14931}$	382432 $_{665}$	8918220 $_{795}$
11214	125 75 37 96	1410 203 068 344	896176 $_{4721}$	873110 $_{14931}$	383097 $_{666}$	8917425 $_{795}$
11215	125 77 62 25	1410 580 363 375	900897 $_{4721}$	888041 $_{14930}$	383763 $_{665}$	8916630 $_{795}$
11216	125 79 86 56	1410 957 725 696	905618 $_{4721}$	902971 $_{14929}$	384428 $_{665}$	8915835 $_{795}$
11217	125 82 10 89	1411 335 155 313	910339 $_{4721}$	917900 $_{14929}$	385093 $_{665}$	8915040 $_{795}$
11218	125 84 35 24	1411 712 652 232	915060 $_{4721}$	932829 $_{14928}$	385758 $_{666}$	8914245 $_{795}$
11219	125 86 59 61	1412 090 216 459	919781 $_{4720}$	947757 $_{14927}$	386424 $_{665}$	8913450 $_{794}$
11220	125 88 84 00	1412 467 848 000	924501 $_{4721}$	962684 $_{14927}$	387089 $_{665}$	8912656 $_{794}$
11221	125 91 08 41	1412 845 546 861	929222 $_{4720}$	977611 $_{14926}$	387754 $_{665}$	8911862 $_{794}$
11222	125 93 32 84	1413 223 313 048	933942 $_{4719}$	992537 $_{14926}$	388419 $_{665}$	8911068 $_{794}$
11223	125 95 57 29	1413 601 146 567	938661 $_{4720}$	*007463 $_{14924}$	389084 $_{665}$	8910274 $_{794}$
11224	125 97 81 76	1413 979 047 424	943381 $_{4720}$	022387 $_{14924}$	389749 $_{665}$	8909480 $_{794}$
11225	126 00 06 25	1414 357 015 625	948101 $_{4719}$	037311 $_{14924}$	390414 $_{665}$	8908686 $_{794}$
11226	126 02 30 76	1414 735 051 176	952820 $_{4719}$	052235 $_{14922}$	391079 $_{664}$	8907892 $_{793}$
11227	126 04 55 29	1415 113 154 083	957539 $_{4718}$	067157 $_{14922}$	391743 $_{665}$	8907099 $_{793}$
11228	126 06 79 84	1415 491 324 352	962257 $_{4719}$	082079 $_{14922}$	392408 $_{665}$	8906306 $_{793}$
11229	126 09 04 41	1415 869 561 989	966976 $_{.4718}$	097001 $_{14921}$	393073 $_{665}$	8905513 $_{793}$
11230	126 11 29 00	1416 247 867 000	971694 $_{4718}$	111922 $_{14920}$	393738 $_{664}$	8904720 $_{793}$
11231	126 13 53 61	1416 626 239 391	976412 $_{4718}$	126842 $_{14919}$	394402 $_{665}$	8903927 $_{793}$
11232	126 15 78 24	1417 004 679 168	981130 $_{4718}$	141761 $_{14919}$	395067 $_{665}$	8903134 $_{793}$
11233	126 18 02 89	1417 383 186 337	985848 $_{4718}$	156680 $_{14918}$	395732 $_{664}$	8902341 $_{792}$
11234	126 20 27 56	1417 761 760 904	990566 $_{4717}$	171598 $_{14917}$	396396 $_{665}$	8901549 $_{792}$
11235	126 22 52 25	1418 140 402 875	995283 $_{4717}$	186515 $_{14917}$	397061 $_{664}$	8900757 $_{793}$
11236	126 24 76 96	1418 519 112 256	*000000 $_{4717}$	·201432 $_{14916}$	397725 $_{665}$	8899964 $_{792}$
11237	126 27 01 69	1418 897 889 053	004717 $_{4717}$	216348 $_{14915}$	398390 $_{664}$	8899172 $_{792}$
11238	126 29 26 44	1419 276 733 272	009434 $_{4716}$	231263 $_{14915}$	399054 $_{664}$	8898380 $_{792}$
11239	126 31 51 21	1419 655 644 919	014150 $_{4716}$	246178 $_{14914}$	399718 $_{665}$	8897589 $_{792}$
11240	126 33 76 00	1420 034 624 000	018866 $_{4716}$	261092 $_{14914}$	400383 $_{664}$	8896797 $_{791}$
11241	126 36 00 81	1420 413 670 521	023582 $_{4716}$	276006 $_{14912}$	401047 $_{664}$	8896006 $_{791}$
11242	126 38 25 64	1420 792 784 488	028298 $_{4716}$	290918 $_{14913}$	401711 $_{664}$	8895214 $_{791}$
11243	126 40 50 49	1421 171 965 907	033014 $_{4715}$	305831 $_{14911}$	402375 $_{665}$	8894423 $_{791}$
11244	126 42 75 36	1421 551 214 784	037729 $_{4715}$	320742 $_{14911}$	403040 $_{664}$	8893632 $_{791}$
11245	126 45 00 25	1421 930 531 125	042444 $_{4715}$	335653 $_{14910}$	403704 $_{664}$	8892841 $_{790}$
11246	126 47 25 16	1422 309 914 936	047159 $_{4715}$	350563 $_{14909}$	404368 $_{664}$	8892051 $_{791}$
11247	126 49 50 09	1422 689 366 223	051874 $_{4715}$	365472 $_{14909}$	405032 $_{664}$	8891260 $_{791}$
11248	126 51 75 04	1423 068 884 992	056589 $_{4714}$	380381 $_{14908}$	405696 $_{664}$	8890469 $_{790}$
11249	126 54 00 01	1423 448 471 249	061303 $_{4714}$	395289 $_{14908}$	406360 $_{664}$	8889679 $_{790}$
11250	126 56 25 00	1423 828 125 000	066017	410197	407024	8888889
			106·	335·	22·	0·0000

No. n	Square n²	Cube n³	Square root √n	Sq. rt. of 10n √10n	Cube root ∛n	Reciprocal 1/n
			106·	335·	22·	0·0000
11250	126 56 25 00	1423 828 125 000	066017 4714	410197 14906	407024 664	8888889 790
11251	126 58 50 01	1424 207 846 251	070731 4714	425103 14907	407688 663	8888099 790
11252	126 60 75 04	1424 587 635 008	075445 4713	440010 14905	408351 664	8887309 790
11253	126 63 00 09	1424 967 491 277	080158 4714	454915 14905	409015 664	8886519 789
11254	126 65 25 16	1425 347 415 064	084872 4713	469820 14904	409679 664	8885730 790
11255	126 67 50 25	1425 727 406 375	089585 4713	484724 14903	410343 663	8884940 789
11256	126 69 75 36	1426 107 465 216	094298 4712	499627 14903	411006 664	8884151 790
11257	126 72 00 49	1426 487 591 593	099010 4713	514530 14902	411670 664	8883361 789
11258	126 74 25 64	1426 867 785 512	103723 4712	529432 14902	412334 663	8882572 789
11259	126 76 50 81	1427 248 046 979	108435 4712	544334 14901	412997 664	8881783 788
11260	126 78 76 00	1427 628 376 000	113147 4712	559235 14900	413661 663	8880995 789
11261	126 81 01 21	1428 008 772 581	117859 4712	574135 14899	414324 664	8880206 788
11262	126 83 26 44	1428 389 236 728	122571 4711	589034 14899	414988 663	8879418 789
11263	126 85 51 69	1428 769 768 447	127282 4711	603933 14898	415651 664	8878629 788
11264	126 87 76 96	1429 150 367 744	131993 4711	618831 14898	416315 663	8877841 788
11265	126 90 02 25	1429 531 034 625	136704 4711	633729 14897	416978 663	8877053 788
11266	126 92 27 56	1429 911 769 096	141415 4711	648626 14896	417641 664	8876265 788
11267	126 94 52 89	1430 292 571 163	146126 4710	663522 14896	418305 663	8875477 788
11268	126 96 78 24	1430 673 440 832	150836 4710	678418 14894	418968 663	8874689 787
11269	126 99 03 61	1431 054 378 109	155546 4710	693312 14895	419631 663	8873902 788
11270	127 01 29 00	1431 435 383 000	160256 4710	708207 14893	420294 663	8873114 787
11271	127 03 54 41	1431 816 455 511	164966 4710	723100 14893	420957 663	8872327 787
11272	127 05 79 84	1432 197 595 648	169676 4709	737993 14892	421620 663	8871540 787
11273	127 08 05 29	1432 578 803 417	174385 4709	752885 14892	422283 663	8870753 787
11274	127 10 30 76	1432 960 078 824	179094 4709	767777 14891	422946 663	8869966 786
11275	127 12 56 25	1433 341 421 875	183803 4709	782668 14890	423609 663	8869180 787
11276	127 14 81 76	1433 722 832 576	188512 4708	797558 14890	424272 663	8868393 786
11277	127 17 07 29	1434 104 310 933	193220 4708	812448 14889	424935 663	8867607 787
11278	127 19 32 84	1434 485 856 952	197928 4709	827337 14888	425598 663	8866820 786
11279	127 21 58 41	1434 867 470 639	202637 4707	842225 14887	426261 662	8866034 786
11280	127 23 84 00	1435 249 152 000	207344 4708	857112 14887	426923 663	8865248 786
11281	127 26 09 61	1435 630 901 041	212052 4708	871999 14887	427586 663	8864462 786
11282	127 28 35 24	1436 012 717 768	216760 4707	886886 14885	428249 662	8863677 785
11283	127 30 60 89	1436 394 602 187	221467 4707	901771 14885	428911 663	8862891 785
11284	127 32 86 56	1436 776 554 304	226174 4707	916656 14885	429574 663	8862106 786
11285	127 35 12 25	1437 158 574 125	230881 4706	931541 14883	430237 662	8861320 785
11286	127 37 37 96	1437 540 661 656	235587 4707	946424 14883	430899 663	8860535 785
11287	127 39 63 69	1437 922 816 903	240294 4706	961307 14883	431562 662	8859750 785
11288	127 41 89 44	1438 305 039 872	245000 4706	976190 14881	432224 662	8858965 784
11289	127 44 15 21	1438 687 330 569	249706 4706	991071 14881	432886 663	8858181 785
11290	127 46 41 00	1439 069 689 000	254412 4705	*005952 14881	433549 662	8857396 785
11291	127 48 66 81	1439 452 115 171	259117 4706	020833 14879	434211 662	8856611 784
11292	127 50 92 64	1439 834 609 088	263823 4705	035712 14879	434873 663	8855827 784
11293	127 53 18 49	1440 217 170 757	268528 4705	050591 14879	435536 662	8855043 784
11294	127 55 44 36	1440 599 800 184	273233 4705	065470 14878	436198 662	8854259 784
11295	127 57 70 25	1440 982 497 375	277938 4704	080348 14877	436860 662	8853475 784
11296	127 59 96 16	1441 365 262 336	282642 4704	095225 14876	437522 662	8852691 783
11297	127 62 22 09	1441 748 095 073	287346 4705	110101 14876	438184 662	8851908 784
11298	127 64 48 04	1442 130 995 592	292051 4703	124977 14875	438846 662	8851124 783
11299	127 66 74 01	1442 513 963 899	296754 4704	139852 14874	439508 662	8850341 783
11300	127 69 00 00	1442 897 000 000	301458	154726	440170	8849558
			106·	336·	22·	0·0000

No. n	Square n^2	Cube n^3	Square root $\sqrt{n}$	Sq. rt. of $10n$ $\sqrt{10n}$	Cube root $\sqrt[3]{n}$	Reciprocal $\dfrac{1}{n}$
			106·	336·	22·	0·0000
11300	127 69 00 00	1442 897 000 000	301458 4704	154726 14874	440170 662	8849558 784
11301	127 71 26 01	1443 280 103 901	306162 4703	169600 14873	440832 662	8848774 782
11302	127 73 52 04	1443 663 275 608	310865 4703	184473 14873	441494 662	8847992 783
11303	127 75 78 09	1444 046 515 127	315568 4703	199346 14871	442156 662	8847209 783
11304	127 78 04 16	1444 429 822 464	320271 4703	214217 14872	442818 662	8846426 782
11305	127 80 30 25	1444 813 197 625	324974 4702	229089 14870	443480 661	8845644 783
11306	127 82 56 36	1445 196 640 616	329676 4702	243959 14870	444141 662	8844861 782
11307	127 84 82 49	1445 580 151 443	334378 4702	258829 14869	444803 662	8844079 782
11308	127 87 08 64	1445 963 730 112	339080 4702	273698 14869	445465 661	8843297 782
11309	127 89 34 81	1446 347 376 629	343782 4702	288567 14867	446126 662	8842515 782
11310	127 91 61 00	1446 731 091 000	348484 4701	303434 14868	446788 661	8841733 782
11311	127 93 87 21	1447 114 873 231	353185 4701	318302 14866	447449 662	8840951 781
11312	127 96 13 44	1447 498 723 328	357886 4701	333168 14866	448111 661	8840170 782
11313	127 98 39 69	1447 882 641 297	362587 4701	348034 14865	448772 662	8839388 781
11314	128 00 65 96	1448 266 627 144	367288 4701	362899 14865	449434 661	8838607 781
11315	128 02 92 25	1448 650 680 875	371989 4700	377764 14864	450095 662	8837826 781
11316	128 05 18 56	1449 034 802 496	376689 4700	392628 14863	450757 661	8837045 781
11317	128 07 44 89	1449 418 992 013	381389 4700	407491 14863	451418 661	8836264 781
11318	128 09 71 24	1449 803 249 432	386089 4700	422354 14862	452079 661	8835483 780
11319	128 11 97 61	1450 187 574 759	390789 4700	437216 14861	452740 662	8834703 781
11320	128 14 24 00	1450 571 968 000	395489 4699	452077 14860	453402 661	8833922 780
11321	128 16 50 41	1450 956 429 161	400188 4699	466937 14860	454063 661	8833142 780
11322	128 18 76 84	1451 340 958 248	404887 4699	481797 14860	454724 661	8832362 780
11323	128 21 03 29	1451 725 555 267	409586 4699	496657 14858	455385 661	8831582 780
11324	128 23 29 76	1452 110 220 224	414285 4698	511515 14858	456046 661	8830802 780
11325	128 25 56 25	1452 494 953 125	418983 4699	526373 14858	456707 661	8830022 780
11326	128 27 82 76	1452 879 753 976	423682 4698	541231 14856	457368 661	8829242 779
11327	128 30 09 29	1453 264 622 783	428380 4698	556087 14856	458029 661	8828463 779
11328	128 32 35 84	1453 649 559 552	433078 4697	570943 14856	458690 660	8827684 780
11329	128 34 62 41	1454 034 564 289	437775 4698	585799 14855	459350 661	8826904 779
11330	128 36 89 00	1454 419 637 000	442473 4697	600654 14854	460011 661	8826125 779
11331	128 39 15 61	1454 804 777 691	447170 4697	615508 14853	460672 661	8825346 778
11332	128 41 42 24	1455 189 986 368	451867 4697	630361 14853	461333 660	8824568 779
11333	128 43 68 89	1455 575 263 037	456564 4697	645214 14852	461993 661	8823789 779
11334	128 45 95 56	1455 960 607 704	461261 4696	660066 14851	462654 661	8823010 778
11335	128 48 22 25	1456 346 020 375	465957 4696	674917 14851	463315 660	8822232 778
11336	128 50 48 96	1456 731 501 056	470653 4696	689768 14850	463975 661	8821454 778
11337	128 52 75 69	1457 117 049 753	475349 4696	704618 14850	464636 660	8820676 778
11338	128 55 02 44	1457 502 666 472	480045 4696	719468 14849	465296 661	8819898 778
11339	128 57 29 21	1457 888 351 219	484741 4695	734317 14848	465957 660	8819120 778
11340	128 59 56 00	1458 274 104 000	489436 4695	749165 14847	466617 661	8818342 777
11341	128 61 82 81	1458 659 924 821	494131 4695	764012 14847	467278 660	8817565 778
11342	128 64 09 64	1459 045 813 688	498826 4695	778859 14846	467938 660	8816787 777
11343	128 66 36 49	1459 431 770 607	503521 4695	793705 14846	468598 660	8816010 777
11344	128 68 63 36	1459 817 795 584	508216 4694	808551 14845	469258 661	8815233 777
11345	128 70 90 25	1460 203 888 625	512910 4694	823396 14844	469919 660	8814456 777
11346	128 73 17 16	1460 590 049 736	517604 4694	838240 14844	470579 660	8813679 777
11347	128 75 44 09	1460 976 278 923	522298 4694	853084 14843	471239 660	8812902 777
11348	128 77 71 04	1461 362 576 192	526992 4693	867927 14842	471899 660	8812125 776
11349	128 79 98 01	1461 748 941 549	531685 4694	882769 14842	472559 660	8811349 776
11350	128 82 25 00	1462 135 375 000	536379 106·	897611 336·	473219 22·	8810573 0·0000

No. n	Square n²	Cube n³	Square root √n	Sq. rt. of 10n √10n	Cube root ∛n	Reciprocal 1/n
			106·	336·	22·	0·0000
11350	128 82 25 00	1462 135 375 000	536379 4693	897611 14841	473219 660	8810573 777
11351	128 84 52 01	1462 521 876 551	541072 4693	912452 14840	473879 660	8809796 776
11352	128 86 79 04	1462 908 446 208	545765 4693	927292 14840	474539 660	8809020 775
11353	128 89 06 09	1463 295 083 977	550458 4692	942132 14839	475199 660	8808245 776
11354	128 91 33 16	1463 681 789 864	555150 4692	956971 14838	475859 660	8807469 776
11355	128 93 60 25	1464 068 563 875	559842 4692	971809 14838	476519 660	8806693 775
11356	128 95 87 36	1464 455 406 016	564534 4692	986647 14837	477179 659	8805918 776
11357	128 98 14 49	1464 842 316 203	569226 4692	*001484 14836	477838 659	8805142 775
11358	129 00 41 64	1465 229 294 712	573918 4691	016320 14836	478498 660	8804367 775
11359	129 02 68 81	1465 616 341 279	578609 4692	031156 14835	479158 659	8803592 775
11360	129 04 96 00	1466 003 456 000	583301 4691	045991 14834	479817 660	8802817 775
11361	129 07 23 21	1466 390 638 881	587992 4691	060825 14834	480477 659	8802042 775
11362	129 09 50 44	1466 777 889 928	592683 4690	075659 14833	481136 660	8801267 774
11363	129 11 77 69	1467 165 209 147	597373 4691	090492 14833	481796 659	8800493 775
11364	129 14 04 96	1467 552 596 544	602064 4690	105325 14832	482455 660	8799718 774
11365	129 16 32 25	1467 940 052 125	606754 4690	120157 14831	483115 659	8798944 774
11366	129 18 59 56	1468 327 575 896	611444 4690	134988 14830	483774 660	8798170 774
11367	129 20 86 89	1468 715 167 863	616134 4689	149818 14830	484434 659	8797396 774
11368	129 23 14 24	1469 102 828 032	620823 4689	164648 14829	485093 659	8796622 774
11369	129 25 41 61	1469 490 556 409	625513 4689	179477 14829	485752 660	8795848 773
11370	129 27 69 00	1469 878 353 000	630202 4689	194306 14828	486412 659	8795075 774
11371	129 29 96 41	1470 266 217 811	634891 4689	209134 14827	487071 659	8794301 773
11372	129 32 23 84	1470 654 150 848	639580 4688	223961 14827	487730 659	8793528 773
11373	129 34 51 29	1471 042 152 117	644268 4689	238788 14826	488389 659	8792755 773
11374	129 36 78 76	1471 430 221 624	648957 4688	253614 14825	489048 659	8791982 773
11375	129 39 06 25	1471 818 359 375	653645 4688	268439 14825	489707 659	8791209 773
11376	129 41 33 76	1472 206 565 376	658333 4688	283264 14824	490366 659	8790436 773
11377	129 43 61 29	1472 594 839 633	663021 4687	298088 14823	491025 659	8789663 772
11378	129 45 88 84	1472 983 182 152	667708 4688	312911 14823	491684 659	8788891 773
11379	129 48 16 41	1473 371 592 939	672396 4687	327734 14822	492343 659	8788118 772
11380	129 50 44 00	1473 760 072 000	677083 4687	342556 14821	493002 659	8787346 772
11381	129 52 71 61	1474 148 619 341	681770 4686	357377 14821	493661 659	8786574 772
11382	129 54 99 24	1474 537 234 968	686456 4687	372198 14820	494320 658	8785802 772
11383	129 57 26 89	1474 925 918 887	691143 4686	387018 14820	494978 659	8785030 771
11384	129 59 54 56	1475 314 671 104	695829 4686	401838 14818	495637 659	8784259 772
11385	129 61 82 25	1475 703 491 625	700515 4686	416656 14819	496296 658	8783487 771
11386	129 64 09 96	1476 092 380 456	705201 4686	431475 14817	496954 659	8782716 772
11387	129 66 37 69	1476 481 337 603	709887 4686	446292 14817	497613 658	8781944 771
11388	129 68 65 44	1476 870 363 072	714573 4685	461109 14816	498271 659	8781173 771
11389	129 70 93 21	1477 259 456 869	719258 4685	475925 14816	498930 658	8780402 771
11390	129 73 21 00	1477 648 619 000	723943 4685	490741 14815	499588 659	8779631 770
11391	129 75 48 81	1478 037 849 471	728628 4685	505556 14814	500247 658	8778861 771
11392	129 77 76 64	1478 427 148 288	733313 4684	520370 14813	500905 659	8778090 771
11393	129 80 04 49	1478 816 515 457	737997 4684	535183 14813	501564 658	8777319 770
11394	129 82 32 36	1479 205 950 984	742681 4684	549996 14813	502222 658	8776549 770
11395	129 84 60 25	1479 595 454 875	747365 4684	564809 14811	502880 659	8775779 770
11396	129 86 88 16	1479 985 027 136	752049 4684	579620 14811	503539 658	8775009 770
11397	129 89 16 09	1480 374 667 773	756733 4683	594431 14811	504197 658	8774239 770
11398	129 91 44 04	1480 764 376 792	761416 4683	609242 14809	504855 658	8773469 770
11399	129 93 72 01	1481 154 154 199	766099 4684	624051 14809	505513 658	8772699 769
11400	129 96 00 00	1481 544 000 000	770783	638860	506171	8771930
			106·	337·	22·	0·0000

No. n	Square n^2	Cube n^3	Square root $\sqrt{n}$	Sq. rt. of 10n $\sqrt{10n}$	Cube root $\sqrt[3]{n}$	Reciprocal $\dfrac{1}{n}$
			106·	337·	22·	0·0000
11400	129 96 00 00	1481 544 000 000	770783 4682	638860 14809	506171 658	8771930 770
11401	129 98 28 01	1481 933 914 201	775465 4683	653669 14807	506829 658	8771160 769
11402	130 00 56 04	1482 323 896 808	780148 4682	668476 14808	507487 658	8770391 769
11403	130 02 84 09	1482 713 947 827	784830 4683	683284 14806	508145 658	8769622 769
11404	130 05 12 16	1483 104 067 264	789513 4682	698090 14806	508803 658	8768853 769
11405	130 07 40 25	1483 494 255 125	794195 4681	712896 14805	509461 658	8768084 769
11406	130 09 68 36	1483 884 511 416	798876 4682	727701 14804	510119 658	8767315 768
11407	130 11 96 49	1484 274 836 143	803558 4681	742505 14804	510777 658	8766547 769
11408	130 14 24 64	1484 665 229 312	808239 4682	757309 14804	511435 657	8765778 768
11409	130 16 52 81	1485 055 690 929	812921 4681	772113 14802	512092 658	8765010 768
11410	130 18 81 00	1485 446 221 000	817602 4680	786915 14802	512750 658	8764242 768
11411	130 21 09 21	1485 836 819 531	822282 4681	801717 14801	513408 657	8763474 768
11412	130 23 37 44	1486 227 486 528	826963 4680	816518 14801	514065 658	8762706 768
11413	130 25 65 69	1486 618 221 997	831643 4680	831319 14890	514723 657	8761938 768
11414	130 27 93 96	1487 009 025 944	836323 4680	846119 14799	515380 658	8761170 767
11415	130 30 22 25	1487 399 898 375	841003 4680	860918 14799	516038 657	8760403 767
11416	130 32 50 56	1487 790 839 296	845683 4680	875717 14798	516695 658	8759636 768
11417	130 34 78 89	1488 181 848 713	850363 4679	890515 14797	517353 657	8758868 767
11418	130 37 07 24	1488 572 926 632	855042 4679	905312 14797	518010 658	8758101 767
11419	130 39 35 61	1488 964 073 059	859721 4679	920109 14796	518668 657	8757334 767
11420	130 41 64 00	1489 355 288 000	864400 4679	934905 14795	519325 657	8756567 766
11421	130 43 92 41	1489 746 571 461	869079 4678	949700 14795	519982 657	8755801 767
11422	130 46 20 84	1490 137 923 448	873757 4679	964495 14794	520639 658	8755034 766
11423	130 48 49 29	1490 529 343 967	878436 4678	979289 14794	521297 657	8754268 767
11424	130 50 77 76	1490 920 833 024	883114 4678	994083 14793	521954 657	8753501 766
11425	130 53 06 25	1491 312 390 625	887792 4677	*008876 14792	522611 657	8752735 766
11426	130 55 34 76	1491 704 016 776	892469 4678	023668 14791	523268 657	8751969 766
11427	130 57 63 29	1492 095 711 483	897147 4677	038459 14791	523925 657	8751203 765
11428	130 59 91 84	1492 487 474 752	901824 4677	053250 14790	524582 657	8750438 766
11429	130 62 20 41	1492 879 306 589	906501 4677	068040 14790	525239 657	8749672 766
11430	130 64 49 00	1493 271 207 000	911178 4677	082830 14789	525896 657	8748906 765
11431	130 66 77 61	1493 663 175 991	915855 4677	097619 14788	526553 657	8748141 765
11432	130 69 06 24	1494 055 213 568	920531 4677	112407 14788	527210 657	8747376 765
11433	130 71 34 89	1494 447 319 737	925208 4676	127195 14787	527867 656	8746611 765
11434	130 73 63 56	1494 839 494 504	929884 4675	141982 14786	528523 657	8745846 765
11435	130 75 92 25	1495 231 737 875	934559 4676	156768 14786	529180 657	8745081 765
11436	130 78 20 96	1495 624 049 856	939235 4676	171554 14785	529837 657	8744316 764
11437	130 80 49 69	1496 016 430 453	943911 4675	186339 14785	530494 656	8743552 765
11438	130 82 78 44	1496 408 879 672	948586 4675	201124 14783	531150 657	8742787 764
11439	130 85 07 21	1496 801 397 519	953261 4675	215907 14784	531807 656	8742023 764
11440	130 87 36 00	1497 193 984 000	957936 4674	230691 14782	532463 657	8741259 764
11441	130 89 64 81	1497 586 639 121	962610 4675	245473 14782	533120 656	8740495 764
11442	130 91 93 64	1497 979 362 888	967285 4674	260255 14781	533776 657	8739731 764
11443	130 94 22 49	1498 372 155 307	971959 4674	275036 14781	534433 656	8738967 764
11444	130 96 51 36	1498 765 016 384	976633 4674	289817 14779	535089 657	8738203 763
11445	130 98 80 25	1499 157 946 125	981307 4673	304596 14780	535746 656	8737440 763
11446	131 01 09 16	1499 550 944 536	985980 4674	319376 14778	536402 656	8736677 763
11447	131 03 38 09	1499 944 011 623	990654 4673	334154 14778	537058 657	8735913 763
11448	131 05 67 04	1500 337 147 392	995327 4673	348932 14778	537715 656	8735150 763
11449	131 07 96 01	1500 730 351 849	*000000 4673	363710 14776	538371 656	8734387 763
11450	131 10 25 00	1501 123 625 000	004673 107·	378486 338·	539027 22·	8733624 0·0000

No. n	Square n^2	Cube n^3	Square root $\sqrt{n}$	Sq. rt. of $10n$ $\sqrt{10n}$	Cube root $\sqrt[3]{n}$	Reciprocal $\dfrac{1}{n}$
			107·	338·	22·	0·0000
11450	131 10 25 00	1501 123 625 000	004673 $_{4672}$	378486 $_{14776}$	539027 $_{656}$	8733624 $_{762}$
11451	131 12 54 01	1501 516 966 851	009345 $_{4673}$	393262 $_{14776}$	539683 $_{656}$	8732862 $_{763}$
11452	131 14 83 04	1501 910 377 408	014018 $_{4672}$	408038 $_{14774}$	540339 $_{656}$	8732099 $_{762}$
11453	131 17 12 09	1502 303 856 677	018690 $_{4672}$	422812 $_{14775}$	540995 $_{656}$	8731337 $_{763}$
11454	131 19 41 16	1502 697 404 664	023362 $_{4672}$	437587 $_{14773}$	541651 $_{656}$	8730574 $_{762}$
11455	131 21 70 25	1503 091 021 375	028034 $_{4671}$	452360 $_{14773}$	542307 $_{656}$	8729812 $_{762}$
11456	131 23 99 36	1503 484 706 816	032705 $_{4672}$	467133 $_{14772}$	542963 $_{656}$	8729050 $_{762}$
11457	131 26 28 49	1503 878 460 993	037377 $_{4671}$	481905 $_{14771}$	543619 $_{656}$	8728288 $_{761}$
11458	131 28 57 64	1504 272 283 912	042048 $_{4671}$	496676 $_{14771}$	544275 $_{656}$	8727527 $_{762}$
11459	131 30 86 81	1504 666 175 579	046719 $_{4671}$	511447 $_{14771}$	544931 $_{656}$	8726765 $_{762}$
11460	131 33 16 00	1505 060 136 000	051390 $_{4670}$	526218 $_{14769}$	545587 $_{655}$	8726003 $_{761}$
11461	131 35 45 21	1505 454 165 181	056060 $_{4670}$	540987 $_{14769}$	546242 $_{656}$	8725242 $_{761}$
11462	131 37 74 44	1505 848 263 128	060730 $_{4671}$	555756 $_{14768}$	546898 $_{656}$	8724481 $_{761}$
11463	131 40 03 69	1506 242 429 847	065401 $_{4670}$	570524 $_{14768}$	547554 $_{655}$	8723720 $_{761}$
11464	131 42 32 96	1506 636 665 344	070071 $_{4669}$	585292 $_{14767}$	548209 $_{656}$	8722959 $_{761}$
11465	131 44 62 25	1507 030 969 625	074740 $_{4670}$	600059 $_{14766}$	548865 $_{656}$	8722198 $_{761}$
11466	131 46 91 56	1507 425 342 696	079410 $_{4669}$	614825 $_{14766}$	549521 $_{655}$	8721437 $_{760}$
11467	131 49 20 89	1507 819 784 563	084079 $_{4669}$	629591 $_{14765}$	550176 $_{656}$	8720677 $_{761}$
11468	131 51 50 24	1508 214 295 232	088748 $_{4669}$	644356 $_{14765}$	550832 $_{655}$	8719916 $_{760}$
11469	131 53 79 61	1508 608 874 709	093417 $_{4669}$	659121 $_{14763}$	551487 $_{655}$	8719156 $_{760}$
11470	131 56 09 00	1509 003 523 000	098086 $_{4668}$	673884 $_{14764}$	552142 $_{656}$	8718396 $_{760}$
11471	131 58 38 41	1509 398 240 111	102754 $_{4669}$	688648 $_{14762}$	552798 $_{655}$	8717636 $_{760}$
11472	131 60 67 84	1509 793 026 048	107423 $_{4668}$	703410 $_{14762}$	553453 $_{655}$	8716876 $_{760}$
11473	131 62 97 29	1510 187 880 817	112091 $_{4668}$	718172 $_{14761}$	554108 $_{656}$	8716116 $_{760}$
11474	131 65 26 76	1510 582 804 424	116759 $_{4667}$	732933 $_{14761}$	554764 $_{655}$	8715356 $_{759}$
11475	131 67 56 25	1510 977 796 875	121426 $_{4668}$	747694 $_{14760}$	555419 $_{655}$	8714597 $_{759}$
11476	131 69 85 76	1511 372 858 176	126094 $_{4667}$	762454 $_{14759}$	556074 $_{655}$	8713838 $_{760}$
11477	131 72 15 29	1511 767 988 333	130761 $_{4667}$	777213 $_{14759}$	556729 $_{655}$	8713078 $_{759}$
11478	131 74 44 84	1512 163 187 352	135428 $_{4667}$	791972 $_{14758}$	557384 $_{655}$	8712319 $_{759}$
11479	131 76 74 41	1512 558 455 239	140095 $_{4667}$	806730 $_{14757}$	558039 $_{655}$	8711560 $_{759}$
11480	131 79 04 00	1512 953 792 000	144762 $_{4666}$	821487 $_{14757}$	558694 $_{655}$	8710801 $_{758}$
11481	131 81 33 61	1513 349 197 641	149428 $_{4667}$	836244 $_{14756}$	559349 $_{655}$	8710043 $_{759}$
11482	131 83 63 24	1513 744 672 168	154095 $_{4666}$	851000 $_{14755}$	560004 $_{655}$	8709284 $_{758}$
11483	131 85 92 89	1514 140 215 587	158761 $_{4666}$	865755 $_{14755}$	560659 $_{655}$	8708526 $_{759}$
11484	131 88 22 56	1514 535 827 904	163427 $_{4665}$	880510 $_{14754}$	561314 $_{655}$	8707767 $_{758}$
11485	131 90 52 25	1514 931 509 125	168092 $_{4666}$	895264 $_{14754}$	561969 $_{655}$	8707009 $_{758}$
11486	131 92 81 96	1515 327 259 256	172758 $_{4665}$	910018 $_{14752}$	562624 $_{655}$	8706251 $_{758}$
11487	131 95 11 69	1515 723 078 303	177423 $_{4665}$	924770 $_{14753}$	563279 $_{654}$	8705493 $_{758}$
11488	131 97 41 44	1516 118 966 272	182088 $_{4665}$	939523 $_{14751}$	563933 $_{655}$	8704735 $_{757}$
11489	131 99 71 21	1516 514 923 169	186753 $_{4665}$	954274 $_{14751}$	564588 $_{655}$	8703978 $_{758}$
11490	132 02 01 00	1516 910 949 000	191418 $_{4664}$	969025 $_{14750}$	565243 $_{654}$	8703220 $_{757}$
11491	132 04 30 81	1517 307 043 771	196082 $_{4664}$	983775 $_{14750}$	565897 $_{655}$	8702463 $_{757}$
11492	132 06 60 64	1517 703 207 488	200746 $_{4664}$	998525 $_{14749}$	566552 $_{654}$	8701706 $_{758}$
11493	132 08 90 49	1518 099 440 157	205410 $_{4664}$	*013274 $_{14748}$	567206 $_{655}$	8700948 $_{757}$
11494	132 11 20 36	1518 495 741 784	210074 $_{4664}$	028022 $_{14748}$	567861 $_{654}$	8700191 $_{756}$
11495	132 13 50 25	1518 892 112 375	214738 $_{4663}$	042770 $_{14747}$	568515 $_{655}$	8699435 $_{757}$
11496	132 15 80 16	1519 288 551 936	219401 $_{4663}$	057517 $_{14747}$	569170 $_{654}$	8698678 $_{757}$
11497	132 18 10 09	1519 685 060 473	224064 $_{4663}$	072264 $_{14745}$	569824 $_{655}$	8697921 $_{756}$
11498	132 20 40 04	1520 081 637 992	228727 $_{4663}$	087009 $_{14746}$	570479 $_{654}$	8697165 $_{757}$
11499	132 22 70 01	1520 478 284 499	233390 $_{4663}$	101755 $_{14744}$	571133 $_{654}$	8696408 $_{756}$
11500	132 25 00 00	1520 875 000 000	238053 107·	116499 339·	571787 22·	8695652 0·0000

231

No. n	Square n^2	Cube n^3	Square root $\sqrt{n}$	Sq. rt. of $10n$ $\sqrt{10n}$	Cube root $\sqrt[3]{n}$	Reciprocal $\dfrac{1}{n}$
			107·	339·	22·	0·0000
11500	132 25 00 00	1520 875 000 000	238053 4662	116499 14744	571787 654	8695652 756
11501	132 27 30 01	1521 271 784 501	242715 4663	131243 14743	572441 655	8694896 756
11502	132 29 60 04	1521 668 638 008	247378 4662	145986 14743	573096 655	8694140 756
11503	132 31 90 09	1522 065 560 527	252040 4661	160729 14742	573750 654	8693384 756
11504	132 34 20 16	1522 462 552 064	256701 4662	175471 14741	574404 654	8692629 756
11505	132 36 50 25	1522 859 612 625	261363 4661	190212 14741	575058 654	8691873 755
11506	132 38 80 36	1523 256 742 216	266024 4662	204953 14740	575712 654	8691118 756
11507	132 41 10 49	1523 653 940 843	270686 4661	219693 14739	576366 654	8690362 756
11508	132 43 40 64	1524 051 208 512	275347 4660	234432 14739	577020 654	8689607 755
11509	132 45 70 81	1524 448 545 229	280007 4661	249171 14738	577674 654	8688852 755
11510	132 48 01 00	1524 845 951 000	284668 4660	263909 14738	578328 654	8688097 755
11511	132 50 31 21	1525 243 425 831	289328 4661	278647 14736	578982 654	8687343 754
11512	132 52 61 44	1525 640 969 728	293989 4660	293383 14737	579636 654	8686588 755
11513	132 54 91 69	1526 038 582 697	298649 4659	308120 14735	580289 653	8685833 754
11514	132 57 21 96	1526 436 264 744	303308 4660	322855 14735	580943 654	8685079 754
11515	132 59 52 25	1526 834 015 875	307968 4659	337590 14734	581597 653	8684325 754
11516	132 61 82 56	1527 231 836 096	312627 4660	352324 14734	582250 653	8683571 754
11517	132 64 12 89	1527 629 725 413	317287 4659	367058 14733	582904 654	8682817 754
11518	132 66 43 24	1528 027 683 832	321946 4658	381791 14732	583558 653	8682063 754
11519	132 68 73 61	1528 425 711 359	326604 4659	396523 14732	584211 654	8681309 753
11520	132 71 04 00	1528 823 808 000	331263 4658	411255 14731	584865 653	8680556 754
11521	132 73 34 41	1529 221 973 761	335921 4658	425986 14730	585518 654	8679802 753
11522	132 75 64 84	1529 620 208 648	340579 4658	440716 14730	586172 653	8679049 753
11523	132 77 95 29	1530 018 512 667	345237 4658	455446 14729	586825 653	8678296 753
11524	132 80 25 76	1530 416 885 824	349895 4658	470175 14729	587478 654	8677543 753
11525	132 82 56 25	1530 815 328 125	354553 4657	484904 14728	588132 653	8676790 753
11526	132 84 86 76	1531 213 839 576	359210 4657	499632 14727	588785 653	8676037 753
11527	132 87 17 29	1531 612 420 183	363867 4657	514359 14727	589438 653	8675284 752
11528	132 89 47 84	1532 011 069 952	368524 4657	529086 14726	590091 654	8674532 753
11529	132 91 78 41	1532 409 788 889	373181 4657	543812 14725	590745 653	8673779 752
11530	132 94 09 00	1532 808 577 000	377838 4656	558537 14725	591398 653	8673027 752
11531	132 96 39 61	1533 207 434 291	382494 4656	573262 14724	592051 653	8672275 752
11532	132 98 70 24	1533 606 360 768	387150 4656	587986 14723	592704 653	8671523 752
11533	133 01 00 89	1534 005 356 437	391806 4656	602709 14723	593357 653	8670771 752
11534	133 03 31 56	1534 404 421 304	396462 4655	617432 14722	594010 653	8670019 752
11535	133 05 62 25	1534 803 555 375	401117 4656	632154 14721	594663 653	8669267 751
11536	133 07 92 96	1535 202 758 656	405773 4655	646875 14721	595316 653	8668516 751
11537	133 10 23 69	1535 602 031 153	410428 4655	661596 14721	595969 653	8667765 751
11538	133 12 54 44	1536 001 372 872	415083 4655	676317 14719	596622 653	8667013 752
11539	133 14 85 21	1536 400 783 819	419737 4655	691036 14719	597274 653	8666262 751
11540	133 17 16 00	1536 800 264 000	424392 4654	705755 14718	597927 653	8665511 751
11541	133 19 46 81	1537 199 813 421	429046 4654	720473 14718	598580 652	8664760 751
11542	133 21 77 64	1537 599 432 088	433700 4654	735191 14717	599232 653	8664010 750
11543	133 24 08 49	1537 999 120 007	438354 4654	749908 14716	599885 653	8663259 751
11544	133 26 39 36	1538 398 877 184	443008 4654	764624 14716	600538 652	8662509 750
11545	133 28 70 25	1538 798 703 625	447662 4653	779340 14715	601190 653	8661758 751
11546	133 31 01 16	1539 198 599 336	452315 4653	794055 14715	601843 652	8661008 750
11547	133 33 32 09	1539 598 564 323	456968 4653	808770 14714	602495 653	8660258 750
11548	133 35 63 04	1539 998 598 592	461621 4653	823484 14713	603148 652	8659508 750
11549	133 37 94 01	1540 398 702 149	466274 4652	838197 14712	603800 653	8658758 750
11550	133 40 25 00	1540 798 875 000	470926 107·	852909 339·	604453 22·	8658009 0·0000

No. n	Square n^2	Cube n^3	Square root $\sqrt{n}$	Sq. rt. of 10n $\sqrt{10n}$	Cube root $\sqrt[3]{n}$	Reciprocal $\frac{1}{n}$
			107.	339.	22.	0.0000
11550	133 40 25 00	1540 798 875 000	470926 ₄₆₅₃	852909 ₁₄₇₁₂	604453 ₆₅₂	8658009 ₇₅₀
11551	133 42 56 01	1541 199 117 151	475579 ₄₆₅₂	867621 ₁₄₇₁₂	605105 ₆₅₂	8657259 ₇₅₀
11552	133 44 87 04	1541 599 428 608	480231 ₄₆₅₂	882333 ₁₄₇₁₀	605757 ₆₅₃	8656510 ₇₅₀
11553	133 47 18 09	1541 999 809 377	484883 ₄₆₅₁	897043 ₁₄₇₁₀	606410 ₆₅₂	8655760 ₇₄₉
11554	133 49 49 16	1542 400 259 464	489534 ₄₆₅₂	911753 ₁₄₇₁₀	607062 ₆₅₂	8655011 ₇₄₉
11555	133 51 80 25	1542 800 778 875	494186 ₄₆₅₁	926463 ₁₄₇₀₈	607714 ₆₅₂	8654262 ₇₄₉
11556	133 54 11 36	1543 201 367 616	498837 ₄₆₅₁	941171 ₁₄₇₀₈	608366 ₆₅₂	8653513 ₇₄₈
11557	133 56 42 49	1543 602 025 693	503488 ₄₆₅₁	955879 ₁₄₇₀₈	609018 ₆₅₂	8652765 ₇₄₉
11558	133 58 73 64	1544 002 753 112	508139 ₄₆₅₁	970587 ₁₄₇₀₇	609670 ₆₅₂	8652016 ₇₄₉
11559	133 61 04 81	1544 403 549 879	512790 ₄₆₅₀	985294 ₁₄₇₀₆	610322 ₆₅₂	8651267 ₇₄₈
11560	133 63 36 00	1544 804 416 000	517440 ₄₆₅₁	*000000 ₁₄₇₀₆	610974 ₆₅₂	8650519 ₇₄₈
11561	133 65 67 21	1545 205 351 481	522091 ₄₆₅₀	014706 ₁₄₇₀₄	611626 ₆₅₂	8649771 ₇₄₈
11562	133 67 98 44	1545 606 356 328	526741 ₄₆₅₀	029410 ₁₄₇₀₅	612278 ₆₅₂	8649023 ₇₄₈
11563	133 70 29 69	1546 007 430 547	531391 ₄₆₄₉	044115 ₁₄₇₀₃	612930 ₆₅₂	8648275 ₇₄₈
11564	133 72 60 96	1546 408 574 144	536040 ₄₆₅₀	058818 ₁₄₇₀₃	613582 ₆₅₂	8647527 ₇₄₈
11565	133 74 92 25	1546 809 787 125	540690 ₄₆₄₉	073521 ₁₄₇₀₃	614234 ₆₅₂	8646779 ₇₄₈
11566	133 77 23 56	1547 211 069 496	545339 ₄₆₄₉	088224 ₁₄₇₀₂	614886 ₆₅₁	8646031 ₇₄₇
11567	133 79 54 89	1547 612 421 263	549988 ₄₆₄₉	102926 ₁₄₇₀₁	615537 ₆₅₂	8645284 ₇₄₇
11568	133 81 86 24	1548 013 842 432	554637 ₄₆₄₉	117627 ₁₄₇₀₀	616189 ₆₅₂	8644537 ₇₄₈
11569	133 84 17 61	1548 415 333 009	559286 ₄₆₄₈	132327 ₁₄₇₀₀	616841 ₆₅₁	8643789 ₇₄₇
11570	133 86 49 00	1548 816 893 000	563934 ₄₆₄₉	147027 ₁₄₆₉₉	617492 ₆₅₂	8643042 ₇₄₇
11571	133 88 80 41	1549 218 522 411	568583 ₄₆₄₈	161726 ₁₄₆₉₉	618144 ₆₅₂	8642295 ₇₄₆
11572	133 91 11 84	1549 620 221 248	573231 ₄₆₄₈	176425 ₁₄₆₉₈	618796 ₆₅₁	8641549 ₇₄₇
11573	133 93 43 29	1550 021 989 517	577879 ₄₆₄₇	191123 ₁₄₆₉₇	619447 ₆₅₂	8640802 ₇₄₇
11574	133 95 74 76	1550 423 827 224	582526 ₄₆₄₈	205820 ₁₄₆₉₇	620099 ₆₅₁	8640055 ₇₄₆
11575	133 98 06 25	1550 825 734 375	587174 ₄₆₄₇	220517 ₁₄₆₉₆	620750 ₆₅₂	8639309 ₇₄₆
11576	134 00 37 76	1551 227 710 976	591821 ₄₆₄₇	235213 ₁₄₆₉₅	621401 ₆₅₂	8638563 ₇₄₇
11577	134 02 69 29	1551 629 757 033	596468 ₄₆₄₇	249908 ₁₄₆₉₅	622053 ₆₅₁	8637816 ₇₄₆
11578	134 05 00 84	1552 031 872 552	601115 ₄₆₄₇	264603 ₁₄₆₉₄	622704 ₆₅₁	8637070 ₇₄₆
11579	134 07 32 41	1552 434 057 539	605762 ₄₆₄₆	279297 ₁₄₆₉₄	623355 ₆₅₂	8636324 ₇₄₅
11580	134 09 64 00	1552 836 312·000	610408 ₄₆₄₇	293991 ₁₄₆₉₂	624007 ₆₅₁	8635579 ₇₄₆
11581	134 11 95 61	1553 238 635 941	615055 ₄₆₄₆	308683 ₁₄₆₉₃	624658 ₆₅₁	8634833 ₇₄₆
11582	134 14 27 24	1553 641 029 368	619701 ₄₆₄₆	323376 ₁₄₆₉₁	625309 ₆₅₁	8634087 ₇₄₅
11583	134 16 58 89	1554 043 492 287	624347 ₄₆₄₅	338067 ₁₄₆₉₁	625960 ₆₅₁	8633342 ₇₄₅
11584	134 18 90 56	1554 446 024 704	628992 ₄₆₄₆	352758 ₁₄₆₉₁	626611 ₆₅₁	8632597 ₇₄₅
11585	134 21 22 25	1554 848 626 625	633638 ₄₆₄₅	367449 ₁₄₆₈₉	627262 ₆₅₁	8631852 ₇₄₅
11586	134 23 53 96	1555 251 298 056	638283 ₄₆₄₅	382138 ₁₄₆₈₉	627913 ₆₅₁	8631107 ₇₄₅
11587	134 25 85 69	1555 654 039 003	642928 ₄₆₄₅	396827 ₁₄₆₈₉	628564 ₆₅₁	8630362 ₇₄₅
11588	134 28 17 44	1556 056 849 472	647573 ₄₆₄₅	411516 ₁₄₆₈₇	629215 ₆₅₁	8629617 ₇₄₅
11589	134 30 49 21	1556 459 729 469	652218 ₄₆₄₄	426203 ₁₄₆₈₈	629866 ₆₅₁	8628872 ₇₄₄
11590	134 32 81 00	1556 862 679 000	656862 ₄₆₄₅	440891 ₁₄₆₈₆	630517 ₆₅₁	8628128 ₇₄₅
11591	134 35 12 81	1557 265 698 071	661507 ₄₆₄₄	455577 ₁₄₆₈₆	631168 ₆₅₁	8627383 ₇₄₄
11592	134 37 44 64	1557 668 786 688	666151 ₄₆₄₄	470263 ₁₄₆₈₅	631819 ₆₅₁	8626639 ₇₄₄
11593	134 39 76 49	1558 071 944 857	670795 ₄₆₄₃	484948 ₁₄₆₈₅	632470 ₆₅₀	8625895 ₇₄₄
11594	134 42 08 36	1558 475 172 584	675438 ₄₆₄₄	499633 ₁₄₆₈₄	633120 ₆₅₁	8625151 ₇₄₄
11595	134 44 40 25	1558 878 469 875	680082 ₄₆₄₃	514317 ₁₄₆₈₃	633771 ₆₅₁	8624407 ₇₄₄
11596	134 46 72 16	1559 281 836 736	684725 ₄₆₄₃	529000 ₁₄₆₈₃	634422 ₆₅₀	8623663 ₇₄₃
11597	134 49 04 09	1559 685 273 173	689368 ₄₆₄₃	543683 ₁₄₆₈₂	635072 ₆₅₁	8622920 ₇₄₄
11598	134 51 36 04	1560 088 779 192	694011 ₄₆₄₃	558365 ₁₄₆₈₁	635723 ₆₅₀	8622176 ₇₄₃
11599	134 53 68 01	1560 492 354 799	698654 ₄₆₄₂	573046 ₁₄₆₈₁	636373 ₆₅₁	8621433 ₇₄₃
11600	134 56 00 00	1560 896 000 000	703296 107.	587727 340.	637024 22.	8620690 0.0000

No. n	Square n^2	Cube n^3	Square root $\sqrt{n}$	Sq. rt. of 10n $\sqrt{10n}$	Cube root $\sqrt[3]{n}$	Reciprocal $\dfrac{1}{n}$
			107·	340·	22·	0·0000
11600	134 56 00 00	1560 896 000 000	703296 4642	587727 14681	637024 650	8620690 743
11601	134 58 32 01	1561 299 714 801	707938 4643	602408 14681	637674 650	8619947 743
11602	134 60 64 04	1561 703 499 208	712581 4641	617087 14679	638325 651	8619204 743
11603	134 62 96 09	1562 107 353 227	717222 4642	631766 14679	638975 650	8618461 743
11604	134 65 28 16	1562 511 276 864	721864 4642	646444 14678	639626 651	8617718 743
11605	134 67 60 25	1562 915 270 125	726506 4641	661122 14677	640276 650	8616975 742
11606	134 69 92 36	1563 319 333 016	731147 4641	675799 14676	640926 650	8616233 742
11607	134 72 24 49	1563 723 465 543	735788 4641	690475 14676	641576 651	8615491 742
11608	134 74 56 64	1564 127 667 712	740429 4640	705151 14675	642227 650	8614748 743
11609	134 76 88 81	1564 531 939 529	745069 4641	719826 14675	642877 650	8614006 742
11610	134 79 21 00	1564 936 281 000	749710 4640	734501 14674	643527 650	8613264 741
11611	134 81 53 21	1565 340 692 131	754350 4640	749175 14673	644177 650	8612523 742
11612	134 83 85 44	1565 745 172 928	758990 4640	763848 14672	644827 650	8611781 742
11613	134 86 17 69	1566 149 723 397	763630 4640	778520 14672	645477 650	8611039 742
11614	134 88 49 96	1566 554 343 544	768270 4639	793192 14672	646127 650	8610298 741
11615	134 90 82 25	1566 959 033 375	772909 4640	807864 14670	646777 650	8609557 742
11616	134 93 14 56	1567 363 792 896	777549 4639	822534 14671	647427 650	8608815 741
11617	134 95 46 89	1567 768 622 113	782188 4639	837205 14669	648077 650	8608074 741
11618	134 97 79 24	1568 173 521 032	786827 4638	851874 14669	648727 649	8607333 740
11619	135 00 11 61	1568 578 489 659	791465 4639	866543 14668	649376 650	8606593 741
11620	135 02 44 00	1568 983 528 000	796104 4638	881211 14668	650026 650	8605852 741
11621	135 04 76 41	1569 388 636 061	800742 4638	895879 14666	650676 650	8605111 740
11622	135 07 08 84	1569 793 813 848	805380 4638	910545 14667	651326 649	8604371 740
11623	135 09 41 29	1570 199 061 367	810018 4638	925212 14665	651975 650	8603631 740
11624	135 11 73 76	1570 604 378 624	814656 4637	939877 14665	652625 649	8602891 740
11625	135 14 06 25	1571 009 765 625	819293 4638	954542 14665	653274 650	8602151 740
11626	135 16 38 76	1571 415 222 376	823931 4637	969207 14664	653924 650	8601411 740
11627	135 18 71 29	1571 820 748 883	828568 4637	983871 14663	654574 649	8600671 740
11628	135 21 03 84	1572 226 345 152	833205 4636	998534 14662	655223 649	8599931 740
11629	135 23 36 41	1572 632 011 189	837841 4637	*013196 14662	655872 650	8599192 740
11630	135 25 69 00	1573 037 747 000	842478 4636	027858 14661	656522 649	8598452 739
11631	135 28 01 61	1573 443 552 591	847114 4636	042519 14661	657171 649	8597713 739
11632	135 30 34 24	1573 849 427 968	851750 4636	057180 14660	657820 650	8596974 739
11633	135 32 66 89	1574 255 373 137	856386 4636	071840 14659	658470 649	8596235 739
11634	135 34 99 56	1574 661 388 104	861022 4635	086499 14659	659119 649	8595496 739
11635	135 37 32 25	1575 067 472 875	865657 4635	101158 14658	659768 649	8594757 738
11636	135 39 64 76	1575 473 627 456	870292 4636	115816 14658	660417 649	8594019 739
11637	135 41 97 69	1575 879 851 853	874928 4634	130474 14656	661066 650	8593280 739
11638	135 44 30 44	1576 286 146 072	879562 4634	145130 14657	661716 649	8592542 738
11639	135 46 63 21	1576 692 510 119	884197 4635	159787 14655	662365 649	8591803 739
11640	135 48 96 00	1577 098 944 000	888832 4634	174442 14655	663014 649	8591065 738
11641	135 51 28 81	1577 505 447 721	893466 4634	189097 14654	663663 649	8590327 738
11642	135 53 61 64	1577 912 021 288	898100 4634	203751 14654	664312 648	8589589 738
11643	135 55 94 49	1578 318 664 707	902734 4634	218405 14653	664960 649	8588852 738
11644	135 58 27 36	1578 725 377 984	907368 4633	233058 14653	665609 649	8588114 737
11645	135 60 60 25	1579 132 161 125	912001 4633	247711 14651	666258 649	8587377 738
11646	135 62 93 16	1579 539 014 136	916634 4634	262362 14652	666907 648	8586639 737
11647	135 65 26 09	1579 945 937 023	921268 4633	277014 14650	667556 648	8585902 737
11648	135 67 59 04	1580 352 929 792	925901 4632	291664 14650	668204 649	8585165 737
11649	135 69 92 01	1580 759 992 449	930533 4633	306314 14649	668853 649	8584428 737
11650	135 72 25 00	1581 167 125 000	935166	320963	669502	8583691
			107·	341·	22·	0·0000

No. n	Square n^2	Cube n^3	Square root $\sqrt{n}$	Sq. rt. of $10n$ $\sqrt{10n}$	Cube root $\sqrt[3]{n}$	Reciprocal $\dfrac{1}{n}$
			107·	341·	22·	0·0000
11650	135 72 25 00	1581 167 125 000	935166 $_{4632}$	320963 $_{14649}$	669502 $_{648}$	8583691 $_{737}$
11651	135 74 58 01	1581 574 327 451	939798 $_{4632}$	335612 $_{14648}$	670150 $_{649}$	8582954 $_{736}$
11652	135 76 91 04	1581 981 599 808	944430 $_{4632}$	350260 $_{14647}$	670799 $_{648}$	8582218 $_{737}$
11653	135 79 24 09	1582 388 942 077	949062 $_{4632}$	364907 $_{14647}$	671447 $_{649}$	8581481 $_{736}$
11654	135 81 57 16	1582 796 354 264	953694 $_{4631}$	379554 $_{14646}$	672096 $_{648}$	8580745 $_{736}$
11655	135 83 90 25	1583 203 836 375	958325 $_{4632}$	394200 $_{14646}$	672744 $_{649}$	8580009 $_{737}$
11656	135 86 23 36	1583 611 388 416	962957 $_{4631}$	408846 $_{14645}$	673393 $_{648}$	8579272 $_{735}$
11657	135 88 56 49	1584 019 010 393	967588 $_{4631}$	423491 $_{14644}$	674041 $_{649}$	8578537 $_{736}$
11658	135 90 89 64	1584 426 702 312	972219 $_{4630}$	438135 $_{14644}$	674690 $_{648}$	8577801 $_{736}$
11659	135 93 22 81	1584 834 464 179	976849 $_{4631}$	452779 $_{14643}$	675338 $_{648}$	8577065 $_{736}$
11660	135 95 56 00	1585 242 296 000	981480 $_{4630}$	467422 $_{14642}$	675986 $_{648}$	8576329 $_{735}$
11661	135 97 89 21	1585 650 197 781	986110 $_{4630}$	482064 $_{14642}$	676634 $_{649}$	8575594 $_{735}$
11662	136 00 22 44	1586 058 169 528	990740 $_{4630}$	496706 $_{14641}$	677283 $_{648}$	8574859 $_{736}$
11663	136 02 55 69	1586 466 211 247	995370 $_{4630}$	511347 $_{14640}$	677931 $_{648}$	8574123 $_{735}$
11664	136 04 88 96	1586 874 322 944	*000000 $_{4630}$	525987 $_{14640}$	678579 $_{648}$	8573388 $_{735}$
11665	136 07 22 25	1587 282 504 625	004630 $_{4629}$	540627 $_{14639}$	679227 $_{648}$	8572653 $_{735}$
11666	136 09 55 56	1587 690 756 296	009259 $_{4629}$	555266 $_{14639}$	679875 $_{648}$	8571918 $_{734}$
11667	136 11 88 89	1588 099 077 963	013888 $_{4629}$	569905 $_{14638}$	680523 $_{648}$	8571184 $_{735}$
11668	136 14 22 24	1588 507 469 632	018517 $_{4629}$	584543 $_{14637}$	681171 $_{648}$	8570449 $_{734}$
11669	136 16 55 61	1588 915 931 309	023146 $_{4628}$	599180 $_{14637}$	681819 $_{648}$	8569715 $_{735}$
11670	136 18 89 00	1589 324 463 000	027774 $_{4629}$	613817 $_{14636}$	682467 $_{648}$	8568980 $_{734}$
11671	136 21 22 41	1589 733 064 711	032403 $_{4628}$	628453 $_{14636}$	683115 $_{648}$	8568246 $_{734}$
11672	136 23 55 84	1590 141 736 448	037031 $_{4628}$	643089 $_{14634}$	683763 $_{647}$	8567512 $_{734}$
11673	136 25 89 29	1590 550 478 217	c41659 $_{4627}$	657723 $_{14635}$	684410 $_{648}$	8566778 $_{734}$
11674	136 28 22 76	1590 959 290 024	046286 $_{4628}$	672358 $_{14633}$	685058 $_{648}$	8566044 $_{734}$
11675	136 30 56 25	1591 368 171 875	050914 $_{4627}$	686991 $_{14633}$	685706 $_{648}$	8565310 $_{733}$
11676	136 32 89 76	1591 777 123 776	055541 $_{4627}$	701624 $_{14633}$	686354 $_{647}$	8564577 $_{734}$
11677	136 35 23 29	1592 186 145 733	060168 $_{4627}$	716257 $_{14631}$	687001 $_{648}$	8563843 $_{733}$
11678	136 37 56 84	1592 595 237 752	064795 $_{4627}$	730888 $_{14631}$	687649 $_{647}$	8563110 $_{733}$
11679	136 39 90 41	1593 004 399 839	069422 $_{4627}$	745519 $_{14631}$	688296 $_{648}$	8562377 $_{733}$
11680	136 42 24 00	1593 413 632 000	074049 $_{4626}$	760150 $_{14630}$	688944 $_{647}$	8561644 $_{733}$
11681	136 44 57 61	1593 822 934 241	078675 $_{4626}$	774780 $_{14629}$	689591 $_{648}$	8560911 $_{733}$
11682	136 46 91 24	1594 232 306 568	083301 $_{4626}$	789409 $_{14628}$	690239 $_{647}$	8560178 $_{733}$
11683	136 49 24 89	1594 641 748 987	087927 $_{4626}$	804037 $_{14628}$	690886 $_{648}$	8559445 $_{732}$
11684	136 51 58 56	1595 051 261 504	092553 $_{4626}$	818665 $_{14628}$	691534 $_{647}$	8558713 $_{733}$
11685	136 53 92 25	1595 460 844 125	097179 $_{4625}$	833293 $_{14626}$	692181 $_{647}$	8557980 $_{732}$
11686	136 56 25 96	1595 870 496 856	101804 $_{4625}$	847919 $_{14626}$	692828 $_{648}$	8557248 $_{732}$
11687	136 58 59 69	1596 280 219 703	106429 $_{4625}$	862545 $_{14626}$	693476 $_{647}$	8556516 $_{732}$
11688	136 60 93 44	1596 690 012 672	111054 $_{4625}$	877171 $_{14625}$	694123 $_{647}$	8555784 $_{732}$
11689	136 63 27 21	1597 099 875 769	115679 $_{4624}$	891796 $_{14624}$	694770 $_{647}$	8555052 $_{732}$
11690	136 65 61 00	1597 509 809 000	120303 $_{4625}$	906420 $_{14624}$	695417 $_{647}$	8554320 $_{732}$
11691	136 67 94 81	1597 919 812 371	124928 $_{4624}$	921044 $_{14622}$	696064 $_{647}$	8553588 $_{731}$
11692	136 70 28 64	1598 329 885 888	129552 $_{4624}$	935666 $_{14623}$	696711 $_{647}$	8552857 $_{732}$
11693	136 72 62 49	1598 740 029 557	134176 $_{4624}$	950289 $_{14621}$	697358 $_{647}$	8552125 $_{731}$
11694	136 74 96 36	1599 150 243 384	138800 $_{4623}$	964910 $_{14622}$	698005 $_{647}$	8551394 $_{731}$
11695	136 77 30 25	1599 560 527 375	143423 $_{4624}$	979532 $_{14620}$	698652 $_{647}$	8550663 $_{731}$
11696	136 79 64 16	1599 970 881 536	148047 $_{4623}$	994152 $_{14620}$	699299 $_{647}$	8549932 $_{731}$
11697	136 81 98 09	1600 381 305 873	152670 $_{4623}$	*008772 $_{14619}$	699946 $_{647}$	8549201 $_{731}$
11698	136 84 32 04	1600 791 800 392	157293 $_{4623}$	023391 $_{14619}$	700593 $_{647}$	8548470 $_{731}$
11699	136 86 66 01	1601 202 365 099	161916 $_{4622}$	038010 $_{14618}$	701240 $_{647}$	8547739 $_{730}$
11700	136 89 00 00	1601 613 000 000	166538 108·	052628 342·	701887 22·	8547009 0·0000

No. n	Square n^2	Cube n^3	Square root $\sqrt{n}$	Sq. rt. of $10n$ $\sqrt{10n}$	Cube root $\sqrt[3]{n}$	Reciprocal $\dfrac{1}{n}$
			108·	342·	22·	0·0000
11700	136 89 00 00	1601 613 000 000	166538 $_{4623}$	052628 $_{14617}$	701887 $_{647}$	8547009 $_{731}$
11701	136 91 34 01	1602 023 705 101	171161 $_{4622}$	067245 $_{14617}$	702534 $_{646}$	8546278 $_{731}$
11702	136 93 68 04	1602 434 480 408	175783 $_{4622}$	081862 $_{14616}$	703180 $_{647}$	8545548 $_{730}$
11703	136 96 02 09	1602 845 325 927	180405 $_{4622}$	096478 $_{14616}$	703827 $_{647}$	8544818 $_{730}$
11704	136 98 36 16	1603 256 241 664	185027 $_{4621}$	111093 $_{14615}$	704474 $_{646}$	8544087 $_{729}$
11705	137 00 70 25	1603 667 227 625	189648 $_{4622}$	125708 $_{14614}$	705120 $_{647}$	8543358 $_{730}$
11706	137 03 04 36	1604 078 283 816	194270 $_{4621}$	140322 $_{14614}$	705767 $_{646}$	8542628 $_{730}$
11707	137 05 38 49	1604 489 410 243	198891 $_{4621}$	154936 $_{14613}$	706413 $_{647}$	8541898 $_{730}$
11708	137 07 72 64	1604 900 606 912	203512 $_{4621}$	169549 $_{14612}$	707060 $_{646}$	8541168 $_{729}$
11709	137 10 06 81	1605 311 873 829	208133 $_{4620}$	184161 $_{14612}$	707706 $_{647}$	8540439 $_{729}$
11710	137 12 41 00	1605 723 211 000	212753 $_{4621}$	198773 $_{14611}$	708353 $_{646}$	8539710 $_{730}$
11711	137 14 75 21	1606 134 618 431	217374 $_{4620}$	213384 $_{14610}$	708999 $_{646}$	8538980 $_{729}$
11712	137 17 09 44	1606 546 096 128	221994 $_{4620}$	227994 $_{14610}$	709645 $_{647}$	8538251 $_{729}$
11713	137 19 43 69	1606 957 644 097	226614 $_{4620}$	242604 $_{14609}$	710292 $_{646}$	8537522 $_{728}$
11714	137 21 77 96	1607 369 262 344	231234 $_{4620}$	257213 $_{14609}$	710938 $_{646}$	8536794 $_{729}$
11715	137 24 12 25	1607 780 950 875	235854 $_{4619}$	271822 $_{14608}$	711584 $_{647}$	8536065 $_{729}$
11716	137 26 46 56	1608 192 709 696	240473 $_{4619}$	286430 $_{14607}$	712231 $_{646}$	8535336 $_{728}$
11717	137 28 80 89	1608 604 538 813	245092 $_{4619}$	301037 $_{14607}$	712877 $_{646}$	8534608 $_{728}$
11718	137 31 15 24	1609 016 438 232	249711 $_{4619}$	315644 $_{14606}$	713523 $_{646}$	8533880 $_{729}$
11719	137 33 49 61	1609 428 407 959	254330 $_{4619}$	330250 $_{14605}$	714169 $_{646}$	8533151 $_{728}$
11720	137 35 84 00	1609 840 448 000	258949 $_{4618}$	344855 $_{14605}$	714815 $_{646}$	8532423 $_{728}$
11721	137 38 18 41	1610 252 558 361	263567 $_{4619}$	359460 $_{14604}$	715461 $_{646}$	8531695 $_{728}$
11722	137 40 52 84	1610 664 739 048	268186 $_{4618}$	374064 $_{14604}$	716107 $_{646}$	8530967 $_{727}$
11723	137 42 87 29	1611 076 990 067	272804 $_{4617}$	388668 $_{14603}$	716753 $_{646}$	8530240 $_{728}$
11724	137 45 21 76	1611 489 311 424	277421 $_{4618}$	403271 $_{14602}$	717399 $_{646}$	8529512 $_{727}$
11725	137 47 56 25	1611 901 703 125	282039 $_{4618}$	417873 $_{14602}$	718045 $_{646}$	8528785 $_{728}$
11726	137 49 90 76	1612 314 165 176	286657 $_{4618}$	432475 $_{14601}$	718691 $_{645}$	8528057 $_{727}$
11727	137 52 25 29	1612 726 697 583	291274 $_{4617}$	447076 $_{14601}$	719336 $_{645}$	8527330 $_{727}$
11728	137 54 59 84	1613 139 300 352	295891 $_{4617}$	461677 $_{14600}$	719982 $_{646}$	8526603 $_{727}$
11729	137 56 94 41	1613 551 973 489	300508 $_{4617}$	476277 $_{14599}$	720628 $_{646}$	8525876 $_{727}$
11730	137 59 29 00	1613 964 717 000	305125 $_{4616}$	490876 $_{14598}$	721274 $_{645}$	8525149 $_{727}$
11731	137 61 63 61	1614 377 530 891	309741 $_{4616}$	505474 $_{14598}$	721919 $_{646}$	8524422 $_{726}$
11732	137 63 98 24	1614 790 415 168	314357 $_{4616}$	520072 $_{14598}$	722565 $_{645}$	8523696 $_{727}$
11733	137 66 32 89	1615 203 369 837	318973 $_{4616}$	534670 $_{14597}$	723210 $_{646}$	8522969 $_{726}$
11734	137 68 67 56	1615 616 394 904	323589 $_{4616}$	549267 $_{14596}$	723856 $_{645}$	8522243 $_{726}$
11735	137 71 02 25	1616 029 490 375	328205 $_{4616}$	563863 $_{14595}$	724501 $_{646}$	8521517 $_{726}$
11736	137 73 36 96	1616 442 656 256	332821 $_{4615}$	578458 $_{14595}$	725147 $_{645}$	8520791 $_{726}$
11737	137 75 71 69	1616 855 892 553	337436 $_{4615}$	593053 $_{14594}$	725792 $_{646}$	8520065 $_{726}$
11738	137 78 06 44	1617 269 199 272	342051 $_{4615}$	607647 $_{14594}$	726438 $_{645}$	8519339 $_{726}$
11739	137 80 41 21	1617 682 576 419	346666 $_{4615}$	622241 $_{14593}$	727083 $_{645}$	8518613 $_{725}$
11740	137 82 76 00	1618 096 024 000	351281 $_{4614}$	636834 $_{14592}$	727728 $_{646}$	8517888 $_{726}$
11741	137 85 10 81	1618 509 542 021	355895 $_{4614}$	651426 $_{14592}$	728374 $_{645}$	8517162 $_{726}$
11742	137 87 45 64	1618 923 130 488	360509 $_{4615}$	666018 $_{14591}$	729019 $_{645}$	8516437 $_{726}$
11743	137 89 80 49	1619 336 789 407	365124 $_{4613}$	680609 $_{14591}$	729664 $_{645}$	8515711 $_{725}$
11744	137 92 15 36	1619 750 518 784	369737 $_{4614}$	695200 $_{14590}$	730309 $_{646}$	8514986 $_{725}$
11745	137 94 50 25	1620 164 318 625	374351 $_{4614}$	709790 $_{14589}$	730955 $_{645}$	8514261 $_{724}$
11746	137 96 85 16	1620 578 188 936	378965 $_{4613}$	724379 $_{14589}$	731600 $_{645}$	8513537 $_{725}$
11747	137 99 20 09	1620 992 129 723	383578 $_{4613}$	738968 $_{14588}$	732245 $_{645}$	8512812 $_{725}$
11748	138 01 55 04	1621 406 140 992	388191 $_{4613}$	753556 $_{14588}$	732890 $_{645}$	8512087 $_{725}$
11749	138 03 90 01	1621 820 222 749	392804 $_{4613}$	768143 $_{14587}$	733535 $_{645}$	8511363 $_{724}$
11750	138 06 25 00	1622 234 375 000	397417 108·	782730 342·	734180 22·	8510638 0·0000

No. n	Square n^2	Cube n^3	Square root $\sqrt{n}$	Sq. rt. of $10n$ $\sqrt{10n}$	Cube root $\sqrt[3]{n}$	Reciprocal $\dfrac{1}{n}$
			108·	342·	22·	0·0000
11750	138 06 25 00	1622 234 375 000	397417 $_{4613}$	782730 $_{14586}$	734180 $_{645}$	8510638 $_{724}$
11751	138 08 60 01	1622 648 597 751	402030 $_{4612}$	797316 $_{14586}$	734825 $_{645}$	8509914 $_{724}$
11752	138 10 95 04	1623 062 891 008	406642 $_{4612}$	811902 $_{14585}$	735470 $_{644}$	8509190 $_{724}$
11753	138 13 30 09	1623 477 254 777	411254 $_{4612}$	826487 $_{14584}$	736114 $_{645}$	8508466 $_{724}$
11754	138 15 65 16	1623 891 689 064	415866 $_{4612}$	841071 $_{14584}$	736759 $_{645}$	8507742 $_{724}$
11755	138 18 00 25	1624 306 193 875	420478 $_{4611}$	855655 $_{14583}$	737404 $_{645}$	8507018 $_{723}$
11756	138 20 35 36	1624 720 769 216	425089 $_{4612}$	870238 $_{14582}$	738049 $_{644}$	8506295 $_{724}$
11757	138 22 70 49	1625 135 415 093	429701 $_{4611}$	884820 $_{14582}$	738693 $_{645}$	8505571 $_{723}$
11758	138 25 05 64	1625 550 131 512	434312 $_{4611}$	899402 $_{14581}$	739338 $_{645}$	8504848 $_{723}$
11759	138 27 40 81	1625 964 918 479	438923 $_{4611}$	913983 $_{14581}$	739983 $_{644}$	8504125 $_{724}$
11760	138 29 76 00	1626 379 776 000	443534 $_{4610}$	928564 $_{14580}$	740627 $_{645}$	8503401 $_{723}$
11761	138 32 11 21	1626 794 704 081	448144 $_{4611}$	943144 $_{14579}$	741272 $_{644}$	8502678 $_{723}$
11762	138 34 46 44	1627 209 702 728	452755 $_{4610}$	957723 $_{14579}$	741916 $_{645}$	8501955 $_{722}$
11763	138 36 81 69	1627 624 771 947	457365 $_{4610}$	972302 $_{14578}$	742561 $_{644}$	8501233 $_{723}$
11764	138 39 16 96	1628 039 911 744	461975 $_{4610}$	986880 $_{.14578}$	743205 $_{645}$	8500510 $_{722}$
11765	138 41 52 25	1628 455 122 125	466585 $_{4609}$	*001458 $_{14577}$	743850 $_{644}$	8499788 $_{723}$
11766	138 43 87 56	1628 870 403 096	471194 $_{4610}$	016035 $_{14576}$	744494 $_{644}$	8499065 $_{723}$
11767	138 46 22 89	1629 285 754 663	475804 $_{4609}$	030611 $_{14576}$	745138 $_{644}$	8498343 $_{722}$
11768	138 48 58 24	1629 701 176 832	480413 $_{4609}$	045187 $_{14575}$	745783 $_{644}$	8497621 $_{722}$
11769	138 50 93 61	1630 116 669 609	485022 $_{4609}$	059762 $_{14574}$	746427 $_{644}$	8496899 $_{722}$
11770	138 53 29 00	1630 532 233 000	489631 $_{4608}$	074336 $_{14574}$	747071 $_{644}$	8496177 $_{722}$
11771	138 55 64 41	1630 947 867 011	494239 $_{4609}$	088910 $_{14573}$	747715 $_{645}$	8495455 $_{722}$
11772	138 57 99 84	1631 363 571 648	498848 $_{4608}$	103483 $_{14572}$	748360 $_{644}$	8494733 $_{721}$
11773	138 60 35 29	1631 779 346 917	503456 $_{4608}$	118055 $_{14572}$	749004 $_{644}$	8494012 $_{722}$
11774	138 62 70 76	1632 195 192 824	508064 $_{4608}$	132627 $_{14572}$	749648 $_{644}$	8493290 $_{721}$
11775	138 65 06 25	1632 611 109 375	512672 $_{4608}$	147199 $_{14570}$	750292 $_{644}$	8492569 $_{721}$
11776	138 67 41 76	1633 027 096 576	517280 $_{4607}$	161769 $_{14571}$	750936 $_{644}$	8491848 $_{721}$
11777	138 69 77 29	1633 443 154 433	521887 $_{4607}$	176340 $_{14569}$	751580 $_{644}$	8491127 $_{721}$
11778	138 72 12 84	1633 859 282 952	526494 $_{4608}$	190909 $_{14569}$	752224 $_{644}$	8490406 $_{721}$
11779	138 74 48 41	1634 275 482 139	531102 $_{4606}$	205478 $_{14568}$	752868 $_{644}$	8489685 $_{721}$
11780	138 76 84 00	1634 691 752 000	535708 $_{4607}$	220046 $_{14568}$	753512 $_{643}$	8488964 $_{720}$
11781	138 79 19 61	1635 108 092 541	540315 $_{4607}$	234614 $_{14567}$	754155 $_{644}$	8488244 $_{721}$
11782	138 81 55 24	1635 524 503 768	544922 $_{4606}$	249181 $_{14566}$	754799 $_{644}$	8487523 $_{720}$
11783	138 83 90 89	1635 940 985 687	549528 $_{4606}$	263747 $_{14566}$	755443 $_{644}$	8486803 $_{720}$
11784	138 86 26 56	1636 357 538 304	554134 $_{4606}$	278313 $_{14565}$	756087 $_{643}$	8486083 $_{720}$
11785	138 88 62 25	1636 774 161 625	558740 $_{4606}$	292878 $_{14564}$	756730 $_{644}$	8485363 $_{720}$
11786	138 90 97 96	1637 190 855 656	563346 $_{4605}$	307442 $_{14564}$	757374 $_{644}$	8484643 $_{720}$
11787	138 93 33 69	1637 607 620 403	567951 $_{4605}$	322006 $_{14564}$	758018 $_{643}$	8483923 $_{720}$
11788	138 95 69 44	1638 024 455 872	572556 $_{4605}$	336570 $_{14562}$	758661 $_{644}$	8483203 $_{719}$
11789	138 98 05 21	1638 441 362 069	577162 $_{4604}$	351132 $_{14562}$	759305 $_{643}$	8482484 $_{720}$
11790	139 00 41 00	1638 858 339 000	581766 $_{4605}$	365694 $_{14562}$	759948 $_{644}$	8481764 $_{719}$
11791	139 02 76 81	1639 275 386 671	586371 $_{4605}$	380256 $_{14561}$	760592 $_{643}$	8481045 $_{719}$
11792	139 05 12 64	1639 692 505 088	590976 $_{4604}$	394817 $_{14560}$	761235 $_{643}$	8480326 $_{719}$
11793	139 07 48 49	1640 109 694 257	595580 $_{4604}$	409377 $_{14559}$	761878 $_{644}$	8479607 $_{719}$
11794	139 09 84 36	1640 526 954 184	600184 $_{4604}$	423936 $_{14559}$	762522 $_{643}$	8478888 $_{719}$
11795	139 12 20 25	1640 944 284 875	604788 $_{4604}$	438495 $_{14559}$	763165 $_{643}$	8478169 $_{719}$
11796	139 14 56 16	1641 361 686 336	609392 $_{4603}$	453054 $_{14557}$	763808 $_{644}$	8477450 $_{719}$
11797	139 16 92 09	1641 779 158 573	613995 $_{4604}$	467611 $_{14557}$	764452 $_{643}$	8476731 $_{718}$
11798	139 19 28 04	1642 196 701 592	618599 $_{4603}$	482168 $_{14557}$	765095 $_{643}$	8476013 $_{718}$
11799	139 21 64 01	1642 614 315 399	623202 $_{4603}$	496725 $_{14556}$	765738 $_{643}$	8475295 $_{719}$
11800	139 24 00 00	1643 032 000 000	627805 108·	511281 343·	766381 22·	8474576 0·0000

No. n	Square n^2	Cube n^3	Square root $\sqrt{n}$	Sq. rt. of $10n$ $\sqrt{10n}$	Cube root $\sqrt[3]{n}$	Reciprocal $\dfrac{1}{n}$
			108·	343·	22·	0·0000
11800	139 24 00 00	1643 032 000 000	627805 ₄₆₀₃	511281 ₁₄₅₅₅	766381 ₆₄₃	8474576 ₇₁₈
11801	139 26 36 01	1643 449 755 401	632408 ₄₆₀₃	525836 ₁₄₅₅₅	767024 ₆₄₃	8473858 ₇₁₈
11802	139 28 72 04	1643 867 581 608	637010 ₄₆₀₂	540391 ₁₄₅₅₄	767667 ₆₄₃	8473140 ₇₁₈
11803	139 31 08 09	1644 285 478 627	641613 ₄₆₀₃	554945 ₁₄₅₅₃	768310 ₆₄₃	8472422 ₇₁₈
11804	139 33 44 16	1644 703 446 464	646215 ₄₆₀₂	569498 ₁₄₅₅₃	768953 ₆₄₃	8471705 ₇₁₇
11805	139 35 80 25	1645 121 485 125	650817 ₄₆₀₂	584051 ₁₄₅₅₂	769596 ₆₄₃	8470987 ₇₁₈
11806	139 38 16 36	1645 539 594 616	655419 ₄₆₀₁	598603 ₁₄₅₅₂	770239 ₆₄₃	8470269 ₇₁₇
11807	139 40 52 49	1645 957 774 943	660020 ₄₆₀₁	613155 ₁₄₅₅₁	770882 ₆₄₃	8469552 ₇₁₇
11808	139 42 88 64	1646 376 026 112	664622 ₄₆₀₁	627706 ₁₄₅₅₀	771525 ₆₄₃	8468835 ₇₁₇
11809	139 45 24 81	1646 794 348 129	669223 ₄₆₀₁	642256 ₁₄₅₅₀	772168 ₆₄₃	8468118 ₇₁₇
11810	139 47 61 00	1647 212 741 000	673824 ₄₆₀₁	656806 ₁₄₅₄₉	772811 ₆₄₂	8467401 ₇₁₇
11811	139 49 97 21	1647 631 204 731	678425 ₄₆₀₀	671355 ₁₄₅₄₈	773453 ₆₄₃	8466684 ₇₁₇
11812	139 52 33 44	1648 049 739 328	683025 ₄₆₀₁	685903 ₁₄₅₄₈	774096 ₆₄₃	8465967 ₇₁₇
11813	139 54 69 69	1648 468 344 797	687626 ₄₆₀₀	700451 ₁₄₅₄₇	774739 ₆₄₂	8465250 ₇₁₆
11814	139 57 05 96	1648 887 021 144	692226 ₄₆₀₀	714998 ₁₄₅₄₇	775381 ₆₄₃	8464534 ₇₁₇
11815	139 59 42 25	1649 305 768 375	696826 ₄₆₀₀	729545 ₁₄₅₄₆	776024 ₆₄₂	8463817 ₇₁₆
11816	139 61 78 56	1649 724 586 496	701426 ₄₆₀₀	744091 ₁₄₅₄₅	776666 ₆₄₃	8463101 ₇₁₆
11817	139 64 14 89	1650 143 475 513	706026 ₄₅₉₉	758636 ₁₄₅₄₅	777309 ₆₄₂	8462385 ₇₁₆
11818	139 66 51 24	1650 562 435 432	710625 ₄₅₉₉	773181 ₁₄₅₄₄	777951 ₆₄₃	8461669 ₇₁₆
11819	139 68 87 61	1650 981 466 259	715224 ₄₅₉₉	787725 ₁₄₅₄₄	778594 ₆₄₂	8460953 ₇₁₆
11820	139 71 24 00	1651 400 568 000	719823 ₄₅₉₉	802269 ₁₄₅₄₃	779236 ₆₄₃	8460237 ₇₁₆
11821	139 73 60 41	1651 819 740 661	724422 ₄₅₉₉	816812 ₁₄₅₄₂	779879 ₆₄₂	8459521 ₇₁₅
11822	139 75 96 84	1652 238 984 248	729021 ₄₅₉₈	831354 ₁₄₅₄₂	780521 ₆₄₂	8458806 ₇₁₆
11823	139 78 33 29	1652 658 298 767	733619 ₄₅₉₉	845896 ₁₄₅₄₁	781163 ₆₄₃	8458090 ₇₁₅
11824	139 80 69 76	1653 077 684 224	738218 ₄₅₉₈	860437 ₁₄₅₄₀	781806 ₆₄₂	8457375 ₇₁₅
11825	139 83 06 25	1653 497 140 625	742816 ₄₅₉₈	874977 ₁₄₅₄₀	782448 ₆₄₂	8456660 ₇₁₅
11826	139 85 42 76	1653 916 667 976	747414 ₄₅₉₇	889517 ₁₄₅₃₉	783090 ₆₄₂	8455945 ₇₁₅
11827	139 87 79 29	1654 336 266 283	752011 ₄₅₉₈	904056 ₁₄₅₃₉	783732 ₆₄₂	8455230 ₇₁₅
11828	139 90 15 84	1654 755 935 552	756609 ₄₅₉₇	918595 ₁₄₅₃₈	784374 ₆₄₂	8454515 ₇₁₅
11829	139 92 52 41	1655 175 675 789	761206 ₄₅₉₇	933133 ₁₄₅₃₇	785016 ₆₄₂	8453800 ₇₁₅
11830	139 94 89 00	1655 595 487 000	765803 ₄₅₉₇	947670 ₁₄₅₃₇	785658 ₆₄₂	8453085 ₇₁₄
11831	139 97 25 61	1656 015 369 191	770400 ₄₅₉₇	962207 ₁₄₅₃₆	786300 ₆₄₂	8452371 ₇₁₄
11832	139 99 62 24	1656 435 322 368	774997 ₄₅₉₇	976743 ₁₄₅₃₆	786942 ₆₄₂	8451657 ₇₁₅
11833	140 01 98 89	1656 855 346 537	779594 ₄₅₉₆	991279 ₁₄₅₃₅	787584 ₆₄₂	8450942 ₇₁₄
11834	140 04 35 56	1657 275 441 704	784190 ₄₅₉₆	*005814 ₁₄₅₃₄	788226 ₆₄₂	8450228 ₇₁₄
11835	140 06 72 25	1657 695 607 875	788786 ₄₅₉₆	020348 ₁₄₅₃₄	788868 ₆₄₂	8449514 ₇₁₄
11836	140 09 08 96	1658 115 845 056	793382 ₄₅₉₆	034882 ₁₄₅₃₃	789510 ₆₄₂	8448800 ₇₁₃
11837	140 11 45 69	1658 536 153 253	797978 ₄₅₉₅	049415 ₁₄₅₃₃	790152 ₆₄₁	8448087 ₇₁₄
11838	140 13 82 44	1658 956 532 472	802573 ₄₅₉₅	063948 ₁₄₅₃₁	790793 ₆₄₂	8447373 ₇₁₄
11839	140 16 19 21	1659 376 982 719	807169 ₄₅₉₅	078479 ₁₄₅₃₂	791435 ₆₄₂	8446659 ₇₁₃
11840	140 18 56 00	1659 797 504 000	811764 ₄₅₉₅	093011 ₁₄₅₃₀	792077 ₆₄₂	8445946 ₇₁₃
11841	140 20 92 81	1660 218 096 321	816359 ₄₅₉₅	107541 ₁₄₅₃₀	792719 ₆₄₂	8445233 ₇₁₃
11842	140 23 29 64	1660 638 759 688	820954 ₄₅₉₄	122071 ₁₄₅₃₀	793360 ₆₄₂	8444520 ₇₁₃
11843	140 25 66 49	1661 059 494 107	825548 ₄₅₉₅	136601 ₁₄₅₂₉	794002 ₆₄₁	8443806 ₇₁₂
11844	140 28 03 36	1661 480 299 584	830143 ₄₅₉₄	151130 ₁₄₅₂₈	794643 ₆₄₂	8443094 ₇₁₃
11845	140 30 40 25	1661 901 176 125	834737 ₄₅₉₄	165658 ₁₄₅₂₇	795285 ₆₄₁	8442381 ₇₁₃
11846	140 32 77 16	1662 322 123 736	839331 ₄₅₉₄	180185 ₁₄₅₂₇	795926 ₆₄₂	8441668 ₇₁₃
11847	140 35 14 09	1662 743 142 423	843925 ₄₅₉₄	194712 ₁₄₅₂₇	796568 ₆₄₁	8440956 ₇₁₂
11848	140 37 51 04	1663 164 232 192	848519 ₄₅₉₃	209239 ₁₄₅₂₅	797209 ₆₄₁	8440243 ₇₁₃
11849	140 39 88 01	1663 585 393 049	853112 ₄₅₉₃	223764 ₁₄₅₂₆	797850 ₆₄₁	8439531 ₇₁₂
11850	140 42 25 00	1664 006 625 000	857705 108·	238290 344·	798492 22·	8438819 0·0000

238

No. n	Square n^2	Cube n^3	Square root $\sqrt{n}$	Sq. rt. of 10n $\sqrt{10n}$	Cube root $\sqrt[3]{n}$	Reciprocal $\frac{1}{n}$
			108.	344.	22.	0·0000
11850	140 42 25 00	1664 006 625 000	857705 4593	238290 14524	798492 641	8438819 713
11851	140 44 62 01	1664 427 928 051	862298 4593	252814 14524	799133 641	8438106 711
11852	140 46 99 04	1664 849 302 208	866891 4593	267338 14523	799774 642	8437395 712
11853	140 49 36 09	1665 270 747 477	871484 4592	281861 14523	800416 641	8436683 712
11854	140 51 73 16	1665 692 263 864	876076 4593	296384 14522	801057 641	8435971 712
11855	140 54 10 25	1666 113 851 375	880669 4592	310906 14521	801698 641	8435259 711
11856	140 56 47 36	1666 535 510 016	885261 4592	325427 14521	802339 641	8434548 711
11857	140 58 84 49	1666 957 239 793	889853 4592	339948 14521	802980 641	8433837 712
11858	140 61 21 64	1667 379 040 712	894444 4592	354469 14519	803621 641	8433125 711
11859	140 63 58 81	1667 800 912 779	899036 4591	368988 14519	804262 641	8432414 711
11860	140 65 96 00	1668 222 856 000	903627 4591	383507 14519	804903 641	8431703 711
11861	140 68 33 21	1668 644 870 381	908218 4591	398026 14517	805544 641	8430992 710
11862	140 70 70 44	1669 066 955 928	912809 4591	412543 14517	806185 641	8430282 711
11863	140 73 07 69	1669 489 112 647	917400 4590	427060 14517	806826 641	8429571 711
11864	140 75 44 96	1669 911 340 544	921990 4591	441577 14516	807467 640	8428860 710
11865	140 77 82 25	1670 333 639 625	926581 4590	456093 14515	808107 641	8428150 710
11866	140 80 19 56	1670 756 009 896	931171 4590	470608 14515	808748 641	8427440 710
11867	140 82 56 89	1671 178 451 363	935761 4590	485123 14514	809389 641	8426730 710
11868	140 84 94 24	1671 600 964 032	940351 4589	499637 14514	810029 641	8426020 710
11869	140 87 31 61	1672 023 547 909	944940 4590	514151 14513	810670 641	8425310 710
11870	140 89 69 00	1672 446 203 000	949530 4589	528664 14512	811311 640	8424600 710
11871	140 92 06 41	1672 868 929 311	954119 4589	543176 14511	811951 641	8423890 709
11872	140 94 43 84	1673 291 726 848	958708 4589	557687 14512	812592 640	8423181 710
11873	140 96 81 29	1673 714 595 617	963297 4588	572199 14510	813232 641	8422471 709
11874	140 99 18 76	1674 137 535 624	967885 4589	586709 14510	813873 640	8421762 709
11875	141 01 56 25	1674 560 546 875	972474 4588	601219 14509	814513 641	8421053 709
11876	141 03 93 76	1674 983 629 376	977062 4588	615728 14509	815154 640	8420344 709
11877	141 06 31 29	1675 406 783 133	981650 4588	630237 14508	815794 640	8419635 709
11878	141 08 68 84	1675 830 008 152	986238 4587	644745 14507	816434 640	8418926 709
11879	141 11 06 41	1676 253 304 439	990825 4588	659252 14507	817075 640	8418217 709
11880	141 13 44 00	1676 676 672 000	*995413 4587	673759 14506	817715 640	8417508 708
11881	141 15 81 61	1677 100 110 841	*000000 4587	688265 14506	818355 640	8416800 708
11882	141 18 19 24	1677 523 620 968	004587 4587	702771 14504	818995 640	8416092 709
11883	141 20 56 89	1677 947 202 387	009174 4587	717275 14505	819635 640	8415383 708
11884	141 22 94 56	1678 370 855 104	013761 4586	731780 14504	820275 640	8414675 708
11885	141 25 32 25	1678 794 579 125	018347 4586	746284 14503	820915 640	8413967 708
11886	141 27 69 96	1679 218 374 456	022933 4586	760787 14502	821555 640	8413259 707
11887	141 30 07 69	1679 642 241 103	027519 4586	775289 14502	822195 640	8412552 708
11888	141 32 45 44	1680 066 179 072	032105 4586	789791 14501	822835 640	8411844 708
11889	141 34 83 21	1680 490 188 369	036691 4586	804292 14501	823475 640	8411136 707
11890	141 37 21 00	1680 914 269 000	041277 4585	818793 14500	824115 640	8410429 707
11891	141 39 58 81	1681 338 420 971	045862 4585	833293 14500	824755 640	8409722 708
11892	141 41 96 64	1681 762 644 288	050447 4585	847793 14498	825395 640	8409014 707
11893	141 44 34 49	1682 186 938 957	055032 4585	862291 14499	826035 639	8408307 707
11894	141 46 72 36	1682 611 304 984	059617 4584	876790 14497	826674 640	8407600 706
11895	141 49 10 25	1683 035 742 375	064201 4585	891287 14497	827314 640	8406894 707
11896	141 51 48 16	1683 460 251 136	068786 4584	905784 14497	827954 639	8406187 707
11897	141 53 86 09	1683 884 831 273	073370 4584	920281 14495	828593 640	8405480 706
11898	141 56 24 04	1684 309 482 792	077954 4584	934776 14496	829233 640	8404774 706
11899	141 58 62 01	1684 734 205 699	082538 4583	949272 14494	829873 639	8404068 707
11900	141 61 00 00	1685 159 000 000	087121 109.	963766 344.	830512 22.	8403361 0·0000

No. n	Square n^2	Cube n^3	Square root $\sqrt{n}$	Sq. rt. of 10n $\sqrt{10n}$	Cube root $\sqrt[3]{n}$	Reciprocal $\dfrac{1}{n}$
			109·	344·	22·	0·0000
11900	141 61 00 00	1685 159 000 000	087121	963766	830512	8403361
11901	141 63 38 01	1685 583 865 701	091705 4584	978260 14494	831152 640	8402655 706
11902	141 65 76 04	1686 008 802 808	096288 4583	992754 14494	831791 640	8401949 706
11903	141 68 14 09	1686 433 811 327	100871 4583	*007246 14492	832431 640	8401243 706
11904	141 70 52 16	1686 858 891 264	105454 4583	021738 14492	833070 639	8400538 705
			4582	14492	639	706
11905	141 72 90 25	1687 284 042 625	110036	036230	833709	8399832
11906	141 75 28 36	1687 709 265 416	114619 4583	050721 14491	834349 640	8399126 706
11907	141 77 66 49	1688 134 559 643	119201 4582	065211 14490	834988 639	8398421 705
11908	141 80 04 64	1688 559 925 312	123783 4582	079701 14490	835627 639	8397716 705
11909	141 82 42 81	1688 985 362 429	128365 4582	094190 14489	836266 639	8397011 705
			4581	14489	639	705
11910	141 84 81 00	1689 410 871 000	132946	108679	836905	8396306
11911	141 87 19 21	1689 836 451 031	137528 4582	123166 14487	837545 640	8395601 705
11912	141 89 57 44	1690 262 102 528	142109 4581	137654 14488	838184 639	8394896 705
11913	141 91 95 69	1690 687 825 497	146690 4581	152140 14486	838823 639	8394191 705
11914	141 94 33 96	1691 113 619 944	151271 4581	166626 14486	839462 639	8393487 704
			4581	14486	639	705
11915	141 96 72 25	1691 539 485 875	155852	181112	840101	8392782
11916	141 99 10 56	1691 965 423 296	160432 4580	195597 14485	840740 639	8392078 704
11917	142 01 48 89	1692 391 432 213	165013 4581	210081 14484	841379 639	8391374 704
11918	142 03 87 24	1692 817 512 632	169593 4580	224565 14484	842018 639	8390670 704
11919	142 06 25 61	1693 243 664 559	174173 4580	239048 14483	842656 638	8389966 704
			4580	14482	639	704
11920	142 08 64 00	1693 669 888 000	178753	253530	843295	8389262
11921	142 11 02 41	1694 096 182 961	183332 4579	268012 14482	843934 639	8388558 704
11922	142 13 40 84	1694 522 549 448	187911 4579	282493 14481	844573 639	8387854 704
11923	142 15 79 29	1694 948 987 467	192491 4580	296974 14481	845211 638	8387151 703
11924	142 18 17 76	1695 375 497 024	197070 4579	311454 14480	845850 639	8386448 703
			4578	14479		704
11925	142 20 56 25	1695 802 078 125	201648	325933	846489	8385744
11926	142 22 94 76	1696 228 730 776	206227 4579	340412 14479	847127 638	8385041 703
11927	142 25 33 29	1696 655 454 983	210805 4578	354890 14478	847766 639	8384338 703
11928	142 27 71 84	1697 082 250 752	215384 4579	369367 14477	848404 638	8383635 703
11929	142 30 10 41	1697 509 118 089	219962 4578	383844 14477	849043 639	8382932 703
			4577	14477	638	702
11930	142 32 49 00	1697 936 057 000	224539	398321	849681	8382230
11931	142 34 87 61	1698 363 067 491	229117 4578	412797 14476	850320 639	8381527 703
11932	142 37 26 24	1698 790 149 568	233694 4577	427272 14475	850958 638	8380825 702
11933	142 39 64 89	1699 217 303 237	238272 4578	441746 14474	851596 638	8380122 703
11934	142 42 03 56	1699 644 528 504	242849 4577	456220 14474	852235 638	8379420 702
			4577	14473		702
11935	142 44 42 25	1700 071 825 375	247426	470693	852873	8378718
11936	142 46 80 96	1700 499 193 856	252002 4576	485166 14473	853511 638	8378016 702
11937	142 49 19 69	1700 926 633 953	256579 4577	499638 14472	854150 639	8377314 702
11938	142 51 58 44	1701 354 145 072	261155 4576	514110 14472	854788 638	8376612 702
11939	142 53 97 21	1701 781 729 019	265731 4576	528581 14471	855426 638	8375911 701
			4576	14470	638	702
11940	142 56 36 00	1702 209 384 000	270307	543051	856064	8375209
11941	142 58 74 81	1702 637 110 621	274883 4576	557521 14470	856702 638	8374508 701
11942	142 61 13 64	1703 064 908 888	279458 4575	571990 14469	857340 638	8373807 701
11943	142 63 52 49	1703 492 778 807	284034 4575	586458 14468	857978 638	8373106 701
11944	142 65 91 36	1703 920 720 384	288609 4575	600926 14468	858616 638	8372405 701
			4575	14467		701
11945	142 68 30 25	1704 348 733 625	293184	615393	859254 638	8371704
11946	142 70 69 16	1704 776 818 536	297758 4574	629860 14467	859892 638	8371003 701
11947	142 73 08 09	1705 204 975 123	302333 4575	644326 14466	860530 637	8370302 701
11948	142 75 47 04	1705 633 203 392	306907 4574	658791 14465	861167 638	8369602 700
11949	142 77 86 01	1706 061 503 349	311482 4575	673256 14465	861805 638	8368901 701
			4574	14464		700
11950	142 80 25 00	1706 489 875 000	316056	687720	862443	8368201
			109·	345·	22·	0·0000

No. n	Square n^2	Cube n^3	Square root $\sqrt{n}$	Sq. rt. of 10n $\sqrt{10n}$	Cube root $\sqrt[3]{n}$	Reciprocal $\frac{1}{n}$
			109·	345·	22·	0·0000
11950	142 80 25 00	1706 489 875 000	316056 4573	687720 14464	862443 638	8368201 700
11951	142 82 64 01	1706 918 318 351	320629 4574	702184 14463	863081 637	8367501 700
11952	142 85 03 04	1707 346 833 408	325203 4573	716647 14462	863718 638	8366801 700
11953	142 87 42 09	1707 775 420 177	329776 4574	731109 14462	864356 638	8366101 700
11954	142 89 81 16	1708 204 078 664	334350 4573	745571 14461	864994 637	8365401 700
11955	142 92 20 25	1708 632 808 875	338923 4572	760032 14461	865631 638	8364701 700
11956	142 94 59 36	1709 061 610 816	343495 4573	774493 14460	866269 637	8364001 700
11957	142 96 98 49	1709 490 484 493	348068 4573	788953 14460	866906 638	8363302 700
11958	142 99 37 64	1709 919 429 912	352641 4573	803412 14459	867544 637	8362602 699
11959	143 01 76 81	1710 348 447 079	357213 4572	817871 14459	868181 637	8361903 699
11960	143 04 16 00	1710 777 536 000	361785 4572	832329 14458	868818 638	8361204 699
11961	143 06 55 21	1711 206 696 681	366357 4572	846787 14457	869456 637	8360505 699
11962	143 08 94 44	1711 635 929 128	370928 4571	861244 14456	870093 637	8359806 699
11963	143 11 33 69	1712 065 233 347	375500 4571	875700 14456	870730 638	8359107 698
11964	143 13 72 96	1712 494 609 344	380071 4571	890156 14455	871368 ·637	8358409 699
11965	143 16 12 25	1712 924 057 125	384642 4571	904611 14455	872005 637	8357710 698
11966	143 18 51 56	1713 353 576 696	389213 4571	919066 14454	872642 637	8357012 699
11967	143 20 90 89	1713 783 168 063	393784 4571	933520 14453	873279 637	8356313 698
11968	143 23 30 24	1714 212 831 232	398355 4570	947973 14453	873916 637	8355615 698
11969	143 25 69 61	1714 642 566 209	402925 4570	962426 14452	874553 637	8354917 698
11970	143 28 09 00	1715 072 373 000	407495 4570	976878 14451	875190 637	8354219 698
11971	143 30 48 41	1715 502 251 611	412065 4570	*991329 14451	875827 637	8353521 698
11972	143 32 87 84	1715 932 202 048	416635 4570	*005780 14451	876464 637	8352823 697
11973	143 35 27 29	1716 362 224 317	421205 4569	020231 14449	877101 637	8352126 698
11974	143 37 66 76	1716 792 318 424	425774 4569	034680 14449	877738 637	8351428 697
11975	143 40 06 25	1717 222 484 375	430343 4569	049129 14449	878375 637	8350731 698
11976	143 42 45 76	1717 652 722 176	434912 4569	063578 14448	879012 637	8350033 697
11977	143 44 85 29	1718 083 031 833	439481 4569	078026 14447	879649 636	8349336 697
11978	143 47 24 84	1718 513 413 352	444050 4568	092473 14447	880285 637	8348639 697
11979	143 49 64 41	1718 943 866 739	448618 4568	106920 14446	880922 637	8347942 697
11980	143 52 04 00	1719 374 392 000	453186 4568	121366 14445	881559 636	8347245 696
11981	143 54 43 61	1719 804 989 141	457754 4568	135811 14445	882195 637	8346549 697
11982	143 56 83 24	1720 235 658 168	462322 4568	150256 14445	882832 637	8345852 696
11983	143 59 22 89	1720 666 399 087	466890 4567	164701 14443	883469 636	8345156 697
11984	143 61 62 56	1721 097 211 904	471457 4568	179144 14443	884105 637	8344459 696
11985	143 64 02 25	1721 528 096 625	476025 4567	193587 14443	884742 636	8343763 696
11986	143 66 41 96	1721 959 053 256	480592 4567	208030 14442	885378 636	8343067 696
11987	143 68 81 69	1722 390 081 803	485159 4567	222472 14441	886014 637	8342371 696
11988	143 71 21 44	1722 821 182 272	489726 4566	236913 14441	886651 636	8341675 696
11989	143 73 61 21	1723 252 354 669	494292 4566	251354 14440	887287 637	8340979 695
11990	143 76 01 00	1723 683 599 000	498858 4567	265794 14439	887924 636	8340284 696
11991	143 78 40 81	1724 114 915 271	503425 4566	280233 14439	888560 636	8339588 695
11992	143 80 80 64	1724 546 303 488	507991 4565	294672 14438	889196 636	8338893 696
11993	143 83 20 49	1724 977 763 657	512556 4566	309110 14438	889832 637	8338197 695
11994	143 85 60 36	1725 409 295 784	517122 4565	323548 14437	890469 636	8337502 695
11995	143 88 00 25	1725 840 899 875	521687 4566	337985 14437	891105 636	8336807 695
11996	143 90 40 16	1726 272 575 936	526253 4565	352422 14436	891741 636	8336112 695
11997	143 92 80 09	1726 704 323 973	530818 4564	366858 14435	892377 636	8335417 695
11998	143 95 20 04	1727 136 143 992	535382 4565	381293 14434	893013 636	8334722 694
11999	143 97 60 01	1727 568 035 999	539947 4565	395727 14435	893649 636	8334028 695
12000	144 00 00 00	1728 000 000 000	544512	410162	894285	8333333
			109·	346·	22·	0·0000

No. n	Square n^2	Cube n^3	Square root $\sqrt{n}$	Sq. rt. of $10n$ $\sqrt{10n}$	Cube root $\sqrt[3]{n}$	Reciprocal $\dfrac{1}{n}$
			109·	346·	22·	0·0000
12000	144 00 00 00	1728 000 000 000	544512 4564	410162 14433	894285 636	8333333 694
12001	144 02 40 01	1728 432 036 001	549076 4564	424595 14433	894921 636	8332639 694
12002	144 04 80 04	1728 864 144 008	553640 4564	439028 14432	895557 636	8331945 694
12003	144 07 20 09	1729 296 324 027	558204 4563	453460 14432	896193 635	8331251 695
12004	144 09 60 16	1729 728 576 064	562767 4564	467892 14431	896828 636	8330556 693
12005	144 12 00 25	1730 160 900 125	567331 4563	482323 14430	897464 636	8329863 694
12006	144 14 40 36	1730 593 296 216	571894 4563	496753 14430	898100 636	8329169 694
12007	144 16 80 49	1731 025 764 343	576457 4563	511183 14429	898736 636	8328475 694
12008	144 19 20 64	1731 458 304 512	581020 4563	525612 14429	899371 636	8327781 693
12009	144 21 60 81	1731 890 916 729	585583 4563	540041 14428	900007 636	8327088 693
12010	144 24 01 00	1732 323 601 000	590146 4562	554469 14427	900643 635	8326395 694
12011	144 26 41 21	1732 756 357 331	594708 4562	568896 14427	901278 636	8325701 693
12012	144 28 81 44	1733 189 185 728	599270 4562	583323 14427	901914 635	8325008 693
12013	144 31 21 69	1733 622 086 197	603832 4562	597750 14425	902549 636	8324315 693
12014	144 33 61 96	1734 055 058 744	608394 4561	612175 14425	903185 635	8323622 692
12015	144 36 02 25	1734 488 103 375	612955 4562	626600 14425	903820 636	8322930 693
12016	144 38 42 56	1734 921 220 096	617517 4561	641025 14424	904456 635	8322237 693
12017	144 40 82 89	1735 354 408 913	622078 4561	655449 14423	905091 635	8321544 692
12018	144 43 23 24	1735 787 669 832	626639 4561	669872 14422	905726 636	8320852 692
12019	144 45 63 61	1736 221 002 859	631200 4561	684294 14422	906362 635	8320160 692
12020	144 48 04 00	1736 654 408 000	635761 4560	698716 14422	906997 635	8319468 693
12021	144 50 44 41	1737 087 885 261	640321 4560	713138 14421	907632 635	8318775 691
12022	144 52 84 84	1737 521 434 648	644881 4560	727559 14420	908267 635	8318084 692
12023	144 55 25 29	1737 955 056 167	649441 4560	741979 14420	908902 636	8317392 692
12024	144 57 65 76	1738 388 749 824	654001 4560	756399 14419	909538 635	8316700 692
12025	144 60 06 25	1738 822 515 625	658561 4560	770818 14418	910173 635	8316008 691
12026	144 62 46 76	1739 256 353 576	663121 4559	785236 14418	910808 635	8315317 692
12027	144 64 87 29	1739 690 263 683	667680 4559	799654 14417	911443 635	8314625 691
12028	144 67 27 84	1740 124 245 952	672239 4559	814071 14417	912078 635	8313934 691
12029	144 69 68 41	1740 558 300 389	676798 4559	828488 14416	912713 635	8313243 691
12030	144 72 09 00	1740 992 427 000	681357 4558	842904 14415	913348 634	8312552 691
12031	144 74 49 61	1741 426 625 791	685915 4559	857319 14415	913982 635	8311861 691
12032	144 76 90 24	1741 860 896 768	690474 4558	871734 14414	914617 635	8311170 690
12033	144 79 30 89	1742 295 239 937	695032 4558	886148 14414	915252 635	8310480 691
12034	144 81 71 56	1742 729 655 304	699590 4558	900562 14413	915887 635	8309789 691
12035	144 84 12 25	1743 164 142 875	704148 4557	914975 14413	916522 634	8309098 690
12036	144 86 52 96	1743 598 702 656	708705 4558	929388 14411	917156 635	8308408 690
12037	144 88 93 69	1744 033 334 653	713263 4557	943799 14412	917791 635	8307718 690
12038	144 91 34 44	1744 468 038 872	717820 4557	958211 14410	918426 634	8307028 690
12039	144 93 75 21	1744 902 815 319	722377 4557	972621 14410	919060 635	8306338 690
12040	144 96 16 00	1745 337 664 000	726934 4556	987031 14410	919695 634	8305648 690
12041	144 98 56 81	1745 772 584 921	731490 4557	*001441 14409	920329 635	8304958 690
12042	145 00 97 64	1746 207 578 088	736047 4556	015850 14408	920964 634	8304268 689
12043	145 03 38 49	1746 642 643 507	740603 4556	030258 14408	921598 635	8303579 690
12044	145 05 79 36	1747 077 781 184	745159 4556	044666 14407	922233 634	8302889 689
12045	145 08 20 25	1747 512 991 125	749715 4556	059073 14406	922867 634	8302200 689
12046	145 10 61 16	1747 948 273 336	754271 4556	073479 14406	923501 635	8301511 689
12047	145 13 02 09	1748 383 627 823	758827 4555	087885 14405	924136 634	8300822 689
12048	145 15 43 04	1748 819 054 592	763382 4555	102290 14405	924770 634	8300133 689
12049	145 17 84 01	1749 254 553 649	767937 4555	116695 14404	925404 634	8299444 689
12050	145 20 25 00	1749 690 125 000	772492	131099	926038	8298755
			109·	347·	22·	0·0000

242

No. n	Square n²	Cube n³	Square root √n	Sq. rt. of 10n √10n	Cube root ∛n	Reciprocal 1/n
			109·	347·	22·	0·0000
12050	145 20 25 00	1749 690 125 000	772492 (4555)	131099 (14404)	926038 (635)	8298755 (688)
12051	145 22 66 01	1750 125 768 651	777047 (4554)	145503 (14403)	926673 (634)	8298067 (689)
12052	145 25 07 04	1750 561 484 608	781601 (4555)	159906 (14402)	927307 (634)	8297378 (688)
12053	145 27 48 09	1750 997 272 877	786156 (4554)	174308 (14401)	927941 (634)	8296690 (689)
12054	145 29 89 16	1751 433 133 464	790710 (4554)	188709 (14402)	928575 (634)	8296001 (688)
12055	145 32 30 25	1751 869 066 375	795264 (4554)	203111 (14400)	929209 (634)	8295313 (688)
12056	145 34 71 36	1752 305 071 616	799818 (4553)	217511 (14400)	929843 (634)	8294625 (688)
12057	145 37 12 49	1752 741 149 193	804371 (4554)	231911 (14399)	930477 (634)	8293937 (688)
12058	145 39 53 64	1753 177 299 112	808925 (4553)	246310 (14399)	931111 (634)	8293249 (687)
12059	145 41 94 81	1753 613 521 379	813478 (4553)	260709 (14398)	931745 (634)	8292562 (688)
12060	145 44 36 00	1754 049 816 000	818031 (4553)	275107 (14398)	932379 (633)	8291874 (688)
12061	145 46 77 21	1754 486 182 981	822584 (4553)	289505 (14397)	933012 (634)	8291186 (687)
12062	145 49 18 44	1754 922 622 328	827137 (4552)	303902 (14396)	933646 (634)	8290499 (687)
12063	145 51 59 69	1755 359 134 047	831689 (4553)	318298 (14396)	934280 (634)	8289812 (687)
12064	145 54 00 96	1755 795 718 144	836242 (4552)	332694 (14395)	934914 (633)	8289125 (687)
12065	145 56 42 25	1756 232 374 625	840794 (4552)	347089 (14394)	935547 (634)	8288438 (687)
12066	145 58 83 56	1756 669 103 496	845346 (4552)	361483 (14394)	936181 (634)	8287751 (687)
12067	145 61 24 89	1757 105 904 763	849898 (4551)	375877 (14393)	936815 (633)	8287064 (687)
12068	145 63 66 24	1757 542 778 432	854449 (4552)	390270 (14393)	937448 (634)	8286377 (686)
12069	145 66 07 61	1757 979 724 509	859001 (4551)	404663 (14392)	938082 (633)	8285691 (687)
12070	145 68 49 00	1758 416 743 000	863552 (4551)	419055 (14392)	938715 (634)	8285004 (686)
12071	145 70 90 41	1758 853 833 911	868103 (4551)	433447 (14391)	939349 (633)	8284318 (686)
12072	145 73 31 84	1759 290 997 248	872654 (4551)	447838 (14390)	939982 (634)	8283632 (687)
12073	145 75 73 29	1759 728 233 017	877204 (4551)	462228 (14390)	940616 (633)	8282945 (686)
12074	145 78 14 76	1760 165 541 224	881755 (4550)	476618 (14389)	941249 (633)	8282259 (686)
12075	145 80 56 25	1760 602 921 875	886305 (4550)	491007 (14389)	941882 (634)	8281573 (685)
12076	145 82 97 76	1761 040 374 976	890855 (4550)	505396 (14388)	942516 (633)	8280888 (686)
12077	145 85 39 29	1761 477 900 533	895405 (4550)	519784 (14387)	943149 (633)	8280202 (686)
12078	145 87 80 84	1761 915 498 552	899955 (4549)	534171 (14387)	943782 (633)	8279516 (685)
12079	145 90 22 41	1762 353 169 039	904504 (4549)	548558 (14386)	944415 (633)	8278831 (685)
12080	145 92 64 00	1762 790 912 000	909053 (4549)	562944 (14386)	945048 (634)	8278146 (686)
12081	145 95 05 61	1763 228 727 441	913602 (4549)	577330 (14385)	945682 (633)	8277460 (685)
12082	145 97 47 24	1763 666 615 368	918151 (4549)	591715 (14384)	946315 (633)	8276775 (685)
12083	145 99 88 89	1764 104 575 787	922700 (4549)	606099 (14384)	946948 (633)	8276090 (685)
12084	146 02 30 56	1764 542 608 704	927249 (4548)	620483 (14383)	947581 (633)	8275405 (684)
12085	146 04 72 25	1764 980 714 125	931797 (4548)	634866 (14383)	948214 (633)	8274721 (685)
12086	146 07 13 96	1765 418 892 056	936345 (4548)	649249 (14382)	948847 (633)	8274036 (684)
12087	146 09 55 69	1765 857 142 503	940893 (4548)	663631 (14381)	949480 (632)	8273352 (685)
12088	146 11 97 44	1766 295 465 472	945441 (4548)	678012 (14381)	950112 (633)	8272667 (684)
12089	146 14 39 21	1766 733 860 969	949989 (4547)	692393 (14380)	950745 (633)	8271983 (684)
12090	146 16 81 00	1767 172 329 000	954536 (4547)	706773 (14380)	951378 (633)	8271299 (684)
12091	146 19 22 81	1767 610 869 571	959083 (4547)	721153 (14379)	952011 (633)	8270615 (684)
12092	146 21 64 64	1768 049 482 688	963630 (4547)	735532 (14378)	952644 (632)	8269931 (684)
12093	146 24 06 49	1768 488 168 357	968177 (4547)	749910 (14378)	953276 (633)	8269247 (684)
12094	146 26 48 36	1768 926 926 584	972724 (4546)	764288 (14377)	953909 (633)	8268563 (684)
12095	146 28 90 25	1769 365 757 375	977270 (4547)	778665 (14377)	954542 (632)	8267879 (683)
12096	146 31 32 16	1769 804 660 736	981817 (4546)	793042 (14376)	955174 (633)	8267196 (684)
12097	146 33 74 09	1770 243 636 673	986363 (4546)	807418 (14375)	955807 (632)	8266512 (683)
12098	146 36 16 04	1770 682 685 192	990909 (4545)	821793 (14375)	956439 (633)	8265829 (683)
12099	146 38 58 01	1771 121 806 299	995454 (4546)	836168 (14375)	957072 (632)	8265146 (683)
12100	146 41 00 00	1771 561 000 000	*000000	850543	957704	8264463
			110·	347·	22·	0·0000

R*

No. n	Square n^2	Cube n^3	Square root $\sqrt{n}$	Sq. rt. of $10n$ $\sqrt{10n}$	Cube root $\sqrt[3]{n}$	Reciprocal $\dfrac{1}{n}$
			110·	347·	22·	0·0000
12100	146 41 00 00	1771 561 000 000	000000 $_{4545}$	850543 $_{14373}$	957704 $_{633}$	8264463 $_{683}$
12101	146 43 42 01	1772 000 266 301	004545 $_{4546}$	864916 $_{14373}$	958337 $_{632}$	8263780 $_{683}$
12102	146 45 84 04	1772 439 605 208	009091 $_{4545}$	879289 $_{14373}$	958969 $_{632}$	8263097 $_{683}$
12103	146 48 26 09	1772 879 016 727	013636 $_{4544}$	893662 $_{14372}$	959601 $_{633}$	8262414 $_{682}$
12104	146 50 68 16	1773 318 500 864	018180 $_{4545}$	908034 $_{14371}$	960234 $_{632}$	8261732 $_{683}$
12105	146 53 10 25	1773 758 057 625	022725 $_{4544}$	922405 $_{14371}$	960866 $_{632}$	8261049 $_{682}$
12106	146 55 52 36	1774 197 687 016	027269 $_{4545}$	936776 $_{14370}$	961498 $_{632}$	8260367 $_{683}$
12107	146 57 94 49	1774 637 389 043	031814 $_{4544}$	951146 $_{14370}$	962130 $_{633}$	8259684 $_{682}$
12108	146 60 36 64	1775 077 163 712	036358 $_{4543}$	965516 $_{14368}$	962763 $_{632}$	8259002 $_{682}$
12109	146 62 78 81	1775 517 011 029	040901 $_{4544}$	979884 $_{14369}$	963395 $_{632}$	8258320 $_{682}$
12110	146 65 21 00	1775 956 931 000	045445 $_{4544}$	994253 $_{14368}$	964027 $_{632}$	8257638 $_{682}$
12111	146 67 63 21	1776 396 923 631	049989 $_{4543}$	*008621 $_{14367}$	964659 $_{632}$	8256956 $_{681}$
12112	146 70 05 44	1776 836 988 928	054532 $_{4543}$	022988 $_{14366}$	965291 $_{632}$	8256275 $_{682}$
12113	146 72 47 69	1777 277 126 897	059075 $_{4543}$	037354 $_{14366}$	965923 $_{632}$	8255593 $_{681}$
12114	146 74 89 96	1777 717 337 544	063618 $_{4543}$	051720 $_{14366}$	966555 $_{632}$	8254912 $_{682}$
12115	146 77 32 25	1778 157 620 875	068161 $_{4542}$	066086 $_{14364}$	967187 $_{632}$	8254230 $_{681}$
12116	146 79 74 56	1778 597 976 896	072703 $_{4543}$	080450 $_{14365}$	967819 $_{632}$	8253549 $_{681}$
12117	146 82 16 89	1779 038 405 613	077246 $_{4542}$	094815 $_{14363}$	968451 $_{632}$	8252868 $_{681}$
12118	146 84 59 24	1779 478 907 032	081788 $_{4542}$	109178 $_{14363}$	969083 $_{631}$	8252187 $_{681}$
12119	146 87 01 61	1779 919 481 159	086330 $_{4542}$	123541 $_{14363}$	969714 $_{632}$	8251506 $_{681}$
12120	146 89 44 00	1780 360 128 000	090872 $_{4541}$	137904 $_{14362}$	970346 $_{632}$	8250825 $_{681}$
12121	146 91 86 41	1780 800 847 561	095413 $_{4542}$	152266 $_{14361}$	970978 $_{632}$	8250144 $_{680}$
12122	146 94 28 84	1781 241 639 848	099955 $_{4541}$	166627 $_{14360}$	971610 $_{631}$	8249464 $_{681}$
12123	146 96 71 29	1781 682 504 867	104496 $_{4541}$	180987 $_{14360}$	972241 $_{632}$	8248783 $_{680}$
12124	146 99 13 76	1782 123 442 624	109037 $_{4541}$	195347 $_{14360}$	972873 $_{631}$	8248103 $_{680}$
12125	147 01 56 25	1782 564 453 125	113578 $_{4540}$	209707 $_{14359}$	973504 $_{632}$	8247423 $_{680}$
12126	147 03 98 76	1783 005 536 376	118118 $_{4541}$	224066 $_{14358}$	974136 $_{632}$	8246743 $_{680}$
12127	147 06 41 29	1783 446 692 383	122659 $_{4540}$	238424 $_{14358}$	974768 $_{631}$	8246063 $_{680}$
12128	147 08 83 84	1783 887 921 152	127199 $_{1540}$	252782 $_{14357}$	975399 $_{631}$	8245383 $_{680}$
12129	147 11 26 41	1784 329 222 689	131739 $_{4540}$	267139 $_{14356}$	976030 $_{632}$	8244703 $_{680}$
12130	147 13 69 00	1784 770 597 000	136279 $_{4540}$	281495 $_{14356}$	976662 $_{631}$	8244023 $_{680}$
12131	147 16 11 61	1785 212 044 091	140819 $_{4540}$	295851 $_{14356}$	977293 $_{632}$	8243343 $_{679}$
12132	147 18 54 24	1785 653 563 968	145359 $_{4539}$	310207 $_{14354}$	977925 $_{631}$	8242664 $_{679}$
12133	147 20 96 89	1786 095 156 637	149898 $_{4539}$	324561 $_{14354}$	978556 $_{631}$	8241985 $_{680}$
12134	147 23 39 56	1786 536 822 104	154437 $_{4539}$	338915 $_{14354}$	979187 $_{631}$	8241305 $_{679}$
12135	147 25 82 25	1786 978 560 375	158976 $_{4539}$	353269 $_{14353}$	979818 $_{632}$	8240626 $_{679}$
12136	147 28 24 96	1787 420 371 456	163515 $_{4538}$	367622 $_{14352}$	980450 $_{631}$	8239947 $_{679}$
12137	147 30 67 69	1787 862 255 353	168053 $_{4539}$	381974 $_{14352}$	981081 $_{631}$	8239268 $_{678}$
12138	147 33 10 44	1788 304 212 072	172592 $_{4538}$	396326 $_{14351}$	981712 $_{631}$	8238590 $_{679}$
12139	147 35 53 21	1788 746 241 619	177130 $_{4538}$	410677 $_{14351}$	982343 $_{631}$	8237911 $_{679}$
12140	147 37 96 00	1789 188 344 000	181668 $_{4538}$	425028 $_{14350}$	982974 $_{631}$	8237232 $_{678}$
12141	147 40 38 81	1789 630 519 221	186206 $_{4538}$	439378 $_{14349}$	983605 $_{631}$	8236554 $_{679}$
12142	147 42 81 64	1790 072 767 288	190744 $_{4537}$	453727 $_{14349}$	984236 $_{631}$	8235875 $_{678}$
12143	147 45 24 49	1790 515 088 207	195281 $_{4538}$	468076 $_{14348}$	984867 $_{631}$	8235197 $_{678}$
12144	147 47 67 36	1790 957 481 984	199819 $_{4537}$	482424 $_{14348}$	985498 $_{631}$	8234519 $_{678}$
12145	147 50 10 25	1791 399 948 625	204356 $_{4537}$	496772 $_{14347}$	986129 $_{631}$	8233841 $_{678}$
12146	147 52 53 16	1791 842 488 136	208893 $_{4536}$	511119 $_{14346}$	986760 $_{631}$	8233163 $_{678}$
12147	147 54 96 09	1792 285 100 523	213429 $_{4537}$	525465 $_{14346}$	987391 $_{630}$	8232485 $_{677}$
12148	147 57 39 04	1792 727 785 792	217966 $_{4536}$	539811 $_{14345}$	988021 $_{631}$	8231808 $_{678}$
12149	147 59 82 01	1793 170 543 949	222502 $_{4536}$	554156 $_{14345}$	988652 $_{631}$	8231130 $_{677}$
12150	147 62 25 00	1793 613 375 000	227038	568501	989283	8230453
			110·	348·	22·	0·0000

244

No. n	Square n^2	Cube n^3	Square root $\sqrt{n}$	Sq. rt. of $10n$ $\sqrt{10n}$	Cube root $\sqrt[3]{n}$	Reciprocal $\dfrac{1}{n}$
			110.	348.	22.	0.0000
12150	147 62 25 00	1793 613 375 000	227038 $_{4536}$	568501 $_{14344}$	989283 $_{631}$	8230453 $_{678}$
12151	147 64 68 01	1794 056 278 951	231574 $_{4536}$	582845 $_{14344}$	989914 $_{630}$	8229775 $_{677}$
12152	147 67 11 04	1794 499 255 808	236110 $_{4536}$	597189 $_{14343}$	990544 $_{631}$	8229098 $_{677}$
12153	147 69 54 09	1794 942 305 577	240646 $_{4535}$	611532 $_{14342}$	991175 $_{631}$	8228421 $_{677}$
12154	147 71 97 16	1795 385 428 264	245181 $_{4536}$	625874 $_{14342}$	991806 $_{630}$	8227744 $_{677}$
12155	147 74 40 25	1795 828 623 875	249717 $_{4535}$	640216 $_{14341}$	992436 $_{631}$	8227067 $_{677}$
12156	147 76 83 36	1796 271 892 416	254252 $_{4534}$	654557 $_{14340}$	993067 $_{630}$	8226390 $_{676}$
12157	147 79 26 49	1796 715 233 893	258786 $_{4535}$	668897 $_{14340}$	993697 $_{630}$	8225714 $_{677}$
12158	147 81 69 64	1797 158 648 312	263321 $_{4535}$	683237 $_{14340}$	994328 $_{630}$	8225037 $_{676}$
12159	147 84 12 81	1797 602 135 679	267856 $_{4534}$	697577 $_{14338}$	994958 $_{630}$	8224361 $_{677}$
12160	147 86 56 00	1798 045 696 000	272390 $_{4534}$	711915 $_{14339}$	995588 $_{631}$	8223684 $_{676}$
12161	147 88 99 21	1798 489 329 281	276924 $_{4534}$	726254 $_{14337}$	996219 $_{630}$	8223008 $_{676}$
12162	147 91 42 44	1798 933 035 528	281458 $_{4534}$	740591 $_{14337}$	996849 $_{630}$	8222332 $_{676}$
12163	147 93 85 69	1799 376 814 747	285992 $_{4533}$	754928 $_{14337}$	997479 $_{630}$	8221656 $_{676}$
12164	147 96 28 96	1799 820 666 944	290525 $_{4534}$	769265 $_{14336}$	998109 $_{631}$	8220980 $_{676}$
12165	147 98 72 25	1800 264 592 125	295059 $_{4533}$	783601 $_{14335}$	998740 $_{630}$	8220304 $_{676}$
12166	148 01 15 56	1800 708 590 296	299592 $_{4533}$	797936 $_{14334}$	999370 $_{630}$	8219628 $_{675}$
12167	148 03 58 89	1801 152 661 463	304125 $_{4533}$	812270 $_{14334}$	*000000 $_{630}$	8218953 $_{676}$
12168	148 06 02 24	1801 596 805 632	308658 $_{4533}$	826604 $_{14334}$	000630 $_{630}$	8218277 $_{675}$
12169	148 08 45 61	1802 041 022 809	313191 $_{4532}$	840938 $_{14334}$	001260 $_{630}$	8217602 $_{675}$
12170	148 10 89 00	1802 485 313 000	317723 $_{4532}$	855271 $_{14332}$	001890 $_{630}$	8216927 $_{675}$
12171	148 13 32 41	1802 929 676 211	322255 $_{4532}$	869603 $_{14332}$	002520 $_{630}$	8216252 $_{675}$
12172	148 15 75 84	1803 374 112 448	326787 $_{4532}$	883935 $_{14331}$	003150 $_{630}$	8215577 $_{675}$
12173	148 18 19 29	1803 818 621 717	331319 $_{4532}$	898266 $_{14331}$	003780 $_{630}$	8214902 $_{675}$
12174	148 20 62 76	1804 263 204 024	335851 $_{4531}$	912597 $_{14329}$	004410 $_{630}$	8214227 $_{675}$
12175	148 23 06 25	1804 707 859 375	340382 $_{4532}$	926926 $_{14330}$	005040 $_{630}$	8213552 $_{674}$
12176	148 25 49 76	1805 152 587 776	344914 $_{4531}$	941256 $_{14329}$	005670 $_{629}$	8212878 $_{675}$
12177	148 27 93 29	1805 597 390 233	349445 $_{4531}$	955585 $_{14328}$	006299 $_{630}$	8212203 $_{674}$
12178	148 30 36 84	1806 042 263 752	353976 $_{4531}$	969913 $_{14327}$	006929 $_{630}$	8211529 $_{674}$
12179	148 32 80 41	1806 487 211 339	358507 $_{4530}$	984240 $_{14327}$	007559 $_{630}$	8210855 $_{674}$
12180	148 35 24 00	1806 932 232 000	363037 $_{4531}$	*998567 $_{14327}$	008189 $_{629}$	8210181 $_{674}$
12181	148 37 67 61	1807 377 325 741	367568 $_{4530}$	*012894 $_{14326}$	008818 $_{629}$	8209507 $_{674}$
12182	148 40 11 24	1807 822 492 568	372098 $_{4530}$	027220 $_{14325}$	009448 $_{630}$	8208833 $_{674}$
12183	148 42 54 89	1808 267 732 487	376628 $_{4530}$	041545 $_{14324}$	010077 $_{630}$	8208159 $_{674}$
12184	148 44 98 56	1808 713 045 504	381158 $_{4529}$	055869 $_{14325}$	010707 $_{630}$	8207485 $_{673}$
12185	148 47 42 25	1809 158 431 625	385687 $_{4530}$	070194 $_{14323}$	011337 $_{629}$	8206812 $_{674}$
12186	148 49 85 96	1809 603 890 856	390217 $_{4529}$	084517 $_{14323}$	011966 $_{629}$	8206138 $_{673}$
12187	148 52 29 69	1810 049 423 203	394746 $_{4529}$	098840 $_{14322}$	012595 $_{630}$	8205465 $_{673}$
12188	148 54 73 44	1810 495 028 672	399275 $_{4529}$	113162 $_{14322}$	013225 $_{629}$	8204792 $_{674}$
12189	148 57 17 21	1810 940 707 269	403804 $_{4529}$	127484 $_{14321}$	013854 $_{630}$	8204118 $_{673}$
12190	148 59 61 00	1811 386 459 000	408333 $_{4529}$	141805 $_{14321}$	014484 $_{629}$	8203445 $_{672}$
12191	148 62 04 81	1811 832 283 871	412862 $_{4528}$	156126 $_{14319}$	015113 $_{629}$	8202773 $_{673}$
12192	148 64 48 64	1812 278 181 888	417390 $_{4528}$	170445 $_{14320}$	015742 $_{629}$	8202100 $_{673}$
12193	148 66 92 49	1812 724 153 057	421918 $_{4528}$	184765 $_{14319}$	016371 $_{630}$	8201427 $_{673}$
12194	148 69 36 36	1813 170 197 384	426446 $_{4528}$	199084 $_{14318}$	017001 $_{629}$	8200754 $_{672}$
12195	148 71 80 25	1813 616 314 875	430974 $_{4528}$	213402 $_{14317}$	017630 $_{629}$	8200082 $_{672}$
12196	148 74 24 16	1814 062 505 536	435502 $_{4527}$	227719 $_{14317}$	018259 $_{629}$	8199410 $_{673}$
12197	148 76 68 09	1814 508 769 373	440029 $_{4527}$	242036 $_{14317}$	018888 $_{629}$	8198737 $_{672}$
12198	148 79 12 04	1814 955 106 392	444556 $_{4527}$	256353 $_{14316}$	019517 $_{629}$	8198065 $_{672}$
12199	148 81 56 01	1815 401 516 599	449083 $_{4527}$	270669 $_{14315}$	020146 $_{629}$	8197393 $_{672}$
12200	148 84 00 00	1815 848 000 000	453610	284984	020775	8196721
			110.	349.	23.	0.0000

No. n	Square n²	Cube n³	Square root √n	Sq. rt. of 10n √10n	Cube root ∛n	Reciprocal 1/n
			110·	349·	23·	0·0000
12200	148 84 00 00	1815 848 000 000	453610	284984	020775	8196721
12201	148 86 44 01	1816 294 556 601	458137 4527	299299 14315	021404 629	8196050 671
12202	148 88 88 04	1816 741 186 408	462663 4526	313613 14314	022033 629	8195378 672
12203	148 91 32 09	1817 187 889 427	467190 4527	327926 14313	022662 629	8194706 672
12204	148 93 76 16	1817 634 665 664	471716 4526	342239 14313	023291 629	8194035 671
12205	148 96 20 25	1818 081 515 125	476242 4526	356551 14312	023920 628	8193363 672
12206	148 98 64 36	1818 528 437 816	480768 4526	370863 14312	024548 629	8192692 671
12207	149 01 08 49	1818 975 433 743	485293 4525	385174 14311	025177 629	8192021 671
12208	149 03 52 64	1819 422 502 912	489819 4526	399485 14311	025806 629	8191350 671
12209	149 05 96 81	1819 869 645 329	494344 4525	413795 14310	026435 628	8190679 671
12210	149 08 41 00	1820 316 861 000	498869 4525	428104 14309	027063 629	8190008 671
12211	149 10 85 21	1820 764 149 931	503394 4525	442413 14309	027692 629	8189337 671
12212	149 13 29 44	1821 211 512 128	507918 4525	456721 14308	028321 628	8188667 670
12213	149 15 73 69	1821 658 947 597	512443 4524	471029 14308	028949 629	8187996 671
12214	149 18 17 96	1822 106 456 344	516967 4524	485336 14307	029578 628	8187326 670
12215	149 20 62 25	1822 554 038 375	521491 4524	499642 14306	030206 629	8186656 670
12216	149 23 06 56	1823 001 693 696	526015 4524	513948 14306	030835 628	8185986 670
12217	149 25 50 89	1823 449 422 313	530539 4523	528254 14304	031463 628	8185316 670
12218	149 27 95 24	1823 897 224 232	535062 4524	542558 14304	032091 629	8184646 670
12219	149 30 39 61	1824 345 099 459	539586 4523	556862 14304	032720 628	8183976 670
12220	149 32 84 00	1824 793 048 000	544109 4523	571166 14303	033348 628	8183306 670
12221	149 35 28 41	1825 241 069 861	548632 4523	585469 14302	033976 628	8182636 670
12222	149 37 72 84	1825 689 165 048	553155 4523	599771 14302	034604 628	8181967 669
12223	149 40 17 29	1826 137 333 567	557677 4523	614073 14301	035233 628	8181298 670
12224	149 42 61 76	1826 585 575 424	562200 4522	628374 14301	035861 628	8180628 669
12225	149 45 06 25	1827 033 890 625	566722 4522	642675 14300	036489 628	8179959 669
12226	149 47 50 76	1827 482 279 176	571244 4522	656975 14299	037117 628	8179290 669
12227	149 49 95 29	1827 930 741 083	575766 4522	671274 14299	037745 628	8178621 669
12228	149 52 39 84	1828 379 276 352	580288 4521	685573 14298	038373 628	8177952 668
12229	149 54 84 41	1828 827 884 989	584809 4521	699871 14298	039001 628	8177284 669
12230	149 57 29 00	1829 276 567 000	589330 4522	714169 14297	039629 628	8176615 669
12231	149 59 73 61	1829 725 322 391	593852 4521	728466 14297	040257 628	8175946 669
12232	149 62 18 24	1830 174 151 168	598373 4521	742763 14296	040885 628	8175278 668
12233	149 64 62 89	1830 623 053 337	602893 4520	757059 14295	041513 628	8174610 668
12234	149 67 07 56	1831 072 028 904	607414 4521	771354 14295	042141 628	8173941 669
12235	149 69 52 25	1831 521 077 875	611934 4520	785649 14294	042769 627	8173273 668
12236	149 71 96 96	1831 970 200 256	616454 4520	799943 14293	043396 628	8172605 668
12237	149 74 41 69	1832 419 396 053	620975 4521	814236 14293	044024 628	8171938 667
12238	149 76 86 44	1832 868 665 272	625494 4519	828529 14293	044652 627	8171270 668
12239	149 79 31 21	1833 318 007 919	630014 4520	842822 14292	045279 628	8170602 668
12240	149 81 76 00	1833 767 424 000	634533 4519	857114 14291	045907 628	8169935 667
12241	149 84 20 81	1834 216 913 521	639053 4520	871405 14291	046535 627	8169267 668
12242	149 86 65 64	1834 666 476 488	643572 4519	885696 14291	047162 628	8168600 667
12243	149 89 10 49	1835 116 112 907	648091 4519	899986 14290	047790 627	8167933 667
12244	149 91 55 36	1835 565 822 784	652610 4519	914275 14289	048417 628	8167266 667
12245	149 94 00 25	1836 015 606 125	657128 4518	928564 14288	049045 627	8166599 667
12246	149 96 45 16	1836 465 462 936	661646 4518	942852 14288	049672 627	8165932 667
12247	149 98 90 09	1836 915 393 223	666165 4519	957140 14287	050299 628	8165265 667
12248	150 01 35 04	1837 365 396 992	670683 4518	971427 14287	050927 627	8164598 666
12249	150 03 80 01	1837 815 474 249	675200 4517	985714 14286	051554 627	8163932 667
12250	150 06 25 00	1838 265 625 000	679718	*000000	052181	8163265
			110·	350·	23·	0·0000

No. n	Square n²	Cube n³	Square root √n	Sq. rt. of 10n √10n	Cube root ∛n	Reciprocal 1/n
			110·	350·	23·	0·0000
12250	150 06 25 00	1838 265 625 000	679718 4518	000000 14285	052181 628	8163265 666
12251	150 08 70 01	1838 715 849 251	684236 4517	014285 14285	052809 627	8162599 666
12252	150 11 15 04	1839 166 147 008	688753 4517	028570 14285	053436 627	8161933 666
12253	150 13 60 09	1839 616 518 277	693270 4517	042855 14283	054063 627	8161267 666
12254	150 16 05 16	1840 066 963 064	697787 4516	057138 14283	054690 627	8160601 666
12255	150 18 50 25	1840 517 481 375	702303 4517	071421 14283	055317 627	8159935 666
12256	150 20 95 36	1840 968 073 216	706820 4516	085704 14282	055944 628	8159269 666
12257	150 23 40 49	1841 418 738 593	711336 4517	099986 14281	056572 627	8158603 665
12258	150 25 85 64	1841 869 477 512	715853 4515	114267 14281	057199 627	8157938 666
12259	150 28 30 81	1842 320 289 979	720368 4516	128548 14280	057826 626	8157272 665
12260	150 30 76 00	1842 771 176 000	724884 4516	142828 14280	058452 627	8156607 665
12261	150 33 21 21	1843 222 135 581	729400 4515	157108 14279	059079 627	8155942 666
12262	150 35 66 44	1843 673 168 728	733915 4516	171387 14278	059706 627	8155276 665
12263	150 38 11 69	1844 124 275 447	738431 4515	185665 14278	060333 627	8154611 664
12264	150 40 56 96	1844 575 455 744	742946 4514	199943 14277	060960 627	8153947 665
12265	150 43 02 25	1845 026 709 625	747460 4515	214220 14277	061587 626	8153282 665
12266	150 45 47 56	1845 478 037 096	751975 4515	228497 14276	062213 627	8152617 665
12267	150 47 92 89	1845 929 438 163	756490 4514	242773 14276	062840 627	8151952 664
12268	150 50 38 24	1846 380 912 832	761004 4514	257048 14275	063467 626	8151288 664
12269	150 52 83 61	1846 832 461 109	765518 4514	271323 14275	064093 627	8150624 665
12270	150 55 29 00	1847 284 083 000	770032 4514	285598 14274	064720 627	8149959 664
12271	150 57 74 41	1847 735 778 511	774546 4513	299872 14273	065347 626	8149295 664
12272	150 60 19 84	1848 187 547 648	779059 4514	314145 14272	065973 627	8148631 664
12273	150 62 65 29	1848 639 390 417	783573 4513	328417 14272	066600 626	8147967 664
12274	150 65 10 76	1849 091 306 824	788086 4513	342689 14272	067226 627	8147303 663
12275	150 67 56 25	1849 543 296 875	792599 4513	356961 14271	067853 626	8146640 664
12276	150 70 01 76	1849 995 360 576	797112 4513	371232 14270	068479 626	8145976 664
12277	150 72 47 29	1850 447 497 933	801625 4512	385502 14270	069105 627	8145312 663
12278	150 74 92 84	1850 899 708 952	806137 4512	399772 14269	069732 626	8144649 663
12279	150 77 38 41	1851 351 993 639	810649 4512	414041 14268	070358 626	8143986 664
12280	150 79 84 00	1851 804 352 000	815161 4512	428309 14268	070984 626	8143322 663
12281	150 82 29 61	1852 256 784 041	819673 4512	442577 14268	071610 627	8142659 663
12282	150 84 75 24	1852 709 289 768	824185 4512	456845 14267	072237 626	8141996 662
12283	150 87 20 89	1853 161 869 187	828697 4511	471112 14266	072863 626	8141334 663
12284	150 89 66 56	1853 614 522 304	833208 4511	485378 14265	073489 626	8140671 663
12285	150 92 12 25	1854 067 249 125	837719 4511	499643 14265	074115 626	8140008 662
12286	150 94 57 96	1854 520 049 656	842230 4511	513908 14265	074741 626	8139346 663
12287	150 97 03 69	1854 972 923 903	846741 4511	528173 14264	075367 626	8138683 662
12288	150 99 49 44	1855 425 871 872	851252 4510	542437 14263	075993 626	8138021 662
12289	151 01 95 21	1855 878 893 569	855762 4510	556700 14263	076619 626	8137359 662
12290	151 04 41 00	1856 331 989 000	860272 4511	570963 14262	077245 626	8136697 663
12291	151 06 86 81	1856 785 158 171	864783 4509	585225 14262	077871 626	8136034 661
12292	151 09 32 64	1857 238 401 088	869292 4510	599487 14261	078497 626	8135373 662
12293	151 11 78 49	1857 691 717 757	873802 4510	613748 14260	079123 625	8134711 662
12294	151 14 24 36	1858 145 108 184	878312 4509	628008 14260	079748 626	8134049 661
12295	151 16 70 25	1858 598 572 375	882821 4509	642268 14259	080374 626	8133388 662
12296	151 19 16 16	1859 052 110 336	887330 4509	656527 14259	081000 626	8132726 661
12297	151 21 62 09	1859 505 722 073	891839 4509	670786 14258	081626 625	8132065 662
12298	151 24 08 04	1859 959 407 592	896348 4509	685044 14257	082251 626	8131403 661
12299	151 26 54 01	1860 413 166 899	900857 4508	699301 14257	082877 625	8130742 661
12300	151 29 00 00	1860 867 000 000	905365	713558	083502	8130081
			110·	350·	23·	0·0000

No. n	Square n^2	Cube n^3	Square root $\sqrt{n}$	Sq. rt. of 10n $\sqrt{10n}$	Cube root $\sqrt[3]{n}$	Reciprocal $\frac{1}{n}$
			110.	350.	23.	0.0000
12300	151 29 00 00	1860 867 000 000	905365 4508	713558 14257	083502 626	8130081 661
12301	151 31 46 01	1861 320 906 901	909873 4508	727815 14255	084128 625	8129420 660
12302	151 33 92 04	1861 774 887 608	914381 4508	742070 14256	084753 626	8128760 660
12303	151 36 38 09	1862 228 942 127	918889 4508	756326 14254	085379 626	8128099 661
12304	151 38 84 16	1862 683 070 464	923397 4508	770580 14254	086004 626	8127438 660
12305	151 41 30 25	1863 137 272 625	927905 4507	784834 14254	086630 625	8126778 661
12306	151 43 76 36	1863 591 548 616	932412 4507	799088 14253	087255 626	8126117 660
12307	151 46 22 49	1864 045 898 443	936919 4507	813341 14253	087881 625	8125457 660
12308	151 48 68 64	1864 500 322 112	941426 4507	827593 14252	088506 625	8124797 660
12309	151 51 14 81	1864 954 819 629	945933 4506	841845 14251	089131 625	8124137 660
12310	151 53 61 00	1865 409 391 000	950439 4507	856096 14250	089756 626	8123477 660
12311	151 56 07 21	1865 864 036 231	954946 4506	870346 14250	090382 625	8122817 660
12312	151 58 53 44	1866 318 755 328	959452 4506	884596 14250	091007 625	8122157 659
12313	151 60 99 69	1866 773 548 297	963958 4506	898846 14249	091632 625	8121498 659
12314	151 63 45 96	1867 228 415 144	968464 4506	913095 14248	092257 625	8120838 659
12315	151 65 92 25	1867 683 355 875	972970 4505	927343 14248	092882 625	8120179 660
12316	151 68 38 56	1868 138 370 496	977475 4505	941591 14247	093507 625	8119519 659
12317	151 70 84 89	1868 593 459 013	981981 4505	955838 14246	094132 625	8118860 659
12318	151 73 31 24	1869 048 621 432	986486 4505	970084 14246	094757 625	8118201 659
12319	151 75 77 61	1869 503 857 759	990991 4504	984330 14245	095382 625	8117542 659
12320	151 78 24 00	1869 959 168 000	995495 4505	998575 14245	096007 625	8116883 659
12321	151 80 70 41	1870 414 552 161	*000000 4504	*012820 14244	096632 625	8116224 658
12322	151 83 16 84	1870 870 010 248	004504 4505	027064 14244	097257 625	8115566 659
12323	151 85 63 29	1871 325 542 267	009009 4504	041308 14243	097882 624	8114907 658
12324	151 88 09 76	1871 781 148 224	013513 4504	055551 14243	098506 625	8114249 659
12325	151 90 56 25	1872 236 828 125	018017 4503	069794 14242	099131 625	8113590 658
12326	151 93 02 76	1872 692 581 976	022520 4504	084036 14241	099756 624	8112932 658
12327	151 95 49 29	1873 148 409 783	027024 4503	098277 14241	100380 625	8112274 658
12328	151 97 95 84	1873 604 311 552	031527 4503	112518 14240	101005 625	8111616 658
12329	152 00 42 41	1874 060 287 289	036030 4503	126758 14239	101630 624	8110958 658
12330	152 02 89 00	1874 516 337 000	040533 4503	140997 14239	102254 625	8110300 658
12331	152 05 35 61	1874 972 460 691	045036 4502	155236 14239	102879 624	8109642 657
12332	152 07 82 24	1875 428 658 368	049538 4503	169475 14238	103503 625	8108985 658
12333	152 10 28 89	1875 884 930 037	054041 4502	183713 14237	104128 624	8108327 657
12334	152 12 75 56	1876 341 275 704	058543 4502	197950 14237	104752 625	8107670 657
12335	152 15 22 25	1876 797 695 375	063045 4502	212187 14236	105377 624	8107013 658
12336	152 17 68 96	1877 254 189 056	067547 4502	226423 14235	106001 624	8106355 657
12337	152 20 15 69	1877 710 756 753	072049 4501	240658 14235	106625 625	8105698 657
12338	152 22 62 44	1878 167 398 472	076550 4501	254893 14235	107250 624	8105041 657
12339	152 25 09 21	1878 624 114 219	081051 4502	269128 14233	107874 624	8104384 656
12340	152 27 56 00	1879 080 904 000	085553 4501	283361 14234	108498 624	8103728 657
12341	152 30 02 81	1879 537 767 821	090054 4500	297595 14232	109122 624	8103071 657
12342	152 32 49 64	1879 994 705 688	094554 4501	311827 14232	109746 625	8102415 657
12343	152 34 96 49	1880 451 717 607	099055 4500	326059 14232	110371 624	8101758 656
12344	152 37 43 36	1880 908 803 584	103555 4501	340291 14231	110995 624	8101102 656
12345	152 39 90 25	1881 365 963 625	108056 4500	354522 14230	111619 624	8100446 657
12346	152 42 37 16	1881 823 197 736	112556 4500	368752 14230	112243 624	8099789 656
12347	152 44 84 09	1882 280 505 923	117055 4500	382982 14229	112867 624	8099133 656
12348	152 47 31 04	1882 737 888 192	121555 4500	397211 14229	113491 624	8098477 655
12349	152 49 78 01	1883 195 344 549	126055 4499	411440 14228	114115 624	8097822 656
12350	152 52 25 00	1883 652 875 000	130554	425668	114739	8097166
			111.	351.	23.	0.0000

248

No. n	Square n^2	Cube n^3	Square root $\sqrt{n}$	Sq. rt. of $10n$ $\sqrt{10n}$	Cube root $\sqrt[3]{n}$	Reciprocal $\frac{1}{n}$
			III.	351.	23.	0·0000
12350	152 52 25 00	1883 652 875 000	$130554_{\,4499}$	$425668_{\,14227}$	$114739_{\,623}$	$8097166_{\,656}$
12351	152 54 72 01	1884 110 479 551	$135053_{\,4499}$	$439895_{\,14227}$	$115362_{\,624}$	$8096510_{\,655}$
12352	152 57 19 04	1884 568 158 208	$139552_{\,4499}$	$454122_{\,14227}$	$115986_{\,624}$	$8095855_{\,655}$
12353	152 59 66 09	1885 025 910 977	$144051_{\,4498}$	$468349_{\,14225}$	$116610_{\,624}$	$8095200_{\,656}$
12354	152 62 13 16	1885 483 737 864	$148549_{\,4499}$	$482574_{\,14225}$	$117234_{\,624}$	$8094544_{\,655}$
12355	152 64 60 25	1885 941 638 875	$153048_{\,4498}$	$496799_{\,14225}$	$117858_{\,623}$	$8093889_{\,655}$
12356	152 67 07 36	1886 399 614 016	$157546_{\,4498}$	$511024_{\,14224}$	$118481_{\,624}$	$8093234_{\,655}$
12357	152 69 54 49	1886 857 663 293	$162044_{\,4498}$	$525248_{\,14223}$	$119105_{\,624}$	$8092579_{\,655}$
12358	152 72 01 64	1887 315 786 712	$166542_{\,4497}$	$539471_{\,14223}$	$119729_{\,623}$	$8091924_{\,654}$
12359	152 74 48 81	1887 773 984 279	$171039_{\,4498}$	$553694_{\,14223}$	$120352_{\,624}$	$8091270_{\,655}$
12360	152 76 96 00	1888 232 256 000	$175537_{\,4497}$	$567917_{\,14221}$	$120976_{\,623}$	$8090615_{\,655}$
12361	152 79 43 21	1888 690 601 881	$180034_{\,4497}$	$582138_{\,14221}$	$121599_{\,624}$	$8089960_{\,654}$
12362	152 81 90 44	1889 149 021 928	$184531_{\,4497}$	$596359_{\,14221}$	$122223_{\,623}$	$8089306_{\,654}$
12363	152 84 37 69	1889 607 516 147	$189028_{\,4497}$	$610580_{\,14220}$	$122846_{\,623}$	$8088652_{\,654}$
12364	152 86 84 96	1890 066 084 544	$193525_{\,4497}$	$624800_{\,14219}$	$123470_{\,623}$	$8087997_{\,654}$
12365	152 89 32 25	1890 524 727 125	$198022_{\,4496}$	$639019_{\,14219}$	$124093_{\,623}$	$8087343_{\,654}$
12366	152 91 79 56	1890 983 443 896	$202518_{\,4496}$	$653238_{\,14219}$	$124716_{\,624}$	$8086689_{\,654}$
12367	152 94 26 89	1891 442 234 863	$207014_{\,4496}$	$667457_{\,14217}$	$125340_{\,623}$	$8086035_{\,653}$
12368	152 96 74 24	1891 901 100 032	$211510_{\,4496}$	$681674_{\,14217}$	$125963_{\,623}$	$8085382_{\,654}$
12369	152 99 21 61	1892 360 039 409	$216006_{\,4496}$	$695891_{\,14217}$	$126586_{\,623}$	$8084728_{\,654}$
12370	153 01 69 00	1892 819 053 000	$220502_{\,4495}$	$710108_{\,14216}$	$127209_{\,624}$	$8084074_{\,653}$
12371	153 04 16 41	1893 278 140 811	$224997_{\,4495}$	$724324_{\,14215}$	$127833_{\,623}$	$8083421_{\,653}$
12372	153 06 63 84	1893 737 302 848	$229492_{\,4496}$	$738539_{\,14215}$	$128456_{\,623}$	$8082768_{\,654}$
12373	153 09 11 29	1894 196 539 117	$233988_{\,4495}$	$752754_{\,14214}$	$129079_{\,623}$	$8082114_{\,653}$
12374	153 11 58 76	1894 655 849 624	$238483_{\,4494}$	$766968_{\,14214}$	$129702_{\,623}$	$8081461_{\,653}$
12375	153 14 06 25	1895 115 234 375	$242977_{\,4495}$	$781182_{\,14213}$	$130325_{\,623}$	$8080808_{\,653}$
12376	153 16 53 76	1895 574 693 376	$247472_{\,4494}$	$795395_{\,14213}$	$130948_{\,623}$	$8080155_{\,653}$
12377	153 19 01 29	1896 034 226 633	$251966_{\,4494}$	$809608_{\,14212}$	$131571_{\,623}$	$8079502_{\,652}$
12378	153 21 48 84	1896 493 834 152	$256460_{\,4495}$	$823820_{\,14211}$	$132194_{\,623}$	$8078850_{\,653}$
12379	153 23 96 41	1896 953 515 939	$260955_{\,4493}$	$838031_{\,14211}$	$132817_{\,623}$	$8078197_{\,653}$
12380	153 26 44 00	1897 413 272 000	$265448_{\,4494}$	$852242_{\,14210}$	$133440_{\,623}$	$8077544_{\,652}$
12381	153 28 91 61	1897 873 102 341	$269942_{\,4494}$	$866452_{\,14210}$	$134063_{\,622}$	$8076892_{\,652}$
12382	153 31 39 24	1898 333 006 968	$274436_{\,4493}$	$880662_{\,14209}$	$134685_{\,623}$	$8076240_{\,653}$
12383	153 33 86 89	1898 792 985 887	$278929_{\,4493}$	$894871_{\,14208}$	$135308_{\,623}$	$8075587_{\,652}$
12384	153 36 34 56	1899 253 039 104	$283422_{\,4493}$	$909079_{\,14208}$	$135931_{\,023}$	$8074935_{\,652}$
12385	153 38 82 25	1899 713 166 625	$287915_{\,4493}$	$923287_{\,14207}$	$136554_{\,622}$	$8074283_{\,651}$
12386	153 41 29 96	1900 173 368 456	$292408_{\,4492}$	$937494_{\,14207}$	$137176_{\,623}$	$8073632_{\,652}$
12387	153 43 77 69	1900 633 644 603	$296900_{\,4493}$	$951701_{\,14206}$	$137799_{\,623}$	$8072980_{\,652}$
12388	153 46 25 44	1901 093 995 072	$301393_{\,4492}$	$965907_{\,14206}$	$138422_{\,622}$	$8072328_{\,652}$
12389	153 48 73 21	1901 554 419 869	$305885_{\,4492}$	$980113_{\,14206}$	$139044_{\,623}$	$8071676_{\,651}$
12390	153 51 21 00	1902 014 919 000	$310377_{\,4492}$	$*994318_{\,14205}$	$139667_{\,622}$	$8071025_{\,651}$
12391	153 53 68 81	1902 475 492 471	$314869_{\,4492}$	$*008523_{\,14204}$	$140289_{\,623}$	$8070374_{\,652}$
12392	153 56 16 64	1902 936 140 288	$319360_{\,4491}$	$022727_{\,14203}$	$140912_{\,622}$	$8069722_{\,651}$
12393	153 58 64 49	1903 396 862 457	$323852_{\,4491}$	$036930_{\,14203}$	$141534_{\,623}$	$8069071_{\,651}$
12394	153 61 12 36	1903 857 658 984	$328343_{\,4491}$	$051133_{\,14202}$	$142157_{\,622}$	$8068420_{\,651}$
12395	153 63 60 25	1904 318 529 875	$332834_{\,4491}$	$065335_{\,14201}$	$142779_{\,622}$	$8067769_{\,651}$
12396	153 66 08 16	1904 779 475 136	$337325_{\,4491}$	$079536_{\,14202}$	$143401_{\,623}$	$8067118_{\,650}$
12397	153 68 56 09	1905 240 494 773	$341816_{\,4491}$	$093738_{\,14200}$	$144024_{\,622}$	$8066468_{\,651}$
12398	153 71 04 04	1905 701 588 792	$346307_{\,4490}$	$107938_{\,14200}$	$144646_{\,622}$	$8065817_{\,650}$
12399	153 73 52 01	1906 162 757 199	$350797_{\,4490}$	$122138_{\,14199}$	$145268_{\,623}$	$8065167_{\,651}$
12400	153 76 00 00	1906 624 000 000	355287	136337	145891	8064516
			III.	352.	23.	0·0000

No. n	Square n²	Cube n³	Square root √n	Sq. rt. of 10n √10n	Cube root ∛n	Reciprocal 1/n
			111.	352.	23.	0.0000
12400	153 76 00 00	1906 624 000 000	355287 4490	136337 14199	145891 622	8064516 650
12401	153 78 48 01	1907 085 317 201	359777 4490	150536 14199	146513 622	8063866 650
12402	153 80 96 04	1907 546 708 808	364267 4490	164734 14198	147135 622	8063216 650
12403	153 83 44 09	1908 008 174 827	368757 4489	178932 14198	147757 622	8062566 650
12404	153 85 92 16	1908 469 715 264	373246 4490	193129 14197	148379 622	8061916 650
12405	153 88 40 25	1908 931 330 125	377736 4489	207325 14196	149001 622	8061266 650
12406	153 90 88 36	1909 393 019 416	382225 4489	221521 14196	149623 622	8060616 650
12407	153 93 36 49	1909 854 783 143	386714 4489	235717 14194	150245 622	8059966 649
12408	153 95 84 64	1910 316 621 312	391203 4488	249911 14194	150867 622	8059317 650
12409	153 98 32 81	1910 778 533 929	395691 4489	264105 14194	151489 622	8058667 649
12410	154 00 81 00	1911 240 521 000	400180 4488	278299 14193	152111 622	8058018 650
12411	154 03 29 21	1911 702 582 531	404668 4488	292492 14193	152733 622	8057368 649
12412	154 05 77 44	1912 164 718 528	409156 4488	306685 14191	153355 621	8056719 649
12413	154 08 25 69	1912 626 928 997	413644 4487	320876 14192	153976 622	8056070 649
12414	154 10 73 96	1913 089 213 944	418131 4488	335068 14191	154598 622	8055421 649
12415	154 13 22 25	1913 551 573 375	422619 4487	349259 14190	155220 621	8054772 648
12416	154 15 70 56	1914 014 007 296	427106 4487	363449 14189	155841 622	8054124 649
12417	154 18 18 89	1914 476 515 713	431593 4487	377638 14189	156463 622	8053475 648
12418	154 20 67 24	1914 939 098 632	436080 4487	391827 14189	157085 621	8052827 649
12419	154 23 15 61	1915 401 756 059	440567 4487	406016 14188	157706 622	8052178 648
12420	154 25 64 00	1915 864 488 000	445054 4486	420204 14187	158328 621	8051530 648
12421	154 28 12 41	1916 327 294 461	449540 4486	434391 14187	158949 622	8050882 649
12422	154 30 60 84	1916 790 175 448	454026 4486	448578 14186	159571 621	8050233 648
12423	154 33 09 29	1917 253 130 967	458512 4486	462764 14186	160192 622	8049585 648
12424	154 35 57 76	1917 716 161 024	462998 4486	476950 14185	160814 621	8048938 648
12425	154 38 06 25	1918 179 265 625	467484 4486	491135 14184	161435 621	8048290 648
12426	154 40 54 76	1918 642 444 776	471970 4485	505319 14184	162056 622	8047642 648
12427	154 43 03 29	1919 105 698 483	476455 4485	519503 14183	162678 621	8046994 647
12428	154 45 51 84	1919 569 026 752	480940 4485	533686 14182	163299 621	8046347 647
12429	154 48 00 41	1920 032 429 589	485425 4485	547869 14182	163920 622	8045700 648
12430	154 50 49 00	1920 495 907 000	489910 4484	562051 14182	164542 621	8045052 647
12431	154 52 97 61	1920 959 458 991	494394 4485	576233 14181	165163 621	8044405 647
12432	154 55 46 24	1921 423 085 568	498879 4484	590414 14180	165784 621	8043758 647
12433	154 57 94 89	1921 886 786 737	503363 4484	604594 14180	166405 621	8043111 647
12434	154 60 43 56	1922 350 562 504	507847 4484	618774 14180	167026 621	8042464 647
12435	154 62 92 25	1922 814 412 875	512331 4484	632954 14178	167647 621	8041817 646
12436	154 65 40 96	1923 278 337 856	516815 4484	647132 14179	168268 621	8041171 647
12437	154 67 89 69	1923 742 337 453	521298 4483	661311 14177	168889 621	8040524 646
12438	154 70 38 44	1924 206 411 672	525782 4483	675488 14177	169510 621	8039878 646
12439	154 72 87 21	1924 670 560 519	530265 4483	689665 14177	170131 621	8039231 646
12440	154 75 36 00	1925 134 784 000	534748 4483	703842 14176	170752 621	8038585 646
12441	154 77 84 81	1925 599 082 121	539231 4482	718018 14175	171373 621	8037939 646
12442	154 80 33 64	1926 063 454 888	543713 4483	732193 14175	171994 620	8037293 646
12443	154 82 82 49	1926 527 902 307	548196 4482	746368 14174	172614 621	8036647 646
12444	154 85 31 36	1926 992 424 384	552678 4482	760542 14174	173235 621	8036001 645
12445	154 87 80 25	1927 457 021 125	557160 4482	774716 14173	173856 620	8035356 646
12446	154 90 29 16	1927 921 692 536	561642 4482	788889 14172	174476 621	8034710 646
12447	154 92 78 09	1928 386 438 623	566124 4481	803061 14172	175097 621	8034064 645
12448	154 95 27 04	1928 851 259 392	570605 4482	817233 14171	175718 620	8033419 645
12449	154 97 76 01	1929 316 154 849	575087 4481	831404 14171	176338 620	8032774 645
12450	155 00 25 00	1929 781 125 000	579568	845575	176959	8032129
			111.	352.	23.	0.0000

No. n	Square n²	Cube n³	Square root √n	Sq. rt. of 10n √10n	Cube root ∛n	Reciprocal 1/n
			111·	352·	23·	0·0000
12450	155 00 25 00	1929 781 125 000	579568 4481	845575 14171	176959 620	8032129 646
12451	155 02 74 01	1930 246 169 851	584049 4481	859746 14169	177579 621	8031483 645
12452	155 05 23 04	1930 711 289 408	588530 4481	873915 14169	178200 620	8030838 644
12453	155 07 72 09	1931 176 483 677	593011 4480	888084 14169	178820 621	8030194 645
12454	155 10 21 16	1931 641 752 664	597491 4480	902253 14168	179441 620	8029549 645
12455	155 12 70 25	1932 107 096 375	601971 4480	916421 14167	180061 621	8028904 645
12456	155 15 19 36	1932 572 514 816	606451 4480	930588 14167	180682 620	8028259 645
12457	155 17 68 49	1933 038 007 993	610931 4480	944755 14166	181302 620	8027615 644
12458	155 20 17 64	1933 503 575 912	615411 4480	958921 14166	181922 620	8026971 645
12459	155 22 66 81	1933 969 218 579	619891 4479	973087 14165	182542 621	8026326 644
12460	155 25 16 00	1934 434 936 000	624370 4479	987252 14164	183163 620	8025682 644
12461	155 27 65 21	1934 900 728 181	628849 4479	*001416 14164	183783 620	8025038 644
12462	155 30 14 44	1935 366 595 128	633328 4479	015580 14164	184403 620	8024394 644
12463	155 32 63 69	1935 832 536 847	637807 4479	029744 14163	185023 620	8023750 643
12464	155 35 12 96	1936 298 553 344	642286 4478	043907 14162	185643 620	8023107 644
12465	155 37 62 25	1936 764 644 625	646764 4479	058069 14162	186263 620	8022463 644
12466	155 40 11 56	1937 230 810 696	651243 4478	072231 14161	186883 620	8021819 643
12467	155 42 60 89	1937 697 051 563	655721 4478	086392 14160	187503 620	8021176 643
12468	155 45 10 24	1938 163 367 232	660199 4478	100552 14160	188123 620	8020533 644
12469	155 47 59 61	1938 629 757 709	664677 4477	114712 14160	188743 620	8019889 643
12470	155 50 09 00	1939 096 223 000	669154 4478	128872 14159	189363 620	8019246 643
12471	155 52 58 41	1939 562 763 111	673632 4477	143031 14158	189983 620	8018603 643
12472	155 55 07 84	1940 029 378 048	678109 4477	157189 14158	190603 619	8017960 643
12473	155 57 57 29	1940 496 067 817	682586 4477	171347 14157	191222 620	8017317 642
12474	155 60 06 76	1940 962 832 424	687063 4477	185504 14156	191842 620	8016675 643
12475	155 62 56 25	1941 429 671 875	691540 4476	199660 14156	192462 620	8016032 642
12476	155 65 05 76	1941 896 586 176	696016 4476	213816 14156	193082 619	8015390 643
12477	155 67 55 29	1942 363 575 333	700492 4477	227972 14155	193701 620	8014747 642
12478	155 70 04 84	1942 830 639 352	704969 4476	242127 14154	194321 619	8014105 642
12479	155 72 54 41	1943 297 778 239	709445 4475	256281 14154	194940 620	8013463 642
12480	155 75 04 00	1943 764 992 000	713920 4476	270435 14153	195560 620	8012821 642
12481	155 77 53 61	1944 232 280 641	718396 4475	284588 14152	196180 620	8012179 642
12482	155 80 03 24	1944 699 644 168	722871 4476	298740 14152	196799 619	8011537 642
12483	155 82 52 89	1945 167 082 587	727347 4475	312892 14152	197418 620	8010895 642
12484	155 85 02 56	1945 634 595 904	731822 4475	327044 14151	198038 619	8010253 641
12485	155 87 52 25	1946 102 184 125	736297 4474	341195 14150	198657 620	8009612 642
12486	155 90 01 96	1946 569 847 256	740771 4475	355345 14150	199277 619	8008970 641
12487	155 92 51 69	1947 037 585 303	745246 4474	369495 14149	199896 619	8008329 642
12488	155 95 01 44	1947 505 398 272	749720 4475	383644 14149	200515 620	8007687 641
12489	155 97 51 21	1947 973 286 169	754195 4474	397793 14148	201135 619	8007046 641
12490	156 00 01 00	1948 441 249 000	758669 4473	411941 14147	201754 619	8006405 641
12491	156 02 50 81	1948 909 286 771	763142 4474	426088 14147	202373 619	8005764 641
12492	156 05 00 64	1949 377 399 488	767616 4474	440235 14147	202992 619	8005123 640
12493	156 07 50 49	1949 845 587 157	772090 4473	454382 14146	203611 619	8004483 641
12494	156 10 00 36	1950 313 849 784	776563 4473	468528 14145	204230 619	8003842 641
12495	156 12 50 25	1950 782 187 375	781036 4473	482673 14145	204849 619	8003201 640
12496	156 15 00 16	1951 250 599 936	785509 4473	496818 14144	205468 619	8002561 640
12497	156 17 50 09	1951 719 087 473	789982 4472	510962 14144	206087 619	8001920 640
12498	156 20 00 04	1952 187 649 992	794454 4473	525105 14143	206706 619	8001280 640
12499	156 22 50 01	1952 656 287 499	798927 4472	539248 14143	207325 619	8000640 640
12500	156 25 00 00	1953 125 000 000	803399	553391	207944	8000000
			111·	353·	23·	0·0000

No. n	Fourth Power n^4	Fifth Power n^5	Sixth Power n^6	Seventh Power n^7
1	1	1	1	1
2	16	32	64	128
3	81	243	729	2187
4	256	1024	4096	16384
5	625	3125	15625	78125
6	1296	7776	46656	2 79936
7	2401	16807	1 17649	8 23543
8	4096	32768	2 62144	20 97152
9	6561	59049	5 31441	47 82969
10	10000	1 00000	10 00000	100 00000
11	14641	1 61051	17 71561	194 87171
12	20736	2 48832	29 85984	358 31808
13	28561	3 71293	48 26809	627 48517
14	38416	5 37824	75 29536	1054 13504
15	50625	7 59375	113 90625	1708 59375
16	65536	10 48576	167 77216	2684 35456
17	83521	14 19857	241 37569	4103 38673
18	1 04976	18 89568	340 12224	6122 20032
19	1 30321	24 76099	470 45881	8938 71739
20	1 60000	32 00000	640 00000	12800 00000
21	1 94481	40 84101	857 66121	18010 88541
22	2 34256	51 53632	1133 79904	24943 57888
23	2 79841	64 36343	1480 35889	34048 25447
24	3 31776	79 62624	1911 02976	45864 71424
25	3 90625	97 65625	2441 40625	61035 15625
26	4 56976	118 81376	3089 15776	80318 10176
27	5 31441	143 48907	3874 20489	1 04603 53203
28	6 14656	172 10368	4818 90304	1 34929 28512
29	7 07281	205 11149	5948 23321	1 72498 76309
30	8 10000	243 00000	7290 00000	2 18700 00000
31	9 23521	286 29151	8875 03681	2 75126 14111
32	10 48576	335 54432	10737 41824	3 43597 38368
33	11 85921	391 35393	12914 67969	4 26184 42977
34	13 36336	454 35424	15448 04416	5 25233 50144
35	15 00625	525 21875	18382 65625	6 43392 96875
36	16 79616	604 66176	21767 82336	7 83641 64096
37	18 74161	693 43957	25657 26409	9 49318 77133
38	20 85136	792 35168	30109 36384	11 44155 82592
39	23 13441	902 24199	35187 43761	13 72310 06679
40	25 60000	1024 00000	40960 00000	16 38400 00000
41	28 25761	1158 56201	47501 04241	19 47542 73881
42	31 11696	1306 91232	54890 31744	23 05393 33248
43	34 18801	1470 08443	63213 63049	27 18186 11107
44	37 48096	1649 16224	72563 13856	31 92778 09664
45	41 00625	1845 28125	83037 65625	37 36694 53125
46	44 77456	2059 62976	94742 96896	43 58176 57216
47	48 79681	2293 45007	1 07792 15329	50 66231 20463
48	53 08416	2548 03968	1 22305 90464	58 70683 42272
49	57 64801	2824 75249	1 38412 87201	67 82230 72849
50	62 50000	3125 00000	1 56250 00000	78 12500 00000

No. n	Eighth Power n^8	Ninth Power n^9	Tenth Power n^{10}
1	1	1	1
2	256	512	1024
3	6561	19683	59049
4	65536	2 62144	10 48576
5	3 90625	19 53125	97 65625
6	16 79616	100 77696	604 66176
7	57 64801	403 53607	2824 75249
8	167 77216	1342 17728	10737 41824
9	430 46721	3874 20489	34867 84401
10	1000 00000	10000 00000	1 00000 00000
11	2143 58881	23579 47691	2 59374 24601
12	4299 81696	51597 80352	6 19173 64224
13	8157 30721	1 06044 99373	13 78584 91849
14	14757 89056	2 06610 46784	28 92546 54976
15	25628 90625	3 84433 59375	57 66503 90625
16	42949 67296	6 87194 76736	109 95116 27776
17	69757 57441	11 85878 76497	201 59939 00449
18	1 10199 60576	19 83592 90368	357 04672 26624
19	1 69835 63041	32 26876 97779	613 10662 57801
20	2 56000 00000	51 20000 00000	1024 00000 00000
21	3 78228 59361	79 42800 46581	1667 98809 78201
22	5 48758 73536	120 72692 17792	2655 99227 91424
23	7 83109 85281	180 11526 61463	4142 65112 13649
24	11 00753 14176	264 18075 40224	6340 33809 65376
25	15 25878 90625	381 46972 65625	9536 74316 40625
26	20 88270 64576	542 95036 78976	14116 70956 53376
27	28 24295 36481	762 55974 84987	20589 11320 94649
28	37 78019 98336	1057 84559 53408	29619 67666 95424
29	50 02464 12961	1450 71459 75869	42070 72333 00201
30	65 61000 00000	1968 30000 00000	59049 00000 00000
31	85 28910 37441	2643 96221 60671	81962 82869 80801
32	109 95116 27776	3518 43720 88832	1 12589 99068 42624
33	140 64086 18241	4641 14844 01953	1 53157 89852 64449
34	178 57939 04896	6071 69927 66464	2 06437 77540 59776
35	225 18753 90625	7881 56386 71875	2 75854 73535 15625
36	282 11099 07456	10155 99566 68416	3 65615 84400 62976
37	351 24794 53921	12996 17397 95077	4 80858 43724 17849
38	434 77921 38496	16521 61012 62848	6 27821 18479 88224
39	535 20092 60481	20872 83611 58759	8 14040 60851 91601
40	655 36000 00000	26214 40000 00000	10 48576 00000 00000
41	798 43252 29121	32738 19343 93961	13 42265 93101 52401
42	968 26519 96416	40667 13838 49472	17 08019 81216 77824
43	1168 82002 77601	50259 26119 36843	21 61148 23132 84249
44	1404 82236 25216	61812 18395 09504	27 19736 09384 18176
45	1681 51253 90625	75668 06425 78125	34 05062 89160 15625
46	2004 76122 31936	92219 01626 69056	42 42074 74827 76576
47	2381 12866 61761	1 11913 04731 02767	52 59913 22358 30049
48	2817 92804 29056	1 35260 54605 94688	64 92506 21085 45024
49	3323 29305 69601	1 62841 35979 10449	79 79226 62976 12001
50	3906 25000 00000	1 95312 50000 00000	97 65625 00000 00000

No. n	Fourth Power n^4	Fifth Power n^5	Sixth Power n^6	Seventh Power n^7
51	67 65201	3450 25251	1 75962 87801	89 74106 77851
52	73 11616	3802 04032	1 97706 09664	102 80717 02528
53	78 90481	4181 95493	2 21643 61129	117 47111 39837
54	85 03056	4591 65024	2 47949 11296	133 89252 09984
55	91 50625	5032 84375	2 76806 40625	152 24352 34375
56	98 34496	5507 31776	3 08409 79456	172 70948 49536
57	105 56001	6016 92057	3 42964 47249	195 48974 93193
58	113 16496	6563 56768	3 80686 92544	220 79841 67552
59	121 17361	7149 24299	4 21805 33641	248 86514 84819
60	129 60000	7776 00000	4 66560 00000	279 93600 00000
61	138 45841	8445 96301	5 15203 74361	314 27428 36021
62	147 76336	9161 32832	5 68002 35584	352 16146 06208
63	157 52961	9924 36543	6 25235 02209	393 89806 39167
64	167 77216	10737 41824	6 87194 76736	439 80465 11104
65	178 50625	11602 90625	7 54188 90625	490 22278 90625
66	189 74736	12523 32576	8 26539 50016	545 51607 01056
67	201 51121	13501 25107	9 04583 82169	606 07116 05323
68	213 81376	14539 33568	9 88674 82624	672 29888 18432
69	226 67121	15640 31349	10 79181 63081	744 63532 52589
70	240 10000	16807 00000	11 76490 00000	823 54300 00000
71	254 11681	18042 29351	12 81002 83921	909 51201 58391
72	268 73856	19349 17632	13 93140 69504	1003 06130 04288
73	283 98241	20730 71593	15 13342 26289	1104 73985 19097
74	299 86576	22190 06624	16 42064 90176	1215 12802 73024
75	316 40625	23730 46875	17 79785 15625	1334 83886 71875
76	333 62176	25355 25376	19 26999 28576	1464 51945 71776
77	351 53041	27067 84157	20 84223 80089	1604 85232 66853
78	370 15056	28871 74368	22 51996 00704	1756 55688 54912
79	389 50081	30770 56399	24 30874 55521	1920 39089 86159
80	409 60000	32768 00000	26 21440 00000	2097 15200 00000
81	430 46721	34867 84401	28 24295 36481	2287 67924 54961
82	452 12176	37073 98432	30 40066 71424	2492 85470 56768
83	474 58321	39390 40643	32 69403 73369	2713 60509 89627
84	497 87136	41821 19424	35 12980 31616	2950 90346 55744
85	522 00625	44370 53125	37 71495 15625	3205 77088 28125
86	547 00816	47042 70176	40 45672 35136	3479 27822 21696
87	572 89761	49842 09207	43 36262 01009	3772 54794 87733
88	599 69536	52773 19168	46 44040 86784	4086 75596 36992
89	627 42241	55840 59449	49 69812 90961	4423 13348 95529
90	656 10000	59049 00000	53 14410 00000	4782 96900 00000
91	685 74961	62403 21451	56 78692 52041	5167 61019 35731
92	716 39296	65908 15232	60 63550 01344	5578 46601 23648
93	748 05201	69568 83693	64 69901 83449	6017 00870 60757
94	780 74896	73390 40224	68 98697 81056	6484 77594 19264
95	814 50625	77378 09375	73 50918 90625	6983 37296 09375
96	849 34656	81537 26976	78 27577 89696	7514 47478 10816
97	885 29281	85873 40257	83 29720 04929	8079 82844 78113
98	922 36816	90392 07968	88 58423 80864	8681 25533 24672
99	960 59601	95099 00499	94 14801 49401	9320 65347 90699
100	1000 00000	1 00000 00000	100 00000 00000	10000 00000 00000

No. n	Eighth Power n^8	Ninth Power n^9	Tenth Power n^{10}
51	4576 79445 70401	2 33416 51730 90451	119 04242 38276 13001
52	5345 97285 31456	2 77990 58836 35712	144 55510 59490 57024
53	6225 96904 11361	3 29976 35918 02133	174 88747 03655 13049
54	7230 19613 39136	3 90430 59123 13344	210 83251 92649 20576
55	8373 39378 90625	4 60536 65839 84375	253 29516 21191 40625
56	9671 73115 74016	5 41616 94481 44896	303 30548 90961 14176
57	11142 91571 12001	6 35146 19553 84057	362 03333 14568 91249
58	12806 30817 18016	7 42765 87396 44928	430 80420 68994 05824
59	14683 04376 04321	8 66299 58186 54939	511 11675 33006 41401
60	16796 16000 00000	10·07769 60000 00000	604 66176 00000 00000
61	19170 73129 97281	11 69414 60928 34141	713 34291 16628 82601
62	21834 01055 84896	13 53708 65462 63552	839 29936 58683 40224
63	24815 57802 67521	15 63381 41568 53823	984 93029 18817 90849
64	28147 49767 10656	18 01439 85094 81984	1152 92150 46068 46976
65	31864 48128 90625	20 71191 28378 90625	1346 27433 44628 90625
66	36004 06062 69696	23 76268 00137 99936	1568 33688 09107 95776
67	40606 76775 56641	27 20653 43962 94947	1822 83780 45517 61449
68	45716 32396 53376	31 08710 02964 29568	2113 92282 01572 10624
69	51379 83744 28641	35 45208 78355 76229	2446 19406 06547 59801
70	57648 01000 00000	40 35360 70000 00000	2824 75249 00000 00000
71	64575 35312 45761	45 84850 07184 49031	3255 24355 10098 81201
72	72220 41363 08736	51 99869 78142 28992	3743 90624 26244 87424
73	80646 00918 94081	58 87158 67082 67913	4297 62582 97035 57649
74	89919 47402 03776	66 54041 07750 79424	4923 99039 73558 77376
75	1 00112 91503 90625	75 08468 62792 96875	5631 35147 09472 65625
76	1 11303 47874 54976	84 59064 38465 78176	6428 88893 23399 41376
77	1 23573 62915 47681	95 15169 44491 71437	7326 68047 25862 00649
78	1 37011 43706 83136	106 86892 09132 84608	8335 77583 12361 99424
79	1 51710 88099 06561	119 85159 59826 18319	9468 27608 26268 47201
80	1 67772 16000 00000	134 21772 80000 00000	10737 41824 00000 00000
81	1 85302 01888 51841	150 09463 52969 99121	12157 66545 90569 28801
82	2 04414 08586 54976	167 61955 04097 08032	13744 80313 35960 58624
83	2 25229 22321 39041	186 94025 52675 40403	15516 04118 72058 53449
84	2 47875 89110 82496	208 21574 85309 29664	17490 12287 65980 91776
85	2 72490 52503 90625	231 61694 62832 03125	19687 44043 40722 65625
86	2 99217 92710 65856	257 32741 73116 63616	22130 15788 88030 70976
87	3 28211 67154 37121	285 54415 42430 29527	24842 34141 91435 68849
88	3 59634 52480 55296	316 47838 18288 66048	27850 09760 09402 12224
89	3 93658 88057 02081	350 35640 37074 85209	31181 71992 99661 83601
90	4 30467 21000 00000	387 42048 90000 00000	34867 84401 00000 00000
91	4 70252 52761 51521	427 92980 01297 88411	38941 61181 18107 45401
92	5 13218 87313 75616	472 16136 32865 56672	43438 84542 23632 13824
93	5 59581 80966 50401	520 41108 29884 87293	48398 23071 79293 18249
94	6 09568 93854 10816	572 99480 22286 16704	53861 51140 94899 70176
95	6 63420 43128 90625	630 24940 97246 09375	59873 69392 38378 90625
96	7 21389 57898 38336	692 53399 58244 80256	66483 26359 91501 04576
97	7 83743 35943 76961	760 23105 86545 65217	73742 41268 94928 26049
98	8 50763 02258 17856	833 74776 21301 49888	81707 28068 87546 89024
99	9 22744 69442 79201	913 51724 74836 40899	90438 20750 08804 49001
100	10 00000·00000 00000	1000 00000 00000 00000	1 00000 00000 00000 00000

n	n^{11}	n^{12}	n^{13}
1	1	1	1
2	2048	4096	8192
3	1 77147	5 31441	15 94323
4	41 94304	167 77216	671 08864
5	488 28125	2441 40625	12207 03125
6	3627 97056	21767 82336	1 30606 94016
7	19773 26743	1 38412 87201	9 68890 10407
8	85899 34592	6 87194 76736	54 97558 13888
9	3 13810 59609	28 24295 36481	254 18658 28329
10	10 00000 00000	100 00000 00000	1000 00000 00000

n	n^{14}	n^{15}	n^{16}
1	1	1	1
2	16384	32768	65536
3	47 82969	143 48907	430 46721
4	2684 35456	10737 41824	42949 67296
5	61035 15625	3 05175 78125	15 25878 90625
6	7 83641 64096	47 01849 84576	282 11099 07456
7	67 82230 72849	474 75615 09943	3323 29305 69601
8	439 80465 11104	3518 43720 88832	28147 49767 10656
9	2287 67924 54961	20589 11320 94649	1 85302 01888 51841
10	10000 00000 00000	1 00000 00000 00000	10 00000 00000 00000

n	n^{17}	n^{18}
1	1	1
2	1 31072	2 62144
3	1291 40163	3874 20489
4	1 71798 69184	6 87194 76736
5	76 29394 53125	381 46972 65625
6	1692 66594 44736	10155 99566 68416
7	23263 05139 87207	1 62841 35979 10449
8	2 25179 98136 85248	18 01439 85094 81984
9	16 67718 16996 66569	150 09463 52969 99121
10	100 00000 00000 00000	1000 00000 00000 00000

n	n^{19}	n^{20}
1	1	1
2	5 24288	10 48576
3	11622 61467	34867 84401
4	27 48779 06944	109 95116 27776
5	1907 34863 28125	9536 74316 40625
6	60935 97400 10496	3 65615 84400 62976
7	11 39889 51853 73143	79 79226 62976 12001
8	144 11518 80758 55872	1152 92150 46068 46976
9	1350 85171 76729 92089	12157 66545 90569 28801
10	10000 00000 00000 00000	1 00000 00000 00000 00000

BINOMIAL COEFFICIENTS

n	Coefficients
1	1, 1
2	1, 2, 1
3	1, 3, 3, 1
4	1, 4, 6, 4, 1
5	1, 5, 10, 10, 5, 1
6	1, 6, 15, 20, 15, 6, 1
7	1, 7, 21, 35, 35, 21, 7, 1
8	1, 8, 28, 56, 70, 56, 28, 8, 1
9	1, 9, 36, 84, 126, 126, 84, 36, 9, 1
10	1, 10, 45, 120, 210, 252, 210, 120, 45, 10, 1
11	1, 11, 55, 165, 330, 462, 462, 330, 165, 55, 11, 1
12	1, 12, 66, 220, 495, 792, 924, 792, 495, 220, 66, 12, 1

CONSTANTS

π	3·14159 26535 89793	$\dfrac{1}{\pi}$	0·31830 98861 83791
π^2	9·86960 44010 89359	$\dfrac{1}{\pi^2}$	0·10132 11836 42338
$\sqrt{\pi}$	1·77245 38509 05516	$\dfrac{1}{\sqrt{\pi}}$	0·56418 95835 47756
$\sqrt{2\pi}$	2·50662 82746 31001	$\dfrac{1}{\sqrt{2\pi}}$	0·39894 22804 01433
$\sqrt{\dfrac{\pi}{2}}$	1·25331 41373 15500	$\sqrt{\dfrac{2}{\pi}}$	0·79788 45608 02865
$\sqrt[3]{\pi}$	1·46459 18875 61523	$\sqrt[3]{\dfrac{1}{\pi}}$	0·68278 40632 55296
e	2·71828 18284 59045	$\dfrac{1}{e}$	0·36787 94411 71442
e^2	7·38905 60989 30650	$\dfrac{1}{e^2}$	0·13533 52832 36613
$\sqrt{e}$	1·64872 12707 00128	$\dfrac{1}{\sqrt{e}}$	0·60653 06597 12633
$M = \log_{10}e$	0·43429 44819 03252	$\dfrac{1}{M} = \log_e 10$	2·30258 50929 94046
1 radian	57°·29577 95130 82321	1°	0ʳ·01745 32925 19943
„	3437'·746 77078 49393	1′	0ʳ·00029 08882 08666
„	206264″ ·80624 70964	1″	0ʳ·00000 48481 36811
$\sqrt{2}$	1·41421 35623 73095	$\sqrt[3]{2}$	1·25992 10498 94873
$\sqrt{3}$	1·73205 08075 68877	$\sqrt[3]{10}$	2·15443 46900 31884
$\sqrt{10}$	3·16227 76601 68379	$\sqrt[3]{100}$	4·64158 88336 12779

n	B''	Notation
·0000		
	·00	Function Diff.
·0204		
	− ·01	f_{-1}
·0641		a
	− ·02	f_0
·1127		b
	− ·03	f_1
·1683		c
	− ·04	f_2
·2354		
	− ·05	
·3267		Formula
	− ·06	
·6732		$f_n = f_0 + nb + B''(c - a)$
	− ·05	
·7645		
	− ·04	
·8316		In using the table ascend in critical cases.
	− ·03	
·8872		
	− ·02	Examples
·9358		
	− ·01	
·9795		
	·00	
·9999		

Examples

n	B''
·1234	− ·03
·4567	− ·06
·8316	− ·04

TABLE FOR FINDING THE
FIRST FIGURE OF CUBE ROOTS

First group of number	First figure of root
0	
	1
7	
	2
26	
	3
63	
	4
124	
	5
215	
	6
342	
	7
511	
	8
728	
	9
999	

$\sqrt[3]{10}$ 2·15443 46900

$\sqrt[3]{100}$ 4·64158 88336

In critical cases ascend.